CALIFORNIA

CALIFORNIA : :

LAND OF CONTRAST

DAVID W. LANTIS
Chico State College

in collaboration with

RODNEY STEINER
Long Beach State College

ARTHUR E. KARINEN
Chico State College

WADSWORTH PUBLISHING COMPANY, INC.

Belmont, California

CALIFORNIA: LAND OF CONTRAST
by David W. Lantis, Rodney Steiner, and Arthur E. Karinen

L.C. Cat. Card No.: 63-19465
Printed in the United States of America

To Helen, Florence, and Phyllis

And with appreciation

to the hundreds of students in our California geography classes

who have contributed so much to our knowledge of the Golden State.

CONTENTS

viii : : CONTENTS

FORETHOUGHTS

This is a geography of California—a land made golden by its poppies, its sycamores and its aspen, its golden trout, the seared gold of its sun-parched hills during the heat of rainless summers, the golden yellow of its ripening crops of wheat, barley, rice, safflower, and baled alfalfa, the gold of its lemons and oranges.

Over a century ago its gold fields began luring the young, the ambitious, the bold. After decades of more or less continuous growth California has become the nation's most populous state—its *new* aureity lies in its academic achievement and its industrial output, evidenced by a score of Nobel Prize winners at its universities and its impressive assignment of national defense contracts.

SITUATION

California, third largest of the fifty states (158,693 square miles), extends along the Pa-

This section has been reviewed by Raymond W. Stanley, San Jose State College, and James N. Wilson, Long Beach State College.

cific shores through nearly 10 degrees of latitude and has a coastline of 1264 miles. Despite several fine harbors, much of the seacoast, bordered by a mountain wall that ascends almost from the water's edge, has no extensive coastal plains.

The "eccentric" location of California within the nation and the Western world has colored its modern evolution. In the sixteenth century, it was even deemed to be an island. More recently its distance from northeastern United States has been a vital consideration in the rise of agriculture and manufacturing. Comparatively empty spaces still separate California from eastern United States. When state boundaries were established in 1850, political leaders made no effort to encompass much of the Spanish Southwest—its relative barrenness provided little hint of any future value. Mountains still somewhat isolate much of California from neighboring Mexico, Arizona, Nevada, and Oregon. Provinciality would be an anticipated result of such remoteness—it has been minimized by the continuing flood of immigrants.

THE APPROACH

Colorful description, factual detail, provocative generalities, imaginative theory, and scholarly documentation contribute to desired studies of man on the land. We wish that all of these factors could have been amalgamated in this book. But in our quest of the ideal we have had yet another goal: the creation of a work that might be read with enjoyment by those who wish to amplify their knowledge of the Golden State. We feel that the urgent need, short of basic research, is a reader-oriented treatise. Erudite analysis, superficial survey, and factual compendium each has its unique contribution, and has already been made available. We refer, wherever appropriate, to other sources throughout this book; the sources are documented in the bibliography at the end of the book. The reader is further encouraged to refer to the bibliography for examples of additional sources.

PRESENTATION

Geography can be studied either *regionally*, through discussion of local areas, or *systematically*, through separate consideration of such topics as landforms, agriculture, and population—we have employed both methods. We have given priority to the regional approach on the contention that the physical subdivisions of California are so obvious and well known that they provide familiar mental routes for the reader. We begin with the less complex eastern margins of the state and move on to the more dynamic areas of Southern California, the Central Coast, and the Great Central Valley.

The systematic approach is presented in the appendices and through separate subject-matter sections within each chapter; those who wish to emphasize the systematic approach may do so. For those who prefer the combined regional-systematic approach, there are succinct summaries at the beginning of chapters.

We visualize geography as involving both land and man; hence, we have tried to avoid slanting toward either the physical or the cultural.

SEQUENT OCCUPANCE

There have been three principal stages in the successive occupance of California: (1) American Indian, (2) colonial (Spanish and Mexican), and (3) American. Evidences of all three have continued into the present.

No other state has had a comparable diversity of Indian populations; in part this has reflected the differing environments of the *several* Californias. Anthropologists have identified five language stocks and twenty-six tribal groupings within California. Descendants of the twenty-four groups still extant in the state number more than 10,000. Where these first citizens have vanished, place names and land routes still echo their presence.

Most California Indians were hunter-gatherers before the Europeans arrived. Those in dry habitats and mountainous terrain had the least material prosperity, and their numbers were limited. Most environments allowed simple shelters and little clothing. The Southern California Indians enjoyed a mild land, which permitted indolence. Those in the Central Valley occupied an environment that required a little more fortitude. The Northwest, with its perennial salmon streams and its conifer forests, was the wealthy portion of the state.

California represented the northwestern perimeter of Spanish settlement in the Americas—its existence was known for over two centuries before colonial occupance of the area began. Between 1769 and 1822 a chain of twenty-one missions was extended northward to Sonoma; the mission landscape included approximately a sixth of the present state (i.e., the coastal lands with an extensive Indian population, which was best suited to the missionaries' program). Besides the Franciscan *padres,* soldiers manned frontier outposts and small numbers of colonists moved northward out of Mexico. Several of California's larger cities originated as *pueblos* (villages). A background for present-day agriculture was initiated with beginnings of irrigation and introduction of crops that subsequently have been quite important. Attempts to Christianize and civilize the Indians were somewhat less than successful. Place names, agricultural practices, highway routes, customs, speech, architectural design, and foods of present-day California reflect the Spanish period.

The Mexican era lasted only a generation (1822-1846) but during that time some 800 large individual holdings (*ranchos*) were awarded; toward the end of the period some properties were even given to Americans and Europeans who accepted Mexican citizenship. However, Mexico scarcely had time to colonize its most distant province, and present-day Americans occasionally reason that this justified the taking of California from our neighboring republic. Perhaps the most lasting results of the Mexican period have been its genetic influences upon today's population and its effects upon subsequent land titles.

The American period began at the end of the Mexican War. Within a year North America's most spectacular Gold Rush had commenced. The subsequent century has been characterized by these economic successions: (1) a pastoral era of cattle and sheep ranching, widely prevalent until the 1880's; (2) grain farming, especially important from the 1870's until 1900; (3) the rise of irrigation agriculture, principally since 1900; (4) industrialization (and urbanization), mostly since World War I, with dramatic expansion and addition since 1940. These periods have overlapped, and not all portions of the state have experienced all four. Evolution has been most elaborate and the change from rural to urban life most complete in the three largest of the metropolitan areas. Over much of the Golden State population is sparse and livestock ranching persists. As early as the census of 1860 it was evident that the California population was beginning to be concentrated in urban clusters—86 percent of the residents are now city folk.

The American period has essentially reflected the westward movement, or "westering," suggested by Horace Greeley in *To Aspiring Young Men* in 1846:

If you have no family or friends to aid you, and no prospect opened to you there (in a father's workshop or his farm), turn your face to the great West, and there build up a home and fortune.

The earlier years witnessed immigration from the Atlantic seaboard—New England and the Middle Atlantic states (especially New York). From the 1880's until World War I this movement was augmented by significant migration from the Middle West—California almost became New Illinois. The 1930's brought victims of depression and Great Plains drought and dust by the thousands. Then during World War II there almost seemed a Confederate invasion, sprinkled with thousands of Negroes and many people from the Rocky Mountain states. After World War II came vast numbers of ex-G.I.'s and their young brides, to populate the new housing tracts and soon jam the schools with their little ones. Despite immigrants from Europe and from eastern Asia, California has essentially been an all-American melting pot—it has lured its millions from all other states. California is no longer a virgin land; even the long-held image of Southern California with miles of orange groves has disappeared before the blade of the bulldozers, clearing the land for more homes.

MANY MILLIONS

As America's most populous state, it is understandable that California should have more dwellings, more house trailers, and more motor boats than any other. Traditionally, new residents have been welcomed, but some Californians are beginning to wonder if the state is to become "America's China."[1] More than a thousand residents of the other forty-nine states are moving into the Golden State daily; coupled with natural California increase the annual addition exceeds the total

[1] Robert de Roos, in "Los Angeles," *National Geographic Magazine* (October 1962), p. 467, comments: "In a recent letter to the *Los Angeles Times*, Dan Jenkins, a friend of mine who came from New Jersey, wrote somewhat tongue-in-cheek:
'When I get back east, I make a point of talking about nothing but our smog, fires, floods, landslides, earthquakes, freeways, parking problems, impossible traffic conditions, early-morning fog, late-afternoon fog, debilitating lack of seasons, constantly increasing property taxes, Mickey Cohen, and the miserable showing of the 1961 Dodgers and Rams.'
Jenkins claims he has dissuaded all of 16 persons from moving to Los Angeles."

population of Baltimore, the nation's sixth largest city in 1960. The 1960 inhabitants of the Los Angeles Lowlands alone rivaled the total California population only twenty years earlier. The Golden State housed 6 million in 1940, 10 million in 1950, and 15 million in 1960. Despite this increase the statewide density (in 1960) was only an eighth that of New Jersey or Rhode Island. Yet most of the people are concentrated within three metropolitan complexes: Los Angeles Lowlands, San Francisco Bay Area, and greater San Diego. Remote mountain districts still afford ample opportunity to escape city congestion. However, many places that provide pleasant residence are hampered by limited economic opportunity. (Population is discussed in Appendix E.)

ECONOMIC BASE

The Golden State has steadily gained prestige and stature. Californians have been making important national contributions for decades, but as late as 1945 many "outlanders" were satisfied to dismiss the state as an agrarian paradise with orange groves and palm trees, a pleasant place in which to spend one's later years. Recently, economic opportunity and climatic amenities have lured many talented Americans in all fields of endeavor, and California has loomed increasingly large as an appealing "money market." Living standards are significantly higher than those in most of the nation, and Californians have more formal education than the average American.

Economic aspects have undergone much alteration—and the rate of continuing change often hampers advance planning. There have been major relocations of such important commodities as oranges, walnuts, truck crops, market milk, and cut flowers. Agriculture (discussed in Appendix F) is also considered within each chapter. California is the nation's agricultural leader; its diverse environments permit the growing of most middle-latitude and subtropical crops, and more than 200 are grown commercially. Despite the concentration of population within a few large metropolitan centers, most California counties are still largely agriculturally oriented.

Few portions of the earth of comparable dimensions have yielded such a wealth and a variety of minerals. Gold mining has almost ceased and petroleum output is declining, but California has ranked among the top three mineral-producing states nationally for over half a century. The heyday of the old-time prospector, seeker of gold and silver, is gone; today the volume of mineral income, in excess of $1.4 billion annually, is derived from industrial minerals (petroleum, iron ore, sand and gravel, salines, cement minerals).

Tourism continues to be important; many regard California as the nation's most beautiful state. The fact that most Americans now have relatives in the Golden State likewise promotes tourism. Facilities, both urban and rural, become increasingly congested as the population of the state rises. Remote areas are being made accessible by improved highways.

Since World War II California has gained a position among the leading industrial states. Manufacturing is concentrated especially in the Los Angeles Lowlands and the San Francisco Bay Area, although food processing is more widely distributed and a few industrial plants are found in most counties. The scope of the California retail market alone, protected as it is by distance against Middlewestern competition, warrants a considerable output of virtually every type of commodity demanded by the "American way of life." Only textiles, among major industrial types, is not well represented. There is much emphasis upon defense contracts—perhaps the most impressive change since 1950 has been the rise of the electronics industry. Such activity is lucrative and requires well-educated and skilled personnel, but it is subject to international tensions and political decisions in Washington, D.C., and thus is somewhat unpredictable.

Military installations have markedly influenced the economy since 1940. Although army outposts played an important part in Spanish activity—some large bases had their origins a century ago—many new facilities have been added since 1945. A number of sizable communities are quite dependent upon military payrolls and large civilian work forces; additions to or subtractions from installations seriously affect the local economy. The Mojave Desert, Southern California, the Central Coast, and the Great Central Valley are particularly important foci for training and testing—with all services and National Aeronautics and Space Administration (N.A.S.A.) well represented.

Transportation makes a signal contribution to the California economy, partly because of the size and population of the state and partly because of regional differences (i.e., the several Californias). Distance from industrial northeastern United States has long promoted interstate transport; as was noted it permitted much local industrial growth. California agricultural products are shipped across the nation and to international markets. A large volume of raw materials from the forest, the sea, and the mine moves to processing centers.

There are three major north-south passageways in California—the most important, benefiting from terrain, differing local economies, and population distribution, extends from San Diego and Los Angeles northward through the Great Central Valley into western Oregon. It is served by two major railroads and U.S. highway 99. (In Chapter 3 the importance of the Mojave Desert as a corridor is stressed.) Rail transportation has declined relatively with expansion of highway commerce. No other state has so many automobiles and trucks or has built so extensive a network of multilane highways. Ocean commerce has also become less important, especially for passenger traffic. By contrast a significant air commerce has developed. Los Angeles in particular conducts a tremendous volume of passenger and freight traffic with other parts of the nation and the world.

REGIONS

California has nearly the physical diversity of the other forty-nine states combined. It constitutes a wonderful laboratory for the physiographer, because it contains examples of virtually all geologic processes. (Landforms are discussed in each chapter and in Appendix

B.) Were it not for summer drought the state might approach the climatic diversity of the other states combined. Summer desert temperatures are as high as any in the nation; winter minimums in the Northeast suggest Maine and Minnesota. Sections of the Northwest approach southeastern Alaska and the Olympic Peninsula of Washington in wetness, whereas the deserts are as dry as any part of North America. Altitude in the High Sierra suggests the Alaska Arctic in temperatures. (Climate too is discussed in individual chapters and in Appendix A.) These two major aspects of the physical earth help explain the variety of natural vegetation and soils present in California.

Regionally California is considered a Pacific coast state. None the less some geographers label this portion of Anglo-America as "Pacific Borderlands," whereas others prefer terms like "Pacific Mountains and Valleys." Eastern California, however, beyond the barrier of the Cascade Range, the Sierra Nevada, and the Peninsular Ranges, is generally recognized as part of the "Intermontane Region," which lies between these highlands and the Rocky Mountain system. This eastern march does not connote California to people of other states and nations—in fact its own residents, particularly those in the Northeast, have felt upon occasion that they were a forgotten people.

Since its inception this book has been developed in the belief that the whole (i.e., California) is the sum of its parts (i.e., the several Californias)—regional units with different environments, unique histories, varied outlooks, and diverse problems. These factors make it futile to generalize about the state without recognizing the regional heterogeneity. The most apparent division exists between the "north" and the "south," widely accepted as the lands on opposite sides of the Tehachapi (i.e., southwesternmost Sierra Nevada). At least eight serious proposals since 1850 to divide California into two or even three states reflect the geographic diversity. As late as 1956 the ten northernmost counties proposed to secede and become the new state of Shasta. The informed Californian should recognize

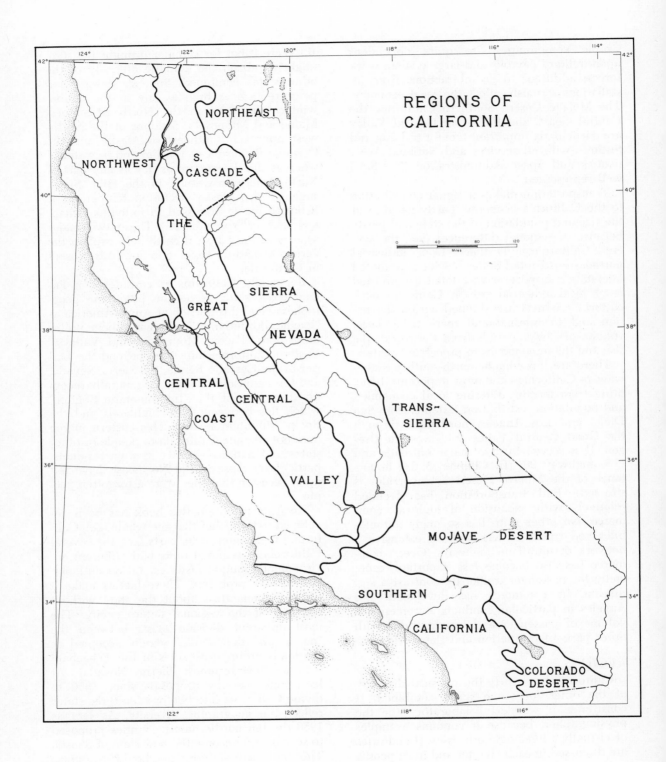

REGIONS OF
CALIFORNIA

NORTHEAST

NORTHWEST

S. CASCADE

THE

GREAT

SIERRA

NEVADA

CENTRAL

CENTRAL

COAST

TRANS-
SIERRA

VALLEY

MOJAVE   DESERT

SOUTHERN

CALIFORNIA

COLORADO
DESERT

that there are differing contacts and varying degrees of isolation still—few residents of the Golden State are truly intimate with all its parts and its geographic diversity.

There is obvious physical basis for California's regional differences—magnification has resulted from specialization within the present economy. Landforms prompted subdivision into ten regions whose names generally have local acceptance (see map opposite). *Part One,* the first four chapters, describes California segments of the Intermontane Region. A text concerned with Anglo-America would probably assign the remaining six units to the "Pacific Borderlands." But in discussion of a single state of such diversity, the majestic barrier of California's high mountain backbone with its singular human utilization merits further compartmentation, hence *Part Two,* the Sierra-Cascade. *Part Three,* designated as Pacific Borderlands, considers the heartland of California with its preponderance of people and economic achievements. A final chapter tells of the peripheral Northwest, a charming land that affords a tasty "dessert."

PROSPECTS

Present prospects for the future portend the probability of continued population increase in the Golden State—hence, creation of more congestion around metropolitan areas, greater pressure on water and all other resources, the necessity of providing more schools and more freeways and tens of thousands of new jobs. Increased difficulty is anticipated in allocating resources between commercial users and recreational-residential users. A growing emphasis upon social problems (crime, civil rights, housing, traffic, smog, etc.) rather than resource development problems seems imminent as the state urbanizes and industrializes. Yet change and expansion do not appear likely to affect all parts of California. Large population increases are not justifiable forecasts at present for much of the Mojave Desert, the Trans-Sierra, the Northeast, the Sierra Nevada, the Southern Cascades, and the Northwest.

The California landscape changes as rapidly as any in the fifty states. In relating the regional geography of the Golden State, we have fully realized that dynamic growth and alteration will make this book historic before the book comes off the press. Some facts will quickly become dated while others may even seem erroneous. We have avoided specific statistics whenever possible and have endeavored to present impressions and concepts that may have more lasting validity.

ACKNOWLEDGMENTS

We owe a debt of gratitude to dozens of professional geographers, to the many hundreds of students who have attended our classes in geography of California since 1950, and to the thousands of others who have added to the impressive body of knowledge concerning this state. Good friends in a number of California colleges and universities have reviewed portions of the manuscript. In recognition of their critical efforts we have identified their assistance in individual chapters. *It should not be assumed that they acquiesce in all of the views we have presented.*

We acknowledge special thanks to Richard F. Logan, University of California at Los Angeles, who has shown an interest in this project almost from its inception and who reviewed a large portion of the manuscript and offered valuable critical suggestions.

David W. Lantis prepared the original text. He has flown extensively over California, traveled virtually every road which appears on highway maps and conducted preliminary field work in all ten regions. Rodney Steiner, especially, and Arthur E. Karinen have participated in the rewriting; however, Lantis recognizes that shortcomings and errors are basically his responsibility. Karinen prepared all of the maps, and Steiner wrote the original drafts of the appendices.

PART ONE : :

THE INTERMONTANE REGION

THE INTERMONTANE REGION

The Intermontane Region is an extensive area, little of which is actually within California. The over-all description presented here is given as a background for subsequent consideration of its California segments. The four parts of the Golden State that lie within this region are not what the world's citizenry envisages when they hear the word "California." These four subdivisions are considered in the first part of this book, which concerns the dry third of the state: the Northeast, the Trans-Sierra, the Mojave Desert, and the Colorado Desert. In fact, had the boundaries of our eleven western states been determined simultaneously, it is probable that no part of the Intermontane Region would have been included within California.

The Intermontane Region, that great land between the Rocky Mountains on the east and the Sierra Nevada-Cascade on the west, extends from the Gulf of California to the Canadian boundary.[1] Despite an Occidental heritage dating from Spanish conquistadors, the Lewis and Clark expedition, and the "mountain men" of the early nineteenth century, this vast realm remains almost devoid of human occupance over wide expanses. Describing parts of it, J. Russell Smith has written:

This is a vast region. Everywhere the rain is so slight, the summer so hot, that the farmer with his plow is not the symbol of settlement. Instead it is the cowboy with his lariat and the leather leggings that keep the cactus from pricking him. Someone has said that this is a region where there are more streams and less water, more cows and less milk, and where one can look farther and see less, than any other place in the world.[2]

Man's activities may differ on the wooded slopes of Oregon's Blue Mountains and in the scorching summer heat of southern Arizona, but almost everywhere they are curtailed by water shortage. The Intermontane Region is essentially surrounded by lofty mountains that wring out moisture from either the Atlantic or Pacific ocean before it reaches this parched land.

Many famed explorers have traversed various portions of the Intermontane Region since the Coronado expedition of the sixteenth century, yet their efforts seldom lured settlers into this dry country. Even after the Atlantic and

[1] Earl B. Shaw, *Anglo-America: A Regional Geography* (New York: John Wiley & Sons, Inc., 1959), identifies it as "The Intermontane Plateaus" (Chapter 13, pp. 342-381). Alfred J. Wright, *The United States and Canada: A Regional Geography*, 2nd ed. (New York: Appleton-Century-Crofts, Inc., 1956), perceives this area as "Western Intermontane Area" (Chapter 17, pp. 406-431). C. Langdon White and Edwin J. Foscue, *Regional Geography of Anglo-America*, 2nd ed. (Englewood Cliffs, N. J.: Prentice-Hall, Inc., 1954), call it "Intermontane Basins and Plateaus" (Chapter 13, pp. 329-374).

[2] J. Russell Smith and M. Ogden Phillips, *North America* (New York: Harcourt, Brace & World, Inc., 1942), p. 545.

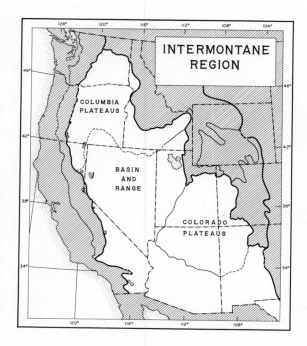

INTERMONTANE REGION

COLUMBIA PLATEAUS

BASIN AND RANGE

COLORADO PLATEAUS

Over a century ago the Mormons moved into the Salt Lake Basin and demonstrated that with irrigation agriculture could succeed in this land of sunshine. Later, irrigation agriculture developed elsewhere, along the Snake River in southern Idaho, in the Yakima and Wenatchee valleys of Washington, and in the twentieth century, in the Salt-Gila Basin of Arizona and the Imperial Valley of California. Technological advances permitted construction of such dams as Hoover, Grand Coulee, and Roosevelt and the drilling of pump wells in Antelope Valley and the Coachella, enabling expansion of cropped acreage. Yet much of the water used to irrigate the land must come from peripheral mountains. The niggardliness of the rain gods prevents agricultural utilization of most of the region.

In the automotive age and especially since the late 1920's, highway travel and recreation have helped to diversify the regional economy. Federal highways 2, 30, 40, 66, 80, and 91 represent major transcontinental routes that contribute considerably to the economic well-being of the region. In this century Grand Canyon, Bryce Canyon, and Death Valley have gained renown as natural wonderlands. Man's works, such as Grand Coulee Dam and Lake Mead, are on the agenda of growing numbers of visitors to western America. In the desert, man has erected places of sport and relaxation such as Reno and Las Vegas, Tucson, and Palm Springs.

Lately portions of the Intermontane Region have been acclaimed "the modern American frontier." One accustomed to thinking of exceedingly small populations for Arizona and Nevada reads in astonishment the latest census statistics and anticipated growth for the remainder of this century.

Pacific slopes were linked by railroads in the nineteenth century, the population density of the region remained low. Whereas cycles of heavier rainfall encouraged settlement of the Great Plains, the persistent dryness of the Intermontane Region afforded hope for dry-land farming only locally.

Mineral deposits have formed an important inducement to attract man into these barren lands. Famed mine camps have boomed and then usually have declined to become ghost towns. Among the more renowned of such centers, some still active, have been the Comstock Lode, Death Valley, Bingham Canyon, Bodie, Cerro Gordo, Douglas, and Bisbee.

Fig 1-1. THE MODOC PLATEAU—*a somber and lonesome land. View from Schonchin Butte northeastward toward Tule Lake Basin reveals absence of table-top flatness.* (Mary Hill)

CHAPTER ONE :: THE NORTHEAST

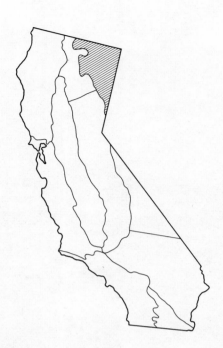

THE NORTHEAST

To most Californians the Northeast is an alien land sketchily known and unvisited. This roughly triangular jumble of lava country, essentially in Modoc and Lassen counties (see Fig. 1-2), is separated from the remainder of the state by the Sierra Nevada and the southern Cascade. To some it suggests a transplanted Wyoming; high-level, relatively flat surfaces prevail, yet mountains are frequently in view (see Fig. 1-1). Alturas almost presents the climatic analogue of Cheyenne in average July and January temperatures, annual precipitation and especially snowfall totals. As in Wyoming, the vegetation cover over wide stretches is disappointingly sparse, with sagebrush being the dominant plant.

Largely because of the dry-summer climate and the prevalence of porous rocky surfaces, water and cultivable land are prized. Thus streams from the highlands are carefully tapped in the few areas where terrain and alluvial soils permit irrigation—a recent map

This chapter has been reviewed by Robert Pease, Los Angeles City Schools, and Robert Middleton, Lassen Union High School, Susanville.

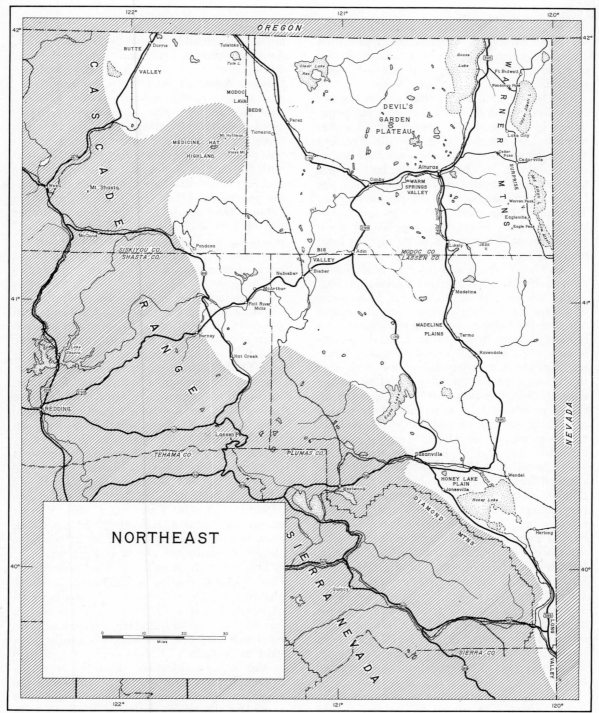

Fig. 1-2. MAP OF THE NORTHEAST.

shows thirty-six irrigation reservoirs within the area. Paradoxically, poor drainage forms a major obstacle to springtime grazing on the numerous wet meadows that are otherwise valuable.

The Northeast is larger than any of the nation's nine smallest states, but its total population, less than 40,000, would not fill a significant Los Angeles suburb. Wide stretches are empty yet most residents are either ranchers or hamlet dwellers. Nearly half of the total populace resides in two small sectors, the **Honey Lake Plain** with 10,000 people and the **Tule Lake Basin** with 5000. Cities are understandably few; Susanville, the largest community, must derive much of its support from mountains west of this land.

Ranching is the dominant source of Northeastern livelihood. Livestock, primarily beef cattle, but also sheep, dictate ranch economy and form the leading source of rural income. Summer feed comes from the open range, extensively controlled by the federal government within national forests or Taylor grazing districts. Governmental policy prescribes the adjustment of animal population to the natural "carrying capacity" of these lands; there are additional restrictions where timber growth or watershed protection is involved. Growing season variability (range grass is available one year in February, the next in May) plus the "multiple-use" program for the national forests, makes ideal grazing intensity difficult, both scientifically and politically, and precipitates continuing controversy between rancher and federal administrator. Winter feed is provided by hay and grain, the most extensively cultivated crops in the Northeast. Irrigated lands commonly produce livestock feeds, although some grain is dry-farmed and some natural forage comes from wet meadows. The only significant variation from this theme occurs in the Tule Lake Basin, where under differing administrative and social conditions potatoes furnish the chief income although occupying only 14 percent of the irrigated acreage.

Forestry, the other major source of income, is also sharply restricted by federal policy, hence assuring some permanence. It should be noted that here, as elsewhere in the West, much timberland is outside the national forest, whereas much nontimbered grazing land is within such forest. The Northeast produces between 5 and 10 percent of California's lumber, predominantly western yellow (Ponderosa and Jeffrey) pine. Processing is nearly as dispersed as livestock ranching, although three of the eighteen scattered mills are in Susanville. For the Northeast, in combination with the eastern slopes of the nearby Cascade and Sierra Nevada, saw timber cut is exceeding regrowth. Moreover, a large proportion (about two thirds) of the annual timber growth here is classed as "cull and breakage," reflecting less than ideal climate and soils for tree growth. Large areas of the Northeast have greater immediate value for grazing.

The other major asset of the Northeast is its abundance of open space. Yet, despite spiraling metropolitan growth, California still possesses an adequacy of this resource in areas more accessible than the Northeast and more benign climatically. Somber-hued lava fields hold limited attraction for the average tourist, whereas the number of hunters and fishermen who might otherwise visit this area tends to be curtailed because of its location. Position alone sets the Northeast apart from major interstate travel routes save for Butte Valley in the extreme northwest, which lies athwart the route of heaviest California-Oregon rail and bus (but *not* automobile) traffic. Hence scenic attractions like Lava Beds, Glass Mountain, Eagle Lake, and the Warner Mountains remain comparatively unvisited; even the military has limited its activities to the Sierra Ordnance Depot at Herlong.

The Northeast then is a distinct, albeit relatively isolated, portion of California. Nowhere else in the state is there so extensive an area of nearly flat lava surfaces. No other section has an economy so singularly dependent upon extensive livestock ranching. Physically more akin to Nevada and to eastern Oregon than to the "other Californias" discussed in subsequent chapters, the Northeast culturally too bears an out-state orientation, attached as it is to the shopping centers of Klamath Falls and Reno and to federal land policies formulated in Washington, D.C. Yet the Northeast is bound firmly to its state by all-compelling political ties, by markets for much of its livestock and its forest products, by tourist sources, and by inclusion within the San Francisco wholesale trade area.

THE LAND

TABLELANDS AND FAULT BLOCKS

The Northeast is plateau country, but it does not represent the textbook illustration of billiard-table flatness. Characteristic elevation is around 4500 feet, yet surfaces vary from 3000 to 10,000 feet above sea level.

Much of the present topography was created before or during the Pleistocene Ice Age (i.e., the last million years). Successive basaltic lava outpourings from multitudinous vents largely buried the older north-trending fault blocks. The oldest flows postdate the creation of Mount Shasta, whereas the youngest, only a few centuries old, are so little weathered that the rocky surface is destitute of plant cover.

There are three principal physiographic units: (1) the Modoc Plateau, a part of the extensive Columbia Plateaus to the north; (2) the Honey Lake Plain; (3) the Warner Mountains and contiguous Surprise Valley. The latter two areas constitute small portions of the Great Basin. The major portion of the Northeast is encompassed within the Modoc Plateau.[1]

The Modoc Plateau has widespread basaltic lava flows and scattered cinder cones. Its principal subdivision is the Devil's Garden Plateau north of the Pit River Valley, bounded by an impressive scarp on the south and east. South of the Pit Valley, Modoc lavas have almost buried older fault blocks, although bold cliffs such as the Hat Creek Escarpment are locally prominent. On the northwestern edge of the Modoc, Lava Beds National Monument has appeal to geologists as well as vaca-

[1] Although it has wide local acceptance, Pease has suggested substitution of the term "Volcanic Tableland" because of the poor definition of the extent of the Modoc Plateau. His Tableland would include the Warner Mountains.

Fig. 1-3. CEDARVILLE AND THE WARNER RANGE. Alluvial aprons along the eastern base of this impressive fault scarp are utilized for livestock ranching. (David W. Lantis)

tionists, with its flows, cinder cones, Mammoth Crater, and several hundred caverns (lava tubes). The Modoc is less arid than the paucity of surface streams would suggest. The lavas are highly permeable and this is one of the principal areas of large springs within the United States. The major river is the Pit, which rises on the western slopes of the Warner Range and is a principal tributary of the Sacramento.

The Warner Range, suggesting a miniature Sierra Nevada, is the westernmost basin range in this area. It is a complex fault block about 90 miles long and of variable width, 8 to 20 miles. Its higher peaks with their small glacial lakes reach elevations of 8000 to 10,000 feet. Lateral and longitudinal faults have divided the range into a group of blocks, so that the north end is a horst, the south end a tilted block that blends into shield volcanoes and lava flows. The Surprise Valley fault, along its steep east face, has a vertical displacement of 6000 feet (see Fig. 1-3).

Appreciable portions of the Northeast have been covered with lake silts of pluvial origin and much of the cultivated land is restricted to such surfaces as Honey Lake Plain, Surprise Valley, the alluvial Pit River Valley, and Tule Lake Basin. Most of the lakes are Ice Age relics (remnants of once larger bodies), much diminished as a result of desiccation, drainage, and irrigation practices.

Surprise Valley is a structural basin in a small rift between the Warner Range and the Hay Canyon Range in Nevada. Its floor, at 4600 feet, is typical for much of the Northeast. Periglacial Lake Surprise, whose old shorelines and terraces now stand as much as 550 feet above the basin floor, shriveled to become the three intermittent Alkali Lakes, sometimes known as Upper, Middle, and Lower. Alluvial aprons flank the bolson (basin without external drainage) and are more impressive at the base of the better-watered Warner Range.

Honey Lake Plain, between the Diamond Mountain segment of the Sierra Nevada to the west and the Amadee-Skedaddle Range to the east, like Surprise Valley, has a pluvial period history. The plain represents the California portion of the bed of Pleistocene Lake Lahontan, an extensive Ice Age mass that was largely in Nevada. Honey Lake is itself an intermittent remnant of Lake Lahontan, whose much greater depth and size are shown by ancient yet prominent wave-cut terraces. Honey Lake receives the discharge of the Susan River and lesser streams, yet much stream flow has been diverted for irrigation, and summer evaporation from the surface of this shallow body is high. The surrounding plain is relatively flat with alluvial aprons sloping toward the lake and widespread lacustrine sediments. There are also lava outcroppings, especially near Janesville.

SAGEBRUSH AND CONIFERS

The natural vegetation represents a transition between Great Basin types and those of the mountains to the west. The Northeast is California's largest area of Great Basin sagebrush, found in association with bunch grass, the chief forage plant, bitterbrush, and saltbrush. The eastside Sierra forest, primarily pines and fir, covers sizable tracts in the western half of the area and also in the Warner Mountains.

Timber constitutes a ranking natural resource of the Northeast, which is not usually appreciated by those traveling along U.S. highway 395 as it follows a belt of western juniper (*J. occidentalis*) extending north-south along the central portion of the area. Lassen and Modoc both rank among California's top eight counties in reserves of available marketable timber acreages.

Vegetation distribution is influenced by terrain, altitude, water availability, and soils. Where young lava flows are insufficiently weathered, the ground has little cover. Locally, aspen glades are found within the Warner Mountain forests, and tule rushes extend along some stream courses on the Honey Lake Plain and in Tule Lake Basin.

SNOWSTORMS AND THUNDERSHOWERS

Much of the Northeast has a dry-summer, humid middle-latitude climate (called *Ds* by Russell, considered subhumid to semiarid by Thornthwaite—see Bibliography) that contrasts with the aridity usually associated with California's Intermontane segments. Most of the precipitation, frequently as snow, is brought by cyclonic storms out of the north Pacific in winter. Although annual totals are low in comparison with mountain areas to the west, the snowfall compares favorably to that received by portions of central United States with a continental climate. Limited summer moisture commonly comes from convectional showers.

The Northeast has suggestions of the seasonal changes associated with interior middle-latitude environments. There is a January to July mean monthly range of 35 to 40 degrees

Fahrenheit, although altitude tends to produce rather cool summers (Alturas averages 67°F. in July). The growing season (approximately four months) tends to be short and frosts have occurred in all months. Winter temperatures average only slightly below freezing, but polar outbursts can bring sharp cold spells; —36°F. recorded in Madeline represents the all-time minimum winter extreme. At such times a person may suspect that the only barrier holding back the cold blasts of the Arctic is a barbed wire fence. Weather stations commonly record a seasonal snowfall total of 3 to 4 feet. In midwinter, dense radiation fogs sometimes occur around Honey Lake and Tule Lake.

A STONY LAND

Good soils are restricted; hence only a tenth of the Northeast is suitable for cultivation. Silts and loams of alluvial or lacustrine origin are characteristic in tilled areas. But over extensive acreages the young volcanic rocks have not weathered sufficiently to provide deep soils.

SETTLEMENT

Occupance of the Northeast has been less elaborate than that of much of California. The area was beyond the confines of Spanish and Mexican activity. More recently, the settlement history has been relatively simple.

THE INDIANS

Prior to Anglo-American settlement the Northeast was shared by American Indian tribes, representing four different families. None of these groups was agrarian, although all except the Northern Paiute were semisedentary.

The eastern fringes, including Surprise Valley and the eastern Honey Lake Plain, represented the western periphery of *Northern Paiute* lands. These little-known Uto-Aztecans were materially inferior to the other three peoples. Dress was surprisingly brief for the environment; whereas crude conical huts, covered with brush or bark, sufficed as winter shelters. Seeds, nuts, and insects, gathered

with assiduous effort, were common foodstuffs; grasshoppers were regarded as a delicacy, and small game (especially rabbits) was prized in the winter diet. Sustaining life was not easy in a dry land with meager resources.

The *Maidu,* mountain-valley Penutian folk, occupied portions of the northern Sierra Nevada and southern Cascade west of Honey Lake Plain. Possibly they utilized the fringes of the plain, although it was peripheral territory. These hunter-fisher folk resided in brush houses in summer and larger earthcovered abodes in winter. Their basic foods, salmon and deer, suggest that their use of the Northeast was limited.

The *Achomawi* of the Hokan family occupied the largest portion of the Northeast, the drainage basin of the Pit. They were a riparian people whose resource economy was based upon fish, waterfowl, and deer. They resided outdoors in summer, in bark houses in winter.

The *Modoc,* a small and closely knit tribe, resided around the lakes by the northern basins. Because of their success in delaying American settlement, especially through the Modoc War of 1872-73, the Modoc have been considered a valorous warlike people. They were lake dwellers who used tule (bulrush) for clothing, basketry, dwellings, and rafts. Their diet was basically fish and wokas (yellow water-lily seeds). The marshy lake fringes provided large quantities of wokas, yet considerable labor was necessitated in food preparation.

THE AMERICANS

Settlement commenced soon after California achieved statehood, and homesteads were established on favorable surfaces near Susanville, Alturas, and Cedarville. Cattle ranching was the principal way of life; the easily flooded alluvial meadows provided forage. Livestock were usually expected to range for themselves, then were slaughtered for their hides and tallow or trailed to markets on the west side of the Sierra.

Transportation was arduous and market conditions unfavorable; hence settlement proceeded slowly. The Northeast was not an appealing portion of the West as long as less isolated localities were available.

Geographic seclusion from more populous parts of California and physiographic ties with the desert country of Nevada resulted in a spirit of independence among early residents of the Northeast. In 1855 Peter Lassen and Isaac Roop proclaimed the "Territory of Nataqua," but Congress never recognized the short-lived entity. The "Sagebrush War" of the following decade resulted from disagreement between Nevada and California over the interstate boundary. Again in 1959 validity of the state line was challenged by a prominent Nevada legislator.

CONTEMPORARY USE

The Northeast remains sparsely populated. Its simple economy is based upon cattle ranching, farming, lumbering, and tourism. Away from the main roads and the few larger towns an individual might walk for many hours or even days without the sight of another human being. With possible exception of the Trans-Sierra, considered in the next chapter, nowhere else in California has man so little altered the landscape.

A generation of accelerated lumbering, 1939-1959, has been followed by recent decline. The Northeast is no longer a surplus timber source because of depletion of private stands. Operations have ceased at such places as Tionesta, Big Lakes, and Willow Ranch.

Around 800 men have been employed in lumbering operations. In the 1950's output of pine decreased, whereas white fir, not used before 1940, increased. Except for the still virgin Weyerhaeuser tract on the northern Devil's Garden, much of the timber must come from national forests, insuring some continued operation. Old logging railroads have been replaced by trucks, which transport logs as far as 75 miles, often over private trails, and permit logging from smaller stands, which is uneconomical with rail operations. Location east of the Sierran front results in slightly lower freight rates; hence considerable lumber is shipped east by rail.

Minerals have never had the major part in

Northeastern economy that they have had in the areas discussed in the next two chapters. A little gold and silver was taken from the northern Warner Range before World War I. Various deposits have been worked for highway construction. A drained lake bed in Jess Valley has been one of the state's few commercial sources of peat moss. Extensive diatomaceous earth deposits west of Big Valley remain unused.

SURPRISE VALLEY

Surprise Valley [2] has the highest rural population concentration in the Northeast. Its area (250 square miles) is small, and easterly portions have intermittent lakes, salt flats, and migrating sand dunes. Cultivation is restricted to a narrow 50-mile-long belt, where a score of small creeks issue from the eastern flank of the Warner Range. Four withering ranch villages are found here (see Fig. 1-2). The largest, Cedarville, is a crossroads junction with a lumber mill (Fig. 1-3). Its white frame houses, like those of a New England rural hamlet, suggest the nineteenth century. The towns are joined by a paved highway; elsewhere there are dirt roads.

Surprise Valley, despite its continuing seclusion, was the earliest center of livestock ranching in Modoc County. There has never been a local railhead, and beef is now trucked to market. Through the years ranches have been consolidated; hence the population has not increased. Transhumance (seasonal migration) is practiced, with livestock hauled into uplands of northwest Nevada in spring. The abrupt fault face of the Warner has discouraged its use from the east. Making hay for local feed is the principal summer activity; alfalfa seed is a commercial product despite ravages of the alfalfa weevil. Stream flow is diverted into contour ditches on the alluvial

2 Erwin G. Gudde suggests in *California Place Names* (Berkeley, Calif.: University of California Press, 1949), p. 348, that early immigrants on a California offshoot of the Oregon Trail named the valley after crossing the Black Rock Desert of Nevada and finding grass and sweet-tasting water. The subsequent research by Pease indicates the valley was named by its settlers in 1863 (personal communication).

fans and some pump irrigation is now employed. As elsewhere in the Northeast, cattle—either yearlings or two-year-olds—are usually marketed in the fall as "feeders." Due to rain-shadow position east of the Warner there is less snowcover than over much of the Northeast, and the livestock can be meadow-pastured much of the winter, which demands less hay.

THE WARNER RANGE

Isolation has prevented the Warner Range from receiving deserved recognition. If this alpine fastness were adjacent to Los Angeles it would be a nationally known playground. A little logging is conducted, and thousands of livestock graze on its meadows in summer. The most significant value of the range, however, is as a storage reservoir for moisture falling from east-moving air masses. To the limited number who know and enjoy these mountains, hiking, camping, trout fishing, and autumnal deer hunting are attractions.

The U.S. Forest Service has set aside the loftier south portion as the 75,000-acre South Warner Wild Area.[3] Here are found Eagle Peak (9934 ft.) and other summits, snow-fed glacial lakes stocked with trout, a scenic Summit Trail, and campsites.

The range does not create a serious barrier to east-west movement, despite the sheer eastern wall, because two deep notches with summits above 6000 feet provide passways. Cedar Pass affords an easy crossing for the paved highway between Cedarville and Alturas. Little-used Fandango Pass farther north was named by early immigrants.

THE PIT RIVER BASIN

The Pit River and its two headwater forks follow a crudely Y-shaped depression across the Modoc Plateau. There are two foci of ranching, the upper basin just west of the Warner and Big Valley downstream.

[3] Wild areas (less than 100,000 acres) and Wilderness areas (over 100,000 acres) are portions of the national forests that are to remain largely in the primitive state for enjoyment by nature lovers. There are eighteen such preserves within California.

The basin of the upper Pit includes Goose Lake Valley, South Fork Valley, and Warm Springs Valley (see map, Fig. 1-2). Ranching in Goose Lake Valley is limited because of the insufficiency of available water from the lower northern segment of the Warner, unfavorable soil conditions, and the small pasturage allotments within the range.

The basic land-use pattern in South Fork Valley was created in 1886 with consolidation of properties to form the large Corporation Ranch. After this property was sold, in 1947, the northern portion was used to raise malt barley. However, in 1959 Southern California interests purchased the ranch and an additional 18,000 acres on the Madeline Plains; the entire holding is now used for cattle ranching with extensive hay meadows. In summer, cattle pasture on Warner Mountain meadows.

Warm Springs Valley, westward from Alturas, is more productive than the sections of the upper Pit mentioned above; its ranchers tend to have incomes above the countywide average. One-time homesteads have gradually been consolidated into larger holdings. Meadows along the Pit are flooded and produce native hay; adjacent uplands provide dry pasturage. Some ranchers have summer range on Devil's Garden.

Alturas (2800)[4] is the seat of Modoc County and the second city of the Northeast. The service center for an extensive area, its commercial importance is enhanced by limited facilities elsewhere in Modoc County. Situated at the junction of federal highways 299 and 395, the city is about midway between Los Angeles and Seattle. Motels, restaurants, and filling stations have appeared beside older two-story business blocks along Main Street. This is the only Modoc community with specialty retail shops and automobile agencies. A westside lumber mill, established after most in the county, benefits from the railhead for shipment. Most of the remaining Indians of the Northeast reside in squalor

[4] Throughout the book population statistics are based upon the 1960 census, but rounded off slightly.

on the outskirts. Mansions are lacking here; residences are modest. Although it is a division point on the Southern Pacific's Lakeport branch, Alturas has lost most of its livestock shipment because cattle are now trucked to market.

BIG VALLEY

Big Valley, erstwhile lake bed along the middle Pit, has been partially drained. Homesteaders entered the area in the 1870's and 1880's after occupance of areas around Susanville and Alturas. The original 160-acre homesteads proved too small; hence holdings have been consolidated. Contemporary ranches average between 1000 and 2000 acres, partially irrigated.

This district, now a producer of feeder beef for California markets, suffers from poor marginal lands for summer pasturage. In addition to native hay, shallow-rooted alfalfa is now grown. Dairying is no longer significant; since highways have been improved the valley cannot compete against operators west of the Sierra-Cascade.

Big Valley towns are small (see map, Fig. 1-2). **Nubieber**, created upon linkage of Great Northern and Western Pacific tracks in 1931, failed to grow as anticipated; with the shift to diesel locomotives its roundhouse lost its importance. Lumbering contributes to the economy of **Adin**.

MADELINE PLAINS

The Madeline Plains is an ancient lake bed south of the upper Pit Basin. This locality has productive soils but lacks sufficient water despite winter swamps, which provide excellent duck and geese hunting. Storage in Tule Lake reservoir permits some irrigation, but dry-farmed grains are typical. A few extensive cattle ranches are scattered across the treeless expanse. The several diminutive communities have rail sidings, service stations, taverns, and shanties. Many travelers along U.S. 395 never slacken their speed as they traverse this plain.

THE NORTHERN BASINS

The western portion of the Northeast, unlike much of the land to the east, has been forested. For a generation after 1930 lumbering was significant, but this locale had limited use before it was crossed by rail lines and improved highways. Contemporary settlement nuclei are beds of pluvial lakes in northeast Siskiyou County: Butte Valley and Tule Lake Basin, partially separated by volcanic uplands containing Lava Beds National Monument. Elsewhere pine lumbering has been the economic mainstay. Reserves of sugar and yellow pine, cedar and red fir, were considerable, and sawn timber increased in value after 1930. The principal center was **Tionesta**, a company town established in the 1930's and once leading lumber producer and second town of Modoc County. When its timber was depleted, operations ceased; Tionesta has disappeared from maps.

BUTTE VALLEY

A group of Brethren, a Pennsylvania Dutch sect from the Middle West, established a colony in Butte Valley in the early 1900's following construction of the Southern Pacific's Shasta route into Klamath Falls. Attempts to apply humid-land farming techniques were unsuccessful. Although the "Dunkards" acquired a knowledge of irrigation agriculture, Butte Valley Irrigation District is critically deficient in water. The principal center is **Dorris** (1000), popular with sportsmen, a highway town that also has a lumber mill.

TULE LAKE BASIN

Development of the Tule Lake Basin into the principal agricultural area of the Northeast came late. After the Bureau of Reclamation constructed Clear Lake reservoir on Lost River the level of Tule Lake receded, permitting agricultural utilization. World War I veterans began homesteading on 80-acre tracts in 1922. During World War II, Nisei placed in a resettlement center reclaimed more land. After the war additional lands were made available for veterans to homestead; so many demanded land that it was necessary to employ a lottery to determine successful applicants.

The characteristic regional pattern of grains, native hay, and alfalfa and livestock

Fig. 1-4. BARLEY HARVEST, TULE LAKE BASIN. An appreciable amount of barley is sold to brewers; the remainder provides feed for local livestock. (Tulelake Chamber of Commerce and Tulelake Growers Association)

has developed but with modifications. For instance, the 80-acre homesteads are markedly smaller than the usual Northeastern ranch. Tule Lake, like the contiguous Klamath Basin in Oregon, produces late potatoes (Fig. 1-5). The basin suffers from its location, however. Salinas Valley and Central Valley deltaland growers are much closer to urban markets. A considerable portion of the barley (Fig. 1-4) is sold to brewers. Contrary to usual Northeastern practice, much alfalfa is marketed elsewhere. Since 1954 the basin has been the only west coast producer of durum wheat. Despite national shortage of this hard wheat, federal acreage controls prevent expanded acreage.

The 30,000-acre Tulelake National Wildlife Refuge west of the farming area was opened in the 1930's. It forms an integral part of the Pacific "flyway" for waterfowl; each autumn the basin becomes a mecca for duck hunters.

Tulelake (950), third largest community in the Northeast, is the newest center in the entire area; its continued growth reflects agricultural expansion (Fig. 1-6). The significance of agricultural shipment is evidenced by facilities along the rail tracks; it also forms the service center for the basin.

THE HONEY LAKE PLAIN

The Honey Lake Plain is a locale rich in early California history. For a century it has been a major gateway into the Sacramento Valley and all northern California. In early days Nobel's Road, Humboldt Road, and other routes reached across the mountains northwestward from Susanville, avoiding higher Sierran country and deeper snowpacks to the south. Discovery of gold in the northern Sierra evoked a brief period of boom and lawlessness. The dispute over the northern portion of the California-Nevada border was centered here, with the outbreak of the so-called "Sagebrush War" in the early 1860's. Briefly the area had even been part of the 50,000-square-mile Territory of Nataqua referred to previously.

The Plain was for a long while the only occupied portion of Lassen County, and much of the county's population remains concentrated here. The area northeast of Honey Lake, drier and hotter, is still little utilized.

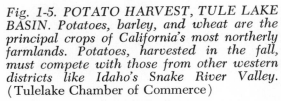

Fig. 1-5. POTATO HARVEST, TULE LAKE BASIN. Potatoes, barley, and wheat are the principal crops of California's most northerly farmlands. Potatoes, harvested in the fall, must compete with those from other western districts like Idaho's Snake River Valley. (Tulelake Chamber of Commerce)

Fig. 1-6. TULELAKE AND THE TULE LAKE BASIN. This thriving community serves as trade center and shipping point for the Basin—a structural depression whose western wall (rear) rises a thousand feet and culminates in Sheepy Peak (5258 ft.), right. (Tulelake Chamber of Commerce)

Northwest of the lake, lands along the Susan River are cultivated. Irrigation commenced in 1854 with flooding of hay meadows along the streams. Present-day irrigation works were not developed until the 1880's when the arrival of the Southern Pacific railroad fostered increased settlement. However, potatoes, an earlier crop, had been sold to the mine camps.

Yields of alfalfa, the principal crop on irrigated lands, have increased with land leveling. Most of the alfalfa is used locally as winter cattle feed. Grains such as wheat, barley, and rye may be dry-farmed but are also grown under irrigation. Yellow grain fields in late summer form an attractive pattern against the blue skies and the forested Diamond Mountains background. Potato yields are good, but market limitations have restricted vegetable production. Some milk is sold locally, but beef is more important.

The Honey Lake Plain suggests other Intermontane irrigated landscapes, with pastures, cropped fields, groves of trees, and farm buildings (Fig. 1-7). Productive land exists on well-drained terraces southwest of ancient Lake Lahotan and continues through Long Valley, which extends toward Nevada nearly 40 miles southeasterly along U.S. 395.

Susanville (5600), seat of Lassen County,

is the ranking community of the Northeast. The town lies athwart the Susan River, where that stream emerges from its Cascadian canyon (Fig. 1-9). It is supported by diverse incomes despite absence of spectacular growth. County business, rail traffic, farm trade, tourism, and several lumber mills contribute to its prosperity. The payroll at a state correctional institution has recently been added. Susanville serves as an eastern gateway to Lassen Park (see Chapter 6), which brings increasing tourists. Lassen College, a two-year county institution, is the Northeast's single seat of higher learning. Wide Main Street is flanked by many older business blocks. As in Alturas, deciduous shade trees provide a changing seasonal aspect. Newer homes erected on volcanic Cascadian slopes provide a view of the town and Honey Lake Plain from a coniferous setting.

Herlong (unincorp.) was established with location of the Sierra Ordnance Depot east of Honey Lake in 1942. It is a bleak community whose population has fluctuated with changing military demands. At times its population has ranked second to Susanville within the entire Northeast. For a military depot its site possessed advantages of dry climate, isolation, and rail access to Pacific ports. In the

Fig. 1-7. RURAL LANDSCAPE, HONEY LAKE BASIN. Livestock and grains are customary sights on the western edge of this relict of pluvial Lake Lahontan. Diamond Mountains (rear) form the northeastern fringe of Sierra Nevada. (Lassen County Chamber of Commerce, photo by Eastman's Studio)

Fig. 1-8. EAGLE LAKE AND SOUTHERN CASCADE RANGE. Past attempts to divert water from the lake failed; its future appears to relate to recreational use. (Lassen County Chamber of Commerce, photo by Eastman's Studio)

Fig. 1-9. SUSANVILLE, LEADING CITY OF THE NORTHEAST. The seat of Lassen County is situated on the extreme northwestern edge of the Honey Lake Basin at the point where the Susan River issues from its canyon within the Southern Cascade Range. Note lumber mill, lower left. (Lassen County Chamber of Commerce, photo by Eastman's Studio)

Fig. 1-10. CAMPING AT EAGLE LAKE. The vacationist delights in the absence of congestion which is common at more frequented vacation spots in the Golden State. (Shasta-Cascade Wonderland Association, Ken Molino)

late 1950's its prospects seemed unlikely until it was deemed a more satisfactory atomic-age storage site than Benicia in the San Francisco Bay Area (see Chapter 8).

EAGLE LAKE

Eagle Lake, 16 miles north of Susanville, is one of California's larger fresh water bodies and is conceded some prospects as a recreational center. Now accessible by California highway 139, the lake may have potential for water sports and camping. Its distinctive fauna has biologic interest (Fig. 1-8 and Fig. 1-10).

PROSPECTS

The Northeast has not shared much in the tremendous California population growth since 1945. With improved transportation, isolation should reduce somewhat, but the Northeast seems destined to remain on the outer fringe of the state. Urban encroachment upon farms elsewhere may encourage more intensive land use, yet short season and soil limitations will persist. Despite the beauty of the Warner Range and the environs of Eagle Lake, the setting of the Northeast should not encourage rapid recreational development, with the exception of hunting and fishing.

Fig. 2-1. DEATH VALLEY FROM DANTE'S VIEW (5704 ft. elevation). This complex rift is more than a mile deep. Note the long alluvial surfaces descending from the Panamint Mountains to the left. Near the middle of the picture is the lowest spot in the Americas (−282 ft.). (Mary Hill)

CHAPTER TWO:: THE TRANS-SIERRA

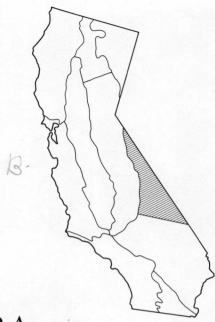

THE TRANS-SIERRA

The silver gray of the mesa
The alkali blotch below
The water pool's sheen where
    the grass grows green
And the far peaks tipped with snow [1]

To the eyes of poet Richard Burton such is the landscape of California on the "far" (east) side of the Sierra Nevada. This Trans-Sierran region, triangular in shape, encompasses 13,000 square miles and is delimited on the west by the abrupt front wall of the mighty Sierra, on the east by the Nevada border, and on the south by the northern limits of San Bernardino County (see Fig. 2-2). The characteristic features of this landscape ignore man-made delimitation and extend eastward into Nevada. The southerly definition is pure literary convenience and, like the ruler-edge political boundary on the east, which most certainly distressed the first

This chapter has been reviewed by Ruth E. Baugh, University of California at Los Angeles.

[1] From *Poems of Earth's Meaning* by Richard Burton. All rights reserved. Reprinted by permission of Holt, Rinehart and Winston, Inc.

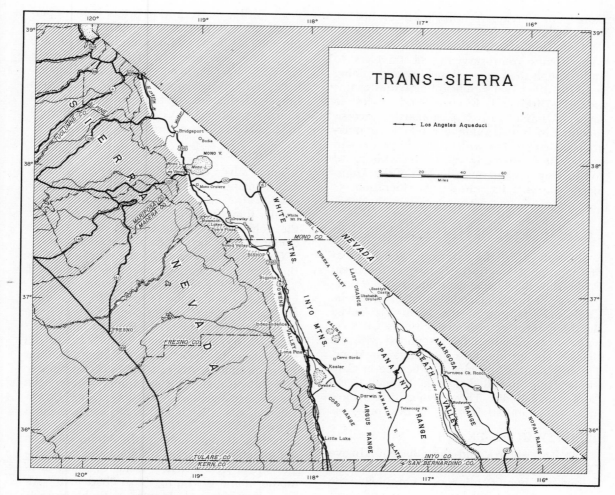

Fig. 2-2. MAP OF THE TRANS-SIERRA.

surveyors, is not indicative of conspicuous physical transformation.

Jupiter's niggardly rains coupled with the generosity of Vulcan have fashioned Trans-Sierran terrain into a striking succession of naked north-south trending mountain blocks and intervening elongated basins with glaring playas.

Man is a persistent intruder in the vast and almost empty Trans-Sierra. About three fourths of the 14,000 permanent inhabitants reside in Owens Valley, which contains all the larger towns. Extensive tracts of federal lands provide a practical indicator of meager re-

sources and sparse population over most of the region. Particularly, these include (1) the unassigned lands still in the public domain under the Bureau of Land Management; (2) Death Valley National Monument—almost a quarter of the region; (3) national forests in the White-Inyo Mountains and the unnamed volcanic tableland between Owens Valley and Mono Basin, dedicated primarily to watershed and range protection rather than forest preservation; (4) military testing grounds—over 700 square miles to the southeast of Owens Lake; (5) Indian reservations —especially that of the Piute, which occupies more than 100 square miles north of Bishop.

Economic supports of Trans-Sierran residents are limited. The dominant source of income comes from servicing of travelers to and through the region. Ranching and mining form the other two significant activities of this area. The former is localized and modest in scope. Mining output customarily exceeds ranching in annual value of product, yet operations fluctuate too widely for this statement ever to be consistently valid. The widespread role mining has had in settlement of the Trans-Sierra warrants its primary consideration.

QUEST FOR MINERALS

Minerals were the economic activity that first prompted Americans to tarry in the Great Basin—this has been as true of the Trans-Sierra as of the larger portion within Nevada. California's portion of the Basin has lacked the dramatic story of famed Virginia City, yet many of its hillsides have resounded with the ring of the prospector's pick against stone. The few centers of major significance in California have included Death Valley, Cerro Gordo, and Bodie. These major strikes have involved a limited portion of this province.

TWENTY-MULE TEAMS

The Trans-Sierra and the adjacent Mojave Desert have provided almost the entire world output of borate minerals. Originally the borates were associated with waters and gases that accompanied vulcanism; later these salines were deposited in lakes that eventually became playas (dry lakes or alkali flats). New borax deposits were discovered near the center of Death Valley in the last quarter of the nineteenth century. In 1882 working of the deposits commenced at the Harmony Borax Works. The refined product was hauled to Mojave, the nearest railhead, for shipment to Los Angeles.[2] Production continued for five

[2] The twenty-mule teams reputedly were eighteen mules and two lead horses. The 165-mile trip required ten days each way. Each wagon-trailer outfit carried 36½ tons, plus animal feed and water. The major production in Death Valley occurred after construction of the Tonopah and Tidewater Railroad northward from Ludlow (on the Santa Fe) in 1907.

years until a sharp drop in prices halted operations. Shortly thereafter a richer borax-bearing mineral, colemanite, was discovered, and production was resumed in 1890. The Pacific Coast Borax Company finally ceased operations at Ryan, its largest mine, in 1927 when lower production costs were achieved at Kramer (and still more recently near Boron) in the Mojave Desert (see Chapter 3).

PRECIOUS METALS

Three silver camps—Cerro Gordo, Darwin, and Panamint City—developed in this area shortly after the Comstock Lode. Less spectacular than the major Nevada silver center or the gold mines of the Sierra's Mother Lode Country, they have been almost forgotten.

Cerro Gordo, two miles above sea level in the White-Inyo Range nine miles northeast of Keeler, was the major factor in the economic growth of Los Angeles in the 1870's according to Remi Nadeau in *The City Makers*. Some millions of dollars were taken from Cerro Gordo between 1868 and 1877. Early in the 1900's the mine was again the state's leading silver producer. An electric bucket tramway was substituted for the mule teams on the steep switchbacks of its "Yellow Grade" downhill to Keeler. The mine has not been operated since 1940.

Gold was recovered in the Mono Basin in the nineteenth century. Among the more important centers of the "Mono diggings" was **Bodie**, home of the mythical "bad man." Although gold was discovered at Bodie in 1859, production did not reach a maximum until the 1870's, when the town had 12,000 population. A little mining was carried on again in the 1930's. Bodie is now a ghost town and is visited by a growing number of tourists, especially since it became a state park.

RECENT MINING

If all the mines ever operated in the Trans-Sierra were still active, what a lively land this would be! Yet as the foregoing historical review has shown, mining has been as ephemeral as desert lakes. Contemporary products are commonly extracted mechanically and shipped after minimum processing; hence much of the ultimate income is "exported" too. Most of the mining is economically marginal and therefore extremely responsive to slight price changes and especially to federal policies involving protective tariffs, defense purchases, and direct exploration incentives.

A major example of intermittent operation is Black Rock mine in the Benton Mountains 25 miles north of Bishop, which yielded more than $10 million in tungsten from 1954 to 1956, but has since closed (in 1963) owing to cessation of the government purchase program. Another prime example of intermittent operation is the Darwin district east of Owens Lake, where there has been irregular activity since 1874. Mines owned by the Anaconda Copper Company were reactivated in 1955 after a one-year closure, yielded between $5 and $10 million in lead and zinc through 1957, and subsequently were shut down with declining prices.

Momentarily uranium and borax have greater demand. The government has sponsored exploratory uranium drilling in the Darwin district, and small scale borax extraction has been occurring in four scattered localities—including the historic site in eastern Death Valley.

Two other minerals, talc and soda ash, have been extracted more consistently. Talc from Deep Springs and Keeler districts is used in such ceramics as wall tile. Soda ash, for detergents and window glass, has been obtained in increasing volume from the dry bed of Owens Lake by a Pittsburgh Plate Glass Company affiliate.

Owens Lake has yielded such salines as soda ash continuously since the early 1880's and qualifies as the most enduring "mine" in the region. Climatic change after the pluvial period in the late Great Ice Age eliminated overflow southward, and as the lake shriveled a concentration of salines occurred. Despite the mining, the limited population around Owens Lake emphasizes the inability of mining to support a permanent Trans-Sierran population. Although Bishop has served as the concentration and supply center for Black Rock and Sierran tungsten and Lone Pine continues to be a supply point for Darwin and Owens Lake, no major town in the area depends chiefly upon mining. Both these communities acquire much greater support from tourism.

THIS BARREN LAND

The Trans-Sierra is a land of desolation for many city-dwellers, a wilderness of sparsely vegetated mountains and seemingly flat basins. For the student of earth sciences, the prospector, and the "rockhound," it seems a paradise where the workings of nature lie exposed without the dense blanket of soil and vegetation characteristic of humid lands. To many a stranger from wetter climes it appears monotonous and barren. To one familiar with dry regions the land is a maze of intricacies resulting from slight variations in slope, relief, soils, and water availability.

THE GREAT BASIN

The Trans-Sierra belongs physiographically to that portion of the Basin and Range known as the Great Basin, nine tenths of which is outside of California. Its trademarks are attenuated youthful north-trending "splinter" ranges separated by alluvium-filled basins. No Trans-Sierran streams drain to the sea; this Great Basin characteristic also applies to much California desert country farther to the southeast. In fact, most basins have no external drainage—that is, they are *bolsons*. The flattish central portion of a bolson is a *playa*, which was a lake bottom during the pluvial period of the late Ice Age. With internal drainage, playas become intermittent, though shallow, lakes.

The Trans-Sierran ranges form three *en echelon* files and include some of the more majestic blocks in the Great Basin (Figs. 2-2 and 2-3). Their geologic histories, lithologies, and structures are too complex to permit simple description. It is sufficient here to note that these three rows generally decrease eastward in elevation and consequently in moisture supply.

The western row includes a magnificent horst, the White-Inyo Range, in the north, which has a group of high summits culminating in 14,242-foot White Mountain Peak, site of the University of California's High Altitude

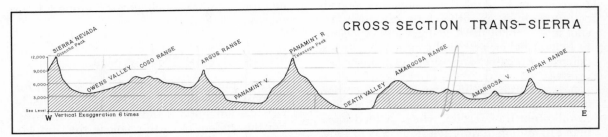

Fig. 2-3. CROSS SECTION OF THE TRANS-SIERRA. The parallel arrangement of the north-south trending succession of fault-block ranges and intervening bolsons, representative of Great Basin physiography, is well shown.

Research Area, and the Coso-Argus-Slate ranges in the south.[3] The middle grouping includes the Last Chance Range in the north and in the south the anticlinal Panamint Range, sufficiently cool to serve as summer headquarters for the Death Valley National Monument. Its single crestline reaches an apex in Telescope Peak (11,049 feet). The eastern tier, collectively the Amargosa Range, is generally remembered by visitors who have explored its colorful formations east of Death Valley at such places as Titus Canyon and Artist's Drive.

The four series of elongated basins that occur between the Sierra Nevada and the Nevada line are as remarkable as the ranges. The westernmost row, the Sierra Forelands, includes West Walker Valley and Bridgeport Valley in the extreme north and Owens Valley, 120 miles long, toward the south (Fig. 2-5). Between these two depressions is Mono Basin with its Volcanic Tableland through whose southern edge the Owens River has cut the gorge containing the sites for the city of Los Angeles hydroelectric production. The second group, least frequented, consists from north to south of Fish Lake, Eureka, Saline, and Panamint valleys. The four are separated by outliers of adjacent ranges so that each has a separate drainage system and playa floor. The third trough is occupied by Death Valley, a great depression with graben-like structure and including a salt-encrusted playa and bordering alluvial fans that often merge

into the pediments of surrounding mountains (Fig. 2-1). The easternmost basin is the Amargosa Valley, not a true bolson, since it contains the intermittent Amargosa River, which follows a U-shaped course around the south end of the Amargosa Range to terminate in Death Valley.

A SUMMER FURNACE

The Trans-Sierra is known for its sizzling summers. Such heat is more common in lower-lying Death Valley (lowest elevation —282 feet), where Furnace Creek averages 102°F. in July, and in Panamint Valley than it is in Owens Valley (Lone Pine has a July average of 75°F.) and Mono Basin. Actually, there is sufficient difference in temperature that the latter areas are recognized as middle-latitude, desert-steppe transition, the former as subtropical deserts (see Appendix A). A dome of high pressure over the area yields high temperatures and clear skies in summer; by contrast, midwinter days are generally pleasant (Furnace Creek has an average December temperature of 52°F.). Dominance of the Trans-Sierra by polar air, however, may bring subfreezing temperatures. Vertical zonation prevails in such mountain ranges as the Panamint, and higher summits in the White Mountains display alpine conditions.

Precipitation everywhere is slight; only on higher summits does it exceed 10 inches annually (Bishop averages 6.05 inches). Within proximity of the snow-laden Sierra Nevada surface water is somewhat more plentiful; scorched eastern portions of the region lack

---

[3] The White-Inyo Range is known as the Inyo Mountains in Inyo County.

sufficient grass for grazing. The chief source of moisture is winter storms from the north Pacific, although most of the moisture has been wrung out of the air masses in crossing the Coast Ranges and the Sierra Nevada. Although specific figures are generally lacking, the upper slopes of the ranges receive more precipitation. Such summits as White Mountain Peak and Telescope Peak are likely to wear snowy caps above 10,000 feet during much of the winter.

Uncommon but sometimes locally spectacular rainfall in summer may accrue from cloudbursts. Such precipitation infrequently results from westward movement of superior air from the western side of the Azores (North Atlantic) High. Turbulence over the ranges more frequently produces cumulus cotton balls that delight the photographer of Trans-Sierran landscapes. Usually however the precipitation from the cumulo-nimbus clouds (thunderheads) is modest—it may even evaporate before striking the ground.

SAGEBRUSH AND SHADSCALE

There are four principal vegetation associations in the Trans-Sierra. Sagebrush (*Artemisia tridentata*) prevails in the north and through much of Owens Valley. In the south its struggle against summer heat is indicated by stunted size. It is gradually replaced by the creosote bush (*Larrea divaricata*), which is dominant over much of southwestern Inyo County including the lower mountain slopes. The low, dry eastern basins support a shadscale (*Atriplex confertifolia*) formation. The higher slopes of the ranges possess a piñon pine (*Pinus monophyllia*) and juniper (*J. californica*) woodland, which usually includes mountain mahogany (*Cercocarpus betuloides*). Lesser cover includes bunch grass over parts of Owens Valley and the east Sierran pine forest, which prevails upon the Volcanic Tableland at elevations over 6000 feet. This is the single stand of marketable timber, although the piñon-juniper provided charcoal to smelt the lead-silver ores locally in earlier mining operations.

To the stranger the vegetation of the basins usually appears monotonously similar. Yet there are local variations resultant from changes in soil chemistry, water availability, soils, and slope. An impressive example is the desert holly (*Atriplex hymenélytra*) around Ubehebe Crater in Death Valley. Following rains, an impressive showing of annual wildflowers flourishes briefly.

THE SIERRA FORELANDS

The Sierra Forelands, consisting of the better-watered alluvial slopes along the eastern face of the Sierra Nevada from the West Walker Valley southward through Owens Valley (see Fig. 2-2), is the favored portion of the Trans-Sierra (Fig. 2-4). This dry land, whose stream flow comes from an adjacent mountain oasis, might well have become comparable on a lesser scale to Utah's Salt Lake Basin or the Colorado Piedmont if much of its modest water supply had not been tapped by the city of Los Angeles through its Aqueduct (Fig. 2-7).

HOME OF THE MONO

Before Anglo-American settlement the area was occupied by the Mono, a little-known primitive Uto-Aztecan people. As hunters and food gatherers rather than farmers, these folk doubtless had an arduous existence. Yet the streams provided fish and the grass-covered plains game; hence life was probably less difficult for the Mono than it was for their cousins the Koso, who occupied less fertile country to the east.

CATTLEMEN AND FARMERS

The first cattlemen settled in the Forelands in 1861 although Mono hostility discouraged settlement until Ft. Independence was established the next year; intermittent Indian troubles continued until 1865. The mining camp at Cerro Gordo afforded an early outlet for beef. Gradually, as the homesteaders increased, there was a shift toward irrigation agriculture. Ditches were constructed in the 1870's and the 1880's, but lack of a local market hampered farming for many years. Cattle and sheep, sold irregularly to mining camps but more often in Los Angeles, were the dominant products. By the 1890's some dairying was being attempted. Unseasonable frosts discouraged efforts to raise deciduous fruits.

By the early years of the twentieth century much of the readily available water was being used in Owens Valley, which contained around 40,000 acres under cultivation (in contrast to less than 10,000 in the 1960's). Much of the ranching was concentrated in the northern part of the valley (known locally as Round Valley and Bishop Valley) although Lone Pine and Independence farther south were growing market towns. Agricultural prosperity of the valley had been enhanced by the gold boom in Tonopah, Nevada. At this time a Bureau of Reclamation survey party visited the area and located an excellent reservoir site at the north end of the Owens Gorge near Tom's Place; this prompted Forelands ranchers to envisage much agricultural expansion. Before their hopes were realized, the city of Los Angeles had acted and constructed the Los Angeles Aqueduct.

A CITY SEEKS WATER

The city of Los Angeles relied upon the waters of the Los Angeles River through the nineteenth century. But as the metropolis grew it became obvious that in times of recurrent drought this supply was inadequate. Led by former mayor Fred Eaton and water engineer William Mulholland, Los Angeles embarked upon construction of the Los Angeles Aqueduct in 1908. This monumental municipal program, a five-year project, cost $23 million. It resulted in a 223-mile conduit comprising open and concrete-lined ditches and steel and concrete pipes, which in places were tunneled through mountain ranges. It required the creation of cement plants, a rail line, a telephone system, and construction camps. The Aqueduct (Fig. 2-7), with a capacity of 400 second feet, takes water from the Owens River north of Independence and delivers it to the San Fernando Reservoir for distribution to Los Angeles mains.

Continued growth of the city, coupled with cycles of drier years, prompted Los Angeles in the 1920's to purchase ranch lands and water rights (to augment municipal water supply) in the northern part of Owens Valley. Construction of the Long Valley Dam, storing 183,000 acre-feet in Crowley Lake, was undertaken in 1935 to supplement the supply. A few years later the Mono Extension was made, including an 11-mile tunnel through the dormant Mono Craters, so as to divert waters of Sierran streams contributing to Mono Lake into the Aqueduct.

Ranching population in Owens Valley and the Mono Basin has been severely restricted since Los Angeles requisitioned a water supply; presently the city obtains two thirds of its water and a tenth of its electricity from these areas. Having acquired much land as well as water rights, Los Angeles leases some 200,000 acres for grazing as well as such water for irrigation as is momentarily excessive of city needs. Inyo County leads the state in proportion of lease-operated ranch land.

EXODUS OF THE FARMER

Removal of much of its water supply markedly altered the economy of Owens Valley. Original aqueduct construction, accompanied by political maneuvering in Washington, D.C., did not change existing rural land-use in Owens Valley; however, in the southern part of the area it ended plans for irrigation expansion with water from a dam the Bureau of Reclamation projected in Long Valley.

Purchase of properties and water rights in northern Owens Valley in the 1920's markedly affected the economy of the basin. The decline of their rural trade areas was particularly difficult for the merchants of Owens Valley communities. Installation of pump wells by the Los Angeles Department of Water and Power on city-owned ranch land served to lower the water table during dry years. A considerable population decline in Owens Valley took place during the 1930's. This decline coincided with years of economic depression elsewhere. Many Valley farmers were fortunate in being able to sell to the city at a fair price.

Fig. 2-4. BEEF CATTLE, OWENS VAL-
LEY. *The rural population of this basin has
declined since Los Angeles built its aqueduct
half a century ago. White-Inyo Range is in the
distance.* (Mary Hill)

Fig. 2-5. SOUTHEASTERN FRINGE OF
OWENS LAKE AND THE COSO RANGE.
*The sparse vegetation cover and the gravelly
surface in the foreground are typical of the
structural basins. Unlike the pluvial lakes,
Owens Lake held water until Los Angeles
eliminated its natural sources. Now it is a
playa.* (Mary Hill)

Fig. 2-6. LONE PINE AND THE HIGH
SIERRA. *Lone Pine provides a gateway to the
loftiest portion of the Sierra Nevada. Mt.
Whitney (14,495 ft.) rises above the Alabama
Hills, which extend across the middle of the
picture.* (Southern Inyo Chamber of Commerce, photo by Bob White's Flying Service)

Fig. 2-7. THE LOS ANGELES AQUE-
DUCT AND SOUTH END OF THE HIGH
SIERRA. *The Aqueduct, with its extension
into the Mono Basin, has a length of 338 miles
and now provides the chief source of water
consumed within the city of Los Angeles.
Olancha Peak (rear) rises to 12,135 feet above
sea level.* (Los Angeles Dept. of Water and
Power)

WATER, RANCHING, AND TOURISTS

Cattle and sheep ranching, the dominant pre-irrigation activity in Owens Valley, has again become the chief mode of rural land-use since the construction and expansion of the Los Angeles Aqueduct. Only the occasional groves of cottonwood and willow indicate the previous position of farm houses. Aqueduct seepage has significance in providing grass forage around Lone Pine, Independence, Bigpine, and Bishop and in Round and Long valleys.

The evaporation of Owens Lake permitted establishment of processing plants to utilize the concentration of mineral salts on the lake floor. Borax and soda ash extraction, centered at Keeler and Bartlett, has been especially important.

The city of Los Angeles has become one of the major employers in Owens Valley. In addition to the maintenance crews required by the Aqueduct itself there has been almost continuous construction of additional facilities, including dams and power plants.

The tourist trade, largely a reflection of growth of Los Angeles coupled with construction of paved highways leading to the eastern Sierra, has become a major factor in the economy of the Forelands since 1940. This trade is unquestionably the reason that the population of Inyo County is more than twice as large today as it was before the Los Angeles Aqueduct was built. Most Owens Valley communities serve as gateways into the canyons of the Sierra's eastern face.

A COMMERCIAL CORRIDOR

Traversed by portions of two federal highways (routes 6 and 395) functioning as a single road (the Sierra Highway) through Owens Valley, the Forelands constitutes a north-south corridor of growing significance (Fig. 2-8), which might be described appropriately as "the back door into Southern California." Repeated road improvement coupled with absence of large cities permits rapid movement. Easternmost of California's three major north-south routes, U.S. 395 is popular with commercial travelers between Southern California and the Pacific Northwest and constitutes the main thoroughfare between Los Angeles and Reno. The highway is increasingly used by truckers engaged in hauling livestock from divers parts of the Intermontane Region into Los Angeles. In summer the route is the all-important avenue of approach for eastern Sierran vacation centers; winter brings snow enthusiasts.

For many years Owens Valley lacked a rail connection with the rest of California. In conjunction with construction of the Los Angeles Aqueduct the Southern Pacific built a broad-gauge line northward from Mojave to link with the narrow gauge that originally connected with lines serving Nevada mine camps. The line has functioned in later years as a freight route and no longer carries passengers except on trains used for motion picture or television films.

THE NORTHERN BASINS

Rural land-use is restricted in the northern basins to West Walker Valley and Bridgeport Valley.[4] The Mono Basin is largely a barren volcanic wilderness with little opportunity even for grazing. Landmark of the area is highly mineralized Mono Lake, thoughtfully labeled "undrinkable" on a recent map issued by the city of Los Angeles.

Mountain-girt Bridgeport Valley, well watered by the East Walker River, provides summer pasturage for hundreds of beef cattle. In the early days, homesteaders sold cattle and hay to such camps as Bodie and Aurora. With the decline of the mining camps, the homesteaders sold out to Kerman and Rickey, who planned to become cattle barons like Miller and Lux. When the firm went into bankruptcy, their Valley holdings were divided into five sizable parcels, averaging 4000 acres each. Because of the altitude (7000 ft.) and cold winters, no attempt is made at year-round feeding. In the late fall cattle are taken to lower-lying basins in Nevada (especially Carson, Mason, and Smith valleys).

[4] West Walker Valley indeed emphasizes the tragedy of the straight-line California-Nevada border. The bulk of the cultivated land is located within Nevada.

Fig. 2-8. THE SIERRAN HIGHWAY (U.S. 395), SOUTH OF BIGPINE. This improved thoroughfare, easternmost of California's three leading north-south highways, affords the principal gateway from Southern California into Sierra Nevada. It also provides a "short cut" to Reno, much of the Intermontane Region, and the Pacific Northwest. (California Division of Highways)

COMMUNITIES

Most Forelands towns are of the strassendorf (single-street village) form—seasonally green ribbons along U.S. 395. With groves of cottonwood and willow they remind one more of typical irrigated oases than of desert hamlets. Importance of tourism is reflected in the ubiquitous motels, cafes, filling stations, curio shops, and sporting goods stores. The width of the single thoroughfare (the highway) is suggestive of Mormon villages.

Bishop (2900), sufficiently distant from Reno and Los Angeles, acts as service center for an extensive area and contains a fourth of the entire Trans-Sierran population. Along its Main Street modern business blocks have replaced false fronts; there is a radio station as well as varied specialty shops. Plural func-

tions include (1) junction town (U.S. routes 395 and 6); (2) operations center for two tungsten mines and lesser mineral operations; (3) headquarters for Inyo National Forest, third most frequented in California; and (4) modest lumbering.

Tourism has evident significance in all Forelands towns; on summer weekends, motels display "no vacancy" signs. Bishop alone claims over half a million visitors annually. **Independence** (unincorp., circa 300), whose principal buildings are the yellow Inyo County courthouse and the Los Angeles Water and Power maintenance structure, is a cluster of single-story false fronts and residences along highway 395. **Bigpine** (unincorp., circa 200), whose farm trade vanished after Los Angeles purchased Big Pine Ditch and around 5000 acres of farmland in 1923, is a "wide spot" catering to wayfarers. **Tom's Place** (unincorp., circa 50), gateway to Rock Creek, Mammoth Lakes, and Lake Crowley, is an assemblage of tourist services despite the surrounding pine forests of the Volcanic Tableland that provides a different setting. **LeeVining** (unincorp., circa 200), distinguished by nearabsence of vegetation, lies near the junction with U.S. 395 of Tioga Pass Road (California 120) into Yosemite Park.

Bridgeport and Lone Pine have more appeal than LeeVining. **Bridgeport** (unincorp., circa 200), Mono County seat, has an ornate Victorian courthouse but neither bank nor high school.[5] It has a strassendorf pattern; false-front blocks are prettied with white paint despite an absence of sidewalks along much of the street. **Lone Pine** (1310), second city of the Trans-Sierra, has specialty shops as well as service stations and motels (Fig. 2-6). It forms the eastern approach into the Mt. Whitney area and lies at the junction of a Death Valley highway (California 190) with U.S. 395. The town serves as focal point for scattered mining operations.

[5] Mono County is an historical accident. Bridgeport became the seat of government when the early settlers discovered that their courthouse in Aurora was inside Nevada.

DEATH VALLEY

The eastern portion of the Trans-Sierra is more characteristic of the Great Basin as a whole. Mining operations are dispersed but neither Panamint or Saline Valley possesses a village. Remote Fish Lake Valley has a few cattle ranches and an expensive "dude ranch" junior college.

LAND OF THE KOSO

The aboriginal inhabitants of the eastern Trans-Sierra were the Koso, who were among the poorest members, materially, of the Uto-Aztecans. Life was most difficult for these people, and Kroeber (see Bibliography) doubts if their numbers exceeded 500. They resided in the mountain canyons but roamed widely in quest of food. Despite the poverty of their environment the Koso used it well. Juniper provided wood for bows; wild hemp, the string; and willows, the arrows. Such game as rabbits, rats, lizards, and even fly grubs were scarce; hence principal food items included piñon nuts, various seeds, mesquite beans, and even prickly pear cactus. The Koso often had to boil or wash their foods to remove concentrations of unpalatable salts.

A NATIONAL MONUMENT

For decades after its discovery Death Valley remained a wasteland, dreaded for tales of summer heat (the American record, 134°F., was measured here) and encumbered since immigrant days by its appropriate appellation. Borax mining over half a century contributed to a tourist industry through transportation and resort facilities developed by the mining company. In 1933 the Valley became a 3000-square-mile national monument operated by the National Park Service to preserve its landscape for recreational use.[6] Mining facilities

Fig. 2-9. *TEXAS SPRING CAMPGROUND, DEATH VALLEY. The modest facilities of this National Monument become congested during the cooler season of the year.* (David W. Lantis)

and commercial resorts that predate establishment of the monument remain privately owned.

A GEOLOGIC MUSEUM

Accessibility to densely populated portions of California, coupled with construction of paved highways, has been a major factor in the use of Death Valley as a winter playground.[7] The season, which lasts from October until May, usually has pleasant weather although sometimes winter storms bring general discomfort.

The main appeal of the Valley is its geology—it is veritably a physiographic museum. The best panorama of the area accessible by auto is from Dante's View in the Black Mountains (Fig. 2-1). Popular sites include Zabriskie Point, with its badlands; the salt pond at Badwater, which is near the lowest spot on the continent (—282 feet); the Devil's Golf

[6] In contrast to the national parks, national monuments are established by and may be abolished by Presidential proclamation with approval of Congress.

[7] Some thousands of persons now cross Death Valley each summer. Park rangers regularly patrol the roads in air-conditioned pickups. Visitors are given specific instructions regarding action in case of vehicular breakdown.

Course, which is the salt-caked bed of ancient Lake Manly; the pastel hues of Titus Canyon in the Grapevine Mountains; the Stovepipe sand dunes; and Ubehebe volcanic crater. Most visitors inspect the relics of the borax-mining era. There is also a variety of recreational activities. Accommodations are limited and at times become congested. Texas Spring campground, near the park headquarters, is popular with campers (Fig. 2-9).

PROSPECTS

There seems little likelihood of much change in utilization of the Trans-Sierra. Importance of the Sierra Forelands as a commercial corridor and as a Sierran gateway should increase, and Death Valley tourism is expanding. But for the size of this region, its economic contribution to California development is limited.

Fig. 3-1. THE MOJAVE—land of transit. View southwest toward Ivanpah Mountains. This introduction to the Desert awaits travelers on U.S. 91 (Interstate 15), motoring from Las Vegas across Ivanpah Valley. Note the many washes on the alluvial fan. (California Division of Highways)

CHAPTER THREE:: THE MOJAVE DESERT

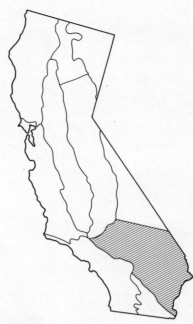

THE MOJAVE DESERT

Each summer many Middlewestern residents receive postcards like this one:

Los Angeles
July 10

Dear Folks:

We've had a hectic week trying to see and do everything here in California and we are beginning the homeward trek tonight—we'll need a vacation after we arrive! Bob does not want to cross the Mojave in daytime heat. We should get home in about four days.

Love,
Ann

Such a postal note relates two facts about the Mojave Desert: (1) its position athwart major communications routes between the North American interior and coastal California; and (2) its dreaded summer heat.

The Mojave Desert occupies one sixth of California (see maps, pp. xvi and 35). Although its general position is easily identified,

This chapter has been reviewed by Jeanne Garrison, El Camino College.

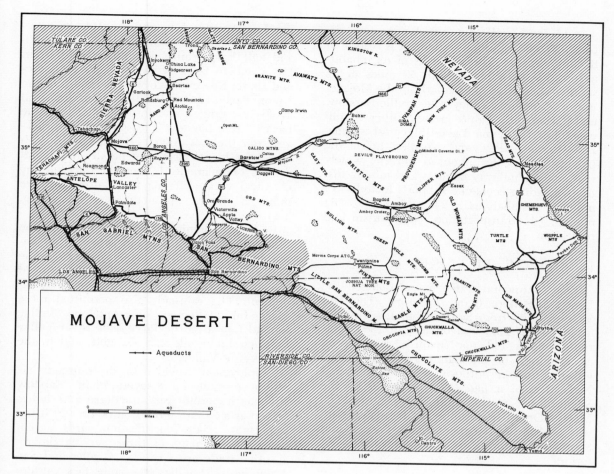

Fig. 3-2. MAP OF THE MOJAVE DESERT.

its extent is less precise.[1] All authorities seem in common accord, however, that the Desert is basically a natural phenomenon. By common acceptance it is restricted entirely to the state of California. The Desert, as described in this chapter, is bounded as follows: on the north by the southern limits of Inyo County, on the west and south by an almost continuous mountain wall (from northwest to southeast the Sierra Nevada including the Tehachapi Range, San Gabriel, Little San Bernardino, Orocopia, and Chocolate mountains), and on the east by the Nevada and Arizona lines.

The Mojave is possibly as naturally appealing to man as any desert of this size can be. Water is locally available, seasonal temperatures are less extreme than those of dry lands to both north and south, the terrain offers scenic variety, mineral-rich rocks are widely exposed, and it is accessible from the Los

[1] The following include some of the many definitions given for the Desert: (1) the dry portion of San Bernardino County; (2) the area bounded by the Garlock Fault, San Andreas Fault, and the Colorado River; (3) the southern California desert over 1000 feet in elevation above sea level; (4) the southern California desert with a normal growth season of less than 10 months; (5) the land of the creosote bush minus the ocotillo; (6) that desert northeast of Los Angeles. Many prominent Southern California geographers contend that the Mojave Desert "blends" into the Colorado Desert approximately at the San Bernardino County line.

Angeles Lowlands. Its population now exceeds 200,000 although settlement is restricted to limited areas. Three fourths of its inhabitants reside in a belt within 50 miles of its southwestern edge, particularly in the Mojave-Boron, Antelope Valley, Victorville-Barstow, and Twentynine Palms locales. Other significant clusters, China Lake-Ridgecrest, Trona, Palo Verde Valley, and Needles, house the balance except for about 5 percent widely scattered in highway hamlets and mining districts. Leading economic supports include (1) military installations, (2) agriculture, (3) mining, (4) transportation, (5) tourism and recreation.

LAND OF TRANSIT

Transcontinental traffic has challenged the Desert for more than a century. The **Old Spanish Trail** from Santa Fe to Los Angeles across Cajon Pass was opened in 1830. This route, neither "old" nor "Spanish," represented an extension of the **Santa Fe Trail**, which linked Mexican outposts in California and New Mexico; it had been projected by the Spanish even in the eighteenth century. The Mojave Desert is still athwart the major gateway (Needles-Barstow-Cajon Pass) into Southern California from the continental interior.

RAILROADS

Two of the five major rail corridors into California from the east cross the Mojave through trackage of two major carriers, the Santa Fe and the Union Pacific. The routes tend to follow the shortest courses permitted by the terrain. Today, as in the past, topography is a major consideration, but the waterhole, once so essential for locomotive water, is no longer important since the advent of diesel engines.

Transcontinental traffic commenced in 1885 when the Santa Fe Railroad extended its tracks from Needles to Amboy to Barstow, skirting the fringes of basins around the margins of the ranges. From Barstow the rail line follows the Mojave River Valley, then crosses Cajon Pass into San Bernardino and

the Los Angeles Lowlands. Later, construction in 1905 of the San Pedro, Los Angeles, and Salt Lake Railroad southwestward from Las Vegas to Barstow gave the Desert a second route; this trackage was merged into the Union Pacific system in 1921. This line also avoids the ranges, and in general follows the basins. From Barstow it leases Santa Fe trackage into the Los Angeles Lowlands. Branch lines have been extended generally to mineral centers (Permanente Cement at Lucerne, the chemical works at Trona, and Kaiser's iron ore mine at Eagle Mountain—see map, Fig. 3-2).

Railroads dominated traffic through the Mojave until the 1920's and provided an important measure of economic support in the Desert. Presence of local railheads reduced transit costs and hence favored mining development. The railroads also permitted more successful settlement of Antelope Valley around Lancaster, in the Mojave River Valley between Victorville and Daggett, and in the Palo Verde Valley.

Employment provided by the railroads has also been significant at several points. **Barstow** still has important rail functions: (1) it has served as a Santa Fe division point; (2) it has important freight classification yards significant in assemblage of trains serving the respective trade areas of Los Angeles and San Francisco; (3) it has the Santa Fe's western diesel shops. These facilities collectively employ approximately 1300. **Mojave**, of lesser consequence than Barstow, has still benefited as a division point on the Southern Pacific's Valley line at the eastern base of Tehachapi Pass. The Santa Fe facilities in **Needles** have been a major factor in the well-being of that community; in fact Needles originated as a railroad town.

UTILITY LINES

The average highway traveler probably has little awareness of another vital aspect of Mojave "transit"—the wires and pipes that deliver fresh water, natural gas, and electricity to coastal California. Oldest of such facilities is the Los Angeles Aqueduct, reaching across the western Mojave from the Trans-Sierra into

Fig. 3-3. LANDMARKS OF THE DESERT. *Joshua Trees, seen here in Joshua Tree National Monument, are among the most distinctive plants in the Mojave. They grow on well-drained surfaces, generally above 2500 feet elevation, and often indicate soils that are quite productive under irrigation.* (National Park Service)

Fig. 3-4. ROSAMOND DRY LAKE—"typical" playa. *These saline surfaces, often destitute of vegetation, are scattered throughout the Mojave. The sun-baked clay becomes a maze of cracks. Evaporation of the ephemeral lakes leaves a residue of saline minerals. This playa serves as an emergency landing field for aircraft.* (U.S. Air Force)

Fig. 3-5. JAWBONE SIPHON ON LOS ANGELES AQUEDUCT. *This is one of ten inverted siphons along the 338-mile-long aqueduct. The Mojave is an important corridor for transmission of water, electricity, and natural gas to coastal California.* (Los Angeles Department of Water and Power)

Fig. 3-6. PROVIDENCE MOUNTAINS—a *small-scale Sierra Nevada. The impressive escarpment of this faulted block rises a mile above the alluvial fan in the foreground. The vegetation is principally creosote bush.* (David W. Lantis)

Los Angeles (Fig. 3-5). In 1941 the Colorado River Aqueduct was completed across the southeastern Mojave from Parker Dam into the Los Angeles Lowlands (Fig. 3-8). Hoover Dam affords a major source of electrical energy for Los Angeles; transmission lines cross the Desert. Since 1947 natural gas has been piped across the Mojave. The first line, from the Permian Basin of eastern New Mexico, was opened in 1947; it enters California at Blythe and crosses the Mojave into Southern California. A decade later another gas line, from New Mexico's San Juan Basin, was completed into California; it enters the state at Topock to provide fuel for central and northern California.

HIGHWAYS

Since the 1920's highways have had increasing importance in the economy of the Mojave. Earlier routes tended to parallel the rail lines. Now the region is traversed by important north-south and east-west routes (map, Fig. 3-2). Two east-west roads, U.S. 60-70 and 66 (Interstate 40), are segments of major year-round transcontinental highways. The Sierra Highway, U.S. 6 and 395 (which becomes a single road across Owens Valley to the north), is the major California artery east of the Sierra Nevada, as was indicated in the two previous chapters. U.S. 91 (Interstate 15) from Barstow northeastward carries much Los Angeles–Las Vegas traffic (Fig. 3-1); its western extension (U.S. 466) has been used increasingly in recent years. Highways have tended to become more direct, showing less regard for terrain, older trails, and water holes; principal thoroughfares are being converted into freeways.

The Desert is laced with numerous unpaved roads. These frequently extend for miles over empty areas; strangers are advised to travel on them with caution, especially in summer.

HIGHWAY TOWNS

Services for wayfarers have fostered establishment of many retail businesses. Garrison estimates that at least a thousand families rely directly upon highway travelers for their livelihood. Larger towns are major nocturnal stopping points with motels and restaurants prominent. The life of many Mojave Desert communities depends upon the motorist. **Baker** is a prime example of a town whose entire existence is related to tourist services —it is largely an assemblage of service stations, motels, cafes, garages, and bars.

AIRLINES

The Desert is relatively unaffected by major transcontinental air travel. However, feeder service is provided by Bonanza Airlines (Los Angeles–Apple Valley–Las Vegas) and Pacific Air Lines (Los Angeles–Lancaster–northern and central California cities).

THE PHYSICAL DESERT

A person unfamiliar with dry lands may assume that all deserts are alike because of water deficiency and sparse population. Yet each of the three California deserts, the Great Basin (or Trans-Sierra, see Chapter 2), the Mojave, and the Colorado (see Chapter 4), has its own distinctive characteristics. There are differences in topography, climate, and vegetation; understandably there is difference in human utilization. For example, some Mojave surfaces (steep slopes, sandy areas, playas) hamper land-use, although terrain affords no handicap over considerable areas.

DRY LAKES AND
WORN MOUNTAINS

The Mojave is a land of broad flattish basins and generally low mountains, much eroded. Whereas the same processes operated here as those which produced the younger Great Basin, there is a wide difference in the geologic time calendar of landform creation, despite the fact that rocks date from very old to quite recent. There are four principal topographic types in the Mojave: (1) untilted blocks, (2) young fault blocks, (3) old fault blocks, (4) basins (bolsons). Locally, recent volcanism has also been of consequence.

The western Mojave is characterized by broad alluvial surfaces. Antelope Valley, a triangular area whose apex points westward, exemplifies the untilted block. Flanking its northwestern and southwestern sides respectively are the Garlock and San Andreas fault zones. The brunt of upward thrust was apparently exerted against the Tehachapi and the Portal Ridge–San Gabriel masses (see map, Fig. 3-2), whereas the Antelope itself has retained limited elevation. Consequently it has received alluvial burden from adjacent highlands with a spectacular series of coalescing alluvial fans descending from the San Gabriel and the Tehachapi. Several small tectonic protuberances, known locally as "buttes," disrupt the regularity of its surface.

The older fault block, worn by longtime erosion, and perhaps almost buried by its surrounding alluvial waste pile is especially typical in the central Mojave. The names of some ranges suggest their dissected physiognomy: Old Dad, Dome, Old Woman. Contemporary surfaces of some highlands doubtless reflect several periods of mountain evolution. Summits may still be quite craggy, even angular. At the base of fault cliffs terrain may still be rocky and rugged with steep stream gradients. Flaring outward are the deposits of intermittent streams that are gravelly upslope and that become sandy as they descend toward the adjacent basin, which is often quite extensive. The alluvium frustrates the detective work of the geologist who endeavors to trace the history of the Desert.

Younger and loftier fault blocks are especially conspicuous in the eastern Mojave; they include the Ivanpah, New York and Providence, Turtle, and Avawatz ranges. The abrupt west face of the Providence Mountains (Fig. 3-6), almost a mile high, affords difficult climbing and is suggestive of the eastern wall of the Sierra Nevada (Chapter 5). By contrast the nearby Cima Dome is so gently rounded as to suggest a giant blister on the earth—it can be traversed easily with a jeep. This difference suggests the intricacy of Mojave Desert geology, as do the impressive sand hills of this locality known as the Devil's Playground.

The many small ranges separate the lower-lying terrain into around fifty individual basins of varying size and altitude. Antelope Valley, described above as an untilted block, is considerably larger than most of the basins. Other better-known basins include Chuckwalla, Searles, Morongo, and Palo Verde. The typical basin looks flat from a mountain peak, but from its low point it slopes gently upward in all directions like a shallow bowl. Differences in natural vegetation reflect soils, depth of water table, and salinity. In the center of many basins are relics of extensive Ice Age lakes, such as Muroc, Rosamond, and Soda. These playas, or intermittent lakes, are usually dry, and their hardpacked clay surfaces may glisten with mineral salts (Fig. 3-4). After flash summer storms and winter cyclonic precipitation they will briefly be covered with shallow water.

OVEN HOT AND WIND SWEPT

The stranger, unfamiliar with the Desert, may dread its summer heat and with some justification, as this news account indicates:

DESERT HEAT KILLS TWO ON SEARCH FOR GOLD

L.A. Men's Truck Fails Near Amboy

The bodies of two Los Angeles men who died from heat and exposure when their truck broke down during a desert prospecting trip were brought out of Bristol Dry Lake in San Bernardino County yesterday by a four-wheel Sheriff's caravan.[2]

The above lead relates an incident that occurred only 14 miles from U.S. 66. The Mojave Desert is a land that experiences blistery summers yet frequent winter mildness, little rain, and abundance of sunshine. It is best considered a middle-latitude desert despite its "subtropical" (33° to 36°) position. Statistics are limited, yet topographic differences between basins and nearby ranges obviously create climatic variations. Average annual precipitation tends to be slight everywhere.

Precipitation follows the typical California seasonal pattern of winter maximum with an-

[2] *Los Angeles Times*, August 17, 1957.

Fig. 3-7. THUNDERHEAD OVER WILD HORSE MESA. Sufficient rain fell locally with this cloudburst to bring several years' "average precipitation." (Richard F. Logan)

nual totals ranging in amounts from about 15 inches in western Antelope Valley to less than five inches over much of the central and eastern Desert. East-moving Pacific storms, whose tracks are frequently well to the north (see Appendix A), lose much moisture over the Coast Ranges and the Sierra Nevada; hence even when overcast skies prevail across the Mojave slight rainfall is likely. The storms are relatively infrequent—even in winter the Desert receives 60 to 80 percent of potential sunshine. The average rainfall at Bagdad over a period of seventeen years was 2.28 inches—this includes three years during which no moisture was recorded! Winter precipitation, which increases on slopes of such higher ranges as the Providence Mountains, may even fall as snow.

The eastern Mojave is particularly subject to summer cloudbursts when low pressure prevails over the interior of southwestern United States and when position of the Azores (North Atlantic) High fosters westerly move-ment of unstable superior (i.e., upper altitude) tropical Gulf air masses. Even if no rain falls, impressive cumulus thunderheads may form (Fig. 3-7).

Temperature ranges, seasonal as well as diurnal, tend to be considerable. Because of clear air and nocturnal cooling, the daily summer range may be 30° to 45°F. and maximums above 100°F. are frequent.[3] The lower-lying eastern Mojave tends to be 10° to 15°F. warmer than the western Desert. Winter daytime temperatures are usually pleasant (with a maximum of 50° to 70°F.), except for periods when a polar air mass pushes southward from the Trans-Sierra or during passage of a cyclonic storm. Winter mildness contrib-

[3] Lantis has crossed the Mojave almost every summer since 1948. His most memorable experience was reading a temperature of 114°F. on the wall of an Amboy cafe at 10:30 p.m., August 10, 1958. Professor Logan of U.C.L.A. can provide more detailed information as result of his Mojave research.

utes to the recreational use discussed later.[4] Nocturnal temperatures, often well below freezing, preclude growth of midwinter and early spring crops.

Winds are a characteristic feature of Mojave climate and in winter and spring tend to be stronger and more frequent, with regional differences in temperature and pressure. Although the strong windstorms commonly associated with desert lands do not seem too prevalent, upon occasion it is possible for a car to receive a good sandblast, with the windshield becoming so pitted that it requires replacement. Additional winds include little dust devils, rising currents suggestive of a miniature tornado, common on summer afternoons. Relatively strong mountain and valley breezes also prevail.

BARRELS OF WATER

Water supply is a critical factor in Mojave occupance. Much of the water used in the region comes from nearby highlands through surface or subterranean flow; Antelope Valley and the Mojave River Valley are more fortunate than most of the Desert because of the adjacent Transverse Ranges. Over wide stretches of the Mojave no surface water is available. Along the Santa Fe Railroad and U.S. 66 east of Barstow water is shipped in by barrel or tank for the railroad, mines, towns, and highway points except where wells tap a subterranean supply of potable water. Locally there are a few springs at the base of mountains, but the flow is limited. It is understandable that Desert residents have keen interest in the California Water Plan (see Chapter 9).

CREOSOTE AND BURROWEED

The natural vegetation of the Mojave Desert, once significant to American Indians as a food supply, now has value for scenic appeal. The dominant vegetation type is the brownish green creosote bush (*Larrea tri-*

[4] Barstow temperature varies from 30°F. to 65°F. in January; 12°F. is the record low there. Contrast this with the record minimum of —36°F. at Madeline cited in Chapter 1.

dentata), sometimes called "false grease-wood," which grows in association with burroweed (*Franseria dumosa*). Widespread distribution of the resinous and evergreen creosote bush, growing 2 to 7 feet high, lends landscape monotony for the highway traveler and obscures the actual variety of vegetation types (Fig. 3-6). Actually there is considerable variation as a consequence of slope, depth of water table, soil conditions, and precipitation, although meager rainfall promotes a limited density.

Four vegetation associations merit note: (1) Such salt-tolerant species as pickleweed or sea blite may grow upon playas even though these highly alkaline surfaces may be devoid of vegetation. (2) On better drained hills and plains where desert shrubs are characteristic, saltbush, burroweed, and encelia lend variety to the widespread creosote bush. (3) Along the floodplains of the Mojave and Colorado rivers are riparian groves of cottonwood and mesquite thickets (Fig. 3-15). (4) On the upper mountain slopes there may be thin stands of juniper and piñon.

Well-known California desert plants add variety to these associations. The yucca, known as "Spanish dagger," is found on many hillsides below 2500 feet elevation, whereas another "lily," the Joshua tree, grows 10 to 20 feet high in groves on well-drained alluvial fans and lower mountain slopes above 2500 feet elevation (see Fig. 3-3)—it is especially prevalent in Antelope Valley and Joshua Tree National Monument. The palo verde, ironwood, and honey mesquite are especially common along sandy washes in the southern basins.

The somber-hued desert becomes splashed with color when the perennials burst into bloom at the end of a wintry rainy season— the red-flowered ocotillo, the yellow-blossomed palo verde, and the white waxy spikes of the yucca have particular attraction. When rainfall is sufficient the long-dormant seeds of annuals grow rapidly. California poppies and lupines are especially abundant in Antelope Valley. After a cloudburst, annuals with a brief life cycle may appear on basin floors despite summer heat.

KANGAROO RATS AND SCORPIONS

Animal life is surprisingly varied—although there is an impressive number of lower forms, the density of larger herbivores (and carnivores also) tends to be low, despite the bighorn sheep found in higher ranges like the Providence Mountains. Burrowing animals include the kangaroo rat, the white-footed mouse, and the jack rabbit. One occasionally hears the mournful yip of the coyote. There are spotted skunks, badgers, and diminutive kit foxes. Many of these creatures are nocturnal and seek shade during the heat of summer days. Reptiles include numerous lizards, the desert tortoise, the desert rattlesnake, and also the sidewinder, a rattler that has adopted a curious sideward method of keeping as much of his body as possible off the hot ground. There are a multitude of insects, including ants, flies, grasshoppers, and beetles; some, like the scorpion, are poisonous.

OCCUPANCE

The Desert, though broad expanses are now regarded as wasteland, has been frequented by man for thousands of years. The Pinto Basin in Joshua Tree National Monument is a significant site in investigation of early man in western America. During the pluvial period the Mojave was quite possibly a more attractive home for primitive peoples than it has been during the Christian era. At the time of the Spanish Conquest the Desert was sparsely populated by three American Indian groups, Serrano and Chemehuevi (representing the Uto-Aztecan family), and Mohave (warlike Hokan people). Yet the Desert was sufficiently empty that the European could occupy it without serious aboriginal opposition.

HUNTERS AND TILLERS

The *Chemehuevi* were a miserably impoverished people who occupied the central Mojave Desert after moving northward within historic times. A small tribe totaling less than a thousand members, the Chemehuevi were hunter-gatherers who eked out a scanty living from rabbits, rats, and reptiles and seeds of such plants as the mesquite. They even attempted a little agriculture where there was spring water. Their favored habitat appears to have been the higher, slightly damper area around the Providence Mountains. They avoided the hot basin floors as they migrated from range to range.

The *Serrano* representatives were not the true Serrano of the San Bernardino Mountains but the Kitanemuk of Antelope Valley and the Vanyuma of the Mojave River Valley; they were impecunious hunters whose livelihood was quite primitive.

The *Mohave* by contrast were sedentary riparian folk who dwelled along the Colorado River in the Needles Area. These were odd farmers who were both warlike and enthusiastic travelers, although they seldom borrowed the skills and techniques that they witnessed in their visits to other Indians. Mohave agriculture, the flood-basin type practiced elsewhere in the Southwest, depended upon utilization of the high water table immediately following recession of Colorado River flood waters. An actual application of water to the land was not undertaken. Crops such as corn, beans, pumpkins, and melons were planted with digging sticks and grew rapidly in the hot environment. In view of the fertility of river silts, yields were probably satisfactory. The Mohave also planted wild grasses and collected seeds from untilled floodplain plants. They did not have too much meat, but they relied upon fish from the river, which were caught by seines or by driving the fish in scoops along sloughs. The Mohave Indians retain much of the Needles Area, with Fort Mohave Indian Reservation encompassing a portion of the Colorado River valley in both California and Arizona. For many years the Indians were a familiar sight at the Needles rail station, where they sold trinkets.

MINERS AND FARMERS

The Mojave Desert remained largely unknown to the white man until the American period. The energetic Franciscan explorer Francisco Garcés visited the Desert in the 1770's and made friends with the Chemehuevi and Mohave Indians, but the Spanish established no settlements. As was indicated earlier, the Old Spanish Trail was not opened until the Mexican period (1823-1847). This route was pursued by the first American immigrant party overland to southern California in 1841 and was employed by Fremont on the eastward lap of his second expedition. This so-called Pathfinder is usually credited with naming the Mojave River valley—extension of the name to the entire Desert came later. The Mormons, who established a settlement at San Bernardino, made much use of the route also, although early knowledge of the Desert published in English came from governmental rail surveys in the 1850's.

The Gold Rush, railroad construction, population growth in Southern California, and the rise of desert mine camps were important factors in the founding of nineteenth-century towns in the Mojave. Earliest agricultural settlement along the Mojave River occurred in the 1860's, even before the first Desert bonanza strike. But the really dramatic increase in population did not take place until after World War II. Garrison cites these significant technological developments in recent Desert occupance: irrigation, air conditioning, energy sources (such as hydroelectricity and bottled gas), railroads, paved highways, and air transport.

MINING

Mining in the Mojave Desert has been less dramatic than in some parts of California. Still it has had intermittent economic moment since the 1880's. Early silver mining at such places as Calico and in the Rand District occasioned characteristic lawlessness and boom-camp excitement. Before 1900 some of the mine towns alone in the Mojave were more than mere villages. Much of the recent production has come from unspectacular industrial mineral products including cement, iron ore, potash, borax, and scheelite (tungsten). If petroleum is excepted, the Desert ranks high in production of minerals in California—some thirty-six different varieties have

had importance. Water has sometimes been the vital economic factor—often long hauls in tanks by rail or road have been necessary.

GOLD AND SILVER

Popular concepts of desert mining are often associated with gold, but contemporary production of gold in the Mojave Desert is negligible. Over 200 gold claims have been located in this region—outstanding producers have included the Yellow Aster (Randsburg) and the Bagdad-Chase (south of Ludlow). Yet it was silver that brought early development in the Mojave, even though this area has never been a leading producer. The brief activity at Calico in the 1880's subsided within a few years as market prices declined. After a long period of decadence the town was restored as a tourist attraction in the 1950's (Fig. 3-16).

The Rand District has been an intermittent producer of both gold and silver. A cluster of camps flourished following gold discovery in the 1890's. Most lucrative was the open-pit Yellow Aster, which was worked for many years and yielded some millions of dollars. California's major silver producer has been the Rand Silver Mine at Red Mountain, which was operated after World War II.

INDUSTRIAL MINERALS

In recent years the value of mineral products from the Desert has approached $100 million annually. Little of this has come from precious metals, for the Mojave activity is chiefly concerned with industrial minerals, including salines, cement, iron ore, and others.

Salines, particularly borax and potash, are the most important products. **Trona** (1138) is wholly supported by plants that pump brine from beneath the crusted surface of Searles Lake and by complex chemical processes provide various products for export from the Desert—potash and borax have had particular moment (Fig. 3-9). Southeast California contains 90 percent of the world's known borate reserves. At **Boron** in eastern Kern County (Antelope Valley) longtime borax mining has expanded drastically as a result of the demand for boron fuels and other compounds. A re-

Fig. 3-8. PARKER DAM AND LAKE HAVASU. *Parker Dam on the lower Colorado River was built in the late 1930's. Lake Havasu, a 55-mile-long reservoir, is used for recreational purposes while hydroelectricity is generated at the dam. Two miles above the dam is the intake for the Colorado River Aqueduct, which delivers water to the ninety-six cities plus unincorporated localities that belong to the Metropolitan Water District.* (Metropolitan Water District)

Fig. 3-9. TRONA AND SEARLES LAKE. *Desolate Searles Lake, a playa with a solid saline crust 10 feet thick, has highly complex brines. It is one of two major sources of potash within the United States. This elaborate chemical plant processes a variety of potassium, calcium, sodium, lithium, and bromine salts.* (American Potash and Chemical Corporation)

Fig. 3-10. OPEN-PIT BORAX MINE AT BORON. *This vast, near-surface deposit of borax represents one of the more recent mining operations in the Mojave.* (U.S. Borax, Los Angeles)

Fig. 3-11. IRON-ORE MINE AT EAGLE MOUNTAIN. *Ores from this replacement magnetite deposit have been mined since 1948 and are shipped to California's only integrated steel mill at Fontana.* (Kaiser Steel Corporation)

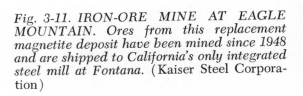

cently developed open-pit mine and $20 million processing plant dominate the landscape here, and settlement has followed (Fig. 3-10). The reserve is large, high in grade, and near the surface. The nearby town of **Desert Lake**, a planned community, has materialized since 1953.

Manufacture of *cement* from local minerals is consequential in the Mojave Desert and is largely a reflection of proximity to Southern California markets. Production commenced around 1910; additional plants have been opened and older facilities enlarged. Specific location has been influenced by extensive limestone deposits and rail facilities. The major concentration is the Mojave River Valley, where Southwestern Portland Cement at Victorville and Riverside Cement at Oro Grande constitute two of the larger plants in western United States. In the late 1950's additional plants were constructed by Permanente Cement at Cushenbury in Lucerne Valley and California Portland Cement near Mojave. The continued population growth in Southern California makes future prospects encouraging.

The Desert has provided *iron ore* for Kaiser Steel at Fontana (Chapter 7) since 1942. The first operation was conducted at the Vulcan Mine on the southwestern side of the Providence Mountains. After completion of a 50-mile rail link with the Southern Pacific, Vulcan was abandoned in favor of Eagle Mountain (north of U.S. 60-70) in 1948. The magnetite replacement deposit here contains over 40 million tons of ore varying in content from 30 to 50 percent (Fig. 3-11). **Eagle Mountain** has been cited in *Time* as a model example of the "new" company mining town.

Scheelite (tungsten) has come especially from Atolia in the Rand District—this is the largest known deposit of high-grade scheelite in the nation. It will be noted (Chapter 5) that tungsten ore has also come from the eastern Sierra Nevada and Trans-Sierra (Chapter 2).

The Desert is characterized by many smaller, widely dispersed enterprises. Some are oriented toward the Los Angeles market and tend to conduct steady operations. For example, gypsum for plasterboard comes from Midland, and common table salt and calcium chloride from the brines of Bristol Lake. The Bristol salt (sodium chloride) is used in industrial chemicals at Henderson, Nevada, and in the water-softening operations of the Metropolitan Water District at La Verne. Despite many playa salt deposits, Bristol Lake is the only one that has been used extensively. Some lesser operations are related to the erratic Federal defense program, such as manganese from the Little Maria Mountains and tungsten from Atolia; hence production tends to be intermittent.

AGRICULTURAL AREAS

The Mojave Desert would make a prosperous farming area, with its advantages of through rail lines and major highways, abundance of flat to rolling land, long growing season, and proximity to Los Angeles markets —*if* only it had water. Where irrigation water is available, agriculture has moment. Other local considerations have included soils, "cheap" land, capital, mechanization, governmental assistance. Most farms are single-family, owner-operated propositions.

Much of the Mojave is not well suited for livestock ranching. The grazing capacity of its natural vegetation is low; it permits no more than five head of cattle per square mile in the northeast. Moreover, the low mountains do not provide alpine grasslands for transhumance. Accordingly vast stretches are devoid of cattle and sheep ranches. Yet it was stockmen rather than miners who constituted the first group of Anglo-Americans to settle in the Desert. By the 1860's there were ranches along the Mojave River and some crops were produced near Victorville. More recent dryland grazing has been restricted largely to the northeastern Mojave Desert around the higher ranges. Grazing is a marginal activity, dependent upon sufficient winter rain and the large California beef market. Over 60,000 acres under irrigation in the Desert is related to livestock feeds—this especially represents raising of alfalfa.

THE ESSEX DISTRICT

The contiguous Clipper and Lanfair valleys north of Essex represent a distinctive grazing area—this part of the Mojave has greater vegetation density than most of the Desert. These somewhat higher surfaces (between 3000 and 4000 feet) carry a cover of bunch grass and shrubs upon which the cattle browse —the loftier Providence and New York mountains trap more moisture than most ranges in the Desert. Even so there are fewer than a dozen cattle ranches. Headquarters are situated in canyons at the base of the ranges where water from limestone formations provides a steady spring flow. Natural forage is sufficiently limited that alfalfa is imported for supplemental feed. Winter isolation from drifting snow, though infrequent, has constituted a hazard. In the past, hundreds of cattle perished—during the winter of 1948-49 a "haylift" (i.e., dropping of hay from low-flying aircraft) was employed.

THE PALO VERDE VALLEY

The Palo Verde Valley,[5] remindful of a miniature Indus or Nile, is a crescentic segment of the lower Colorado River floodplain in the southeastern Mojave. This area, now the Desert's leading agricultural producer, suggests Colorado Desert agricultural landscapes (Chapter 4). Its cultivated fields form a vivid contrast with the barren, uncultivated Chuckwalla Valley to the west along U.S. 60-70.

Palo Verde irrigation development was delayed until the early twentieth century, although San Francisco financier Thomas Blythe acquired title to 39,000 acres under the Swamp and Overflow Act in 1874 and added another 35,000 acres through his "controlled" entrymen under the Desert Act a few years later. In 1877 he made the first California filing for Colorado River water, thus assuring the Valley prior rights on the stream. Blythe died in 1883 before development was scarcely com-

[5] The authors concur with Logan (personal communication) that Palo Verde agriculture more properly belongs in Chapter 4, except it lies outside of the Colorado Desert as it is defined in this book.

menced; during a long period of estate litigation most of the original irrigation works were destroyed by floods. After court decision finally permitted development, the Palo Verde Mutual Water Company sold land and constructed a new irrigation system. Inadequate market outlets posed a problem until ranchers floated bonds and constructed their own rail line, the California Southern, to connect with the Santa Fe mainline at Cadiz in 1915. After completion of the rail outlet, cotton became the chief crop; production was expanded to 32,000 acres in 1919. Cotton remained the principal commodity until the depression period of the 1930's.

LEADING PALO VERDE VALLEY PRODUCTS, 1961
(all values in millions of dollars)

	ACREAGE	VALUE
Truck Crops	12,500	8.0
lettuce	5,800	3.2
cantaloupes	2,800	2.4
watermelons	2,200	1.0
Field Crops	90,000	12.0
cotton	18,000	6.7
alfalfa	28,000	3.5
barley	8,000	0.67
Livestock	—	9.8

Source: Agricultural Commissioner, Riverside County.

Agricultural expansion was delayed until construction of Hoover Dam—frequent Colorado River rampages crippled irrigation works and destroyed crops. In fact, floods required repeated replacement of the granitic barrier across the river, The Weir, which served as an irrigation canal diversion. The Valley has been plagued also by drainage problems— since the land slopes away from the slightly higher natural levee, fields toward the west have had a higher water table. For a time, too, depressed farm prices and a sizable bonded indebtedness occasioned farm abandonment until a Reconstruction Finance Corporation loan was obtained by the irrigation district in 1934.

The Valley, despite its small size (170

square miles), subsequently has become a prosperous agricultural oasis, producing cotton, melons, alfalfa, lettuce, and livestock. Cotton monoculture persisted into the 1930's, but by 1938 acreage of alfalfa, shipped to the Los Angeles dairy belt, exceeded cotton. More recently cotton acreage has been restricted by federal allotments. The season permits five to seven cuttings of alfalfa between March and October. Truck farming (especially lettuce and melons) is usually large scale—considerable absentee-owned land is leased. Cantaloupes and watermelons, harvested "early" (May to July), tend to yield premium prices (Fig. 3-13). Livestock, which is imported from Western rangelands in the fall, fattened and shipped to Los Angeles in late winter, augment farm incomes. The irrigation situation has been improved too, with construction of a low dam to replace The Weir.

Blythe (6000), marketing and shipping point of the Valley, benefits from travelers on U.S. 60-70. The stately palms along its main street and the downtown sidewalk canopies reflect the climate (Fig. 3-12). As the largest city between Phoenix and Indio, Blythe has grown with agricultural expansion; it is also the service center for an extensive area. U.S. 60-70 provides a major highway gateway into California; increased winter travel particularly benefits Blythe establishments. Much freight has been diverted from railroad to highway, and considerable beef and alfalfa move to Los Angeles markets by truck.

ANTELOPE VALLEY

Antelope Valley, occupying 1500 square miles in the westernmost Mojave Desert, is also favored for agriculture more than most of the Desert: (1) the natural funnel produced by convergence of the Tehachapi and San Gabriel ranges produces slightly more rainfall; (2) additional water, both surface and underground flow, comes from these peripheral mountains; (3) terrain and soils are suitable; (4) the Valley is closer to metropolitan Los Angeles than much of the Mojave; (5) U.S. highway 6 and the Valley Line of the Southern Pacific provide good transportation facilities; (6) urbanism in the Los Angeles Lowlands is promoting some agricultural relocation here (see Chapter 7). Approximately 90,000 acres are cultivated, but only about half of this is cropped annually.

Farming has been practiced in the Valley for over three quarters of a century. In the early 1880's bunch grass permitted localized grazing during winter and spring. The "boom of the eighties" in Southern California fostered agriculture in the west and also around Palmdale. Promoters sold many parcels for grain farming, usually to newcomers unfamiliar with rainfall cycles in this nearly arid land. The purchasers were told that the water table was high and that winter rains would provide moisture for grains. The "wet cycle" then prevalent permitted several good grain harvests —750 carloads of wheat were reportedly shipped in 1893. The ensuing drier period was disastrous for many settlers, and much land was abandoned.

Establishment of six irrigation districts in the eastern Antelope Valley paralleled grain farming farther west. Unfortunately the irrigation supply depended upon minute streams draining the north slopes of the San Gabriel Mountains. Southern Antelope Valley Irrigation Company, which spent $180,000 for Little Rock Reservoir and a canal system, was the largest project. Thousands of acres of almonds and prunes were planted. After an eleven-year period of extreme dryness, which commenced in 1893-94, only one irrigation district survived. Many trees perished, and other orchards were severely curtailed. By 1905 only 250 acres of pears, 200 acres of apples, and 50 acres of almonds remained along Little Rock Creek. Forty families had built homes along Rock Creek in the 1890's—within fifteen years only five families remained.

Agricultural curtailment proved temporary. Well drilling had commenced in the 1870's, and settlers were cognizant of a 240-square mile artesian basin under the Valley floor. As early as 1900 some land was being irrigated with artesian flow west of Lancaster. Concentrations of salts produced "white" and "black" alkali and necessitated an experimental period

Fig. 3-12. BLYTHE AND THE PALO VERDE VALLEY. *The Palo Verde Valley, a segment of the lower Colorado River valley, is the most productive agricultural area in the Mojave. Blythe, its trade center, is an important port of entry. Its main street, Hobson Way, lies along the midpoint of the photo, extending eastward toward Arizona's Dome Rock Mountains. (Palo Verde Chamber of Commerce, photo by Bert Watts Photography)*

Fig. 3-13. HONEYDEW MELON HARVEST, PALO VERDE VALLEY. *California is the nation's leading producer of these melons. The Palo Verde Valley is an early season source. (Palo Verde Chamber of Commerce, photo by Bert Watts Photography)*

Fig. 3-14. FLIGHT LINE AT EDWARDS AIR FORCE BASE. *The Air Force tests its new aircraft designs at this Antelope Valley installation. Rogers Dry Lake is in the rear. (U.S. Air Force)*

Fig. 3-15. NEEDLES—*major port of entry. This old railroad division point on the mainline of the Santa Fe and U.S. 66 (Interstate 40), lies at the base of the Sacramento Mountains along the floodplain of the Colorado River. (Needles Chamber of Commerce, photo by Harrison Dhormann)*

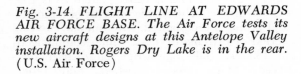

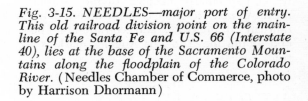

to ascertain most promising land. Continued drilling of wells depleted artesian pressure and pumping was required before 1910. As late as that year most of the Valley had use only for seasonal pasturage. Agriculture gradually stabilized with restriction of cultivation to more productive lands.

LEADING ANTELOPE VALLEY PRODUCTS, 1961
(all values in millions of dollars)

	ACREAGE	VALUE
Fruits and Nuts	2,400	0.7
pears	260	0.28
peaches	370	0.21
almonds	1,580	0.15
Field Crops	48,000	6.1
alfalfa hay	32,000	4.5
wheat	5,400	0.3
irrig. pasture	1,800	0.22
barley	3,500	0.1
Truck Crops	1,260	0.6
potatoes	500	0.28
cantaloupes	350	0.2
Livestock (& products)	—	2.8
beef	—	1.9
milk	—	0.64
sheep	—	0.4
Poultry	—	9.9
turkeys	—	4.4
chickens	—	3.3
eggs	—	1.9

Source: Agricultural Commissioner, Los Angeles County.

The contemporary agricultural mosaic was established essentially by the middle 1920's. It had been learned that the saline fringes of Rosamond Dry Lake were untillable. The pump-well belt, focusing upon Lancaster, is crescentic toward the south and west (much of the water drains from the San Gabriel Mountains). As pumping methods improved with employment of larger motors, it became possible to tap deeper gravel lenses. However, the pumped area tends to be restricted on higher portions of alluvial fans because the water table is too deep. Increasing precipitation toward the west (with higher elevation) permits dry-farming of grains, and even some orchards near the mountains. Surface flow

allows modest canyon-mouth irrigation along Rock Creek and Little Rock Creek. Alfalfa, which had become the principal crop, was shipped to Los Angeles by rail at first, but by the 1920's some shipments were going by truck.

The rural economy of Antelope Valley has been modified since 1940. In the west holdings have been consolidated. Employment of strip farming checks erosion and conserves moisture, and dry-farmed wheat and barley are successful in years of ample rainfall—approximately 40,000 acres are produced. Farms, highly mechanized and owner-operated, average around 1000 acres each. A few almond orchards remain. The pump-well belt to the east benefits from proximity to Los Angeles but is hampered by a steadily declining water table (60 to 200 feet deep). Five and a half cuttings a year of alfalfa are usual, and much hay is trucked to the Los Angeles dairy belt (Chapter 7). Urban markets also afford an outlet for such truck crops as carrots and melons. Many poultry ranches have been established since 1945 as urbanization in the San Fernando Valley (Chapter 7) forced relocation.

Impressive urban growth has occurred around the twin communities of **Lancaster** (26,000) and **Palmdale** (11,500). Lancaster increased fourfold during the 1950's and has become the largest city and ranking service center of the entire Desert. Much growth in both towns has been related to residential functions for activities at Palmdale Airport and Edwards Air Force Base. There has also been considerable expansion of services for travelers on U.S. 6. After 1950, aircraft companies located in metropolitan Los Angeles established testing facilities at the Palmdale Airport. With their housing tracts, both communities resemble newer Los Angeles suburbs. Lancaster has a considerable number of trees for a Mojave Desert town. **Mojave** (1800) to the north remains more singularly concerned with its railroad functions and highway services. Water is too precious to be wasted; hence trees and gardens are almost absent and the town looks bleak.

THE MOJAVE RIVER VALLEY

The Mojave River Valley forms an attenuated ribbon of greenery amidst the gray desert hues as it extends crescent-like for over 60 miles. The Mojave River, which rises on the northeastern slopes of the San Bernardino Mountains, constitutes one of the major streams of the Desert. Although its surface flow generally disappears into its sandy bed upstream from Victorville, its subsurface flow continues past Afton, 50 miles east of Barstow, and can be tapped by shallow wells. During the late Pleistocene its waters fed pluvial lakes Manix (Afton) and Soda, and then flowed into Lake Manly in Death Valley (Chapter 2).

The Valley has been a commercial corridor for more than a century, first as a segment of the Old Spanish Trail, then for emigrant trains and Mormons traveling between Salt Lake and San Bernardino. Then came the main line of the Santa Fe and eventually U.S. 66. The Desert's first cattle ranching was conducted here—this mode of utilization remains significant, and alfalfa fields are commonplace. Availability of water bears out the statement made at the beginning of the section about Desert agriculture. Poultry ranches and fields of potatoes and onions have modified older land-use patterns.

Farming has not been the principal force behind recent growth of Valley towns, however. **Victorville** (5000), site of a new junior college, was a nineteenth-century miners' outfitting point; its false fronts were once popular settings for "western" motion pictures. Today Victorville serves as the center of the upper valley (known locally as Victor Valley) and derives considerable income from wayfarers on U.S. 66, personnel at George Air Force Base, and employees of two large cement plants.

Barstow (12,000), ranking community of the central Desert, is well located; it is readily understandable that it is the second city of the region. It was founded as a rail junction town in 1886 although Daggett to the east served as Calico's railhead. Later Barstow gained importance as a railroad division point. It has extensive freight classification yards and

Fig. 3-16. CALICO LOOKS LIKE A TELEVISION WESTERN LOT. This nineteenth-century mining camp has been restored as a tourist attraction. (David W. Lantis)

since 1945 has been the site of the Santa Fe's "running" diesel repair shops. Other sources of income accrue from services to highway travelers, from its status as a subregional service center, and from the nearby Marine Corps Depot. Garrison in her thesis has described the location of Barstow as a "tank of gas from Los Angeles, Las Vegas, and Needles." Service stations, cafes, and motels are much evident. More than a million visitors annually pass near the city by freeway. Barstow is the shopping center for a hinterland of approximately 10,000 square miles. Several thousand civilian and military personnel are employed at the Marine Corps Depot.

THE NEEDLES AREA

The Needles Oasis, long utilized by the Mohave Indians, has not achieved the agricultural output of the Palo Verde Valley—although it is larger than the downriver area, it has been handicapped much more by Colorado River inundations. Also, much of it is Indian land although prior water rights on the Colorado have not been established.

The Cotton Land Company purchased railroad tracts in 1909 and also leased some acreage from the Fort Mohave Indian Reservation. Crop prospects seemed excellent until the river went on a pre-harvest rampage, and operations were never resumed. In 1953, many years after Hoover Dam had eliminated the flood threat, a revival of farm activity took place, and the Arizona side of the floodplain was cleared of tamarisk and willows. Optimists have anticipated that eventual production may rival that of the Palo Verde Valley. There is very little arable land on the California side.

Needles (4600), which long was the largest community in the entire Desert, was established in 1883 as a projected Santa Fe division point. It has a more settled atmosphere than many Mojave Desert towns (Fig. 3-15), even though it has not achieved the recent growth of Lancaster and Barstow. Although the railroad payroll is still significant, services to travelers on U.S. 66 have become important. The town is lower in elevation than any Mojave community except Blythe; proximity of the Colorado River increases summer humidity. Despite a reputation for summer heat, Needles profits from absence of nearby commercial rivals.

LUCERNE VALLEY

Agricultural development of Lucerne Valley, southeast of Victorville at the base of the San Bernardino Mountains, has been relatively recent. As late as the 1920's much of the limited farming was marginal; by 1925 around 500 acres (in small holdings) were cultivated. Such operations were generally abandoned during the depression years of the 1930's. Contemporary farming tends to be more substantial, and alfalfa is trucked to Los Angeles markets; feeder cattle are pastured on irrigated meadows. There are poultry ranches, some operated by the increasing number of retired couples. Some operators, city residents, are "weekend" farmers. Establishment of a few guest ranches reflects the desire of Angelenos to seek temporary refuge in the desert.

Despite a continuing artesian supply, water continues to be a restricting factor—this area anticipates eventual importation of water from northern California.

MILITARY INSTALLATIONS

The Pacific Theater in World War II and subsequent military preparedness have accounted for persistence of military installations in the Mojave Desert. Space, climate, and communications have been significant permissive considerations. Each of the major services maintains at least one large establishment—such utilization irritates those who decry unnecessary federal waste (i.e., duplication of facilities) despite the apparent worthlessness of much of these reserved tracts. Yet as many as 28,000 military employees and 10,000 civilian contractors' personnel have added to governmental payrolls in the Desert during the past decade.

Installations are space oriented: acreages necessary for testing aircraft and missiles and for target ranges have been available. Approximately a sixth of the entire Mojave is contained within military bases; elsewhere wanderers are cautioned against picking up "duds" remaining from World War II testing activities.

Military installations tend to be climate related, which is one reason for concentration here rather than in the Northeast or the Trans-Sierra. The dry climate permits outdoor preservation of many supplies at the Marine Corps Depot east of Barstow, for example. The Depot constitutes the Marines' chief storage and repair center in western United States. It has excellent highway and rail facilities.

Communications constitute a third locational factor. Although space oriented, the installations have been situated in proximity to rail lines and established communities where supplies and civilian labor forces are available. In the entire Mojave, only China Lake–Ridgecrest represents a new community (since 1940) based upon the military. Elsewhere established towns have gained population because of nearby installations: Barstow, Lancaster, Palmdale, Victorville, Mojave, and Twentynine Palms. The tendency of military activities to gravitate into the western Mojave demonstrates that many of the functions represent "spill-overs" from

Southern California where congestion precluded their establishment. Noteworthy examples are Edwards Air Force Base and Palmdale Airport, where large civilian staffs have been employed to test materiel produced around Los Angeles.

The Naval Ordnance Test Station at China Lake has created one of the Desert's largest communities, China Lake–Ridgecrest. **China Lake** (12,000), within the military reserve, contains offices, laboratories, and housing for military and select civilian personnel. **Ridgecrest** (5000), outside the base, is a modern desert town with air-conditioned stucco tract houses and a shopping center that now serves much of the northern Desert. The test station has rail connections via a branch line to Inyokern; it is used to test ship-fired rockets, some of which have been manufactured in Southern California.

Edwards Air Force Base, a 300,000-acre installation, was established as a training command base during World War II (Fig. 3-14). More recently it has been used as a testing center for new Air Force and Navy aircraft and for missile research. This site has about 350 good flying days per year. Its lengthy runway, completed in 1954, was the world's largest at the time of construction.

George Air Force Base, established north of Victorville in 1941, has served as headquarters for an interceptor squadron whose primary function has been defense of metropolitan Los Angeles and environs from potential air attack. It has also been used for advanced jet training.

The Army and the Marine Corps maintain separate bases for desert training programs. Camp Irwin, the older establishment, is located north of Barstow and was used as an Army training center in preparation for the North African campaign during World War II. Its varied terrain permits a variety of maneuvers. It was inactive between 1944-1951; since then, this 600,000-acre reserve has become the largest military installation in size within California.

The Marine Corps Training Center north of Twentynine Palms was established in 1952 to provide a desert training station—it represented the single site the Corps could find in the Desert with the land (560,000 acres) it wanted. The base, with a capacity of 10,000 trainees, is favorably located with respect to the Corps' Southern California centers in San Diego and at Camp Pendleton.

WINTER PLAYGROUND

Many a grizzled prospector who endured much hardship in the Mojave Desert in the pre-automobile era would shake his head in disbelief at the idea of the Desert as a recreational area. Perhaps it has less appeal than Death Valley or the Grand Canyon of the Colorado, but it benefits from its position relatively near the Los Angeles Lowlands—and the "High Desert" gives urban campers, hunters, bird watchers, flower lovers, and rockhounds a chance to escape briefly from the Gargantuan metropolis. Red Rock Canyon is not another Bryce nor is Mitchell Caverns northwest of Essex comparable to Carlsbad and Mammoth Cave, but these places *are* accessible to the Angeleno.[6] Leading areas are (1) the northern base of the San Bernardino Mountains, from Cajon Pass to Lucerne Valley, and (2) the northern piedmont of the Little San Bernardino Mountains.

Joshua Tree National Monument, established in 1936, was for some years unfrequented—its contemporary popularity apparently results from the desire of the Southern California masses for a change of scenery.[7] At Salton View (5185 ft. elevation) one can look down a mile to the Salton Sea (upon those increasingly rare days when the air is

[6] Residents of Southern California (the South Coast) distinguish between "High Desert" (i.e., most of the Mojave) and "Low Desert" (Colorado Desert and lower Colorado River Valley). The rapidity with which Angelenos discovered the Mojave Desert after World War II is astounding. It was possible to camp at Cottonwood Spring in solitude in 1950—within four years it was jammed with weekend campers.

[7] Without doubt a major factor here and elsewhere in the Mojave Desert has been the publicity given on travel programs on radio and television and the travelogues that appear in Los Angeles newspapers.

not laden with haze, i.e., Los Angeles smog). Despite such other attractions as the Oasis of Mara at the park headquarters, Cottonwood Spring, numerous Joshua trees, the Cholla cactus garden in Pinto Basin, and some good examples of spheroidal weathering of granitoidal rocks, the offerings of the Monument are not comparable to better-known American wonderlands. Its campgrounds are "dry" (i.e., one brings his own firewood or fuel and water) yet winter visitors are supporting a continuing growth of **Twentynine Palms.** Nearby **Morongo Valley, Yucca Valley,** and **Joshua Tree** contain the residences of an increasing number of gregarious desert lovers who cannot or will not afford Palm Springs (Chapter 4).

Apple Valley is a magnificent testimony to the alchemy of a Long Beach oil fortune mixed with a continuous barrage of advertising via radio, television, and highway signs, *and* proximity to Los Angeles. In 1947 Apple Valley seemed unlikely to become the "Palm Springs of the Mojave" despite its extensive new inn. Now it also has a golf course, airport, and paved roads and has become the residence of Los Angeles business executives who commute to their offices by private planes. Recreational activities provide a livelihood for over 1000 people. The 5000-acre Jess Ranch, producer of beef, turkeys, and trout (grown in ponds) is one of the principal attractions for the occasional city visitor.

Southern California affords limited opportunity for fresh-water fishing as there are few lakes and streams tend to be dry beds or, infrequently in winter, raging torrents. Hence many Middlewestern refugees who yearn sufficiently for the old fishin' hole back home will drive several hundred miles, often towing a boat-laden trailer, to fish in the Colorado River. The clear waters here provide bass, bluegill, channel catfish, and crappie. Principal locales include Lake Havasu behind Parker Dam, Needles (where San Bernardino County is developing facilities), the 15-mile section from Parker Dam to Earp, and The Weir site at Blythe. An increasing number of boating enthusiasts make trips along the lower Colorado River.

SUBURBIA IN THE DESERT

It should be obvious from this chapter that the Mojave Desert is sharing in the population spiral of Southern California, albeit on a more modest scale. Logan of U.C.L.A. has identified the following factors as major contributors to this growth: (1) the "discovery" of the beauty and solitude of the Desert; (2) the availability of cheap federal land; (3) the efforts of real estate promoters; (4) technological advances, such as swimming pools and air conditioning, that tend to make this land habitable; (5) the desire to escape the metropolis; (6) polluted air in metropolitan Los Angeles.

The "High Desert," lying above 2000 feet elevation especially along the northern base of the Little San Bernardino, San Bernardino, and San Gabriel ranges has been the focus of much of the development. Devotees imply that the area lacks the intolerable summers of the "Low Desert" (i.e., Colorado Desert), whereas enthusiasts for the latter argue that the summers are miserable in both areas and that the Mojave winters lack the pleasantness found farther south. In any event a string of communities, many established since 1945, stretches about 150 miles from Palmdale through Hesperia, Apple Valley, and Lucerne Valley into Morongo Valley and beyond Twentynine Palms.

The newly arrived South Coast resident may start with a vacation at a luxury resort or dude ranch or even with the filing for a five-acre "jackrabbit homestead." A number of these occasional visitors have become full-time residents. Some have outside incomes (investments or pensions), others creative ability (artists and writers), but many attempt to find local employment. The thousands of desert homesteads provided by the federal government have posed such serious problems for San Bernardino County as road maintenance and police and fire protection. A problem is posed too for the census taker who must decide who is and who is not a "resident" of the Desert. Meanwhile, realtors endeavor to entice more residents, and local Chambers of Commerce strive to widen the economic base by endeavoring to attract industry.

THE FUTURE?

It is risky to prophesy the future for the Mojave Desert, or any other part of California. The senior author, who has felt a personal fascination toward our Southwestern deserts since his childhood, remained skeptical of activities in Antelope Valley as late as 1950. As Southern California's South Coast becomes increasingly congested, the question posed by Edward T. Price of Los Angeles State College in 1958 may be relevant: "Will new migrants from the east be as content with the Desert as previous arrivals have been with the Los Angeles area?"

Technological advances cannot ignore the Desert's dryness. The economic handicap results from a combination of low annual rainfall coupled with high evaporation rates and winters too cold for agriculture. Land slope and the long season would favor more extensive cultivation if rainfall or available irrigation water permitted.

Currently the Mojave Desert has obvious impediments to expanded population. Although the water is perhaps the most crucial, it may be partially resolved through California Water Plan importation from northern California (Chapter 9). The future for mining camps and communities dependent upon military bases is problematic.

Assuredly the Mojave has benefited tremendously since 1920 from its juxtaposition with Southern California athwart principal surface corridors into the coastal sectors. Population growth and agricultural decline in the Los Angeles Lowlands should intensify the utilization of water in the Mojave Desert. In fact the entire future of the region seems related to Los Angeles stimulation (viz., industry, recreation, residence, tourism, travel, mining).

Fig. 4-1. THE DESERT SHALL BLOOM LIKE A ROSE! Evolution of irrigation agriculture in the Colorado Desert is one of the remarkable success stories of reclamation in western United States. (David W. Lantis)

CHAPTER FOUR:: THE COLORADO DESERT

THE COLORADO DESERT

The Colorado Desert, smallest region of California (approximately 4000 square miles), is a breed of arid land different from most desert wastes of the world because it has access to water, the Colorado River. To the west is Southern California, to the north the Mojave Desert, to the east Arizona, and to the south Mexico (see Fig. 4-2).

For decades after early nineteenth-century surveys by Zebulon Pike and Stephen Long, much of North America between the Missouri River and the Sierra Nevada was regarded as the "Great American Desert" and was labeled thus on textbook maps. Although its extent has been sharply reduced by establishment of wheat farms and livestock ranches, the "Great American Desert" is still a fitting title for much of the extreme Southwest, including the Colorado Desert of California. Here edible vegetation is so limited that even grazing is nigh impossible without irrigation—this is a land where the year's rainfall may not total

This chapter has been reviewed by Lauren Post, San Diego State College, and Herbert Blossom, Sacramento City College.

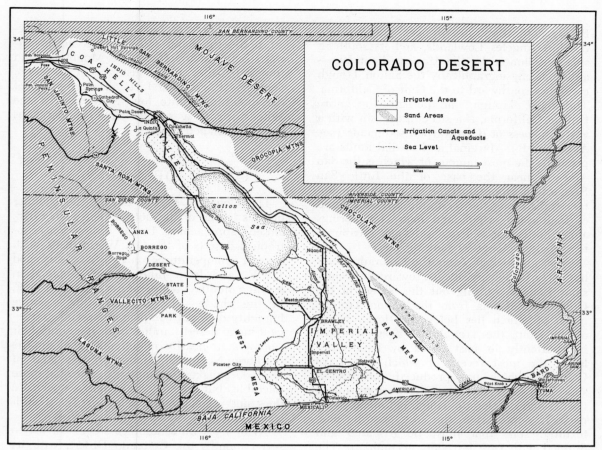

Fig. 4-2. MAP OF THE COLORADO DESERT.

an inch, and where it is literally possible to fry an egg in the sun of a summer afternoon. By whatever standards a scholar devises, and in the terminology of local residents, this area is truly a desert—that is, in its empty, undeveloped three quarters.

The occupied quarter of the Colorado Desert encompasses as its larger southern portion the delta of the Colorado River, whose water is supplemented by subsurface runoff from less arid mountains to the west. Coupled with the advantages of rich soil, long growing season, and access to the prosperous American market, the Colorado Desert understandably has become one of the world's most productive oases. It has also become one of the na-

tion's most famous recreation places, with advantages of a near-ideal winter climate and proximity to the wealthy, populous South Coast (Chapter 7).

THE SALTON TROUGH

The Colorado Desert largely coincides with the landform division called the Salton Trough. It comprises a series of low-lying basins between the Peninsular Ranges of Southern California to the west and the Little San Bernardino, Orocopia, and Chocolate Mountains to the east (see map, Fig. 4-2). Its northwest corner focuses on San Gorgonio

Pass, a natural and heavily used gateway into the Los Angeles Lowlands, and its southern side is delimited by the Mexican boundary—although physiographically the Salton Trough continues southward to the Gulf of California. The entire Trough, and perhaps the entire Gulf of California, is a structural basin with a vast thickness of downwarped sediments (see Appendix B). Marginal and medial faults are present—the most famous of which is the San Andreas near the base of the Little San Bernardino Mountains; the spectacular mountain walls along the west side are considered of fault-scarp origin, and many hot springs along both west and east sides are attributed to seepage in zones of faulting.

From an apex at Yuma the Colorado River has spread a delta westward toward the Peninsular Ranges shutting out the waters of the Gulf of California from the Salton Trough, much of which lies below sea level. North of the Delta the Trough has been occupied intermittently in past times by fresh-water lakes, the most recent of which was Lake Cahuilla, which has produced conspicuous shorelines especially along the western side of the Trough. Colorado Delta sediments were partially deposited in the lake, creating fine-textured soils that must be irrigated and drained with care lest salts accumulate. The north (California) half of the delta drains northwesterly to the Salton Sea—this portion of the Trough is called the **Imperial Valley**. The northern Trough, which slopes southward to the Salton Sea, is called **Coachella Valley**. It is filled with alluvium from the high mountains to the northwest, which is coarser than the Colorado delta sediments—hence in many places it is too porous or full of boulders for agriculture. The center of the Trough is occupied by the **Salton Sea**, which originated as a fresh-water lake in 1905 when the Colorado River surged into irrigation works of the Imperial Canal during flood stage. Surface evaporation has concentrated the salt content of the lake so that it approximates that of the ocean.

Sand dunes, locally conspicuous, presumably represent beach sand blown eastward from the shores of Lake Cahuilla. The largest body, the **Sand Hills**, trends northwestward between the Chocolate Mountains and Imperial Valley for a distance of 40 miles. Some crests rise 300 feet, although most of the dunes are quite low. Southwest of the Salton Sea is a smaller area of barchans (crescent-shaped dunes).

A TORRID DESERT

The Colorado Desert during the summer months is one of the hottest places on earth, closely approaching Death Valley and subtropical deserts of the Old World in its heat. Record temperatures here have reached 126°F., and from June through September, average midday temperatures exceed 100°F. in the shade. The normally low relative humidity does not compensate enough to prevent many desert families from spending their summers in nearby mountains or along the seashore. Nocturnal cooling in this land of clear skies makes the summers somewhat more tolerable, but even at night the temperature does not regularly fall below 70°F. in midsummer.

"Winter" is quite another story—for six to seven months the Colorado Desert, with its mild sunny days and crisp clear nights, is climatically one of the more appealing portions of the United States. In winter as in summer this is one of the sunniest portions of the nation. Agriculturally the Colorado Desert can practically be considered to have a year-around growing season. A low temperature of 13°F. has been recorded, however, and there is an element of risk involved in growing sensitive winter produce.

The Colorado Desert is also one of the more arid portions of the earth, with annual precipitation totals at various stations approximating 3 inches. In both winter and summer the controlling air is typically of local "tropical continental" origin, inasmuch as the location is equally remote from polar Pacific, polar Canadian, and tropical Atlantic air masses. Although close to the subtropical Pacific

Ocean, the Colorado Desert is shielded from its influence by the Pacific High (see Appendix A) and by the western mountains.

Occasional winter storms from the Pacific briefly bring overcast skies, but usually most of the potential rain has been wrung out when the storms cross the Transverse and Peninsular ranges. Accompanying winds, especially near the base of San Gorgonio Pass, are often more significant than precipitation since blowing sand is highly destructive to some crops. Windbreaks of native arrowweed, laboriously hand-set, are a common sight in the truck gardens; elsewhere windbreaks of tamarisk trees are sometimes grown.

Like winter "lows," summer storms are infrequent but often memorable. As moist, unstable air moves northwestward, commonly from the Gulf of Mexico, displays of lightning, winds, insufferable humidity, and occasional torrential rains occur; for example, in 1909, 4 inches of rain fell in 24 hours in mid-August at Yuma on the southeast edge of the Colorado Desert.

SONORAN VEGETATION

The Colorado Desert flora consists predominantly of scattered species of low shrubs, which can survive for months without rainfall. The creosote bush with its olive-hued leaves and the low grayish burroweed are most widespread. The total vegetation has greater complexity than the casual tourist along main highways suspects; botanists have collected hundreds of individual species of native plants. Besides its great variety, much of the plant life is quite distinct from that of the other California deserts—so much so that the term *Sonoran Desert* is sometimes applied in differentiating the flora of the Colorado and other "southern" deserts from the flora of the Mojave Desert.

Distinctive vegetation characteristic of the Sonoran Desert includes a relatively large supply of succulents, such as the cholla cactus (*Opuntia echinocarpa*), the ocotillo (*Fouquieria splendens*), dramatic at Eastertide with its monkey-tail branches tipped with red flowers, and the low but distinctive washbank "forests" of mesquite, palo verde, ironwood, and smoke tree, so celebrated in desert landscape paintings. At opposite extremes are the Washingtonia palms of the mountain canyons and the coarse perennial *galleta* grass, which is an important factor in stabilization of the Sand Hills east of Imperial Valley. For many plants individual rainstorms tend to be more important than seasonal totals. Like other dry portions of California, the Colorado Desert is sometimes vivid with blooms of quick-growing annuals, particularly after spring rains.

DESERT INDIANS

The Colorado Desert was not inviting for aboriginal peoples. Those who reside there, the desert Cahuilla and various Yuman groups, restricted their habitats to favored peripheral locations. The *Cahuilla*, limited in numbers, concentrated about Palm Canyon as they do today. They were formerly food-gatherers who took advantage of Colorado River seepage into the Salton Trough to provide sources of food. Various cacti served in their diet as well as fruits and fleshy portions of some plants. Their staple was the mesquite bean, which was ground in wooden mortars. The seeds and sometimes the pulp of such plants as wild plum, manzanita, and sumac added to their diet. As a nonagricultural people residing in a land with limited game, the Cahuilla necessarily used all available plants; Kroeber noted that they found some sixty varieties useful. Coiled rush and grass baskets, carrying nets, and unadorned red pottery were among the equipment used by these people. Their dwellings were thatched with a sloped roof—daubing mud on the thatching was apparently a technique borrowed from the Spanish. The successful survival of the Cahuilla to the present is significant.

Aboriginal utilization of the Imperial Valley remains uncertain. Kroeber suspected seasonal occupancy by the *Kamia*, a Yuman people of whom there remains scanty information.

They may have been farmers along the Colorado in northern Baja California although Garcés considered them a mountain folk who sought foodstuffs along the lower Colorado. Certainly the Imperial Valley was not a cherished homeland for southwestern Indians.

The *Yuma* were a sedentary people who practiced flood irrigation in a manner like their near relatives upstream, the Mohave (see Chapter 3). Although the name of the former people has been assigned to the family, there were no larger numbers of Yuma than Mohave; the Yuma were apparently less given to warfare and to traveling. The fertility of the Yuma oasis would have discouraged desert forages. Like the Cahuilla, the Yuma have survived to the present, and Fort Yuma reservation has been set aside in Bard Valley.

A TRANSPORTATION CORRIDOR

The overland route between Spanish holdings in Mexico and Alta California crossed the Colorado Desert between Yuma and Anza-Borrego, but the distance between watering places, plus difficulties with Indians, made this land route even more forbidding than the difficult ocean voyage up from Mexico. During the Gold Rush period, when the Desert served as an important corridor in transcontinental travel, the Colorado Crossing continued to parallel the old Spanish route directly west from Yuma to the Peninsular Ranges in order to minimize the waterless intervals. The most famous traffic of this era was John Butterfield's Overland Mail Stage, which operated in 1858-1861 over a 2800-mile route between St. Louis and San Francisco, using several stations in the Colorado Desert.

Federal rail survey teams had crossed the Colorado Desert a few years earlier, but not until 1877 did the present-day transcontinental line of the Southern Pacific Railroad reach the length of the Desert between San Gorgonio Pass and Yuma. Indio, created as the local construction headquarters, remains a major railroad service center. A branch line was built from Niland to Calexico in 1903 after beginnings of farm settlement there. The San Diego and Arizona Eastern (now part of the Southern Pacific), a tortuous line that meanders back and forth across the International Border, was opened in 1919, and provides a second rail outlet to the Pacific Coast.

More recently a network of paved highways has been constructed across the Colorado Desert, and much contemporary commerce moves by truck rather than rail. The most heavily traveled routes are U.S. 99 between San Gorgonio Pass and Calexico, U.S. 60-70 (Interstate 10) east from Indio, and U.S. 80 (Interstate 8) between San Diego and Yuma. Much travel on these routes consists of movement between the South Coast (Southern California) and eastern United States, which perpetuates the role of the Colorado Desert as a transport corridor. Within the region interstate highway traffic is serviced primarily at Indio and El Centro—both towns had developed retail facilities prior to the dawn of the automobile age and both are located conveniently near major highway junctions.

QUEST FOR WATER

Availability of adequate irrigation water has been the key factor in agricultural development of the Colorado Desert. Only after dependable water supplies became available could substantial settlement occur—a condition still true. Dr. Oliver M. Wozencraft, a Gold Rush physician who was serving as Indian Agent in San Francisco, is considered the first to have visualized the irrigation possibilities of the Desert. His efforts to gain the necessary government backing prior to the Civil War were unsuccessful, however. Others apparently lacked Wozencraft's vision, and the Colorado Desert remained untilled during the nineteenth century.

Irrigation eventually resulted from efforts of two experienced water engineers, George Chaffey and Charles Rockwood. Their California Development Company (the C.D.C.), aided considerably by Chaffey's fame as a developer of successful irrigation systems in

Southern California and Australia and by his willingness to reinvest the personal fortune thereby amassed, succeeded in conveying Colorado River water into Imperial Valley by 1901. Hundreds of settlers had already occupied the southern portion of the Valley at the end of the 50-mile ditch that passed through Mexico in order to circumvent the Sand Hills and utilize the bed of the Alamo River, one of the ancient flood channels by means of which the Colorado River had originally built its delta.

Problems of silting and obstacles interposed by the United States and Mexican governments induced the C.D.C. to cut a new but faulty canal entry from the river a few miles below Yuma. Aided by untimely flooding, the Colorado River soon ran uncontrolled into the canal and from March 1905 until February 1907 flowed through Imperial Valley to create the Salton Sea. The floodwaters converted the shallow beds of the New and Alamo rivers into impressive gorges—actually fortunate in view of their present utility as drainageways for surplus irrigation water, which prevents waterlogging and salt accumulation.

The struggle to provide an assured water supply for the Colorado Desert without simultaneously admitting the entire river was not readily ended. In 1910 the Colorado again poured uninvited into one of its former distributary channels. In 1916 a check dam built across the river to divert flow during low stage into the Imperial Valley Canal caused floodwaters to back up and inundate part of Yuma. Finally, increasing use of irrigation water on the Mexican side of the border posed a long-term threat to adequacy of the supply.

A large flood-control dam and a canal entirely within the United States was deemed necessary to utilize effectively the Colorado River for irrigation of the Colorado Desert. Approval by states through which the river flows was not secured until the Colorado River Compact of 1922; financial wherewithal was not forthcoming until Congressional passage of the Boulder Canyon Act of 1928 and availability of Public Works funds in 1933. The task of building the world's highest dam, Hoover, upriver and the All-American Canal (Fig.

4-4) through the Sand Hills took years to complete. The contemporary water system for the Colorado Desert dates from 1940 when the first flow was diverted into Imperial Dam, then desilted in nearby settling basins and conveyed 80 miles into Imperial Valley.

World War II preempted labor from a longer extension, the Coachella Canal, so that Colorado River water did not reach the northern part of the Colorado Desert until 1948. Previously the Coachella Valley depended upon groundwater originating in the Transverse and Peninsular Ranges—an expensive and limited source.

The new canal systems have been a significant stimulus to Colorado Desert agriculture despite the distances involved and the high evaporation losses en route. Their operation is facilitated by continuous downhill flow, which obviates the need for expensive pumping. There is sufficient gradient to permit generation of hydroelectric power at four plants along the All-American Canal.

Populated portions of the Colorado Desert, dependent upon water supplies, consist of distinct "oases" widely separated by raw desert. These subdivisions are: (1) Imperial Valley, (2) Bard Valley, (3) Anza-Borrego Desert, (4) Salton Sea, and (5) Coachella Valley. Each will be considered successively.

IMPERIAL VALLEY

The Imperial Valley, with an irrigated area of some 470,000 acres and a population of 70,-000, is the focus of settlement and productivity in the Colorado Desert. Agriculture is the predominant source of livelihood and is nearly the only basic activity. There is also limited service to wayfarers, military activity at El Centro Naval Air Station, and wallboard manufacture at Plaster City.

Settlement of Imperial Valley commenced at the turn of this century, and the population grew rather rapidly for three decades as irrigation agriculture expanded. Most towns were established before 1910, and they have been influenced by the branch line of the

Southern Pacific, which has permitted commercial export agriculture. The earlier settlers were generally homesteaders who came from the Middle West, often enticed by promotion efforts of the Imperial Land Company, a C.D.C. affiliate. To allay concern that prospective settlers might have had for desert residence the name "Imperial Valley" was coined by the developers.

SEASONAL LABOR

A large number of seasonal farm laborers was needed early, a reflection of the distaste that farmers of European ancestry held for field work in extreme summer heat and of proximity to dependable low-wage Mexican labor. Mexican families, encamped beside irrigation ditches, were an early sight in the Valley.

Reliance upon inexpensive laborers increased so that Mexicans alone did not satisfy the need. Hindus began migrating from Canada in 1907. These people, known as "ragheads" because of their turbans, helped pick the first cotton in 1910. Of those who remained, a number have been socially accepted farm owners, and one member of the India-born group was elected to Congress in 1956, 1958, and 1960. Importation of Filipino workers began in 1920, in the fear that Congress would restrict Mexican immigration; like the Hindus, they have tended to move up the economic ladder. Many Filipinos still in the Valley are now lease farmers. Additional non-Mexican labor, including many Southern Negroes, came to the Valley during the depression-and-dust years of the 1930's.

The Mexican national and the Mexican-American have furnished the chief supply of temporary labor since the beginning of Imperial Valley settlement. Between World Wars I and II thousands came by truck from Sonora and Baja California, ostensibly for the work season; they often remained during the slack season on public welfare rolls. Many were "wetbacks" (illegal entrants), who crossed the border easily and repeatedly in response to seasonal labor needs. Many others became United States citizens and permanent residents; by 1950, 30 percent of the county population had Spanish surnames.

Heavy seasonal low-cost labor remains critical to success of present-day agriculture, especially for truck crops. Since 1950 the illegal entrant has been largely replaced by the Mexican contract worker (*bracero*) whose movement is regulated by agreements between the Mexican and United States governments. The individual rancher must assure work and housing for these laborers. American migratory workers have also been active, and increasingly demand elimination of bracero competition and improvement of farm wages. Increasingly, too, automation of farm production is occurring—even the hard-to-mechanize vegetables are not immune. Many a laborer who once knew more humble tasks now tends impressive farm machines in the Valley.

The period since the mid-1920's has been one of relative agricultural maturity in Imperial Valley. Acreage and population have grown slowly in comparison with the earlier decades, and the general land-use patterns have become persistent.

THE RANCH

The typical Valley ranch is an owner-operated "food factory" of many hundred acres. Today's farmer is the son, or even the grandson, of a homesteader. He is a lifelong resident of the Valley and is thoroughly familiar with local methods and problems. There are also corporation properties, some representing reinvestment of farm money "driven" from the Los Angeles Lowlands by urbanization. Considerable land is leased, perhaps to a Japanese or Filipino truck farmer or to a Salinas lettuce grower. Farm buildings are limited in number and modest in quality. Dwellings are generally single-story frame structures; many are shanties. Many owners reside in town, with a foreman or other employees living on the ranch. There are few outbuildings; many ranches do not contain livestock, and a tin roof on poles suffices as a machinery shed. More recent construction of quality ranch-type bungalows reflects a tendency for some landowners to move back to the country. Fields are large and commonly fenceless. The irrigation lateral (often concrete lined) is ubiquitous, and rural roads are closely spaced, although unpaved to a much greater extent than is typical of so productive an area in California. Cottonwoods, eucalyptus, and tamarisk trees are widely planted for shade and as windbreaks.

PRODUCTS

Settlers experienced a characteristic period of trial and error in the choice of products. The many items that proved physically or economically unsuitable for emphasis included wheat, grapes, deciduous fruit, hogs, turkeys, and potatoes. Dairying rose to significance prior to World War I, and has since declined in the face of competition from areas having milder summers. Summer heat also discouraged production of eggs, potatoes, and deciduous fruit. Maize and grain sorghum once occupied significant acreages, then diminished along with disappearance of their chief consumer, the work horse. Table grapes proved more suitable on the sandy soils of Coachella Valley than in the Imperial.

Several crops of recent years were not part of the earliest agriculture: cotton (since 1910), lettuce (since 1916), carrots (somewhat later), flax (since 1934), and sugar beets (since 1937). Feeding of cattle and sheep on locally grown alfalfa and grain has been a dependable mainstay from the beginning; in 1909 such activity accounted for more than 90 percent of the acreage and the value of Imperial Valley production. Although agriculture has subsequently become more diversified, livestock and feed output have tended to rise. Raising of perishable truck crops is the other major activity that has proved highly successful since the earliest settlement. Export of 297 carloads of cantaloupes was recorded in 1905; cantaloupes remain a leading truck crop. The technique of double-cropping within a single season, unknown in most parts of the United States, has been in vogue almost from the beginning.

DIVERSE OUTPUT

Agriculture in Imperial Valley is characterized by great productivity as well as much diversity. With its essentially year-around growing season, the Valley could raise most types of crops grown elsewhere in the United States; it thus has an inherently wide range of possibilities compared to higher latitude areas. To this initial climatic advantage and the benefits of level terrain and deep soils, farmers have added dependable water supply, efficient farm methods, and aggressive marketing practices. Diversity is further promoted by such factors as ultimate limits to consumption, competitive advantages of other farm areas, local soil variations, and federal policies (price and acreage controls). The accompanying table documents the recent productivity and diversity of Imperial agriculture. Leading products in this table will subsequently be discussed.

LEADING IMPERIAL COUNTY PRODUCTS, 1961
(all values * in millions of dollars)

	ACREAGE	VALUE
Truck Crops	72,000	43.5
lettuce	40,000	26.7
tomatoes	4,000	3.9
cantaloupes	7,000	3.5
watermelons	5,000	2.2
carrots	6,000	2.9
others	10,000	4.3
Feed Crops	272,000	34.1
alfalfa	157,000	24.2
barley	83,000	4.7
sorghum	32,000	2.8
pasture	—	2.4
Livestock (& products)	—	31.5
cattle	—	26.5
sheep (& wool)	—	3.2
others	—	1.8
Cotton (& cottonseed)	60,000	27.6
Sugar Beets	48,000	13.4
Others	20,000	10.0
flaxseed	16,000	1.8
alfalfa seed	—	2.7
fruit & nuts	2,000	1.2
miscellaneous	2,000	4.3

* About 2% of value comes from areas outside Imperial Valley.

Source: Imperial County Agricultural Crop Report, 1961.

TRUCK CROPS

Vegetables and melons constitute the most valuable product group in the Valley. They are raised largely for fresh table-use and are shipped wherever price momentarily promises the best return, be it Los Angeles or Boston. The greater the distance, the greater the potential competition from growers nearer the market; hence timing is of utmost importance in successful production here. Most truck crops in Imperial Valley are planted to mature in midwinter or spring—at times when there are few competing areas in operation (see the table of harvest periods). Planting season traditionally begins after Labor Day, at the time most American farmers are involved with harvests.

a paper "hot cap." In a different way heat is conserved for young tomato plants by building paper and wood shelters the length of each crop row, so oriented as to create a southern exposure.

Most truck crops have common need for a near-perfect water balance (hence land-leveling and irrigation timing must be extremely precise), but specific crops may differ widely in their other environmental preferences. Carrots, for instance, are tolerant of cold, and thus may be grown in more frost-prone portions of the Valley. Lighter textured soils are preferred for a majority of the truck crops, partly because water control is easier and crop quality in some cases is superior; most important, such soils promote faster crop growth. Let-

APPROXIMATE HARVEST MONTHS FOR LEADING CROPS, COLORADO DESERT

	J	F	M	A	M	J	J	A	S	O	N	D
Alfalfa				x	x	x	x					
Barley & Flax					x	x	x					
Lettuce	x	x	x								x	x
Tomatoes		x	x	x	x	x						
Carrots	x	x	x	x	x	x						x
Grapes						x	x	x				
Dates									x	x	x	
Cotton	x								x	x	x	x
Sugar Beets				x	x	x						

Sources: U.S. Farm Placement Service; California Crop & Livestock Reporting Service.

Lettuce, the dominant truck crop, provides a good example of the timing factor. A number of growers operate in the Salinas and Imperial valleys by means of a carefully planned seasonal migration of operations between the two areas (see Chapter 8). By shifting key personnel onto leased land in Imperial Valley and carefully staggering the planting periods, a steady output of lettuce is maintained during the Salinas off-season.

Most truck crops require relatively intense effort—beyond regular fertilization, pest control, weeding, and irrigation. Melons, for instance, are given special temperature advantages by planting them on south-facing furrow ridges—each young plant is then covered with

tuce, however, absorbs wind-blown sand and hence is commonly grown on heavier soils. Vast tracts of lettuce (it occupies more acreage than all other truck crops combined) are thus particularly appropriate for the Imperial Valley, where the majority of soils are heavy textured.

Eighteen separate truck crops were harvested in the Imperial Valley in a recent year. Within the limitations posed by local growing conditions, the choice and extent of truck crops depends upon such factors as planting in other truck-cropping areas. Enterprising growers elsewhere can change marketing prospects quickly; this is the case with Mexican tomato production, which currently is absorbing the winter market. For some crops competition is also severe from southern Texas and Florida in years when good weather conditions prevail there. Consumer preferences have a long-term impact, as in the case of carrots. Decreased output since 1950 reflects loss of eastern markets due to the advent of packaged topped carrots; earlier, the Imperial carrot had an advantage because of more attractive leaves. Another long-range production influence is plant disease. Although diseases are generally kept under control, they constitute one reason for a significant decline in cantaloupe acreage in the last decade.

FEED CROPS

From the earliest days, the bulk of the cultivated area in the Imperial Valley has been devoted to raising livestock feeds, particularly alfalfa and barley. These crops bring the minimum returns per acre, and accordingly are "filler" crops for lands not needed for the more valuable products. Fortunately they tend to be highly tolerant of the alkali soil that plagues much of the Valley, and in addition they are generally soil-builders, especially alfalfa. As the table here indicates, the feeds can be grown later into the summer than is desirable for most truck crops, permitting more complete land-use and encouraging rotation with such short-lived crops as lettuce.

Alfalfa is the dominant feed crop for several reasons. It is a heavy producer—one stand yields six to eight cuttings annually and lasts for three to eight years; it builds a nitrogen supply in the soil; and for many years the Los Angeles dairy belt has been an important consumer for Imperial Valley alfalfa hay. Unfortunately it is the heaviest water user of all major Valley crops, but this habit makes alfalfa particularly useful on the areas of heavier, waterlogged soil.

LIVESTOCK

In common with many irrigated areas in the dry West, the Imperial Valley is a major feeding place where cattle and sheep from rangelands are brought for "finishing" (i.e., final fat-

tening before marketing). Population growth of Southern California has been directly reflected in the livestock boom in the Imperial Valley, within easy trucking distance of the urban packing plants. Valley feeding is done not on extensive ranches but on alfalfa pastures previously cut for hay or, increasingly, at feed lots that have automatic feed mixers and pens able to handle thousands of animals at a time. It has recently been possible, by careful shading for the feed lots, to maintain summer feeding volumes comparable to those in the cooler months. Indeed the summer drought of California rangelands is a major incentive to summer feeding in the Valley. Besides bulk feed crops, by-products from other commodities are utilized, especially cottonseed meal and sugar-beet pulp. Even so, Imperial Valley has momentarily outrun its feed supply and must import the deficit.

COTTON

Despite considerable fluctuation, cotton has tended to remain a leading Valley product since World War I. As elsewhere in the West, cotton long has been "emigrating" from the South to escape the boll weevil, depleted soils, and small upland farms that repel mechanization. Cotton has proved reasonably tolerant of alkaline soils and is only a moderate user of water. Under stimulus of the federal price-support program, cotton is second only to truck crops and fruit in returns per acre, and commonly occupies as much land as acreage quotas will permit. After ginning and baling in the Valley, the cotton is generally trucked to Long Beach or San Diego for export to Asia and elsewhere. The *Acala* variety, with a moderately short length of fiber, is dominant, but not so exclusively as in the San Joaquin Valley. Long staple *Egyptian* and *Delta Pine* are also raised.

SUGAR BEETS

The newest major crop, sugar beets, has impressively added to Valley farm production since World War II. Like cotton, it is well suited to the alkaline, water-short desert environment. Output is stimulated (and to a de-

Fig. 4-3. IMPERIAL DAM AND HEAD-GATES OF THE ALL-AMERICAN CANAL. *The low Imperial Dam, stretching across the Colorado River about 15 miles north of Yuma, permits diversion into the "desilting basins" seen in the middle of the photograph. Water then flows westward into the Imperial and Coachella valleys.* (Imperial Irrigation District)

Fig. 4-4. ALL-AMERICAN CANAL, EAST MESA, AND HYDROELECTRIC PLANT. *The gradient on the Colorado River delta permits generation of electricity at four points along the All-American Canal. This artificial river, with its capacity of 15,000 feet per second, is one of the largest irrigation canals in the world. Note creosote-bush vegetation on East Mesa and Sand Hills in the distance.* (Imperial Irrigation District)

Fig. 4-5. EL CENTRO—METROPOLIS OF THE DESERT. *The view is northwestward across the county seat of Imperial County. Contrast the density of shade trees on the east side (far right) with the southwest quadrant (middle left). Note warehouses and shipping sheds along the rail sidings.* (El Centro Chamber of Commerce)

Fig. 4-6. BORREGO SPRINGS AND PENINSULAR RANGES. *Christmas Circle forms a unique center for this dispersed resort town; many of the residences in Borrego Springs are located to the right of the photo around De Anza Country Club. Wash in upper left descends from Palm Canyon, probably the outstanding feature of Anza-Borrego State Park, located within the San Isidro Range.* (Borrego Sun)

gree regulated) by government policy, and beet pulp furnishes supplemental cattle feed. Unlike cotton, it is a refugee not from the South but from the urbanized lands of the South Coast. Production in the Imperial Valley was stimulated by construction of the first local refinery in 1948 north of El Centro. In keeping with the Valley pattern of unusual timing of its crops, beets are planted in the fall; California beets elsewhere are nearly all spring-planted.

THE URBAN SCENE

Urbanization of the Imperial Valley population has been a continuous process of steady growth. Virtually all towns have experienced this off-the-farm trend; two thirds of Valley residents are now urbanites. The communities are shipping points and of necessity residences for businessmen, ranchers, and farm workers. Remoteness from large cities guarantees existence of considerable retail trade. On the other hand, retired ranchers do not typically elect to remain here nor do these communities have particular tourist appeal—agriculture justifies their existence.

There is a common urban design in the Imperial Valley. Skylines are low and arcaded store fronts characteristic. Water coolers are conspicuous, and stopping places here advertise facilities not as merely air-conditioned but as "refrigerated." [1] Many visitors remember wooden shacks, dust-choked tamarisk trees, and bare earthen yards. Such things to a degree bespeak newness, migratory labor, distinct minority quarters, and absentee ownership. All larger towns except Holtville are located along the major north-south rail line. Adjacent to the tracks one generally finds

[1] Even the rudest shanty will have a water cooler, or swamp cooler, that adds humidity to the air. The more expensive air conditioning, a refrigeration system that takes moisture from the interior, is preferred, especially since the proximity of the Gulf of California brings sticky heat at times. Affluent Imperial Valley residents live in air-conditioned homes, drive air-conditioned automobiles, and work in air-conditioned offices.

shipping sheds and processing plants, and to the west is the central shopping district. East of the tracks is a "Little Mexico," with its shanties, bare ground, and paucity of trees; it is occupied by Negroes as well as Mexicans. In the southwest quadrant there is evidence of affluence in well-landscaped homes. "West side" occupance by a few Hindu ranchers and Japanese businessmen reflects changing social conditions since 1945.

El Centro (16,800) is the "largest city below sea level in the Western Hemisphere" (Fig. 4-5). It functions as the government, shopping, and travel center for Imperial County; this factor is reflected in its many specialty shops, motels, and kindred businesses. Additional patronage comes from the expanding population south of the border in Mexicali Valley. Among its agricultural activities is a flax-fiber plant. Each census since 1910 shows El Centro housing an ever increasing share of the Valley population—now almost one fourth.

Brawley (12,700) near the center of truck cropping, is the chief residence place for farm workers (permanent and migratory) and also affords residence for many prosperous ranchers. It is of course a major shipping center. Until the 1950's Brawley rivaled and for many years exceeded El Centro as the largest Valley town. In the face of an increasingly well-paid labor force and greater population mobility, Brawley is at a disadvantage relative to the drawing power of its county-seat rival.

Calexico (8000), although somewhat distinct in appearance and function as a border crossing, is increasingly reminiscent of the other Valley towns in the direct importance of agriculture to its economy. Its early founding as the tent-city headquarters of the Imperial Land Company at the terminus of the original irrigation canal and its spurt during the Prohibition era as a weekend center for Mexicali-bound farm hands (it was the largest Valley city in 1920) financed permanent urban services that perhaps otherwise would have been located in El Centro.

The other Imperial Valley towns are relatively small, serving essentially as shipping, residence, and weekday trade centers for their respective localities. They include **Imperial** (2600), site of Imperial Valley College, **Holtville** (3000), and **Calipatria** (2500).

BARD VALLEY

The Bard Valley is California's portion of the Yuma Valley on the "upper delta" of the Colorado River. It is separated from the bulk of the Colorado Desert by the Sand Hills and Pilot Knob. Unlike the remainder of the Desert, the upper delta has always had water; hence, it provided an attractive habitat for the Yuma Indians, practitioners of flood irrigation.

More recently this locale has also been important because of the "Yuma Crossing." Below its junction with the Gila, the Colorado is confined to a narrow gorge where it cuts through the low Yuma Range. The Spanish located an ill-fated mission here in 1780. Many forty-niners entered California at this point on the Gila Trail, and Fort Yuma, an Army post, was established in 1852. The Southern Pacific utilized this crossing in 1877 for its southern transcontinental rail line, and U.S. 80 enters California here. Another crossing is made by the siphon that carries Colorado River water, taken from the California side, *under* the river for convenient delivery to Arizona's Yuma Valley. At the north end of Bard Valley is Imperial Dam, where water is diverted into the All-American Canal.

Virtually all of the Bard Valley was encompassed in the 48,000-acre Fort Yuma Indian Reservation established in 1884, but political pressures subsequently forced opening of the northeasterly half of the reservation to non-Indian homesteaders. On the homestead land, the Bard Irrigation District was established with 40-acre tracts. The remaining floodplain was divided among the Yumas, with each Indian receiving five acres of bottomlands. The Indians, who eke out small incomes on their tiny patches, have substandard residences. They have had partial self-government since 1936.

The Bard agricultural environment, as elsewhere in the Colorado Desert, permits wide choice of crops. Present production tends to parallel that in Imperial Valley, with winter truck crops (lettuce and carrots), forage, spring melons, cotton, and livestock-feeding being representative. With numerous shanties and the willow thickets along the Colorado, Bard Valley presents a less well-kept landscape than the Imperial Valley. A distinctive note is added by the fishing resorts and trailer courts along the Colorado.

Partition of the Yuma Valley among California, Arizona, and Mexico represents a tragedy of political geography that has resulted in duplication of such civil services as fire, police, and education. There are three separate irrigation districts. The Colorado River has in historic time shifted its course over the wide floodplain just above the Yuma Crossing, and there long was some doubt as to which state had jurisdiction over a 10-square-mile tract that has "crossed over" onto California's side of the river. Further effects of the boundary are felt in the time-zone change and duplicate incorporation of businesses in both California and Arizona. Many Californians are married in Yuma to avert a three-day wait. **Winterhaven**, the California suburb of Yuma, Arizona, owes its existence partly to the state line. California gasoline taxes have tended to be cheaper than those in Arizona; hence a disproportionate share of Yuma Valley gasoline is sold in Winterhaven. The disorderly assemblage here of filling stations, cafes, and farm workers' dwellings forms a misleading gateway to wealthy California.

ANZA-BORREGO DESERT

The southwestern periphery of the Colorado Desert is perhaps the best contemporary illustration of the "natural" desert. Here in 1933, amidst alternating basins and offshoot ridges of the Peninsular Ranges, was established the 470,000-acre Anza-Borrego Desert State Park, California's largest state park (Fig. 4-7). From November to May the park affords

Fig. 4-7. ANZA-BORREGO STATE PARK. *This remarkable desert park, containing almost half a million acres, is the largest in the California system. Naked rock formations and desert vegetation are two of its noteworthy features. (California Division of Beaches and Parks)*

lished a ranch with hopes of marketing table grapes earlier than elsewhere in California. If Borrego grapes mature sufficiently early, their price is attractive. Expanded Coachella Valley crops, however, offer serious competition. Borrego agriculture is handicapped by high water costs, porous soils, and isolation from markets; yet there has been considerable land speculation, and raw desert land has sold for $600 to $1500 an acre. **Borrego Springs**, a highly dispersed residential community, has developed along the southwest side of the Valley, occupied during the cooler months by retirees and vacationers from the South Coast and from as far away as western Canada (Fig. 4-6). Remoteness and absence of a publicity-conscious clientele result in an appreciably quieter atmosphere than at Palm Springs, despite similarities in scenery and nearly identical climates.

SALTON SEA

The Salton Sea was created and reached its greatest extent in 1905-1907, when it rose to within 198 feet of sea level and forced the Southern Pacific Railroad to relocate on higher ground. Exclusion of the Colorado River and the high desert evaporation rate then conspired to reduce the Sea by 1925 to one half its 1907 extent. Subsequent increases in return flow from nearby irrigation have expanded the Sea now to about two thirds its 1907 extent. Irrigation water is commonly applied by Imperial and Coachella Valley farmers in quantities sufficient to flush out salts that would otherwise accumulate in their soils. The saline water is then drained into the only downhill site available—the Salton Sea. Anticipating no early end to this practice, the irrigators have sought flooding rights to permit a continued rise in the level of the sea.

Of late the Salton Sea has become a recreation place for residents of metropolitan Southern California as their home areas become ever more crowded for recreational activities. Corvina, a near relative of sea bass, has been

a refuge for Southern Californians—hikers, campers, and sightseers. Striking rock formations, representative Sonora Desert flora and fauna, and warm winter sunshine are major attractions, and there is a rich history stemming from early-day travel (noted in the section on transportation).

Most populous of the depressions within this subregion is Borrego Valley. Unlike the other basins, it is surrounded by, but is not part of, the state park. The Valley was homesteaded after World War I but most entrymen failed, and much land was accumulated into a single parcel. After World War II deep wells were drilled to furnish a water supply for agriculture. The principal crops include table grapes, cotton, livestock feeds, and winter vegetables such as asparagus and lettuce. In 1947, DiGiorgio Fruit Company estab-

Fig. 4-8. SALTON CITY—SEASHORE RE-SORT. An abundance of waterfront homesites is available for the desert enthusiast. The community is situated on the west side of the Salton Sea near U.S. 99. (Salton City Resorter)

successfully planted and sports fishing is popular—perhaps ill-fated, however, due to increasing salinity of the Sea. The growing enthusiasm for water sports leads many devotees to trailer-haul their boats from metropolitan Los Angeles. Salton Sea State Park, designed for boat launching and other shoreline activities, has been established on the northeast shore and supplements the older privately operated facilities. The dumping of sewage into the Sea by Imperial Valley cities—in both United States and Mexico—has posed an urgent problem, especially with the expansion of recreational facilities.

Urbanization of the Salton Sea shoreline is being initiated along the north and west sides, where building sites close to main highways are more available than around the southern shores. Construction initially has stressed commercial lodgings and services for the recreation visitor rather than individual private dwellings. Most spectacular has been **Salton City**, where a Los Angeles developer invested $10 million to create an 11,000-lot development with paved streets and water obtained from a deep well several miles away. Within the first year (1958-59) $30 million

worth of lots were sold, although extensive home construction has not materialized (Fig. 4-8).

THE COACHELLA VALLEY

The Coachella Valley, northernmost segment of the Salton Trough, shares with the Imperial an alluvial surface and temperatures and aridity common to the rest of the Colorado Desert. The Coachella is considerably smaller in area and has a generally higher and coarser surface; historically, it found water a scarcer commodity. On the other hand the Coachella Valley is bordered by higher, more scenic mountains and lies closer to metropolitan Los Angeles—both in terms of distance and with regard to position along main traffic routes.

Man-made differences between the Coachella and Imperial Valleys are also conspicuous and result in part from recognition of the significant physical and locational differences. Coachella agriculture stresses orchard crops such as its famous date palms and mini-

Fig. 4-9. STOOP LABOR, COACHELLA TRUCK PATCH. Tedious field labor has long characterized Coachella Valley vegetable farming. The "stoop laborers" in this field are Mexican nationals (braceros). (Bureau of Reclamation, photo by R. C. Middleton)

Fig. 4-10. COACHELLA VINEYARD AND MT. SAN JACINTO. Table grapes constitute the leading cash crop of the Coachella Valley; nowhere else in the nation are fresh grapes marketed so early in the season. There has been a sizable expansion of acreage since 1950. (Bureau of Reclamation, photo by J. R. Cotterill)

mizes livestock production. An even greater distinction is that in the Coachella recreation is virtually on a par with farming as a basis for human settlement, and the name of Palm Springs is perhaps more meaningful to most Californians than the name Coachella stamped on grapefruit rinds or date wrappers. Hence discussion concerns (1) the Agricultural Valley and (2) the San Jacinto Piedmont.

THE AGRICULTURAL VALLEY

The Coachella Valley remained an unoccupied waste, save for its hunter-gatherer Indians, until the Southern Pacific track was laid across it in 1877. Even the name seems to be of late origin, being credited to mapping crews of the U.S. Geological Survey (refuting popular belief that it derives from the Spanish *conchilla*—for the small shells so common in the Valley soils). Considerable filing of land claims took place following arrival of the railroad, but actual settlement was limited until the turn of the century.

In typical desert fashion, agricultural settlement of the Coachella Valley proceeded hand-in-hand with development of the water supply but in a different sequence from the Imperial Valley. Colorado River water was not originally accessible for the Coachella. Seeking water for locomotives, the railroad discovered artesian flows in 1888, and in 1900 introduction of well-drilling methods feasible for agriculture permitted the beginnings of irrigation. For almost half a century thereafter agriculture and population of the Valley grew relatively steadily, but at a very modest rate in comparison to the Imperial Valley boom.

The first decade, and perhaps the entire half century, might be considered as one of agricultural "infancy." During this experimental period, many and possibly all of the products tried in the Imperial were also attempted in the Coachella. Several crops important in the first decade remain significant, especially melons and dates. Although not as consistently successful, other important contemporary crops—especially grapefruit, table grapes, and cotton—were established by 1910. The relatively high water costs, among other conditions, discouraged production of livestock feeds and even of cantaloupes, a fairly high-value crop that nonetheless suffered from Imperial Valley "cheap-water" competition.

THE COLORADO DESERT ::71

Irrigation water was widely shared in the beginning, with farm sizes often of 10 to 80 acres (much smaller than in Imperial Valley).

Available groundwater supplies diminished rapidly in the face of heavy, and often wasteful, usage. Artesian flows declined and finally ceased. As pumping was applied and irrigated acreage expanded, the water table dropped. By 1920 it was obvious that supplemental water supply was necessary if more than a fraction of the Valley was to be permanently irrigated. Coachella farmers joined with Imperial and Southern California water seekers in obtaining Hoover Dam and related Colorado River projects, and in 1948 water deliveries commenced from the Coachella branch of the All-American Canal.

Cropland and population have tripled since 1948, and the Coachella Valley has experienced an era of expansion reminiscent of the pre-1930's in Imperial Valley. Acreage is still increasing and some shifts are occurring in the general pattern of products that had evolved prior to 1948. Expanded livestock-feeding, truck crops, and vineyards are particularly apparent; citrus and cotton also have proliferated notably.

The contemporary landscape of the lower Coachella contrasts impressively with that of the Imperial. Farm properties are noticeably smaller, yet residences are generally more attractive. Trees are markedly more conspicuous—not only the date palms and groves of citrus but also the assorted varieties like tamarisk used as windbreaks. They lend a refreshing green contrast to the colorful though barren mountain border.

The accompanying table suggests the overall diversity, high value, and export orientation of Coachella Valley farm output. Orchards and vineyards dominate in the Coachella to about the same extent that livestock feeding does in the Imperial; however, livestock feeds are less significant in the Coachella than orchards and vineyards are in the Imperial. Truck crops and cotton are important in both areas. The Coachella has a much smaller total production than the Imperial but its output per acre and diversity are greater.

LEADING COACHELLA VALLEY PRODUCTS, 1961
(all values in millions of dollars)

	ACREAGE	VALUE
Fruit Crops	30,000	21.6
grapes	12,000	11.7
dates	4,000	5.9
grapefruit	8,000	1.9
tangerines	3,000	1.6
others	3,000	0.5
Livestock (& products)	—	5.4
Feed Crops	10,000	1.4
Truck Crops	14,000	10.2
carrots	2,000	2.3
tomatoes	1,000	2.2
sweet corn	5,000	2.1
others	6,000	3.6
Cotton (& cottonseed)	6,000	2.3

Source: Agricultural Commissioner, Riverside County.

Succeeding paragraphs describe the three leading agricultural groups: fruit crops, truck crops, and livestock.

FRUIT CROPS

The different appearances of the date palm, citrus tree, and vineyard tend to obscure significant similarities among these three leading Coachella crops. First, they are relatively permanent; second, they are sufficiently high-value products to compensate for their heavy water consumption. Dates, the extreme example, are by far the "thirstiest" desert crop, but at the same time normally return the most value per acre. Fruits are typically grown on higher-lying, coarser soils where waterlogging and akalinity are at a minimum. Of all crops the fruits are best able to repay the higher irrigation costs incurred on these droughty soils. Fruits thus provide a means of using lands that may not be usable for other items. All three fruit crops are shipped predominantly in perishable form, which requires careful handling and transport arrangements.

Grapes, the leading Coachella product, are predominantly of the Thompson seedless variety and are shipped for fresh table-use earlier than their counterparts elsewhere in the state (see table of harvest months, p. 64).

Fig. 4-11. DATE GROVE NEAR INDIO. The date palm, with its roots in hell and its fronds in heaven, has a voracious appetite for water. (Bureau of Reclamation)

Grapefruit also depends heavily upon table consumption in California—a favorable, growing market. High quality and early ripening habit are important advantages for Coachella grapefruit, as opposed to the nondesert varieties.

Dates depend on nationwide markets; about 90 percent of the nation's production comes from Coachella Valley. As in coastal citrus districts, date groves in the Coachella are virtually a "way of life"—their aesthetic and prestige value help compensate for the in-

volved, expensive efforts required for their creation. So successful is Coachella date production that Middle East growers have sent students to study local techniques. Dates, however, are among the few major crops not sharing in Coachella agricultural expansion. Marketing problems have been severe in recent years, aggravated by competition from foreign imports. Moreover the trees are attractive to subdividers for their shade and exotic effect—more so because the date groves happen to be concentrated in what is now the path of urban expansion between Indio and Palm Springs.

TRUCK CROPS

Vegetables and melons account for a quarter of the farm output in the Imperial and Coachella Valleys alike, and the two areas do not differ essentially in the motives and methods. There is repetition of many specific products; for example, carrots and tomatoes are among the leading truck crops in both areas, and more than half the varieties of vegetables grown in the Colorado Desert are raised in both the Imperial and the Coachella. On the other hand, the Coachella has more diversity in kinds of truck crops; no one vegetable is so outstanding as is lettuce in the Imperial. There is a certain exclusiveness of truck crops in the two valleys. Cabbage and garlic, important Imperial products, are currently absent in Coachella; sweet corn and peppers, which occupy considerable Coachella acreage, are not repeated each year in the Imperial.

LIVESTOCK FEEDING

The livestock industries in the Coachella, long subordinate to fruit and truck, are attaining major significance. Water has become more plentiful for raising feed; also, the nearby Southern California market is expanding. As in the Imperial Valley, emphasis is upon fattening of imported cattle with locally grown alfalfa, barley, and sorghum. So far cattle-feeding is concentrated in a single large-scale operation near Thermal. One major packing company is now in process of transferring its Southern California slaughter facilities from Los Angeles to this area.

THE COLORADO DESERT : : 73

The agricultural Coachella Valley has a higher population density than the Imperial, which partially reflects the Coachella's greater per-acre productivity. An expanding majority of the Coachella population consists of town dwellers. Urban growth is favored by compactness of the farm area, close network of rural roads, importance of specialized shipping facilities, and relatively high rural purchasing-power. The four agricultural Coachella towns, established prior to significant highway travel, are located along the railroad. Until recently the more northerly the town, the more it was favored by new irrigation development and routing of main highways, which explains why only two towns, Indio and Coachella, have attained significant size.

Indio (9700) is the dominant farm center and shipping point of Coachella Valley. Although geographically off-center for service to Valley farmers, its superior shipping facilities (as a railroad point and highway junction) gave it an early advantage. Further impetus came from proximity to date groves, producers of relatively high incomes, and a need for elaborate processing facilities in town. The railroad yards, truck traffic, and busy tourist-catering facilities lend an air of year-round activity. A third of the agricultural Valley population resides in Indio.

Coachella (4900) is more exclusively oriented to agriculture, and in a sense is the Brawley of Coachella Valley. Its population fluctuates seasonally with migration of farm workers, but over-all growth has responded to irrigation expansion commencing in the late 1940's.

THE SAN JACINTO PIEDMONT

Recreational activities prevail in the northwestern Coachella as singularly as agriculture does to the southeast. The mild winters of the Colorado Desert compensate for the sweltering summer heat. Accordingly with California population growth, improved transcontinental transportation facilities (especially by air), an expanded leisure group (including many senior citizens), and technological developments (especially air conditioning and swimming pools), the Desert has become one of the nation's smart winter playgrounds. Activity is concentrated along the Piedmont at the base of the San Jacinto Range. Recreational assets include proximity to the Los Angeles Lowlands via San Gorgonio Pass, absence of agricultural utilization, and the spectacular backdrop of the San Jacinto Range.

A string of recreational communities is staggered southward from Desert Hot Springs through Palm Springs to La Quinta. Their "permanent" populace of 26,000 in 1960 rivals that of the agricultural Valley. Originally widely detached, these communities are coalescing along California Route 111. Many of the remaining "open stretches" are occupied by golf courses—there are more than a dozen in all. The area describes itself as "America's winter golfing capital" (Fig. 4-12).

Palm Springs (14,500), an internationally known winter resort, is the primary focus of recreational population along the Piedmont. This once-secluded mineral springs has become a veritable transmogrification of Beverly Hills' Wilshire Boulevard and Hollywood's Sunset Strip into the desert. The city as it exists is the composite product of wealth accumulated in the motion-picture industry, the rise of the sun-tan fad, and creation of *nouveau* West Coast and Midwest fortunes. Its singular excuse for existence is as a winter play place—there are no other visible means of support.

Palm Springs was founded soon after construction of the Southern Pacific route through the desert in the late 1870's. The community remained static until establishment of Desert Inn in 1909—this hotel allegedly first filled when a movie company established a "location" in Palm Springs. During the 1920's the village was transformed into a dreamland Hollywood set complete with palms, movie starlets, and swimming pools. National publicity has attracted many others, including a significant number of vacationists and retired well-to-do from all parts of the nation. Some

Fig. 4-12. WINTER GOLF CAPITAL OF AMERICA. *Such is the contention of boosters of the San Jacinto Piedmont where there are a dozen golf courses—seen here is Bermuda Dunes Country Club.* (Union Pacific Railroad)

Fig. 4-13. PALM SPRINGS. *One of the nation's best-known winter resorts, Palm Springs, lies at the base of Mt. San Jacinto (10,805 ft.). Note the "checkerboard" arrangement of the city. The central district, middle of photo to right, is shown in Fig. 4-15.* (Palm Springs Chamber of Commerce; McFadden and Eddy Associates)

Fig. 4-14. COACHELLA BRANCH OF THE ALL-AMERICAN CANAL. *Completion of the Coachella Branch in 1948 was followed by a marked expansion of irrigation agriculture in the Coachella Valley. A date grove and grapefruit orchard are on the left.* (Bureau of Reclamation, photo by R. C. Middleton)

Fig. 4-15. OLDER SECTION OF PALM SPRINGS. *In few, if any, arid spots have a comparable number of people spent so much for recreation and seasonal residence. With air conditioning, an increasing number remain throughout the year, although the "social season" extends from October to April.* (Union Pacific Railroad)

16 percent of the resident population is over age 65, a figure twice the California average. There is an obvious concentration of wealth, yet sharp contrasts exist. Besides its more affluent visitors some 50,000 "ordinary" Angelenos visit Palm Springs during an average winter weekend to see how the "other 5 percent" lives. Opening of the world's largest aerial tramway, to the upper reaches of the San Jacinto Range, is expected to bring another half million visitors annually.

Palm Springs focuses upon its principal business street, Palm Canyon Drive, which is lined with branches of smart Los Angeles and New York shops, night clubs, and stock brokerage offices. Its service facilities (including hotels, restaurants, and night clubs) exceed those of many large cities. Residences and resorts extend outward more than two miles from the nucleus. The city dispersal is partially due to the alternate mile-squares, which are parts of the Cahuilla Indian reservation centered south of Palm Springs in Palm Canyon. Federal approval in 1957 of long-term leases of Indian lands is promoting a "filling-in" of the "checkerboard" and making ninety-two members of the Cahuilla tribe wealthy.

Desert Hot Springs (1500), at the base of the Little San Bernardino Mountains, lacks affluence and suggests a "poor man's Palm Springs." It is essentially a mineral springs resort.

Palm Desert (1300), southeast of Palm Springs beyond **Cathedral City** (1900), was organized in 1947 by Los Angeles realtors. Despite its golf courses and tourist facilities along Route 111, it is a relatively sedate residential town. Some of its residents are well-to-do displaced Europeans. The new Desert College could become California's most socially oriented junior college.

La Quinta, frequented by wealthy desert enthusiasts, is as uneffusive as Palm Springs is flamboyant.

PROSPECTS

Recreation and agriculture in the Colorado Desert depend upon the stimulation exerted by Southern California metropolitan areas. As the latter flourish so are the resort clientele and the farm markets maintained. At present, continued growth of Southern California population is assumed; thus, no end is seen to expansion of the recreational communities of the San Jacinto Piedmont, Anza-Borrego Desert, and the Salton Sea. Livestock feeding and produce farming can thereby anticipate expanding markets.

The nature of the Colorado Desert itself poses some limitations to added settlement, although one wonders in light of recent developments in environmentally similar central Arizona. Only Coachella Valley is now assured of expanded reclamation in the near future. Adjacent to the cultivated Imperial Valley are large empty wastelands, East Mesa and West Mesa, which are potentially arable (see map, Fig. 4-2). For many years the federal government's General Land Office has prohibited homesteading of these "mesas" pending Supreme Court decision regarding allocation of Colorado River water. West Mesa appears economically out of reach of Colorado water, but East Mesa is partially accessible from the All-American Canal. Under agreement with the federal government the Imperial Irrigation District has sublet a small tract here to Brock Farms, Inc., which is experimenting with a variety of crops brought from many distant parts of the world. Drifting sand and extremely porous soils that demand heavy water applications are major problems.

Water supply for the Desert remains a major limitation, although it appears adequate for present levels of agriculture for many years. After the Palo Verde Valley users upstream (see Chapter 3), Imperial and Coachella farmers enjoy first priority on California's share of Colorado River water. Expansion of this supply is rendered doubtful by the physical and legal shrinkage of the Colorado River. Greater irrigating efficiencies may be demanded; combined with California population growth they may result in greater emphasis upon higher value products with less land devoted to feeds and many field crops. The low altitude of the Desert offers intriguing possibilities if sea-water conversion ever becomes sufficiently inexpensive.

Industrialization of the Desert is not yet a significant trend, although some firms recognize the appeal of the San Jacinto Piedmont as a residential area. Heavy industry is not likely to be welcome in such areas. The expanding electronics industry of central Arizona demonstrates that neither heat nor settlement oriented toward agriculture and recreation prevents industrialization when other conditions are "right." It remains to be seen whether the Colorado Desert is an adequate location for lighter "high-value-added" manufacturing in terms of labor forces, services, communications, and research facilities.

PART TWO : :

THE SIERRA-CASCADE REGION

THE SIERRA-CASCADE REGION

Mountains form the most salient features on the surface of the earth. In North America few ranges can rival the Sierra Nevada and the Cascade for dramatic landscapes and for scenic magnificence. Many have thrilled to the tremendous east wall of the Sierra Nevada from Highway 395 (Fig. 2-6) or the impressive spectacle of Mt. Shasta from a railroad coach.

Some geographers have identified the Sierra Nevada and the Cascade with the lower-lying lands to the west (i.e., the Pacific Borderlands). There is much merit in delineation of broad portions of the earth as regions. Yet the physical contrasts between these loftier mountains and the hills and lowlands to the west alone seems sufficient reason to give them separate status in the study of a single state.

It would be difficult to find companion mountain ranges more unlike in structure than the Sierra Nevada and the Cascade. Both, it is true, are of recent origin in their present form. The name of the latter range has in fact been applied to the orogeny, the Cascade Revolution, which created most of the lordly young mountains of this earth during late geologic times. The southern Cascade of California would not be much of a mountain range were it not for the more prominent cones,

Lassen Peak (10,466 ft.) and Mt. Shasta (14,-162 ft.), which stand thousands of feet above the surrounding tablelands. The Sierra Nevada by contrast is one of the great granitic fault-blocks of the world.

The Sierra-Cascade region serves many important functions. From its snowfields come the rivers that provide domestic water for San Francisco, Los Angeles, and a host of smaller communities. Without the winter moisture accumulation in these ranges the Great Central Valley would not be a great agricultural empire. From the montane forests, too, has come lumber to build cities and hydroelectric power from falling water to foster industrial growth. To the mountains —for health, pleasure, and relaxation—go thousands of Californians and many visitors, to hike and fish and ski—or to relax amidst the grandeur of these alluring summits.

The mountains likewise divide California into two realms, the Pacific Borderlands to the west (Part Three) benefiting from the influence of moisture-laden Pacific air masses, and the dry Intermontane lands (Part One) east of the shadow of the Sierra and the Cascade. Even today the highlands, especially the Sierra, serve as barriers to transportation; hence vehicular traffic is limited to a relatively

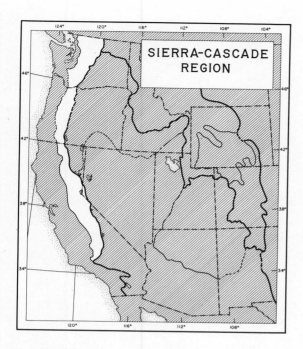

few passes. As was noted earlier, so significant is this wall as a barrier that in early days of California's state history, abortive attempts were made by some Intermontane settlers to join Nevada territory.

Fig. 5-1. THE HIGH SIERRA. Lower Rae Lake, Dragon Peak, and Mt. Rixford are found in eastern Kings Canyon National Park. Many alpine enthusiasts regard this locality as one of the most scenic portions of the Sierra Nevada. (Joseph Wampler)

CHAPTER FIVE:: THE SIERRA NEVADA

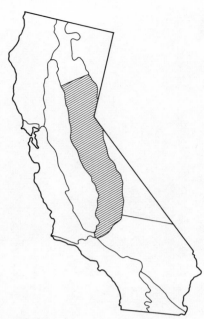

THE SIERRA NEVADA

The Sierra Nevada is a magnificent range. The gods dealt lavishly when they bestowed upon these mountains such attributes as Mt. Whitney (14,495 ft.), long the nation's highest summit;[1] Lake Tahoe, one of the world's loveliest alpine lakes; Yosemite Valley, acclaimed by some as the prime beauty spot of the hemisphere; the giant trees of Sequoia Park; a dozen great chasms; and some of the most awe-inspiring examples of valley glaciation known to man. Here is a mountain range whose charm and appeal usually increases with one's knowledge. And full appreciation of the Sierra must come slowly; much of it is inaccessible except by pack train and afoot.

The Sierra Nevada is a tremendous highland block, extending more than 400 miles from the steep wall that rises above the southern borders of Lassen Park southward to Tejon Pass in Los Angeles County (see map, Fig. 5-2). Its width approximates 70 miles; in the

This chapter has been reviewed by John E. Kesseli, University of California, Berkeley.

[1] That Mt. McKinley is the highest summit in the fifty United States is one of the several geographical "quiz facts" that have resulted from the creation of the two new states.

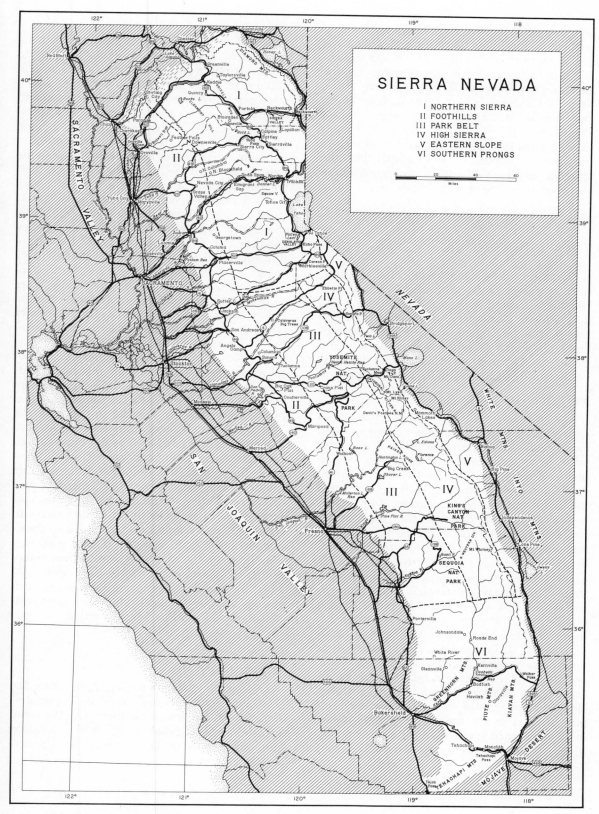

Fig. 5-2. MAP OF THE SIERRA NEVADA.

south it is less than 50 miles and near Lake Tahoe more than 80 miles. The range encompasses more than 27,000 square miles. On the east its precipitous walls rise abruptly above three of California's four Intermontane lands, the Northeast, Trans-Sierra, and Mojave Desert (see Part One). On the west the approach from the Great Central Valley into the Sierra foothills is so gradual that the stranger may be well within the range before he becomes aware of it.

THE DESIGN

The Sierra Nevada is often cited in introductory geography and geology classes as a "textbook example" of the fault block (Fig. 2-6). Such elementary description fails to convey the intricate history of this complex highland which includes a long background of sediment deposition, folding and faulting, volcanism, glaciation, uplift, and erosion.

EVOLUTION

The life story of the Sierra Nevada began with deposition of thousands of feet of sediments into a geosyncline. These particles came from the wearing away of the ancient highland mass, Cascadia, to the west. Then in succession over a long period of geologic time the following changes occurred. (1) Forces within the crust buckled the sedimentary strata upward into folded layers; the deformation was accompanied by violent faulting. Evidence is seen today in the north-south parallelism of foothill terrain (reflected in the twisted shapes of many reservoirs and highway routes). (2) A major event in establishment of this ancestral Sierra was the intrusion beneath the sediments of a vast molten mass that cooled to become a granitic batholith of impressive proportions. Today this light-hued granite, which forms the bulk of the range, imparts the gleaming "range of light" surfaces. Implacement of gold within the Mother Lode also resulted at this time. The original mountains were much lower than the contemporary Sierra; their creation was followed by a long

period of calm as if Mother Nature had been so weakened by the strain of her labor as to require a renewing of strength. (3) Through millions of years the upfolded ridges, which were separated by downfolded troughs and fault basins, were worn so low that the presently dry lands of the Intermontane Region (Part One) were exposed to much more rain falling from Pacific-born air masses. Prior to the wearing down of the highlands, however, their northern end was buried by lava flows. Today we find evidence of past times in the amazingly level interfluves and plateaus (Fig. 5-8), such as the surface into which Yosemite Valley has been cut. (4) The upbowing of the batholith, deprived of much of its sedimentary cover, commenced in the Eocene. With continuing erosion the higher elevations were etched out to produce mountainous terrain. Uparching and erosion, and volcanic activity largely restricted to the northern Sierra, continued intermittently during much of the Tertiary. Today the flows give variety and color to the terrain; they include the many flat-topped interfluves in the foothills, some known as "Table Mountain"—there are several features so named. (5) Toward the close of the Tertiary the maximum uplift took place, concentrated in the east, so that the range began to assume its present unsymmetrical tilt. Toward the end of this deformation large-scale faulting occurred, coupled with the dropping of Owens Valley, to create the dramatic east face of the range. The uplift caused rivers to cut deeply into the subdued upland, thus creating modern stream canyons. Placer gold was deposited in the stream valleys. Present-day fault blocks and escarpments developed. (6) Finally came the ice sculpture discussed next. It was partially caused by the increasing wetness and cold produced by the uplift.

ICE SCULPTURE

Even without the glaciation of the Great Ice Age, the Sierra Nevada would be impressive. Because of ice sculpture there are the deep broad-floored canyons (Fig. 5-16), serrated summits, scores of lakes, spectacular waterfalls, and other features that contribute majesty to the "range of light."

All of the Sierra was not greatly affected by the repeated advances of ice tongues down the canyons. In the north, where the summits were between 6000 and 7000 feet, only small cirque glaciers developed. But from Donner Pass southward into the canyon of the upper Kern, a distance of nearly 300 miles, glaciers filled scores of canyons. Some glaciers were only 10 to 15 miles long but others attained lengths of nearly 60 miles. Around the crest between Lake Tahoe and Cathedral Range in Yosemite Park a small ice cap formed. One of the most effective jobs of erosion was accomplished in the south, where the Great Western Divide bore a dozen glaciers varying in length from five to seven miles.

CONTEMPORARY TERRAIN

The modern Sierra Nevada is a complex fault block that retains some vestiges, particularly around headwaters areas, of ancient trellis drainage patterns associated with the ridge and valley character of its ancestral highlands. It also possesses "superimposed ranges," generally with northwest-southeast trend, that are remnants of its earlier orogeny. Among the better known of these segments are the contiguous Cathedral and Ritter ranges in the Yosemite area, Kaiser Ridge between Huntington Lake and the South Fork of the San Joaquin, and the Great Western Divide in Sequoia Park. The east wall rises, with en echelon fault facets, to the highest summits in the High Sierra around Mt. Whitney. At the northern end of the range faults and differential tilting have produced three parallel blocks with east-facing scarps. From west to east these are Clermont Hill, Grizzly Mountains, and Diamond (Carson) Mountains. Although the eastern Sierra contains a maze of faults, they are often obscured by erosion and by alluvial deposits at the base of the range.

The Sierra Nevada contains only small remnants of the folded sedimentary rocks of the ancestral range. These are commonly found in the western foothills or in the superimposed ranges mentioned above. The bulk of the exposed bedrock of the Sierra consists of granitoidal rocks whose soft gray hues account for the designation "range of light." Weaknesses in the granitics, produced by faulting and other causes, have been responsible for the ease with which water and ice have etched out certain segments of the batholith. Elsewhere lack of jointing accounts for such impressive monoliths as Half Dome, Tehipite Dome, and Moro Rock. In the northern Sierra lavas and schists are responsible for the darker, less attractive rock colors.

The Sierra varies considerably in elevation. Summits are generally under 7000 feet in the north; too, elevations seldom reach 6000 feet in the Greenhorn, the Piute, and the Tehachapi in the south. Seven out of the eleven peaks whose summits exceed 14,000 feet are found in proximity to Mt. Whitney.

Stream drainage, complimented by the work of valley glaciers, has gouged deeply into the gently inclined western slope of the Sierra. The fourteen major rivers (from north to south: Feather, Yuba, Bear, American, Cosumnes, Mokelumne, Calaveras, Stanislaus, Tuolumne, Merced, San Joaquin, Kings, Kaweah, and Kern) have produced a series of canyons that vary in depth from 1500 feet to more than 6000 feet in extreme instances. Whereas the slight tilt of the Sierran block is readily appreciated from interfluve ridges, the marked degree of dissection tends to obscure the gentleness of the westward inclination throughout much of the range.

VERTICAL ZONES

With the greatest relief of any mountain range within conterminous (48 states) United States, length through five degrees of latitude, and intricacy of surface, the Sierra Nevada is characterized by considerable variation in weather and climate, which is reflected in the vegetation zones as well.[2]

[2] Relief is the principal determinant of vertical zonation. Other controls produce such effects as *ubac-adret* (shady slope-sunny slope) and descending timberline elevation northward.

CLIMATE

The Sierra Nevada displays the typical California climatic pattern of dry summers and moist winters. But variations and extremes tend to be greater than in most of the state. Throughout the Sierra there is the expected temperature decrease with rise in elevation.

Even more impressive than temperature gradient is distribution of moisture. Three fourths of the precipitation is concentrated during the winter half-year and less than 3 percent of the annual total falls in summer. Southward migration of the Hawaiian High permits an invasion by cyclonic storms from the North Pacific. The fronts usually pass to the northward; hence most of the moisture comes from the warmer tropical Pacific air masses within the warm sector of the storms.

The upper reaches of the northern Sierra in the vicinity of Donner Summit receive almost the highest annual snowfall recorded in the United States; annual amounts fluctuate between about 200 and 700 inches. The period of maximum precipitation, which lasts longer in the northern Sierra, usually occurs from November through April. The belt of heaviest snowfall (a north-south zone about 80 miles long), which has received more than 30 feet within a single month near Donner Summit, lies between 3000 and 6500 feet elevation. Maximum snowfall is likely during January; with continued low temperatures the snowpack generally increases in depth through February. The deep pack has considerable weight, demanding steep-roofed buildings, snowsheds on the Southern Pacific, and employment of snowfighting equipment on main rail and highway lines (Fig. 5-29). The weight of snowbanks at Blue Canyon in 1914 so bent a fence whose rails consisted of two-inch locomotive boiler flues that they fell out of their posts.

Violent thunderstorms are rare in the Sierra Nevada; river flood stage generally is caused by rapid rise of spring temperatures, accelerating the melting of snowbanks. Some winter floods occur when storms bring rain instead of snow—this is most likely if there has been unusually heavy snowfall early in the season. Although summer precipitation totals are limited, convectional (orographic) storms are ofttimes accompanied by lightning, which brings a threat of fire in the dry forests.

Climatic zones in the Sierra Nevada vary with altitude (and latitude), although the several types all display summer drought (see Appendix A). The *semiarid subtropic* type, restricted to the lower reaches of more southerly stream canyons, has the hot dry summer characteristic of the southern Central Valley. The *warm-summer subtropical (Mediterranean)*, representative of the Sacramento Valley, extends southward along the lower foothill uplands, narrowing toward the south. A rather broad belt of *cooler-summer subtropical* (not separately identified in the appendix) prevails in the upper foothills. Much of the forest land lies within the *dry-summer middle latitude* belt. Winters are cold but temperatures are seldom below zero at 5000 feet. That portion of the High Sierra which lies above timberline is described as *tundra*, or *alpine*. Its midsummer temperatures are akin to those of the arctic slope of Alaska; winter temperatures presumably drop below zero.

SHRUBS AND FORESTS

The natural vegetation of the Sierra Nevada reflects elevation and various climatic ramifications resultant from its bulk and dissection. The vegetation can be grouped into several zones: foothill, montane forest, subalpine forest, alpine meadows, and eastern slope.

The **Foothill Zone**, in addition to other controls, is the product of repeated fire. It begins at the eastern edge of the Great Central Valley and attains its upper limit around 4000 feet in the south (lower in the north). Its lower portion is grasslands, parched during the dry summers in seared hues of straw yellow. Scattered amidst the grasses are groves of interior live oak and valley oak as well as numerous herbs and wildflowers. The middle portion (between 1000 and 4000 feet elevation) contains chaparral, with its various ceanothus and manzanita. Chamise is especially common; the formation also includes scrub oaks, coffeeberry, and many other species. This dwarf evergreen "forest," quite mixed, is generally found on rocky, well-

Fig. 5-3. THE MONTANE FOREST—open and sunny. Note the natural regrowth of ponderosa pine. (U.S. Forest Service)

Fig. 5-4. SUMMER PASTURE IN THE NORTHERN SIERRA. Although transhumance has declined, the summer range remains important. This meadow is part of Plumas National Forest. (U.S. Forest Service)

drained slopes. Some species can survive frequent fires, whereas others are perpetuated through seed survival. Most plants are markedly drought tolerant. The higher foothills, clue to transition into the beautiful forests at higher elevation, support an open digger pine-blue oak woodland. common between 3000 and 4000 feet (in the south). The digger (Pinus sabiniana) is a shaggy tree that is not fit company on the bases of foliage and coloring for the lordly pines of higher altitudes.

The **Montane Forest** is found between 4000 and 7000 feet (north) and between 5000 and 7000 feet or higher farther south. It is a southward continuation of the luxuriant conifer forests of the Cascade Range, yet it seems a different forest—more open and light (Fig. 5-3). Although most of its trees are conifers, it includes such broadleafs as Kellogg oak, bigleaf maple, dogwood, and western azalea —most conspicuous in autumn when the leaves turn; the dogwood leaves become an almost dazzling red. Incense cedar (Libocèdrus decúrrens), Douglas fir, and the pines, especially the sugar, Jeffrey, and ponderosa (yellow), are conspicuous at lower elevations. The ponderosa particularly flourishes on drier slopes and lower altitudes. The Douglas fir (Pseùdotsùga taxifòlia), more abundant in

the northern Sierra, prefers north-facing slopes. Various pines, most commonly the Bishop and Monterey, are likely successors to chaparral on burned patches. The white fir (Àbies cóncolor) becomes a dominant at higher elevations. The Forest includes the giant Sierran redwood, Sequoia gigantèa, whose groves are apt to contain ponderosa and sugar pine and incense cedar. The Sequoia is found only in the southern Sierra; it is sometimes confused with mature incense cedar by strangers. This Forest, with its many variations, includes a wider variety of trees, shrubs, and herbs than any other California life zone. It is decidedly a forest of cone-bearers; sometimes, because of the prevalence of the ponderosa, it is called "the yellow pine forest." Glades and treeless slopes have numerous shrubs; California hazel, gooseberry, thimbleberry, and manzanita are especially common. Moist treeless slopes are particularly popular with such plants. On dry flats, low vegetation includes a variety of grasses and herbs, whereas wet swamps and meadows support water-tolerant grasses, herbs, and shrubs (Fig. 5-4).

The **Subalpine Zone** rises from 5000 feet (7000 feet in the south) to timberline. The red fir (Àbies magnífica), often in heavy

Fig. 5-5. MT. DANA–MINARETS WILD AREA. Summits in the High Country southeast of Yosemite Park reach 13,000 feet. Seen here are Garner Lake, Mt. Ritter, and Mt. Banner. (Joseph Wampler)

stands, is perhaps the most characteristic tree. Other conifers include such pines as western white and lodgepole, mountain hemlock, and white fir. The aspen, most conspicuous in September when its trembling leaves turn golden, is common. Shrubs are found in limited quantities, although gooseberry and waxberry are significant. Herbs too tend to be restricted, but yellow-green lichens are common on tree trunks. Significant modification takes place toward timberline. The pines (whitebark, foxtail, and limber) are still representative, and the Sierran juniper is often prominent at timberline. The red fir is usually not found this high although the lodgepole pine and mountain hemlock flourish. At timberline the oft-contorted juniper and the whitebark pine bear evidence of deep snow and strong winds.

The **Alpine Meadows**, above timberline, are generally found from about 9000 feet to summit ridges and peaks (Fig. 5-5). Besides grasses they afford a garden of elfin plants, both annual and perennial, and constitute one of the delights of a high-country visit. Two blue favorites are gentian and Polemonium. Whereas heather adds its purple, the Indian paintbrush, red—there are many hues from snow white to deep blues and purples. Even such trees as pines and hemlock exist as stunted little sticks not over a foot in height. These plants must grow rapidly, for the season is short. Green shoots appear before the snow has melted. July brings a riot of color; late August, seed pods and dried plants. The discerning eye finds plants wherever there is a bit of soil and a trace of water.

The **Eastern Slope** is a badly fractured reproduction, generally with narrower zones, of the western slope. The red fir is found only in the Carson Range and in the northern Sierra. The montane forest reaches higher elevations and is more open than on the west side. Jeffrey and ponderosa pine are conspicuous dominants. At its base piñon and juniper are found, often associated with cottonwoods and such vegetation from the east as sagebrush. Because of steeper gradients and sparser cover than the western slope, the vegetation of the eastern slope seems more dissimilar than it actually is. The effects of thin soils, drought, and wide extremes of temperature contribute to the feeling of difference between east and west.

SETTLEMENT

THE INDIANS

The Sierra Nevada was occupied by members of three aboriginal families: *Penutians* (west), *Shoshone* (east), and *Washoe* (a Hokan people who occupied the Carson Range and the littoral of Lake Tahoe). Disappointingly little information remains regarding these pre-European inhabitants. Their population, their mode of life, and even their migrations are often in doubt. There is considerably more knowledge about the Penutians than about the Shoshoneans.

These mountains afforded relatively favored environments in their lower reaches and held a far larger proportion of the pre-European inhabitants than the region does of California's contemporary population. "Permanent" abodes were commonly in the canyons, warmer than the uplands and better supplied with fish, game, and water. Despite the rugged terrain there was less cultural diversity than in such regions as the Northwest. The summit of the range posed less of an economic or political barrier than it does today.

The Sierra provided varied resources for the Indians. There was an abundance of acorns; the foothills generally constituted a more attractive environment than the floor of the Great Central Valley. Hill tribes tended to be stabilized with limited need for migration in search of game. The eastern slope provided the Shoshones with a more favorable habitat than that of their relatives to the east in the Great Basin.

Mountain areas have often formed areas of refuge for weaker people; such has been the case with the Sierra Nevada. For example, the Washoe (Hokans) were apparently "senior residents" of California who had been driven into the higher country by later arrivals. With the exception of Southern California and the Northwest, there have been as many reservations established in the Sierra as anywhere in California.

THE SPANISH

The Sierra Nevada was an unknown land to the Spanish; they had neither the numerical strength nor the economic necessity to penetrate so far from coastal missions. Even the present name of the range was originally applied to the Coast Ranges around Monterey Bay by Juan Cabrillo in 1542. It has been assigned to the Sierra only on maps constructed since 1850. Presumably Padre Garcés crossed Tejon Pass in 1776 and was the first white man to see the Sierra Nevada. The Spanish had no influence upon later utilization of the range; the names they assigned some rivers, as *Rio de los Reyes* (Kings), *Rio de las Plumas* (Feather) and *Rio de los Americanos* (American) have been Anglicized so that their Spanish origin is no longer apparent.

FUR TRAPPERS

The principal contribution of the fur trappers, who began entering the Southwest in the 1820's, to American occupance of the Sierra Nevada and California was exploration. The fur trappers first discovered the Sierran passes (see section on Transportation) that were afterwards significant in the economic growth of the state. Jedediah Smith, after presumably camping along the Kings, first failed in a midwinter crossing from the west but later successfully traveled across the Sierra en route to Salt Lake in 1827. The outstanding early exploration was accomplished by Joseph Walker, who apparently crossed the range from the east via tributaries of the East Walker River in November of 1833 in the vicinity of Tioga Road. The following year he returned eastward across Walker Pass. Most fur trappers were not literary; hence only limited records, usually as diaries, remain of their travels. However, they did make a signal contribution to knowledge of the Sierra Nevada.

IMMIGRANT PARTIES

Immigrant parties followed the fur trappers in the 1840's. Their goal was not within the range itself but the lowlands to the west. Their guides were sometimes men who had gained knowledge as fur trappers. In some instances the earlier immigrant groups utilized passes previously unknown to Americans. Thus the Bidwell party, the first company, used Sonora Pass and Stanislaus Canyon in 1841. Then the Chiles group followed Walker Pass, known since the crossing by Walker and his men a decade earlier. The first traverse of Donner Pass in 1844 is described in *The Opening of the California Trail*, edited by George R. Stewart. The name of this famous pass, however, is derived from the tragic Donner Party, which used it in 1846.

LATER EXPLORATION

Objective efforts to examine the Sierra Nevada began with the Fremont expedition of 1843-45 guided by Joseph Walker and Kit Carson. This group visited such locales as the Tehachapi Range, Lake Tahoe, and Kings Canyon. The official expedition map was published in 1848 and was the first to show such features as Carson, Walker, and Kern rivers, Owens and Bonpland (Tahoe) lakes. During the later 1840's specific attempts were made to find the best routes for emigrants.

The extent and general features of the Sierra were known at the time of the Gold Rush. Quest for more feasible transportation routes, foothill settlement, and appreciation of the High Sierra came afterwards. Two federal railroad surveys expanded knowledge: the Williamson survey of 1853 in the south and the Beckwith survey of 1854 in the north. Yosemite and Kings Canyon were appreciated by the early 1850's; Yosemite has been a vacation land since 1855. Sequoia bark from Calaveras Grove was exhibited in United

States and in Europe, and in 1858 the Giant Forest was discovered.

Geologic investigation of the Sierra came relatively early. For a generation California Geologic Survey parties explored and mapped the range. Knowledge of the High Sierra was gained in 1864. Clarence King assumed that he had ascended Whitney (actually he climbed Mt. Langley) in 1871; Whitney's summit had been reached by 1873. Although specific areas had been mapped in the previous decade, orderly survey of the Sierra commenced in the 1890's. Since 1890 the United States Geologic Survey, the Sierra Club, and the National Park Service have contributed much to knowledge of the physical geography.

AMERICAN SETTLEMENT

As it has in many western mountains where mining has been involved, American settlement came to the Sierra Nevada with precipitous suddenness. Within two years after Marshall's discovery of gold on the American River in January 1848, there were perhaps 50,000 working miners in the Sierra. The Gold Rush affected not only the region but the state and the nation. Many miners soon forsook mining for more certain livelihood, frequently outside of the Sierra Nevada. But the effect of the Rush was momentous. Statehood for California was hastened and speedy urbanization of San Francisco, Sacramento, Stockton, and Marysville materialized. Economic development was accelerated: retail establishments, banks, transportation facilities, lumbering, ranching, and industry (especially in San Francisco). Widespread creation of governmental institutions and services took place, including formation of mountain counties. Cultural activities were enhanced: schools, theaters, churches, newspapers. The Gold Rush era left a legacy of artistic and literary richness.

By 1880 most of the Sierra Nevada was confronted with post-Gold Rush settlement and economic stabilization. The boom camps had experienced early chaotic conditions with much lawlessness. They commonly consisted at first of tents and rude shacks, often forming narrow ribbons along stream canyons. Many were plagued by repeated fires. Within a generation some had vanished and many were crumbling. Most contemporary Sierran communities were created in that era. But many towns and entire counties have never reacquired the population they had during their earlier years.

Lumbering, originally an adjunct of the mining boom, has been a persistent source of livelihood. Here, as in the Southern Cascade and the Northwest, the history too frequently has been one of mining the forest. Like the gold camps, some lumber towns have withered and died.

Livestock ranching too had an early start and has become the most unfailing source of livelihood in the region. Yet it has never been responsible for assemblage of sizable populations. Sierran transhumance began with the drought year of 1864 when cattle were taken to high meadows near the source of the San Joaquin River. Ranching, much more than mining, has stabilized the economy of the Sierra over the past century.

Transportation facilities were quickly necessitated because of the Gold Rush. By 1850 crude trails across the Sierra were in regular use and, in the foothills especially, ferries were operating across rivers. For almost a century the region has had railroad routes. Through commerce, like ranching, has continued to be an important factor in settlement stability.

Recreation early made a modest contribution to Sierran economy. Yosemite and Lake Tahoe achieved popularity during the late nineteenth century. But widespread establishment of recreational facilities as a settlement factor has occurred mostly in the twentieth century, especially with the use of the automobile and improvement of highways. Hydroelectric development too has tended to be a twentieth-century stimulant.

TRANSPORTATION

Transportation has contributed much to utilization of the Sierra Nevada, especially since American settlement commenced. The route-finding of fur trappers, emigrants, and others has been noted previously. Despite use since Gold Rush days and notwithstanding technological improvements, the Sierra remains an impediment to east-west surface travel. Conditions that contribute to this barrier effect include (1) continuity of summit height; (2) canyons (i.e., eroded surfaces, especially on the west side); (3) steep slopes; (4) winter storms (especially deep snow and heavy rains followed by landslides; (5) ownership (especially, federal wild areas within the national forests). Although the Sierra presents handicaps, its position athwart routes between Los Angeles and San Francisco (i.e., the Tehachapi Mountains) and between central California and interior United States results in much surface traffic across the range.

RAILROADS

Rail lines have crossed the Sierra Nevada since 1868, when the Southern Pacific (then called the Central Pacific) extended its line eastward into Nevada toward a junction with the Union Pacific in Utah. For the remainder of the nineteenth century this remained the single rail route eastward across the mountains. Although this line has been hampered by steep grades and heavy winter snowfall, which necessitated miles of snowsheds, it was favored by its directness between the Bay Area, Sacramento, and eastern United States.

The Southern Pacific extended its second line across the range in the 1870's when it built its Sunset Route southward through the San Joaquin Valley and across Tehachapi Pass in 1876. This traverse, unhampered by deep snow or high elevation (the summit is at 4025 ft.), was made difficult because of faulting and steep slopes on the northwest face of the Tehachapi (Fig. 5-14).

The feasibility of the Feather River Canyon for an east-west rail crossing of the Sierra Nevada was recognized in the 1860's, even before the Southern Pacific utilized Donner Summit. Beckwourth Pass is almost 2000 feet lower than Donner. But the tortuous nature of the Feather canyon seemed to pose impossible construction problems. Hence it was not until 1909 that another company, the Western Pacific, made a crossing of the Sierra. Its line is not plagued by the heavy snows of Donner Summit, although rain sometimes leads to landslides (Fig. 5-30). The Western Pacific, shortest trackage of the major western rail systems, connects central California with the Middle West through shipping arrangements with the Denver and Rio Grande and with the Burlington Route.

HIGHWAYS

Ten east-west highway routes cross the Sierra Nevada but only half of them can be used throughout the year. These routes generally originated in passages discovered before 1850 and were long used as crude wagon trails.[3] They tend to ascend rapidly the steep eastern slopes of the Sierra, then descend the western slopes gradually following the relatively gentle interfluves. Much improvement has taken place since the 1920's; all of the highways are now paved, although most remain winding two-lane roads with steep grades. In the late 1950's conversion of U.S. 40 (Interstate 80), U.S. 50, and U.S. 466 into freeways was commenced. In the extreme south U.S. 99 (Interstate 5) is a completed freeway, with some eight-lane stretches, into Southern California across Tejon Pass.

East-west travel across the southern half of the Sierra is hampered because many of the state highway routes, utilizing higher passes, are seasonally blocked by snow (Fig. 5-12). In midwinter there is no crossing between U.S. 50 on the north and California 178 (Walker Pass) on the south. In fact, there is no highway between Tioga Road (California 120) and 178. In this portion of the range lies the High Sierra, including California's largest wilderness area, discussed later.[4]

[3] The Feather River highway (U.S. 40A) was not opened until 1937. This arduous engineering achievement in places involved lowering of workmen into the canyon with ropes. Previously, travelers from the adjacent Sacramento Valley took the old wagon road across the uplands to Quincy. This road was closed in winter by deep snow.

[4] Note that residents of the San Joaquin Valley around Fresno are confronted with the absence of a direct eastward route.

Understandably most of the commercial carriers as well as the majority of private vehicles utilize relatively few highways. In the north most of the traffic follows U.S. 40 (Interstate 80) or U.S. 50, and in the south U.S. 466 and U.S. 99 (Interstate 5).

THE PASSES

There are no low passes, although Tejon (4183 ft.), Tehachapi (3988 ft.), and Walker (5250 ft.) are sufficiently low and far enough south that they are seldom closed by snow even briefly.[5] California's highest automobile pass, Tioga (9941 ft.), seasonally forms the eastern entry into Yosemite Park; until recent years a 22-mile stretch of Tioga Road west of the summit represented a wagon trail of the 1880's, merely covered with black-top. Passes northward from Tioga to Echo (U.S. 50) are high: Sonora (9626 ft.), Ebbetts (8731 ft.), and Carson (8573 ft.). From Echo (7377 ft.) northward they tend to be lower: Donner (7089 ft.), Yuba (6701 ft.) and Beckwourth (5221 ft.). Heavy snows necessitate use of large motorized equipment to keep most of these crossings open in winter.

To appreciate more fully the several portions of the Sierra Nevada and their somewhat different usage, the remainder of this chapter will be concerned with subdivisions of the range. These units will be considered successively: (1) High Sierra, (2) Eastern Slope, (3) Southern Prongs, (4) Park Belt, (5) Foothills, (6) Northern Sierra.

THE HIGH SIERRA

The High Sierra, the true alpine back country, is a paradise for the nature lover; it is an unspoiled wilderness uncrossed by high-

[5] California passes tend to be appreciably lower than those in the Colorado Rockies, where Trail Ridge Road (U.S. 34) exceeds 12,000 feet and paved roads reach the summits of Mt. Evans (14,260 ft.) and Pikes Peak (14,110 ft.). However, the base of the Sierra Nevada lies thousands of feet lower than the bases of Rocky Mountain ranges. The highest pass in California is Whitney (13,500 ft.), crossed by the foot trail to the summit of Mt. Whitney.

Fig. 5-6. KINGS CANYON—wilderness park. Its enthusiasts regard Rae Lake as the loveliest in the High Country. Fin Dome adds a photogenic backdrop. (National Park Service, photo by Stagner)

way—not even a single dirt road (Fig. 5-6). Yet with continuing population growth within California the area is, as one writer has expressed it, an unspoiled wilderness "only by courtesy." Only the efforts of organizations of sportsmen and outdoors enthusiasts have prevented its ravishment by commercial interests, such as the group that has proposed an expressway running the length of the High Sierra.

EXTENT

The High Sierra has no definite geographic limits but for its enthusiasts it has positive meaning: it is the alpine wilderness. It can be defined as the alpine belt above the continuous forests—the central one third of the Sierra Nevada. It extends, between transmontane highways, from Walker Pass (California 178) on the south to Tioga Pass on the north. It is, according to description, the area that was covered by a Pleistocene ice cap and where summits exceed 12,000 feet (Fig. 5-8)—in short, it includes all of California's 14,000-foot peaks except Mt. Shasta and White Mountain Peak.

THE LAND

The High Sierra represents one of America's finest examples of scouring by mountain glaciers. It contains over 1200 lakes and tarns; a paternoster (bead-like chain) arrangement of lakes along its U-shaped canyons is common. It has few waterfalls but scores of rapids and cascades along its streams. The ice removed much of the loose or broken rock; today the High Sierra is largely a realm of clean-swept, polished granite of lighter hues. The few dozen glacial remnants (Fig. 5-7) originated less than 4000 years ago in the "Little Ice Age." The vistas include glacial-grooved canyons and serrated ridges, capped by skies whose blueness seems unmatched in populated portions of California.

Climatically the High Sierra is a land of seasonal contrasts; wintry blasts as opposed to the serenity of clear summer skies. Sometimes, however, there are severe thunderstorms in summer and frost is a threat any month of the year. Snowfall is perhaps less than at lower elevations in the range, and summits are sometimes swept clear by strong winds. Yet in canyons and along north-facing

Fig. 5-7. LYELL GLACIER AND MID-SUMMER SNOWBANKS. *Lyell Glacier in southeastern Yosemite National Park is one of the largest glacial remnants in the Sierra Nevada.* (Richard Pillsbury)

slopes snow lingers so long that banks can be found in protected spots even in August.

The High Sierra has few trees, and they are not found in dense stands. Treeline varies from 10,000 feet in the north to over 11,000 feet in the south. Trees are apt to be stunted, even prostrate, at timberline. The characteristic vegetation consists of herbaceous plants, about one third of which are indigenous to California. Among the common ones are columbine, purple polemonium, figwort, and wild mustard. Various grasses and sedges prevail in many wet meadows.

The High Sierra is a harsh land for wild life, which is found in only small numbers.

The fauna includes the marmot, cony, alpine chipmunk, and mountain sheep. Only a small number of the sheep remain. Birds are seasonal residents except for the rosy finch, which remains throughout the year.

THE PRIMITIVE AREAS [6]

The High Sierra is a public domain nearly half of which is contained in the back country of three national parks, **Yosemite**, **Sequoia**, and **Kings Canyon**. The rest of the area is under the supervision of the Forest Service,

[6] All of California's mountain areas have primitive areas. (See Chapters 1, 6, 7, 8, and 10.)

*Fig. 5-8. KERN PLATEAU AND THE GREAT WESTERN DIVIDE. The High
Country westward from Mt. Whitney reveals an area of surprisingly little dissec-
tion. This is a relict of the epoch before the last period of mountain building. (U.S.
Forest Service)*

including all or part of six national forests.
The Forest Service has recognized the feasibility of maintaining portions of the national
forests as unspoiled wilderness, and hence
has established primitive areas.

Beginning in 1930 the Forest Service established portions of the national forests as primitive areas. There are seventy-eight such areas
within the nation, containing about one
twelfth of the total national forest acreage.
Selected as type areas for nature lovers they
are further identified according to size. The
twenty-eight larger units, in excess of 100,000
acres, are identified as "Wilderness areas."
The fifty smaller units known as "Wild Areas"
vary in size from 5000 to 100,000 acres (Fig.
5-5). Within primitive areas roads and
wheeled vehicles, landing of aircraft, use of
motor boats, and commercial lumbering are
prohibited. Limited grazing is allowed *if* the
vegetation is protected. Hunting and fishing
are permitted in accordance with state laws.
The primitive areas provide physical, mental,
and aesthetic values to those who visit them.
On the deficit side their use is restricted to a
hardy few, while the nation loses their potential minerals, lumber, and water power.

Eighth largest of the American wilderness
areas, and the largest within California, is
the **High Sierra Wilderness Area**, established
in 1931 with an area of 615 square miles. This
reserve, which is mostly bare rock country,
encompasses much of both sides of the main
Sierran crest from the vicinity of Mammoth
Lakes southward to the eastern boundary of
Sequoia National Park near Mt. Whitney.

California is fortunate to possess fourteen
of the nation's fifty wild areas. Within the
Sierra Nevada the **Mt. Dana–Minarets Wild
Area** was established in 1931 and has an area
of 136 square miles. Like the High Sierra
Wilderness Area it is mostly barren granite
rock along the main Sierran crest from Minaret
Summit to Mt. Lyell (Fig. 5-7); its high peak
is Mt. Ritter (13,156 ft.). Perhaps not strictly
within the limits of the High Sierra but justifi-
ably included are the **Desolation Valley, Emigrant Basin**, and **Hoover Wild Areas**. Smallest
of the three is the Hoover Wild Area with only
32 square miles. It is situated north of Tuolumne Meadows and adjoining Yosemite Park
and is characterized by glacial topography
and abundance of winter snow. Twice as large
is Desolation Valley Wild Area in the high

country west of Lake Tahoe but somewhat lower in elevation than is usual for the High Sierra. Largest of California's wild areas is Emigrant Basin Wild Area north of Yosemite Park.

A SUMMER PLAYGROUND

With slight exception, the High Sierra serves as a summer playground; winter sports are limited by isolation and absence of lodges and other facilities. Hiking, mountain climbing, fishing, and "packing-in" (from pack stations at lower elevations) are principal forms of recreation. Most of the visitors are neither rock climbers nor fishermen but merely nature lovers who come individually, by couples, families, or groups to "escape civilization" in this serene wilderness. During the summer when the lower Sierra is parched, the High Sierra is a land of spring, with blue skies and green meadows, shimmering lakes, fresh air, and scenic grandeur.

Despite absence of transmontane High Sierra highways there are numerous approach roads that permit the rapid hiker to gain alpine summits within hours after parking his automobile. A score of these roads from U.S. 395 in the east brings the visitor much closer to the summits than do the western approaches which number slightly more than half those from the east. From the west the principal approaches are from Yosemite Valley, Giant Forest Highway into the South Fork of the Kings, California 168 to Florence Lake, and the Mineral King branch of California 198. Residents of Southern California have a near monopoly on eastern approaches because of the absence of highways across the range. The western approaches are employed by people from central and northern California and also from Southern California.

The High Sierra is laced by a network of lateral trails from the canyons across the crest. Some trails, such as several in Yosemite Park, were utilized by Piute Indians in their migrations via Kearsarge, Mono, and Piute passes. Most westside trails were constructed by stockmen in the nineteenth century. Within Yosemite Park the U.S. Army improved the cattle trails when the military administered

Fig. 5-9. *RIDING TO PALISADE GLACIER. The trail through Bigpine Canyon, past the chain of seven paternoster lakes, makes this glacial relict accessible by horse or on foot.* (U.S. Forest Service)

the park. The 13-mile **Mt. Whitney Trail** was opened in 1904; the present crest-crossing via Whitney Pass was completed in 1930. The 48-mile **High Sierra Trail**, built by the National Park Service in 1930-1931, extends from Crescent Meadow on the Giant Forest Highway in Sequoia Park through the alpine country of the Kern-Kaweah headwaters across the Kern-Kaweah Divide to join the Muir Trail.

The stellar High Sierra trail is the **John Muir Trail**, envisioned by Theodore Solomons, pioneer member of the Sierra Club. The route was originally explored between 1892 and 1897. The Club finally established a committee to obtain state aid, and the legislature appropriated $10,000 in 1915. Between 1917 and 1929 four comparable appropriations were made. Construction, supervised by the State Engineer, with the assistance of the Sierra Club and the Forest Service, was completed in 1932 although the route across lofty Forester Pass (13,200 ft.) was not finished until 1938. The Trail, extending 212 miles from Yosemite Valley to Mt. Whitney, is jointly maintained by the Forest Service and the National Park Service. The Muir Pass–Mather Pass portion west of Bishop is conceded to be one of the most scenic sectors, vying with the Sequoia Park portion, which includes the highest pass (Forester), as well as the Kings-Kern Divide and the Mt. Whitney area. Access to the Muir Trail is provided by thirty-eight lateral trails that connect it with automobile roads. Fifty persons traversed the entire length of the route in 1951; thousands have hiked over portions· of it in recent summers. Most popular are the Glen Pass section, the Middle Fork of the San Joaquin basin, and the areas near Evolution Lake and Thousand Island Lake.

Hiking is the principal mode of travel in the High Sierra; for shorter jaunts the hiker can travel virtually unencumbered. The High Sierra has a varied appeal and offers fifty trail passes and 350 miles of improved paths over 10,000 feet elevation.

July and August are the best months in the high country; by July streams are low enough to ford and the early wildflowers abloom. August is the most popular month; there are late flowers. Of the 1600 who signed the register atop Mt. Whitney in a recent summer, 300 did so on Labor Day alone!

Combination camping-hiking pack trips are increasingly popular for groups. With pack animals a rate of one to two miles an hour is possible. Of increasing concern is the problem of grazing by pack animals. Suggested methods of protection for grass include fencing, signs, meadow reseeding, restricted grazing, time limits, rotated meadow use, route planning for larger groups, and feed importation. Since three fourths of the High Sierra lies west of the principal crest, most camping is on that side. Over 2000 pack and riding animals are available for High Sierra trips; during August reservations are usually necessary weeks in advance. Mules are popular for strength and endurance, horses for riding, burros for lighter packs into rugged terrain.

Rock climbing is restricted to the more agile and physically fit. Some find challenge in climbing the maximum number of high summits; others are satisfied with climbs that provide the greatest amount of alpine scenery. Climbers have used artificial aids from the time that George Anderson first ascended Half Dome in 1875.

Ice climbing is an even more restrictive activity, with Lyell, Ritter, and Palisades glaciers as popular spots.

The High Sierra is a paradise for the fly-fisher—a land of snow-fed creeks and lakes with sufficient brush to shade the water, abundance of fish, and not too many fishermen. This is trout country, land of the rainbow, golden, cutthroat, Lock Leven, and Eastern. The bright-hued golden, California's state fish, has its home in the timberline water bodies (Fig. 5-10). In *Waters of the Golden Trout Country,* McDermand lists over a hundred high-country trout lakes and indicates the types of fish in each. Scores of lakes adjoin the Muir Trail alone; some are seldom fished. There are 1200 lakes of an acre or more above 10,000 feet. Among the streams the Kern has long been famous for its trout. The more popular and accessible lakes, such as Rae, Bullfrog, and Shadow, require annual stocking. Most "planting" in high-country lakes is now effected with aircraft—the fingerlings are either rainbow or brook; the golden is no longer hatch-raised.

There is relatively little hunting in the High Sierra since game animals are not plentiful and hunting is forbidden within national parks. The deer usually abandon the High Sierra for lower elevations before hunting season opens.

WINTER WONDERLAND

The High Sierra is a snowy land, seldom visited by man, for eight months out of every year. There are few reasons to enter this winter wonderland, entirely blanketed by a white coat save for the green hues of the conifers and barren rock outcrops. Unobstructed by man, nature in the High Sierra maintains a balance between the hunters (owls, coyotes, hawks) and the hunted (mice and rats).

Snowshoes provide solution for winter travel in the area for those who must go there —such as Southern California Edison crews to Florence Lake. Lila Lofberg, wife of a power company employee, describes life at Florence Lake in *Sierra Outpost.* In Chapter Seven, "An All-Night Trek to See People," she describes snowshoeing from Florence Lake across Kaiser Pass to Big Creek 34 miles away.

Winter in the High Sierra is described by Orland Bartholomew in the *Sierra Club Bulletin* (Vol. 15). Bartholomew stored eleven

Fig. 5-10. HOME OF THE GOLDEN TROUT. California's state fish is indigenous to High Country lakes. One wonders here, "Did the missus have all the luck?" (Joseph Wampler)

caches of food during the autumn, and then in the winter of 1929 skied from Lone Pine to Yosemite, using special skis and a 60-pound pack with a 6-pound tent. He experienced no temperatures below zero above 11,000 feet during his trip and nowhere found snow more than four feet deep. In January he found the summit of Mt. Whitney barren; strong winds restrict snow depth around the heights and account for the relatively "high" temperatures encountered. Even above 10,500 feet he found many flowing creeks. He concluded that with a knowledge of mountaineering and with proper clothing the High Sierra poses no great hazards for winter travel.

THE EASTERN SLOPE

The Eastern Slope of the Sierra Nevada is often considered to be a straight, precipitous fault face, which rises abruptly from the desert country to the east (Fig. 2-6). This is almost true southward from Bishop, but north of Bishop the eastern front becomes more complex. In such places as the Carson Range and the Sweetwater Range (north of Bridgeport) it includes a series of re-entrants. Canyons of the two larger streams, the Walker and Carson rivers, tend to have a lesser gradient eastward.

The abruptness of portions of the eastern Sierran front, coupled with proximity to U.S. 395, makes it accessible to outdoorsmen who like their rugged country in easier doses than the High Sierra. Hence it is a popular vacation area for those who tour by automobile—a much larger group than the hikers who visit the high country. A score of well-maintained lateral access roads, varying in length from 3 to 20 miles, makes some scenic country available from U.S. 395.

Fig. 5-11. CAMPING BESIDE RUSH CREEK. Many thousands of Californians take advantage of the accessibility of national forest campgrounds along the Eastern Slope. (U.S. Forest Service)

RECREATION

The Eastern Slope is one of the more frequented highland areas in the West; tourism has become "big business" here. Varied recreational use prevails, with concentration in canyons, upon lakes, and along streams. Fishing, camping, swimming, and boating, hiking, winter sports, and relaxation constitute major activities. Visitors are far more numerous here than in the High Sierra. Numerous resorts and small communities depend upon tourism.

Sports fishing in this portion of the Sierra suffers from too many fishermen. Few trout stream locales in the nation are more heavily fished, and despite heavy annual stocking the catch compares unfavorably with the High Sierra.

Boating (canoes, rowboats, and small motorboats) is restricted to relatively few water bodies. These include Twin Lakes, June Lakes, Mammoth Lakes, and Lake Sabrina. Swimming is popular at most of these spots on summer afternoons, although some people find the water too cool.

Numerous facilities exist; since much of the area is within national forests, many camping spaces are available (Fig. 5-11). However, many thousands visit the Eastern Slope on summer weekends, and facilities become congested. Cabins are available at many places; areas such as Mammoth Lakes have more pretentious housing. Use of house trailers has become very popular. Mammoth Lakes, Twin Lakes, the Reversed Creek Area (June Lakes), Bishop Creek, and Lone Pine Creek are especially popular for camping.

Roads, lateral trail approaches to the Muir Trail, and gentle hillside slopes are available for the casual hiker who is unable or unwilling to attempt the long and steeper trails of the High Sierra.

A score of commercial packers with ranch headquarters at the base of the eastern front indicate the significance this area has as an outfitting center for high-country trips. Although the packer is confronted with the necessity of maximum return from his livestock and equipment during the short season between May and October, rates are reasonable. The pack train "express" is less expensive—a pack train from a larger station follows a regular daily route. Thus it is sometimes possible to have camping equipment delivered to a definite point while the individual goes afoot.

The Eastern Slope gained popularity as a winter-sports center in the 1950's. Sufficient snow is much more certain here than in the mountains of Southern California. In 1950 Mammoth Mountain (11,034 ft.) was unknown as a winter-sports center; in less than a decade it had become the leading Eastern Slope winter-sports center, with a large lodge, three double-chair lifts, and a ski school. Tows are also located at McGee Creek and Conway Summit on U.S. 395, a peripheral area in the Trans-Sierra.

ALPINE COUNTY

Alpine County dramatizes the economic problems that still afflict much of the Sierra Nevada—in a period when the population of California is increasing rapidly some Sierran counties are either stagnant or even witnessing an actual population decline. Alpine County had 400 inhabitants in 1960.

Settlement of this portion of the range commenced in the early 1850's as a result of the Gold Rush. When Alpine County was formed in 1864, mining was the principal source of California livelihood and establishment of this remote entity seemed valid. A silver boom was underway along Silver Creek south of present-day Markleeville and the original county place, **Silver Mountain City**, was a hustling camp of 3000 residents. By 1875, after the boom collapsed, the county population had declined to 1200. Briefly Alpine forests supplied timbers for the Comstock Lode.

Contemporary Alpine County demonstrates that superlative scenery and pleasant summer weather (Fig. 5-12) cannot compensate for geographic isolation. Despite eastward extension of California 89 to join U.S. 395, much of Alpine County is secluded half of each year from the remainder of California. Hence its residents must look eastward to Minden, Nevada, for many goods and services. Recreation is an important seasonal source of livelihood. Mining, lumbering, and livestock ranching also contribute to local incomes.

Markleeville, the diminutive county seat, is a one-street town of less than a hundred people in a tiny pine-sloped basin at 5500 feet elevation. Its small one-story courthouse suggests a rural schoolhouse.[7]

HYDROELECTRICITY

East-flowing Sierran streams are small in volume but have the advantage of steep gradients along their upper reaches within the Eastern Slope. Rights to the flow of numerous creeks belong to Los Angeles Department of Water and Power, which has power plants in Owens Gorge east of the Sierra and southward along the Los Angeles Aqueduct (Chapter 2). North of the area of Los Angeles activity, private power companies have long utilized the gradient of Mill, LeeVining, Rush, and Bishop creeks, and the Truckee River, to generate hydroelectricity.

Power development has been gradually consolidated into two firms, the Sierra Pacific Electric Company and the California Electric Power Company. Sierra Pacific, the older utility, supplies the larger communities of western Nevada with power generated along the Truckee River. California Electric originated with the demand for electricity at gold-boom Tonopah, Nevada, in 1904. For many years its principal markets have been in southeastern California.[8]

---

[7] The San Francisco *Examiner* (Nov. 23, 1961) noted that Alpine County has no doctor, dentist, practicing attorney, barber, or movie theater.

[8] California Electric was previously called Nevada-California Power. It absorbed local power companies in Goldfield and Tonopah. Then, beginning in 1905, four hydroelectric plants were constructed along Bishop Creek; Lake Sabrina is the largest of three artificial reservoirs that regulate flow. Plants are so staggered along the creek as to permit maximum hydrostatic head between each successive generator; the steep gradient of the Eastern Slope is beneficial. To assure a post-gold-boom market, local firms in the eastern Los Angeles Lowlands were absorbed. California Electric also acquired a company operating to the north that had built hydroelectric plants in the June Lakes district and on Mill Creek west of Mono Lake. Its market area now includes a portion of western Nevada, the Mojave Desert, eastern Los Angeles Lowlands, and the Colorado Desert. An interlacing transmission system joins various communities, and a number of steam plants supplement power from water-driven generators.

Fig. 5-12. SWITZERLAND OF AMERICA. *Alpine, least populous of the fifty-eight counties, has impressive scenery. This shows the locale of Carson Pass (8573 ft.) on California highway 88, which is closed many months of the year.* (Mary Hill)

Fig. 5-13. PINE CREEK MINE. *This operation represents one of the major tungsten producers within the United States.* (Union Carbide Nuclear Division of Union Carbide Corporation, photo by B. Carl Huddleston)

MINING

The Sierra Nevada has never proved a major source of most minerals except for the gold from the Foothills. An exception is Pine Creek mine northwest of Bishop, the state's chief source of tungsten (Fig. 5-13). The mine is located high on the Eastern Slope above 11,000 feet; ore is trucked to the modern mill at the base of the range via spectacular switchbacks.[9] Elsewhere the Leviathan mine in Alpine County has produced sulphur, which has been used in smelting copper ore at Yerington, Nevada.

THE SOUTHERN PRONGS

The Southern Prongs, extending southward from the High Sierra to Tejon Pass, links the Sierra with the Transverse and the southern Coast ranges (see map, Fig. 5-2). To many Californians, this lower portion of the range with its serene pastoral scenes does not con-

[9] The demand for tungsten has expanded with growth of the air-space industry and its use of heat-resistant steels. Wolframite, the common tungsten ore, is usually found in low concentrations in granitic rocks. Another important source has been northeast of Bishop in the Benton Range (part of the White-Inyo Mountains in the Trans-Sierra) where production has been less regular than at Pine Creek. The "Bishop District" has collectively yielded tungsten worth $100 million.

jure the usual image of the Sierra Nevada. Although two of the four principal Sierran crossings (Tehachapi and Tejon Passes) are here, much of the Southern Prongs is little known.

THE LAND

It was noted earlier in the chapter that the Sierra Nevada should not be considered a "simple" fault block. At both the north and south ends of the range, parallel blocks replace the single mass. The units of the Southern Prongs are: (1) Greenhorn (west); (2) Piute (middle); (3) Kiavah (east—this is the continuation of the High Sierra main crest); (4) southward from Tehachapi Pass the blocks merge into the single anticlinal structure, the Tehachapi Range. The Southern Prongs is appreciably lower than the High Sierra; summit elevations of 5000 to 9000 feet are typical. There are many craggy ridges, and the whole landscape has been eroded into a maze of slopes. There is also a series of little intermont basins, such as Walker, Lynn, and Cummings. In addition to the principal canyon, the Kern, there are lesser river valleys.

The Southern Prongs is lower and drier than more northerly portions of the Sierra; the altitude of timberline is higher here than the summit; hence montane forests ascend the ridgetops, and alpine meadows are absent. Grasslands and groves of valley oak are typical on the western slopes of the Greenhorn and the Tehachapi. Chaparral is widespread, whereas desert vegetation, rising upon eastern slopes, is particularly prevalent in the Kiavah. As elsewhere in California, spring is the verdant season. The ensuing long drought season is characterized by seared countrysides—dust prevails until late fall. Although some winter moisture comes as snow, a considerable portion falls as rain.

UTILIZATION

A gold rush in the middle 1850's briefly made the Southern Prongs the economic center of Tulare and Kern counties. The focus of activity was along the Kern River and in the Greenhorn Mountains. Kernville was the principal camp although Havilah, Kern County's first seat, Claraville (in the Piute) and Tailholt (White River) in the Greenhorn were prominent in the period. The gold boom had subsided by the time the Southern Pacific extended its route southward through the southern San Joaquin; many residents moved into the Valley and Southern Prongs towns languished.

Sundry activities support the modest population of the Southern Prongs today—hillside grazing, a little farming in the basins, mining, much through commerce, recreation, lumbering, and hydroelectricity. Cattle ranching is especially widespread on western slopes; much livestock is moved seasonally to irrigated alfalfa fields in the San Joaquin. The drier Kiavah has limited use. There is a little lumbering; **Johnsondale** on the upper Kern is a company-owned producer of pine.

Water makes an important contribution to the Southern Prongs economy, especially along the Kern. Here both Southern California Edison and Pacific Gas and Electric generate hydroelectricity. Construction of **Isabella Dam**, allied with the Central Valley Project (see Chapter 9), created a new boom on the upper Kern in the 1950's. Boating, fishing, and camping are popular; the Southern Prongs is relatively accessible to many Southern Californians. An assemblage of lodges and cafes has appeared between Bodfish and Roads End. Sports fishing is popular at Lake Isabella

Fig. 5-14. *TEHACHAPI LOOP—an engineering wonder of the 1870's. Utilizing 28 miles of track, the Southern Pacific's "Valley Line" ascends 2735 feet in 16 "air-miles."* (Southern Pacific Company, photo by Dorman)

and also farther north along the Kern. Summer cabins have been erected within the montane forest belt, especially by residents of the area around Bakersfield who desire refuge from San Joaquin summers. Residents of the southern San Joaquin ski in the Greenhorn when snow permits.

The use of the Tehachapi tends to be distinctive. First, there is much traffic flow across Tejon and Tehachapi passes—the latter of course carries through railroad (Fig. 5-14) as well as highway commerce. Second, there is ranching (beef and grains) in Tehachapi Valley. Third, cement is manufactured at Monolith. The plant, originally constructed to provide cement for the construction of the Los Angeles Aqueduct, has been a longtime producer. Fourth, much of the range is a vast private domain, Tejon Ranch, used for livestock ranching and grain farming (Fig. 5-15). Such use has negated the recreational utilization that assumedly would have developed be-

Fig. 5-15. BEEF PASTURE IN THE TEHACHAPI. These grasslands are part of the vast Tejon Ranch. (Tejon Ranch Company)

cause of proximity to Los Angeles. The Tejon, a quarter-million-acre estate partially owned by the publishers of the Los Angeles *Times,* was assembled from several Mexican ranchos in the mid-nineteenth century by Edward Beale, Indian Superintendent. The ranch still provides work for local Indians, as stipulated in the terms by which Beale sold the property.

Towns in the Southern Prongs are typically small. Many, like **Kernville** (actually a new resort center; the original site is under Lake Isabella) are tourist centers, whereas others like **Glennville** are supported by the surrounding ranches. **Tehachapi** (3161) has particular importance as a tourist stop.

THE PARK BELT

The Park Belt, the central section of the Sierra Nevada within the montane forest belt along its western slopes where stream-cut canyons have been deepened by ice into tremendous chasms, is the portion of the range most utilized for the singular purpose of recreation (see map, Fig. 5-2). Here there are three national parks as well as less familiar beauty spots.

YOSEMITE NATIONAL PARK

Yosemite National Park, best-known portion of the Sierra, encompasses nearly 1200 square miles; it extends from the Foothills eastward into the High Sierra.[10] It contains the two mighty ice-deepened valleys of the Merced (Yosemite Valley) and Tuolumne (Hetch Hetchy Valley) rivers, the uplands that surround these gorges, and some spectacular examples of alpine glaciation (part of the High Sierra).

Yosemite Valley presumably was "discovered" by the Mariposa Battalion under Major James D. Savage in 1851 during a punitive expedition against the Yosemite, a Miwok tribe residing in the Valley. Later fame of the Valley was enhanced by *Discovery of the Yosemite* written by L. H. Bunnell, an expedition member.

Recreational development of Yosemite began shortly after its discovery. James M. Hutchings led the first "tourists" into the Valley in 1855; soon trails and horseback roads had been constructed. By 1874, 12,000 tourists

[10] It should be stressed that the Park Belt lies above the Foothills and below the High Sierra, in the montane forests, even though the limits of Yosemite and Sequoia "overlap" into the lower and higher altitudes.

THE SIERRA NEVADA : : 105

Fig. 5-16. GLACIAL TROUGH IN THE PARK BELT. The ice-scoured canyon of the Marble Fork of the Kaweah River is seen from Pine Ridge, Sequoia National Park; the Great Western Divide is in the distance. (National Park Service, photo by Stagner)

Fig. 5-17. HALF DOME (8937 ft.), HEADWALL OF YOSEMITE VALLEY. Tongues of ice flowed into Yosemite Valley from Tenaya (left) and Little Yosemite (right) canyons. In the distance lies the High Sierra. (David W. Lantis)

from many lands had journeyed into the area by horseback. A year later three wagon roads (Coulterville, Big Oak Flat, and Mariposa) had been extended into the Valley. Although a rail line was operated from 1907-1937, the automobile rapidly became the chief means of conveyance after 1900.

Government wardship for Yosemite came early; in 1864 the federal government gave the Valley and its surrounding uplands to the state of California. Through efforts of John Muir and others, the state reserve (including the Mariposa sequoia grove) became a national park in 1890. The park was maintained for some years by the U.S. Army, and soldiers constructed pioneer trails. Private land holdings were not entirely eliminated within the park until 1939. The National Park Service assumed control in 1916; its personnel have been continuously confronted by problems of too many visitors, too limited funds, and insufficient staff.[11] Yet an impressive achievement

[11] Yosemite vies with Colorado's Rocky Mountain National Park for volume of annual visitors among western parks. The Park Service, long plagued by low salaries and too few personnel, has been aided materially by the ten-year program known as "Mission '66."

in improvements and maintenance has been effected.

The "theft" of Yosemite Park, the "raid" of Hetch Hetchy Valley, was achieved by the city of San Francisco in 1913 after a five-year struggle in Congress. Hetch Hetchy, the somewhat smaller and less famous "twin" of Yosemite Valley, became the site of a metropolitan reservoir. As numbers of park visitors increase, the seriousness of the loss of Hetch Hetchy for public facilities becomes more evident (Fig. 5-18). It might well have been cheaper to have built a more expensive storage reservoir farther west.

To many visitors the park and Yosemite Valley are synonymous. The Valley, widely acclaimed as one of the world's wonders, has become the victim of its siren-call beauty. On summer weekends visitors arrive by tens of thousands—because of congestion, consideration has been given to removal of all overnight facilities from the Valley. Many visitors do not essay beyond its confines (one mile wide and seven miles long). Most public facilities are concentrated here: Government Center (museum, hospital, etc.), Yosemite Lodge and luxurious Ahwahnee Hotel, the campgrounds,

Fig. 5-18. THE ROAD TO GLACIER POINT, YOSEMITE PARK. *In summer, files of. automobiles on the principal roads within Yosemite Park reduce the pleasure of vacations and demonstrate the need for expanded facilities. Under "Mission '66" additional parking spaces are being built.* (National Park Service, Yosemite Park Museum)

Old Village (the former administrative center). Activities on the Valley floor include trail hikes, horseback riding, swimming and wading, the firefall from Glacier Point, campfire programs, and even nocturnal jazz. Natural attractions include Mirror Lake, the Merced River, and its Happy Isles. The Valley's walls, 4000 feet high, possess the renowned waterfalls (Yosemite, Ribbon, Bridal Veil, and Sentinel) and the great granite domes (El Capitan, Cathedral Rock, Half Dome, and North Dome) (Fig. 5-17).

Roads lead from Yosemite Valley to other portions of the Park. California 120 ascends the north wall via a series of tunnels. From Crane Flat it extends eastward across the High Sierra via Tioga Pass (9941 ft.) to U.S. 395 and LeeVining. A new middle segment of this route bypasses tortuous old Tioga Road, only slightly improved since its construction as a nineteenth-century mine trail. From the Big Oak Flat road another route leads to O'Shaughnessey Dam and Hetch Hetchy reservoir. Southward from the Valley the Wawona Road (California 41) has a turn-off past Badger Pass, famed as a winter ski area, to Glacier Point, which provides dra-

matic views of the Valley and of Little Yosemite Valley (with Nevada and Vernal falls) to the southeast (Fig. 5-17).

Numerous hiking trails from Yosemite Valley, to the falls, Glacier Point, and the High Sierra, are used increasingly. To make isolated back-country portions of the park more accessible and in hopes of reducing Valley congestion, five hikers' camps, approximately 10 miles apart, have been constructed in the High Sierra. The camps afford relatively inexpensive lodging and meals. Vogelsang Camp and Tuolumne Meadows form especially popular points of departure for high-country hikes. The six-day pack trip into the alpine portion of the park is especially popular.

SEQUOIA NATIONAL PARK

Sequoia National Park, half the size of Yosemite Park, forms the south end of the Park Belt. Although its eastern portion has glacial topography similar to that of Yosemite, it is because of the more than a score of groves of Sierra redwood (*Sequoia gigantéa*) that the park was established in 1890.

Hale Thorp, an early San Joaquin Valley

Fig. 5-19. HIGHWAY OF THE GEN-ERALS, SEQUOIA NATIONAL PARK. This road is maintained throughout the year. Snow scenes and minimum traffic reward the winter visitor. (National Park Service, photo by Stagner)

of the Generals Highway, which made the largest trees accessible. Visitors have greatly increased since World War II, a reflection of California population growth and year-round accessibility of the park from San Francisco, Los Angeles, and intermediate points.

There is marked contrast in the settings that form the foci of visitors' attention in Sequoia Park as contrasted with Yosemite and Kings Canyon. Although the eastern portion of Sequoia, from the Great Western Divide to alpine summits around Mt. Whitney, has the glacial topography that typifies the other two parks, most visitors to Sequoia concentrate in the Giant Forest. The Forest is situated on the much-dissected upland between the canyons of the South Fork and the Kings River (north) and the Middle Fork of the Kaweah River (south) at elevations rising from 5000 to 7000 feet.

Despite ever increasing numbers of visitors, park officials have been able to prohibit the development of a carnival atmosphere, fostered by sideshows and nocturnal jazz concerts, which plagues some national parks. Park activity centers at Giant Forest village with its lodge and campgrounds, coffee shop, and general store. In summer emphasis is upon strolls through the forests, visits to Moro Rock with its view of the Great Western Divide (Fig. 5-16), drives along the Generals Highway (Fig. 5-19), a guided tour of Crystal Cave, picnicking at Crescent Meadows, and evening campfire lectures. In winter there is the appeal of the Sequoias underlain by snow and winter sports at Wolverton.

Chief attraction of the park is of course the groves of Sierra redwood. Oldest and bulkiest of living forms, this Sequoia is much restricted in distribution as contrasted with the Coast redwood (see Chapter 10). These related species constitute the remains of a vegetation formation that was widely distributed in the northern hemisphere in past geologic ages. Fortunately the Sierra redwood within the park is reproducing its kind so that extinction of the species in the protected groves does not seem imminent. In addition to bulk, heights exceeding 200 feet, and great

settler, was shown the "Giant Forest" by Kaweah Indians in 1858 in appreciation of his friendship to the natives. Although the discovery roused the curiosity of the botanic world, more than a generation passed before federal efforts were made to establish a national preserve. Meanwhile thousands of sheep and cattle were grazed in this part of the Sierra Nevada. Endeavors of the Kaweah Co-operative Commonwealth Society, a socialistic group founded in 1886 with the intent of taking timber from Giant Forest, prompted local conservationists to speed establishment of a national park. During its first fifteen years the park was under Army administration. Maintenance varied with the command and suffered from persistent shortage of funds. A road into Giant Forest was finally completed in 1914. Numbers of visitors to the park were much accelerated in the 1930's after construction age (in some cases exceeding 3000 years), the species is impressive for its thick, fire-resistant bark.

KINGS CANYON NATIONAL PARK

Kings Canyon National Park, created in 1940, is located north of Sequoia Park. Its establishment culminated a half-century struggle by nature lovers to preserve one of the most scenic portions of the range. Although the sequoia groves of the former General Grant National Park are within its limits, such groves are more characteristic of Sequoia Park.

Kings Canyon lies largely within the confines of the High Sierra; it was established as a wilderness park.[12] Although they are less known than those in Yosemite, Kings Canyon has some of the outstanding granite domes and glacial topography of the Sierra. Only a portion of the South Fork of the Kings Canyon is accessible by automobile. road; the highway is a continuation of California 180 beyond the junction of that route with the Generals Highway at Wilsonia in the General Grant grove. The road terminates near Cedar Grove approaching the western limits of the park. A glance at a highway map will reveal why residents of Fresno and environs desire to have this road extended eastward to a junction with U.S. 395.

The alpine landscapes of Kings Canyon were favorably compared with those of Yosemite by John Muir. The South Fork of the Kings Canyon is neither as wide nor as deep as Yosemite Valley; although it is several miles longer, it lacks the number of waterfalls and granite domes. Toward the east the canyon includes beauteous Zumwalt Meadows and Paradise Valley. The park encompasses other precipitous canyons as well. Along the Middle Fork of the Kings is isolated Tehipite Valley— larger than Yosemite Valley and with loftier walls. Its great Tehipite Dome is one of the striking granite knobs of the Sierra Nevada. Somewhat smaller but impressive are Bubbs

[12] It is hoped that the reader will not be confused because of the overlap between the Park Belt and the High Sierra—there is an obvious overlap.

Fig. 5-20. *THE SYLVAN SETTING OF BASS LAKE. Accessibility, low elevation (3400 ft.), and warm water give this storage reservoir particular appeal for boating and family outings. However, there is much summer congestion.* (Pacific Gas and Electric Company)

Creek Canyon and Cloud Canyon along Roaring River.

Kings Canyon, with limited facilities of the type found in most national parks, is apt to disappoint the tourist who desires comfort. It is the delight of the hiker, camper, and fisherman to whom overcrowded Yosemite Valley is frustrating.

BASS LAKE

For the tourist who yearns for comforts of city life accessible by a good paved road, there is Bass Lake. Only three miles from the Wawona Road in Sierra National Forest at an elevation of 3450 feet, Bass Lake is an artificial water body behind a storage dam belonging to Pacific Gas and Electric Company. Because of its accessibility, warm water for boating, swimming, and water skiing in summer, and its public campgrounds, Bass Lake is popular

Fig. 5-21. HUNTINGTON LAKE, SIERRA NATIONAL FOREST. This artificial lake, part of the Big Creek Project at an elevation of 7000 feet, looks deceivingly natural. Water is diverted through Ward Tunnel (under Kaiser Ridge) from the South Fork of the San Joaquin River. Since Huntington acts as a regulatory unit, its level does not fluctuate much. (Southern California Edison Company)

with families and becomes congested. Despite an attractive sylvan setting and such urban conveniences as newspapers, fresh milk delivery, and postal service in the village of Bass Lake, some feel there is not adequate compensation for the resultant congestion.

HUNTINGTON LAKE COUNTRY

The Huntington Lake Country is a delightful portion of the Park Belt situated in the montane forests (5000-7000 feet elevation) between Kings Canyon and Yosemite parks. Little known to out-of-staters, it has long been frequented by residents of the San Joaquin Valley; more recently, growing numbers of Southern Californians too have come here for relaxation. It lies within Sierra National Forest and has long been approachable by the Tollhouse Road (now California 168). The old wagon road with its switchbacks was sufficiently steep so that most engines would boil; in recent years the highway has been improved.

The Huntington Lake Country includes segments of the San Joaquin and North Fork of the Kings drainage basins.[13] Its artificial lakes (see below) constructed for hydroelectric development look deceivingly natural aside from the dam structures (Fig. 5-21). This is one of the attractive playgrounds in the Sierra Nevada. Its weather is cool, and there are campgrounds, clear water, and conifer forests. Utilization includes water sports (much boating and some swimming), fishing, camping, hunting, and winter sports. Thousands visit the area each fall to hunt deer. Shaver Lake, lower (5370 ft.) and warmer than most reservoirs in the Big Creek Project, is most popular for boating and swimming. China Peak ski area, with its lodge and double-chair lift, has become one of the more frequented winter resorts in the Park Belt.

[13] Reds Meadows and Devil's Postpile National Monument, an interesting formation of columnar basalt, are situated in the headwaters area of the San Joaquin. Because they are reached by road across the main Sierran summit from Mammoth Lakes, they are probably best considered Eastern Slope recreation spots.

Variations in elevation within the Country fosters divergent recreational use. The Country reaches back into the High Sierra at Florence Lake, a good point of departure for high-country trips. Mono Hot Springs to the north has waters beneficial for arthritis sufferers; this federally owned facility has free bath-houses and campgrounds. Huntington Lake, favored for camping, is sufficiently high (6950 ft.) that its water is too cool for most swimmers. Dinkey Creek is lower; besides its warmer waters (at Honeymoon Pool) the stream is well regarded by fishermen; hence its campgrounds become congested. It is a focal point in the Kings River Recreational Area.

The **Big Creek Project**, envisaged by John Eastwood as early as 1886, forms the major hydroelectric development in the Southern California Edison system (Fig. 5-22). Since 1911, this utility company has expended more than $220 million and has constructed fourteen dams, ten tunnels, and eight powerhouses along the upper San Joaquin and its tributaries, using and reusing the force of falling water.[14] Florence Lake and Lake Edison in Mono Basin on the western edge of the High Sierra form the easternmost units. Lake Thomas A. Edison was completed in 1954 and has a capacity of 125,000 acre-feet. The basic project had been completed by 1929 and included 15-foot Ward Tunnel (drilled through 13 miles of solid rock under Kaiser Ridge to transport water from Florence Lake to Huntington Lake), Florence, Huntington (a regulatory body), and Shaver lakes. Mammoth Pool reservoir (3100 ft.) is the lowest and newest storage unit. The whole project focuses upon the company town of **Big Creek**, whose permanency contrasts with many abandoned lumber and mine camps. The 690,000 kilowatts generated at the Big Creek powerhouses is sent 250 miles to metropolitan Los Angeles by four large transmission lines.

Fig. 5-22. *POWERHOUSE NO. 1, BIG CREEK PROJECT. Southern California Edison calls this development, with its eight powerhouses utilizing the South Fork of the San Joaquin, "the hardest working water in the world." Downstream the water is again diverted for irrigation in the San Joaquin Valley.* (Southern California Edison Company)

Another pioneer of the California electric power industry, A. G. Wishon, early discovered that the Kings River drops 7000 feet in 20 miles! In 1962 Pacific Gas and Electric brought his dreams to fruition with completion of the $80 million **Kings River Project**, which generates 313,000 kilowatts for use in central California. Major units include Courtright and Wishon reservoirs, and Haas Powerhouse, an underground unit blasted out of solid rock.

THE FOOTHILLS

The Sierran Foothills, which flank the Great Central Valley on the east from the Feather River Country southward to the canyon of the Kern (see map, Fig. 5-2) has been

[14] The Big Creek and Kings River projects do not affect the use of San Joaquin and Kings water in the San Joaquin Valley of course since they do not remove any of the runoff. The federal government has built two major storage units downstream, Friant on the San Joaquin and Pine Flat on the Kings.

the most intensively utilized portion of the range since the Gold Rush. Elevation varies from less than a thousand feet above sea level on the west to approximately 4000 feet on the east. The uplands (interfluves) rise slowly eastward while stream canyons progressively deepen. The countryside is covered with grassland, with groves of valley oak and digger pine, and sometimes is thickly mantled by thickets of chaparral. Some regard the Foothills as the climatically favored portion of California. Lower elevations are warm in summer but less hot than the Great Central Valley. The high fog of coastal areas and the wintry "tule fog" of interior lowlands is absent. There is definite seasonality but winters are not extremely cold; storms usually bring rains in contrast to the heavy snow of higher lands to the east. Activities have included mining, ranching, through commerce, lumber processing, residence, and recreation.

THE MOTHER LODE COUNTRY

The heart of the Foothills is the Mother Lode Country, situated between Mariposa on the south and Sierra City on the north.[15] This attenuated belt, approximately 15 miles wide and tributary to California 49, has produced the bulk of California's gold. Within its eight counties, today characterized by a somnolent air contrary to that over much of California, over $2 billion worth of gold has been taken. The Mother Lode proper, the discontinuous zone of Jurassic quartz fissure veins outcropping between Mariposa and Georgetown, is of smaller dimensions with a north-south length of about 120 miles.

Far beyond the value of gold removed from the Sierra has been the economic, political, and social significance of the activity fostered by the Gold Rush. The growth of California was quickened by some decades. The cities of San Francisco, Sacramento, and Stockton, as well as a number of smaller communities, resulted

from the Rush. Statehood for California was speeded and economic development of the entire West accelerated. Sierran gold made the nation the world's leading producer of gold during the second half of the nineteenth century; in recent years production has almost ceased.

The major rush to the gold fields began in 1849, more than a year after Marshall found gold in the mill race of Sutter's lumber mill on the South Fork of the American River early in 1848. Local excitement materialized during the summer of 1848, but it involved a few thousand Californians, Mexicans, and residents of other Pacific areas. During the following years perhaps 100,000 came into the Mother Lode Country from many parts of the world. Although many thousands soon left, usually without anticipated fortunes, other thousands remained to help build the state. Most gold seekers were young, robust, and with some means—cost of reaching California eliminated the poverty stricken.

Three modes of mining (placering, lode, and dredging) have accounted for most of the gold production in the Sierra Nevada. Although all three were adapted early, each achieved maximum output at different periods. Most early mining, of a placer nature (i.e., washing of gravels), employed the bulk of the miners and was often conducted with the crudest equipment. *Placering* occurred in a belt 150 miles long by 50 miles wide; it was the principal means of recovery prior to 1880. This technique has resulted in recovery of gold worth $1.3 billion. Early placering took place in the alluvial deposits of stream beds, bars, and adjacent benches. Such deposits represented the reconcentration of Tertiary gravels (originally laid down in streams of the ancestral Sierra) into such contemporary rivers as the American, Feather, and Yuba. The richest nuggets were commonly removed the first year; production gained momentum for several years with a continuing influx of miners despite lessening per capita recovery.

The gold seekers early turned to recovery of placer gold in the long-abandoned channels of Tertiary streams that today constitute

---

[15] *Strictly*, the Mother Lode Country does not include the "Northern Diggings." Although this section discusses mining, it should be kept in mind that much contemporary Foothill activity (discussed in later sections) centers in the Mother Lode Country.

hillsides in the Mother Lode Country. To remove the gold, they used drift mining and hydraulicking. *Drift mining* demanded tunneling into the deposits, a process often expensive because of shoring or risky because of threat of cave-in. Use of running water to cut into the Tertiary gravels was soon adopted, and then followed in 1853 by *hydraulicking* (direction of a stream of water under great pressure from a nozzle on the end of an iron pipe against the hillside). This rapid and inexpensive process was widely used until the courts issued a permanent injunction against hydraulicking, which had led to choked river channels, increased flood threats in the Great Central Valley, and destruction of agricultural lowlands through silting.[16]

Lode mining commenced on Fremont's Mariposa Grant at Mariposa in 1849. It was believed at first that quartz veins might be widespread through the Sierra. The realization came gradually that the gold-bearing country rock was restricted largely to the attenuated Mother Lode with its separate and discontinuous fissures. Scores of mines have contributed to the wealth acquired from hard-rock mining. Most early operations failed despite investments totaling millions. Gradually necessary knowledge of ores, mining techniques, and suitable machinery evolved. Lode mining became the chief means of recovery after the placer decline. Although lode mining persisted into the 1950's, dredging has been more significant in the twentieth century. Half the vein gold of the Mother Lode was acquired from a single 10-mile strip in Amador County. Major mines there, each of which is thousands of feet deep and has yielded gold in excess of $10 million each, include the

Hayward (Old Eureka), Utica group, Keystone, Phoenix, and Argonaut.

Dredging has been the principal recovery technique in the twentieth century with concentration at the edge of the Sierra Nevada from Merced County northward into Butte County. Here hundreds of millions of dollars in gold has been obtained by large-scale operations that have worked deposits uneconomic by other methods. For larger operations floating bucket-dredges weighing several thousand tons each have been employed. The dragline technique has been used for smaller operations. Unfortunately the land used for such activity has often had grazing value; the soil is replaced by sand and gravel by dredging.

Northwest of the Mother Lode proper and and generally considered apart from the better-known area is the "Northern Diggings" focused upon Grass Valley, Nevada City, and the nearby Allegheny District. Much of the mining here, which began in 1852 and survived until the late 1950's, has been of the lode type. For a time, Nevada City, North Columbia, and North Bloomfield were also important centers for hydraulic mining. Ores have averaged sufficiently high in value so that vein mining was resumed for a decade after World War II. Major properties have included the Idaho-Maryland, the Empire-North Star, and the Original Sixteen to One.

A progressive decline in California gold production took place after 1852. From the middle 1860's, annual output ranged in value between $15 and $25 million with decline after World War I and a spectacular but temporary increase after passage of the Gold Reserve Act in 1934. During World War II issuance of Regulation W led to cessation of gold mining. After the war the low price of gold relative to high mining costs discouraged many mines from reopening. Since 1946 most gold has been recovered through dredging in Sacramento and Yuba counties. Now even this activity has nearly ceased.

In recent years production of *cement* in Calaveras and El Dorado counties has had more economic significance than gold mining. The Calaveras Cement plant at San Andreas,

[16] A good example of former hydraulicking is Cherokee, on the north side of Table Mountain near Oroville. The technique demanded 100 miles of ditches and pipes of 30-inch diameter. One pipe crossed the West Branch of the Feather 900 feet above the stream. At the period of maximum operations at Cherokee eighteen monitors (nozzle heads) were being directed against the ancient stream channel. By the time the gold supply was exhausted in 1883, $10 million had been recovered. Each nozzle could blast a stream of water 400 feet.

established in 1926, has expanded its output considerably. The several hundred employees make an important contribution to the economy of a mountain county. The Ione formation, especially around Ione in Amador County, is a major western source of clay for refractory use. The formation is also a source of silica for the California glass industry.

BEEF AND FRUIT

The Foothills began producing foodstuffs during the Gold Rush; markets were restricted almost exclusively to the camps. Often early production was on a subsistence basis; a miner planted a few crops for his own needs. With the mining decline, Foothills agriculture stagnated—transportation was poor and markets almost absent.

The Foothills environment both hampers and favors ranching. Topography is often a major disadvantage; sizable areas are handicapped by steep slopes and thin, rocky soils. The drought season is particularly a disadvantage where terrain has made irrigation impossible. Weather is an asset—intermediate altitudes have a long season. Higher elevations have sufficient rainfall to permit ranching without irrigation. If topography were more suitable the numerous Sierran streams could provide irrigation water even though stream regimes (periodicity of seasonal flow) would demand reservoirs. As elsewhere in California, there is a land-use conflict involving cropping, forestry, grazing, and recreation.

Livestock ranching forms the more extensive land-use type in the Foothills. Beef production commenced during the Gold Rush; as accessible forests were cut, lands suitable for grazing increased. Repeated burnings and overgrazing have reduced the value of some pastures, and chaparral has engulfed many abandoned farms. Many smaller Foothills ranches are combination year-round feeding-grazing properties with production of dry-farmed grains and hay where the environment permits. The importance of the Foothills for beef production increases as the population of California rises—for some years the state has been a "meat-short" producer.

Grazing has had greater relative importance in the economy of the central Foothills counties from Mariposa through Amador. In the pre-automobile era transportation handicaps in these counties, coupled with much terrain unsuitable for cropping and less moisture than farther north, recommended livestock. In these counties considerable numbers of San Joaquin Valley livestock have been pastured during late spring in the course of transhumance to higher grasslands.

Marked expansion of irrigated pasture lands has occurred since the practice was adopted in the 1930's. Two irrigation developments have reduced the topographic problem. Earlier, ditches were plowed on a near contour with breaks to permit water to seep downslope into the next lower ditch. This practice required considerable attention to irrigation; slope and thin soil horizons discouraged land leveling. More recently overhead sprinklers have been adopted. On irrigated grasslands cultivated pastures of ladino clover, annual ryegrass, and fescue grass are considered suitable.

Growth of commercial agriculture in the Foothills tended to occur long after the decline of gold mining. The outlawing of hydraulic mining provided ready-made irrigation systems. The Paradise and Oroville-Wyandotte irrigation districts in Butte County are two examples of mining-era antecedents. Before the days of highways and consequent trucking of produce to market, agriculture was commonly restricted to localities that could market produce by rail. These areas included lands around Ione, Placerville, and Auburn. Demise of the mining constituted a longtime deterrent of agricultural expansion. Many locales farmed during the Gold Rush reverted to chaparral or second-growth forest.

Foothills agriculture has developed specialized aspects; fruit growing and poultry farming are significant. There are many part-time subsistence farms, especially adjacent to major communities and principal transportation arteries.[17] Climate permits a variety of

17 Paradise affords a good illustration. Many people work in Chico, 12 miles to the west, and maintain small acreages.

crops, especially in the so-called "thermal belt" (generally between elevations of 200 and 1200 feet). In the northern Foothills interfluves provide farm land, whereas in the south steeper slopes are a handicap. At least half of the Foothills is either too steep or too rocky for cropping.

Thermal belt mildness, with limited frost, permits oranges in the north near Oroville and in the south near Porterville. Plantings began in both areas with garden trees in the 1860's. The climatic advantage was not fully appreciated until the damaging California frosts of 1879-1880 encouraged establishment of commercial orchards. Both localities have had rail facilities (the Western Pacific at Oroville and the Santa Fe at Porterville), affording transportation long lacking over much of the Foothills. Oroville is on the fringe of the Sacramento Valley but the citrus district surrounding Palermo, Wyandotte, and Bangor, established in the 1880's, extends eastward into the Foothills. Contour, furrow, and sprinkler irrigation has been practiced, with South Fork of the Feather water from ditches originally constructed for mining. Although larger acreages are found on the Kaweah Delta (San Joaquin Valley), oranges are grown in small coves and valleys within the foothills of Tulare County. The thermal advantage permits both areas to make their heaviest shipments in November, before the large post-Christmas shipments from Southern California. With population growth reducing groves in the Los Angeles Lowlands, oranges would appear to have an assured future in the thermal belt. However, citrus production southeast of Oroville has never fully recovered from the effects of the "great freeze of 1932." These Butte and Tulare county districts are also important producers of olives, which are processed locally. Olives are sometimes grown on soils that are thin and not well suited for oranges.

Portions of Placer and El Dorado counties, with such advantages as slope, water, air drainage, and transportation, have produced deciduous fruits at elevations between 1000 and 3000 feet since the Gold Rush. Although peaches, cherries, grapes, and apples are raised, pears (in both counties) and plums (in Placer County) have more value. Plums are found at lower elevations between Loomis and Auburn; spring months are virtually frost-free, and plums mature earlier than elsewhere in California. Production has never fully revived from the overplanting and subsequent decline of the 1930's. Cherries have declined somewhat; production is more risky than for other fruits, in both market fluctuations and production hazards. This area was significant because of its ability to ship early sweet cherries.

These counties, long known for their pears, have become one of the nation's centers for this fruit. Although pears will tolerate more frost than some deciduous fruits, they are grown on the well-drained Aiken lateritic soils. The thermal advantage has permitted later marketing than from some California districts; hence the pears can be marketed as fresh fruit. For a time production was delayed because of investment requirements (especially the period before trees begin bearing). Low prices in the 1930's were an upsetting influence, but more recently production has increased—with urbanization eliminating Santa Clara Valley orchards, additional Foothills acreage has been planted.

Paradise in Butte County is a secondary apple-producing area, with most of the marketing done locally. A variety of apples are grown, but size and color compare unfavorably with the best apples from Washington and Oregon. Growth of Paradise threatens to eliminate the orchards eventually.

A recent agricultural development in the Foothills has been the increased production of poultry, both turkeys and chickens. Poultry is especially important in the rural economies of Placer, Amador, Tuolumne, and Mariposa counties. In Tuolumne County turkeys now provide over half the total farm receipts. Turkeys are more difficult to raise than chickens and are usually grown farther from urban centers; recently they have accounted for two thirds of the Tuolumne income from poultry. Rising California markets, climate, and improved transportation facilities seem to explain the increase.

Fig. 5-23. FRIANT DAM AND THE FRIANT-KERN CANAL. This multipurpose unit provides flood control, irrigation, and recreation. (Bureau of Reclamation, photo by A. G. D'Alessandro)

Fig. 5-24. GRANITE BEACH ON FOLSOM LAKE. Proximity to metropolitan Sacramento has afforded this Central Valley Project reservoir recreational popularity. (Bureau of Reclamation, photo by A. G. D'Alessandro)

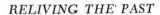

RELIVING THE PAST

Tourist expenditures have considerable value to the Foothills economy. A major portion of such income comes from services to trans-Sierran travelers on main highways (U.S. 40-50). Motels, cafes, service stations, and garages in such communities as Auburn and Placerville derive considerable income from wayfarers. Yosemite-bound vacationists bring much business to Mariposa.

Many visitors, usually Californians, follow Route 49, the **Mother Lode Highway**, to gain impressions of Gold Rush days. The stranger seeks out sites of such once lively camps as Hell's Hills, Hoodoo, Frenchmen's, or Lake City. He will probably visit the mill site on the American where Marshall found gold in 1848 and inspect the locales of placering, the pockmarked Mother Lode itself, or famed lode mines like the Argonaut. The tourist visits the sloped towns with their plain pre-Victorian white cottages, narrow Alianthus-lined streets, weathered brick business blocks with sagging iron shutters and overhanging balconies. Much frequented **Columbia** best maintains the atmosphere of the boom years and has become a state park. There are more old buildings and less suggestion of the contemporary era than in prospering Foothills towns.

Columbia is a "must" for visitors although concessionaries are creating an unappealing commercialism.

Situated between higher portions of the Sierra and the well-populated Great Central Valley, the Foothills is increasingly popular for weekend outings, for summer youth camps, and vacation cottages of lowland dwellers. Spring is delightful, with green hillsides and wildflowers. There is a particular appeal in autumn when the leaves are turning and after the High Sierra becomes snowbound.

Shores of storage reservoirs have increasing popularity as recreation centers. Much frequented by fishermen and boatsmen is Lake Millerton behind Friant Dam, well suited as a recreation area northeast of Fresno (Fig. 5-25). **Turlock Lake State Park** is crammed with campers and boaters throughout the summer. In future years lakes behind Pine Flat, Folsom, and Oroville (under construction) dams, as well as lesser-known reservoirs, should be utilized more and more (Fig. 5-24).

LUMBERING

Lumbering forms a basic source of contemporary Foothills livelihood. Elevations above 2000 feet in the north (higher in the south)

Fig. 5-25. LAKE MILLERTON ON A SUM-MER WEEKEND. This reservoir, backed up behind Friant Dam, is used extensively by boating enthusiasts from Fresno and environs. (Bureau of Reclamation, photo by B. D. Glaha)

Fig. 5-26. POST OFFICE AT COLUMBIA. This famed gold camp, whose restoration commenced during the California statehood centennial, has been converted into a state park and is popular with visitors to the Foothills. (California Division of Beaches and Parks)

are often forested but most of the logs now come from Sierran elevations above the Foothills. Actually, wood industries have had significance since the Gold Rush although emphasis has been shifted in recent years. Earlier lumbering was conducted near the mine camps to provide wood for fuel, for mine props, and for local construction. With the decline of mining, lumbering experienced a decline. Yet by 1900 the more accessible forests had been cut. As farther north in the Cascade, the flume was an important means of transportation before the motor truck, although some logging railroads such as the Sierra Railroad from Oakdale to Tuolumne were also constructed.

The post-World War II lumber expansion in the Foothills has been related to population growth in portions of California away from the Sierra. Logs come almost entirely from the Sierra montane forest sometimes referred to as the "west Sierra pine forest." Timberland is about equally divided between national forest and private ownership. Lumbering is carried on seasonally since winter snowfall precludes year-round operations.

Some tree-farming is developing but exploitative cutting is still too widely practiced on private lands. In the national forests marketable timber is sold on a contract basis and cutting operations are checked by the Forest Service. The price paid by the lumberman depends upon the location of the stand; with less accessible forests and logs that demand transport greater distances to the mill, the timber must be sold at a reduced price. Many operations are of recent development and most cutting is done with chain saws; logs are skidded to the loading point with large tractors. Power equipment, usually converted shovels, is used to load the logs on trucks. Because of terrain, size of operation, and distance to mills, timber is moved almost exclusively by truck. Lack of access roads forms

THE SIERRA NEVADA : : 117

a major handicap in utilization of forests over much of the area tributary to Foothills mills. On federal lands roads are built by the Forest Service.

Lumbering contributes to the economy of all Foothills counties. Operations vary considerably in size and many small firms utilize mobile equipment. The area ranks second in the state—after the Northwest and ahead of the Southern Cascade. Although El Dorado and Tuolumne counties are the ranking producers (both exceed 130 million board feet annually), forest products are the chief source of income only in Sierra and Mariposa counties. Larger operations are located in Auburn, Tuolumne, Sonora, and Angels Camp. Mill workers are generally family men; many operate ranches or subsistence farms on the side since the seasonal nature of lumbering generally does not provide an adequate annual income.

WATER AND POWER

Water, like timber, became an important Foothills resource with the Gold Rush. Early water rights were associated with placer and hydraulic mining. With the demise of mining, ditches and other facilities became available for other purposes. Topography discouraged use of water for irrigation over much of the Foothills; even where the slope was favorable farming was usually delayed in the nineteenth century because of market limitations.

In this century development of water resources in the Foothills has been threefold: urban use, irrigation, and hydroelectric power; flood control and recreation are important adjuncts. Some works have had multiple functions, such as hydroelectricity and then, downstream, irrigation or irrigation coupled with flood control.

Pacific Gas and Electric Company of San Francisco has been the principal firm to utilize water in the Foothills for hydroelectric development. This firm, with one of the nation's three leading systems of private power transmission, was created in 1905 through consolidation of a group of smaller companies. Hydroelectricity was devised as the solution

for power needs of fuels-poor central California in the late nineteenth century; by the time petroleum became available as fuel waterpower development was well established. As the demand for electrical energy increased, Pacific Gas and Electric gradually absorbed additional firms using Sierran streams for power purposes. Today this giant utility corporation generates electricity at scores of powerhouses in the western Sierra from the drainage basin of the Feather River southward into the Kern basin. Some of its more important developments are located on the Feather, Yuba, American, Mokelumne, Kings, and Kern. Power is distributed over thousands of miles of lines throughout the Great Central Valley, the San Francisco Bay Area, the Central Coast, and northwestern California. Hundreds of Foothills residents are employed by this utility firm.[18] In some instances Pacific Gas and Electric uses water "belonging to" irrigation districts; after the water has been fully utilized for power production it is used for agricultural purposes.

Water for domestic purposes is obtained in the western Sierra Nevada by the city of San Francisco and also by the communities of the East Bay. About the time that Los Angeles began its aqueduct southward through Owens Valley, San Francisco sought Sierra water by making a water filing for Lake Eleanor and Hetch Hetchy Valley sites in Yosemite National Park in 1903. The city's plans were opposed by various interests, including the Sierra Club, San Joaquin Valley ranchers, and others; in 1910 San Francisco voters approved a $45 million bond issue. Construction of 343-foot O'Shaughnessy Dam in Hetch Hetchy Valley did not begin, however, until after President Woodrow Wilson signed the Raker Bill in 1913. The project included construction of 68-mile standard-gauge Hetch Hetchy Railroad from Oakdale to the damsite. Water from the reservoir flows down the Tuolumne for 12 miles before it is diverted through the intake into the main 150-mile

18 Pacific Gas and Electric pays 66 percent of all local taxes in Amador County, 63 percent in Plumas County, and 38 percent in Alpine County.

aqueduct, which carries water across the San Joaquin Valley, through the Mt. Diablo Range southwest of Tracy, thence to San Francisco Peninsula. Advantage is taken of a 1400-foot drop in elevation near Moccasin—the city constructed Moccasin Powerhouse. Unlike Los Angeles, San Francisco does not have its own municipal system and hence sells electricity to Pacific Gas and Electric. Morainal Lake Eleanor, northwest of Hetch Hetchy, was likewise converted into a storage reservoir by a dam that raises the level of the natural water body 30 feet. The Hetch Hetchy project was completed in 1934 when Crystal Springs reservoir was constructed on San Francisco Peninsula near Palo Alto. More recently, Cherry reservoir west of Yosemite Park has been created.

Following the San Francisco example, Alameda County cities banded together and organized East Bay Municipal Utility District in 1923. Fewer complications appeared than had been true with San Francisco's Hetch Hetchy site. After investigation of such distant sources as the Feather and McCloud rivers, the District built 358-foot Pardee Dam on the Mokelumne River and in 1931 completed a 94-mile aqueduct to deliver water from the Foothills into reservoirs in the Berkeley-Oakland Hills.

Sierran waters are used for irrigation purposes in a variety of ways. The most spectacular activity has centered around the Central Valley Project (see Chapter 9) with recent construction of Pine Flat Dam on the Kings, Friant on the San Joaquin, and Folsom on the American. Huge Oroville Dam (735 ft.) on the Feather River, first unit under the California Water Plan, is to be a multipurpose project designed to provide water to various users presumably as far south as San Diego; it is now under construction (Fig. 5-35). Prior to development of major Central Valley Project units, water users of the Turlock and Modesto districts constructed Don Pedro reservoir on the Tuolumne downstream from Hetch Hetchy. Other older structures included Exchequer on the Merced and Melones on the Stanislaus.

Water use within the Foothills itself is on a far less grandiose scale. Irrigation works for the Foothills evolved from ditches built by early mining interests. In the twentieth century, following growth of commercial agriculture, several irrigation districts were established. Illustrative is El Dorado Irrigation District, organized in 1925 with assemblage of old mining water rights. Although a million-dollar bond issue was floated in 1927, the District experienced financial difficulties during the depression of the 1930's. Water is still sold in many localities on the basis of the "miner's inch," a legacy of earlier use.

THE CAMPS THAT LIVED

The bulk of the permanent population of the Sierra is found in the Foothills. Towns here almost without exception began as Gold Rush camps; hence there are many common attributes. Many communities are situated along canyons so that a "shoestring pattern" with narrow, winding streets is characteristic. Although most towns experienced a series of destructive fires in the boom period, the unadorned pre-Victorian style of architecture is common—cottages with white siding are characteristic. Business blocks are often of brick; a few buildings in most towns generally date back a century. Foothills towns look more settled than many California communities of comparable size. Few have experienced much recent growth, and large plate-glass windows and neon signs are not conspicuous.

Most Mother Lode camps were born and died within a few years. For many of these towns no physical evidence remains to indicate where thousands of miners congregated. Many of the villages that have survived are small and tranquil, with slight evidence of growth or prosperity.

The flourishing towns have several common attributes. Generally, they are crossroads where north-south California 49 intersects principal east-west arteries. Larger communities are often county seats and serve as local trade centers. Catering to travelers on the trans-Sierran highways usually makes a definite contribution to the economy. The peaceful atmosphere is attracting many senior citizens to settle here. Many persons employed in Great Central Valley cities now reside in the Foothills; this trend is particularly significant within driving distance of Sacramento.

The principal northern communities are Paradise, Grass Valley, and Nevada City. **Paradise** (approx. 12,000) is the largest community in the entire Sierra. This old village, once allegedly Pair-o-Dice, has a statewide reputation as a retirement center. Many Chicoans have escaped the summer heat and midwinter tule fogs of the Sacramento Valley by establishing residence here. Paradise rambles across an uplands between Butte Creek and the West Branch of the Feather River. Unincorporated, unzoned, and conservative, Paradise is a bewildering assemblage of shacks, small fruit-and-poultry farms, and attractive residences in a coniferous setting (Fig. 5-36). Grass Valley and Nevada City, twin communities of Nevada County, have somewhat different economic supports. **Grass Valley** (5000) survived into the 1950's as a hard-rock gold producer; lately it has become the home of many employed at Beale Air Force Base or around Sacramento. **Nevada City** (2400) is a county seat with lumber mills and is popular with senior citizens. Both towns service the surrounding agricultural areas.

Auburn, Placerville, Jackson, Ione, Sutter Creek, and San Andreas, leading towns of the central Foothills, are residential outliers of Sacramento. All except Ione and Sutter Creek are county seats. **Ione** (1100), known as Bedbug in gold-boom years, was never a mining camp; it has remained the center of cattle-ranching Ione Valley. **Sutter Creek** (1200) long persisted because of the Central Eureka mine; an erstwhile favorite residence for retired miners, it has also appealed to senior citizens. **Auburn** (5600) and **Placerville** (4500) rank among the larger incorporated cities of the Foothills. Both are situated on principal trans-Sierran highways; Auburn is also a railroad town. Sierra College, moved to a new campus in nearby Rocklin, is the only collegiate institution within the Sierra Nevada. Both are centers for agricultural districts; Placerville has pear shipping sheds. Auburn's

New Town, rising above the original business district, appears out-of-place among Foothills communities. **Jackson** (1900) was long the epitome of the persistent gold camp; its narrow main street is flanked with old business blocks with overhanging balconies. At first less prosperous than others its deep-shaft Kennedy and Argonaut mines brought continued wealth long after many camps had vanished. **San Andreas** (1400) survives as seat of Calaveras County and has a cement plant; unlike most ranking Foothills towns it is not a gateway on a trans-Sierran highway.

Angels Camp, Sonora, Tuolumne, and Mariposa compose the important southern Mother Lode towns. All except Tuolumne are Sierran gateways; Sonora and Mariposa are county seats. **Tuolumne** (1400) is a ranch center with pine lumber mills and is the eastern terminus of the Sierra Railroad. **Angels Camp** (1100) remembers the writings of Harte and Twain each spring with its jumping frog contest; the town survives because of ranching, lumbering, and mining. **Sonora** (2700) once vied with Columbia as the metropolis of the "southern mines." Among the most picturesque of the surviving camps, its economy is based upon lumbering, tourism, limestone quarries, and local trade. Unincorporated **Mariposa**, in a relatively sterile area, is a county seat that benefits as a stopping point on the All-Year Highway into Yosemite Park.

THE NORTHERN SIERRA

The Northern Sierra lies north of the High Sierra and flanks the Foothills on the east. It has distinctive features that tend to set it aside from the rest of the Sierra Nevada. North of Echo Summit (U.S. 50) elevations of prominent peaks are markedly lower than to the south. Although individual summits exceed 9000 feet around Lake Tahoe, prominent peaks farther north lie between 7000 and 8000 feet. The Northern Sierra, except where glaciation has stripped surfaces to bedrock, is forested across its summits; the alpine zone of the High Sierra is absent. Snowfall is heavy and isolation has been a persistent winter characteristic away from major trans-Sierran crossings (Fig. 5-29).

Topography forms a distinctive feature. Much of the range is a single massive unit but the Northern Sierra, like the Southern Prongs described earlier, consists of three parallel blocks separated by two depressions. The westernmost block, Clermont Hill, is less well defined than Grizzly Mountains (the middle segment) or Diamond Mountains, the easternmost block, which continues southward as the Carson Range of western Nevada (Fig. 1-7). The Feather River, which has cut its canyon through Clermont Hill and the Grizzly Mountains, is suggestive of an antecedent stream. The Tahoe depression and Sierra Valley lie west of the Carson-Diamond mass, whereas small basins like American and Big valleys in the Feather River Country are between the Grizzly Mountains and Clermont Hill.

There has been somewhat limited modification in utilization of most of the Northern Sierra since the Gold Rush period. It shared in the mining activity but with less success than the Mother Lode Country. Lumbering and ranching developed early and still form important adjuncts of the economy. Some counties in this portion of the range have shown little population gain since 1945. The major transition in this century has been the improvement of transportation facilities followed by a marked increase in recreational use.

Four subdivisions of the Northern Sierra will be discussed: Donner-Tahoe Area, Sierra Valley, Yuba Country, and Feather River Country.

THE DONNER-TAHOE AREA

The Donner-Tahoe Area, best-known portion of the Northern Sierra, affords many visitors their first glimpses of California; few Sierran locales could make a more impressive introduction. Although less spectacular than the High Sierra, the Area nevertheless has high summits and a suggestion of ice sculpturing that is conspicuous farther south around Yosemite Park. The contrast between the forested Sierran slopes and the desert country of Nevada is sharp.

Fig. 5-27. *AUBURN SKI HILL. Many winter-sport localities, off U.S. 40, are readily available to residents of the Bay Area and Central California; hence they are much frequented.* (U.S. Forest Service)

This area is the most important commercial corridor into central California. Man has used this crossing in growing numbers since the Gold Rush era. Railroad construction across Donner Summit, noted earlier, took place a century ago. Two major highways, U.S. 40 (Interstate 80) and U.S. 50, provide broad paved ribbons whose easy gradients make the Sierran crossing a pleasure for motorists.

Accessibility to populations of the Central Valley and the San Francisco Bay Area, plus relative assurance of winter snow, has made this district one of the important winter-sports centers of western America (Fig. 5-27). Snow sports developed relatively late although a little skiing was done during the Gold Rush. Absence of transportation facilities and lodgings were longtime limitations. Renewed interest in Sierran skiing came from Europe after World War I; Truckee and Yosemite

Park were early foci. The major impetus came from the university campuses in Palo Alto and Berkeley in the early 1930's when ski clubs were organized. The Sierra Club was also an important force.

The Donner-Tahoe Area has become one of the nation's most frequented ski centers. It has advantages of highway access, and such diverse facilities as lodges and huts, ski schools, tows, and lifts. It possesses slopes suitable for the novice, the skilled, and the expert. Donner Summit has long been the most frequented Sierran winter-sports locality. Its Sugar Bowl is the locale of the annual Silver Belt Race down the drop of more than a thousand feet from Mt. Lincoln. To the north the Sierra Club has its Tappaan Lodge at Norden, whereas to the west are Soda Springs and Beacon Hill, considered good "practice" slopes for the inexperienced. The ski season usually lasts from late November into May, depending upon the winter. A succession of Aleutian storms is deemed ideal, bringing the dry powdery snow that delights the skiing enthusiast. By contrast the central Pacific storms tend to bring mushy snow that makes for disappointing skiing. Usual snow depth and the open forest slopes add to skiing enjoyment. Before World War II the Southern Pacific ran ski trains from the Bay Area; the practice was discontinued during the war. Since 1945 buses and private cars have captured the business and the ski-train service was not resumed. On winter weekends bus schedules are good.

Squaw Valley, six miles north of Lake Tahoe, was unknown until its winter-resort development commenced in 1948 when a New York socialite acquired 640 acres. Several 9000-foot peaks rise above the 2-mile long Valley at 6200 feet. After Squaw Valley was awarded the 1960 Winter Olympic Games, $20 million was spent developing facilities that became a state park after the games. With its heavy winter snowfall and four double-chair lifts it has become one of the nation's outstanding ski centers. Millions of dollars have been expended on private lodges, restaurants, and dwellings adjacent to the park. **Alpine Meadows** in Bear Valley to the south opened in 1962.

Another winter-sports center has developed near Echo Summit on U.S. 50. The best-known site is **Heavenly Valley** with its two chair lifts. Farther south other developments have taken place on lesser trans-Sierran highways 88, 4, and 108. Perhaps the best known is **Dodge Ridge,** north of Yosemite Park on California 108.

Periods of concentration plague the resort operator in the Donner-Tahoe Area. Lake Tahoe is primarily a summer vacation land, although lodges along Highways 40 and 50 gain considerable year-round business from wayfarers as well as winter-sports enthusiasts. Acceleration of winter sports is occurring, but there remains the problem of weekend congestion followed by limited midweek activity.

Truckee (approx. 2000) began as a lumber camp, but its surrounding hillsides have long since been denuded. The ghost camp of Hobart Mills, 6 miles to the north, testifies to the past significance of lumbering. Truckee serves as a lumbering, railroad, and gateway point, benefiting seasonally from services to winter-sports enthusiasts.

Lake Tahoe is a place of breath-taking beauty—enjoyed by millions since it was first made known by the explorations of John C. Fremont in 1844. Set in a structural basin at an elevation of 6225 feet and rimmed by ice-sculptured summits rising above conifer-forested slopes, Tahoe is more than 20 miles long and covers 193 square miles (partially within Nevada). Ice, flowing from the south, deposited a mass of moraine across the depression, thus detaching Tahoe from shallower Fallen Leaf Lake to the south.

Lake Tahoe, like Yosemite Valley, has fallen prey to its own beauty as it has become one of the more frequented highland recreational centers in western America. Thousands of Californian and numerous outlanders visit the Tahoe area, especially in the summer to enjoy the magnificent setting and escape from the hot lowlands (Fig. 5-28). The paved highways that encircle the lake add to its accessibility: California 89 on the west, U.S. 50 on the south and east, and Nevada 28 on the northeast. On summer weekends traffic con-

Fig. 5-28. EMERALD BAY, LAKE TAHOE. Highway 89 follows the fringes of this scenic cove, popular for boating and bathing. (Link Studio, P.O. Box 264, Stateline, California)

gestion becomes as annoying as on many winding city streets. Scores of private lodges, resorts, and cottages front the highway; except for small Bliss State Park and a few public campgrounds and beaches, desirable waterfront sites have long been privately owned. Hundreds of cabins flank the beaches. Congestion is especially acute at the north end of the lake between Tahoe Vista and Crystal Bay and at the southeast end between Stateline and Al Tahoe. **Tahoe City** (unincorp.) and **Al Tahoe** are the largest permanent communities; their small full-time population belies the summer crowds. Tahoe City, focal point for nearby summer estates, has a municipal pier that serves as an aquatic parking lot.

Utilization of the Tahoe Basin has changed much in the past century. Some early Cali-

fornians appreciated Tahoe's resort potential; relaxation as well as hunting and fishing attracted pioneer visitors. Tahoe City was surveyed in 1863 and a hotel was built there the next year. After construction of the Central Pacific across Donner Summit, a wagon road was extended from Truckee. Freighting between California points and the Nevada silver camps supported haymaking in Tahoe Basin in the pre-railroad era. Between 1860 and 1900 considerable lumbering took place on the wooded slopes around the lake; fortunately there has been much second growth. Gradually better-appointed resort hotels were built. A series of lake boats provided excursion facilities. For a time Nevada water-users attempted to lower the level of Tahoe in order to obtain more water. In the pre-automobile era visitors came by horsedrawn vehicle and

Fig. 5-29. *DEEP SNOW PLAGUES DON-NER PASS. Since the days of the pioneer Donner Party, deep winter snow has hampered transit across this 7000-foot summit. Today rail and highway traffic is seldom long delayed because large snowplows are utilized.* (Southern Pacific Company)

Fig. 5-30. *THE FEATHER RIVER CAN-YON. The California Zephyr is seen passing through "Honeymoon Tunnels." Although this Sierran crossing is nearly half a mile lower than Donner Pass, precipitous canyon walls long delayed railroad and highway construction.* (Burlington Route–Rio Grande–Western Pacific Railroads)

remained for a week or so. With the rise of automotive transportation visits became shorter. Increasingly Tahoe has been frequented by weekend visitors, who create the contemporary congestion.

Popular activities at Tahoe include swimming, sunbathing, waterskiing, boating, hiking, fishing, and camping, as well as winter sports on the slopes of Mt. Rose. The shallower (and warmer) waters of Emerald Bay and Fallen Leaf Lake are more popular with bathers than the chilly waters of Tahoe's main body. On the Nevada boundary are gambling casinos. Concentration of the bulk of the tourist trade in summer adds to problems of resort operators.

So large are the multitudes that now frequent the lake annually that only with careful planning and restriction can the beauty of Tahoe and its surroundings be protected. The numbers that visit the Swiss lakes indicate this can be done. The *San Francisco Examiner* (April 9, 1961) concernedly editorialized "Coney Island at Tahoe?" Tahoe Basin seems destined to have the largest population concentration within the Sierra Nevada; it was estimated to be 20,000 in 1962 with a *permanent* population of 75,000 predicted by 1970. A California-Nevada Interstate Compact effected in 1961 should protect the lake against overtapping of its water. However, with rising population, sewage contamination poses a threat despite dispersal plants. A few years ago when Nevada suggested that the main crest of the Sierra be made the state line some Tahoe businessmen favored including all of Tahoe within Nevada in order to permit gambling. Tahoe Keys, a $100 million waterfront development where every lot has its own dockage, suggests that further growth around the lake is likely.

SIERRA VALLEY

Sierra Valley is a flattish, crudely circular plain a mile above sea level. It occupies the north end of the Tahoe rift, and is separated

Fig. 5-31. DOWNIEVILLE. This old camp, situated attractively at the confluence of the Downie and the North Fork of the Yuba, is one of the most picturesque Sierran villages. (David W. Lantis)

from Tahoe Basin by a rolling volcanic upland tributary to Little Truckee River. The upland, once well forested, has been much logged. To the west in the Grizzly Mountains are two beautiful cirque lakes—Independence and Webber—still little known and seldom visited.

Sierra Valley, economic heart of Sierra County, was settled early yet has been apart from main routes—although U.S. 40A and the Western Pacific now skirt its northern edge. The Valley remains little known to many Californians even though it is the principal ranching basin within the Sierra Nevada. Settlement followed establishment of James Beckwourth's trading post in 1852. A number of early occupants were Italian-Swiss dairymen. Land-use has changed only slightly during the past century. Cattle ranching and summer haymaking, pioneer activities, remain the basis of the economy. The Valley center, with extensive marshes, contains one of the sources of the Feather River; it is used by local ranchers and Sacramento Valley cattlemen for summer grazing. Both groups also utilize surrounding slopes for pasturage. Properties are large, with ranch houses concentrated along the highway that encircles the Valley. The roof slope of two-story white frame houses

and large hay barns with steeply pitched roofs testify to winter snows and the necessity of feeding stock. Hardier field crops, especially grains (barley, wheat, and oats), are grown upon the better-drained Valley fringes; short season and frost threats negate many crops. With improved transportation facilities dairying declined in the 1950's. Butter was once shipped to the Central Valley, but now milk is brought from the Sacramento Valley with less cost than Grade-A milk can be produced locally. Good California markets for meat have encouraged a shift to beef cattle.

The western Sierra Valley shares slightly in the growing recreational use of the Northern Sierra. The quiet family resort of **Calpine** is situated amidst the pine forests that descend from the Grizzly Mountains.

Sierra Valley towns, founded early, show little evidence of recent growth. Business blocks tend to retain the false fronts of the nineteenth century. **Loyalton** (900), largest village in the Valley, has long had lumber operations.

YUBA RIVER COUNTRY

The Yuba River Country reaches westward from Sierra Valley to the Foothills tributary to California Routes 20 and 49. This was a

Fig. 5-32. INDIAN VALLEY, AN INTER-MONT BASIN. Cattle ranching is "the way of life" in this small rift between the Diamond and Grizzly Mountains. Indian Falls Ridge in the rear exceeds 7000 feet elevation. (David W. Lantis)

portion of the "Northern Mines" (see Foothills)—nowhere else did gold mining extend so far eastward into the Sierra with as much success as it did here. Understandably much of the accessible timber was cut early; hence there has been nearly a century for reforestation. Timber reserves, now largely contained within national forests, are consequential.

Hillsides in the Yuba River Country are dotted with evidences of gold mining; the western portion in the Foothills contains some of the more impressive evidences of hydraulic mining as well as the famed lode mines of Grass Valley. A little lode mining has persisted into the 1960's around Downieville.

The Yuba has three major tributaries—the North, Middle, and South forks. Economic activity within the Yuba River Country is concentrated along the North Fork, which is followed by California 49. Some of its enthusiasts regard this landscape as more appealing than the Feather River Canyon, which is much better publicized. For many years Pacific Gas and Electric has generated power at Bullards Bar dam. Upstream lumbering has continuing significance on a scale more modest than in portions of the Foothills.

Tourism makes an increasing contribution to the economy of the Yuba River Country. Besides motels and lodges there are a number of picnic spots and campgrounds along the North Fork. Sports fishing for trout is popular. The canyon has ready availability to residents of the Bay Area and the Sacramento Valley.

The "metropolis" of the Yuba Country is **Downieville** (approx. 500), a charming village nestled at the base of pine-covered slopes (Fig. 5-31). During the gold boom it was the center of an area that yielded much placer gold. Today its small populace is supported by county government, tourist, mining, lumbering, and local trade. Residents even include a few senior citizens lured from the city.[19] Its tortuous main street, flanked by nineteenth-century buildings and overhanging balconies, has been used as a setting for "western" movies. Up-canyon **Sierra City**, another tourist stop, continued as a mining center long after boom days; it yielded gold from a quartz ledge at the base of Sierra Buttes (8615 ft.), high promontory in the Yuba Country.

THE FEATHER RIVER COUNTRY

Though it was the upper portion of the "Northern Diggings" during the Gold Rush, much of the Feather River Country remained

[19] Although Downieville has no hospital, helicopter "ambulance service" is available to Sacramento Valley cities.

Fig. 5-33. CARIBOU POWERHOUSE, FEATHER RIVER CANYON. P.G. and E. uses and re-uses the energy of falling water between Lake Almanor and Oroville. This is one of a series of powerhouses on the North Fork of the Feather River. (Pacific Gas and Electric Company)

an isolated wilderness until a late period in California history. More recently as a commercial corridor, as a projected source of water for drier lands to the south, as a playground, as a producer of much hydroelectricity, and as a lumber center, this segment of the Sierra Nevada has become more frequented and better known throughout California.

The Feather River Country is the heartland of the extreme Northern Sierra. It is traversed by the main line of the Western Pacific, a spectacular engineering achievement noted earlier (Fig. 5-30). Usually lower within the canyon than the rail line is U.S. 40A, still an obscure state highway in the early 1950's. It becomes especially important as a California gateway when Highways 40 and 50 become ˉ snowbound. The Feather River crossing is

relatively low (Beckwourth Pass summit is 5221 ft.), which helped explain construction of a wagon road in 1851 (which could not follow the deep canyon below Portola and hence veered off to the northwest).

Considerable portions of the Feather River Country were long covered with virgin forests of ponderosa pine and Douglas fir. Exploitation was encouraged earlier in the twentieth century with construction of the Western Pacific Railroad. After World War II, with expanded consumption of lumber in California, access roads were built away from the highways; widespread logging has taken place and some of California's finest remaining conifers have been cut. Plumas County has become a major producer of timber; more important centers include Greenville, Quincy, and Portola. Because of heavy winter snowfall, lumbering is concentrated in summer and seasonal unemployment is a local problem as elsewhere in northern California.

The Feather River Country comprises the northern end of the Sierran gold belt. Soon after the discovery of gold farther south, portions of the Feather Country in the Foothills were being worked; miners rapidly progressed up the canyons. Such Foothills sites as Bidwell Bar (now a state park), Big Bar, and Rich Bar were important centers, with some of the more spectacular placer operations. The hydraulic activity at Cherokee was noted previously. Farther east, the Plumas-Eureka, near Johnsville, was the best-known lode mine.

The Feather River is the largest stream in the Sierra Nevada; its several branches have become a major focus of hydroelectric development by Pacific Gas and Electric Company. Great Western Power Company (later merged into P.G. and E.), constructed Almanor Dam in 1917, thus creating Lake Almanor, a regulatory body covering Big Meadows. Downstream along the North Fork, P.G. and E. uses and reuses falling water at six powerhouses (Fig. 5-33). There are additional plants on the West Branch and three more power plants have been constructed on the South Fork in connection with new reservoirs for Oroville-Wyandotte Irrigation District. P.G. and E. also hopes to construct generating centers on

Fig. 5-34. KEDDIE—a resort in the pines. Conversion of the Western Pacific section-crew quarters into a resort reflects the rising movement of recreation in the Feather River Country. (English Properties, Inc., photo by Eastman's Studio)

the less accessible Middle Fork in conjunction with irrigation developments. Besides Lake Almanor, another artificial P.G. and E. lake, Bucks, is popular for water sports and for summer cabin sites.

Ranching is relatively unimportant in the Feather River Country although uplands are used whenever possible. The two principal basins, aside from Sierra Valley, which has been discussed, are American Valley at Quincy and Indian Valley (whose chief town is **Taylorsville**). The latter basin, like Sierra Valley, was a dairying center before World War II; its land is now devoted to beef cattle (Fig. 5-32).

The Feather River Country has rising importance as a summer vacation land. Most of

the resorts are located along the North Fork canyon (Fig. 5-34). Sports fishing is popular, although the beauty of this canyon alone makes it attractive for outings. Winter sports have also increased in popularity, with Blairsden as the chief site. However, the Feather River Country is less advantageously located than Mammoth Lakes, Yosemite Park, or the Donner-Tahoe Area. **Blairsden** is the gateway to scenic Lakes Basin Recreation Area in the Grizzly Mountains. Little visited except by local residents until recent years, this glaciated locality on the northern edge of Sierra Buttes is becoming popular for camping and for fishing. Gold Lake is the best known of its several water bodies. Nearby Plumas-Eureka mine is a focal point of a 5600-acre park that

Fig. 5-35. OROVILLE DAM—initial unit of California's water plan. An artist has "dummied in" 735-foot-high Oroville Dam, an earth-fill structure now under construction on the Feather River, depicting how it should look after completion in 1968. It will have a capacity of 3.48 million acre-feet and a shoreline of 167 miles. (California Department of Water Resources)

Fig. 5-36. THE SKYWAY IN PARADISE. The single main street extends for miles along the "Ridge." (Paradise Chamber of Commerce, photo by Henson Studio)

is considered one of the finest in the California state system. It is being developed into a ski center. Another attraction is Feather Falls on the Fall River; this 640-foot waterfall remains accessible only by trail.

The communities of the Feather River Country are small and generally older towns whose slow growth reflects economic limitations of the Northern Sierra. The area includes ghost mine camps and abandoned lumber towns. The two largest communities are Quincy and Portola. **Quincy** (2700), a one-time gold camp, more attractively situated than Portola, is snug against the southern edge of American Valley. A lumber center and tourist stop, it is also important for county government and local trade. Its white marble courthouse and older frame dwellings suggest a Vermont village. **Portola** (1900), which began as a twentieth-century railroad division point, has never entirely lost its frontier appearance. Its economy also depends upon lumbering and tourist trade, which explains a second shopping center along the highway.[20]

[20] A decline in population from 2261 in 1950 reflects the conversion of Western Pacific engines to diesel power. Nubieber (Chapter 1) and Dunsmuir (Chapter 6) are two other northern California communities thus affected by a technological change. Within the North Fork canyon, the attractively situated railroad village of Keddie has made a successful conversion into a year-round resort (Fig. 5-34).

PROSPECTS

California has received a tremendous inheritance in this largest of mountain ranges within the forty-eight "older" states. How much of this legacy is to be squandered by callous individuals who, with disregard for the future, assert that "this land is mine"? Much planning is necessary *soon* if this is to be averted. Prospects for the Sierra Nevada suggest, in consideration of California population growth, ever increasing utilization of this lofty range. As a barrier its significance has already been reduced by technological advances. Modern state and federal highways, and rail lines, have much reduced the effectiveness of its mighty wall. Accelerated population growth indicates expanded utilization as a recreation land. Summer congestion in Yosemite Valley and around Lake Tahoe will doubtless be duplicated at other places now less frequented. Already attractive cabin sites on water are beginning to become expensive. It is doubtful if mining will again have the moment it did during the Gold Rush despite agitation for higher gold prices. However, for generations to come the Foothills will be frequented by those who wish to visualize the atmosphere of that tumultuous period in California history. Water resources will have increasing importance and the need for water conservation more urgency; additional dams will be built. Doubtless, too, increased forest conservation is demanded; eventually tree farming should wholly replace forest mining. An interesting question pertains to the future of the High Sierra. Can this remain a virgin wilderness or will it, like Lake Tahoe and Yosemite Valley, be opened to the masses with construction of paved highways, resorts, and other lures? Large urban centers seem unlikely, yet present trends in Paradise, Placerville, and Tahoe Basin intimate larger cities in the future. Prospects for industrial development are not yet evident.

CHAPTER SIX :: THE SOUTHERN CASCADE

THE SOUTHERN CASCADE

The Cascade Range lies mostly outside California, for it extends from Lassen Peak into southern British Columbia. Yet California possesses two of its better-known summits: **Lassen Peak** and **Mount Shasta**. The Southern Cascade, comparable in size to the Colorado Desert (Chapter 4), has an area within California of approximately 4000 square miles and thus qualifies as the smallest subdivision of the state. Its sparse population slightly exceeds that of the adjacent Northeast (Chapter 1), whose area is four times as large. In the geologic past, the Cascade was the site of magnificent displays of natural fireworks.

The boundaries of the Southern (California) Cascade cannot always be sharply stated (Fig. 6-2). Most definitive is the political California-Oregon line on the north. On the east, the transition from mountains to the Modoc Plateau of the Northeast is sometimes blurred. On the west, Shasta Valley and the

This chapter has been reviewed by Arthur E. Carthew, Los Angeles City College, and John Carthew, University of California at Los Angeles.

134 :: CHAPTER SIX

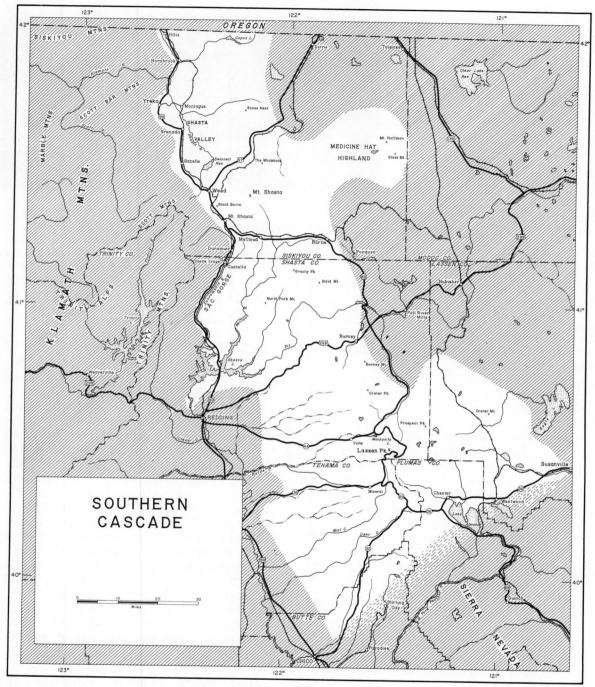

Fig. 6-2. MAP OF THE SOUTHERN CASCADE.

Fig. 6-3. *THE LASSEN VOLCANIC RIDGE. The Cascade Range is ill defined near its southern limits. A cluster of conic peaks rises like giant scoops of ice cream above a basaltic tableland. Surrounding them are scattered lesser cinder cones, some not over 500 years old. View south, with city of Burney, Burney Mountain (7871 ft.), and Lassen Peak.* (David W. Lantis)

Sacramento Gorge occupy a depression between the Cascade and the Klamath Mountains of the Northwest (Chapter 10). On the south, there is a transition from the western slope of the tilted Sierra Nevada to the volcanic cones of the Lassen Peak area; a line drawn between Susanville and Chico approximates such demarcation. Socio-political delimitation is more difficult. From Pacific shores into Nevada, people of extreme northern California tend to have similar interests—and disinterest in many national and international issues. In a recent Congressional election, a local politician, queried about "issues," asked in frustration, "What issues? Nothing besides legislation related to fishing and hunting, water, timber, and ranching seems to concern most of these people."

THE LAND

As elsewhere in California, it is the physical earth that so often seems to form the basis for geographic subdivision. In a sparsely populated land like the Southern Cascade the terrain is particularly conspicuous (Fig. 6-1).

CRATERS AND CINDER CONES

The Southern Cascade consists of a dissected tableland of basaltic sheets, mudflows, and ash, capped by volcanic cones. It constitutes the only region of California in which volcanic features dominate the countryside so completely. Here plutonic activity has been occurring for thousands of years, probably since the Pliocene. South of Mount Shasta the range is rather poorly defined with numerous small cinder cones; prominent summits include Crater Mountain (7418 ft.) and Burney Mountain (7871 ft.), and better known Lassen Peak (10,453 ft.). The area northward from Shasta is more representative of the Cascade, with larger volcanoes rising more impressively above their surroundings. After Mount Shasta, the most noteworthy in California are Whaleback (8536 ft.) and Goose Nest (8289 ft.). The cones are of both andesitic and basaltic composition; some are quite eroded whereas others are well preserved. Many craters have risen from a volcanic shield base.

Mount Shasta (14,162 ft.) is perhaps California's most majestic summit and encompasses the largest single base diameter in the entire range. This magnificent peak completely dominates its surroundings above which it rises almost two miles. Actually Shasta is a double cone; the younger "twin," Shastina, reaches 12,336 ft.; the two summits are surrounded by cinder cones and plug domes. Shasta is wreathed by a cap of valley glaciers whose dimensions, although much reduced over the past century, are still quite impressive. Hotlum on its northeastern slope is the largest of five glacial remnants.

The **Medicine Hat Highland** northeast of Shasta has scores of little cones rising from a shield base. The highest summit is Mt. Hoffman (7928 ft.), and Glass Mountain, an obsidian pile, is nearly as high (7649 ft.).

The southern end of the Cascade is the **Lassen Volcanic Ridge**, much of which lies within the national park (Fig. 6-3). The Ridge, which includes hundreds of small cinder cones, was once dominated by Mt. Tehama, an ancient stratovolcano that collapsed internally; such shield volcanoes as Raker Peak, Prospect Peak, Red Mountain, and Mt. Harkness remain as residues around its outer edges. Lassen Peak, a plug dome, was formed from its heart late, as was Cinder Cone (6913 ft.) to the northeast. Several hundred years ago Chaos Crags arose from the northwest base of Lassen. Lassen was "active" in 1914-1917, when hundreds of minor explosions occurred. Part of these "eruptions" is attributed to the contact of hot lava with snow meltwater. Those Californians who mention it as the only site of recent activity in the United States overlook Hawaii and Alaska.

The western margin of the Southern Cascade is formed by two depressions, Shasta Valley and the Sacramento Gorge; they form a separation from the Klamath Mountains to the west. Oval-like Shasta Valley, 30 miles long by 15 miles wide (east-west), has a highly irregular surface generally between 2400 and 2800 feet elevation. Its eastern half is Pluto's Cave basaltic flow (from the east) named after the largest of its schollendomes (lava caves); the western portion consists of floodplains and alluvial fans. Lava flows have covered extensive portions of the Southern Cascade repeatedly. For a time several thousand years ago the Klamath River was

dammed, thus creating Copco Lake, which at one time was much larger than it is today.

Southward from Shasta Valley beyond Mt. Shasta the Sacramento, fed by streams from the Northeast and swollen with meltwater from the slopes of Shasta, has cut an impressive canyon into the eastern prong of the Klamath Mountains (Fig. 6-7). The McCloud Country, east of the Gorge, is also geologically part of the Klamaths; it is included in this chapter because of its location. Its sedimentary and metamorphic rocks, well revealed in the canyon of the McCloud River, contrast with the younger volcanics of the Cascade.

A SNOWY LAND

The Southern Cascade, like the remainder of California, is plagued by summer drought. Perhaps even more significant here is the effect of varying altitudes, which create vertical zones and climatic complexity. Shasta Valley is semiarid middle latitude, a reflection of its rain-shadow location east of the Klamath Mountains. Eastward lower portions of the tableland grade into the "dry-summer middle latitudes," more extensive in the Northeast (see Chapter 1 and Appendix A). A tundra zone exists above timberline (about 10,000 feet) on Mt. Shasta and Lassen Peak (Fig. 6-1).

Elevation is a major factor as Pacific storms move across northern California in winter. Lowlands receive moisture as either snow or rain; annual snowfall varies between 50 and 100 inches. The slopes of the volcanic cones receive considerably more precipitation, however, and between 20 and 30 feet of snow fall annually on Lassen Peak.

FORESTS OF PINE AND FIR

An open conifer forest, dominated by sugar pine, yellow pine, white fir, and Douglas fir, typifies the terrain between 2000 and 6000 feet elevation. Known as the montane zone (or Sierran transition), this forest represents a continuation of the westside belt in the Sierra Nevada and forms a center of commercial lumbering. Its understory is often a carpet of flowers, green meadows, or chaparral shrubs.

Environmental complexity creates variation in the vegetation. Shasta Valley has sagebrush and Great Basin rabbitbush in the east; there is also considerable grassland here. There is much chaparral in the Southern Cascade. A belt of the "elfin forest," dominated by manzanita, surrounds the base of Mt. Shasta. Above the zone of the pine-fir forests on the slopes of Shasta and Lassen, there is a timberline zone of hemlock and white-bark pine, giving way to alpine meadows with dwarf pines, lichens, daisies, and penstemons.

SETTLEMENT

The Southern Cascade was sparsely populated in pre-Spanish times; even today it is one of the less densely populated portions of California. The mountain "ridge" through the center of the region appreciably reduced its human utilization.

THE SHASTANS

Aboriginal residents of the area were the *Shastans,* members of the Hokan family. They resided principally along the Klamath and the Pit, in Shasta Valley and in Scott Valley (of the Northwest). The northeastern margin of the region toward Butte Valley (of the Northeast) was occupied by their dread neighbors, the Modoc.

The Shastans, hunters and fisherfolk, also gathered acorns and manzanita berries. Their diet was based mainly upon salmon, taken from the rivers, and bear and deer. These peoples were among the more culturally backward American Indians of California, especially in comparison with Northwestern neighbors like the Karok and Yurok.

THE SPANISH-MEXICAN PERIOD

The Southern Cascade remained outside Spanish California. An exploring expedition under Captain Luis Arguello in 1820 skirted the southwestern edge of the region and assigned the name Mt. Joseph to Lassen Peak.

In the final years of the Mexican period several ranchos were awarded in the upper reaches of the Sacramento Valley (Chapter 9); no land grants were made within the Southern Cascade.

American and British fur trappers visited the region between 1827 and 1845. In some instances the trails they followed became the routes of pioneers who followed them. A visit of another nature was made by Lt. George F. Emmons, commanding officer of the U.S.S. *Peacock,* which was lost at the mouth of the Columbia in 1841. Emmons led his command, which was part of the Wilkes exploration expedition, southward from Astoria into the Sacramento Valley.

THE CALIFORNIA-OREGON TRAIL

The California-Oregon Trail, whose central route has become the general course of U.S. 99, connected the Sacramento Valley with the Willamette Valley via the Southern Cascade. Its several segments were logical passages, which doubtless had long been used by the Indians. One branch went west of the Sacramento River Gorge, up the Trinity River, and on into Scott Valley. The route through the Sacramento Gorge was used early by Hudson Bay trappers. The Trail was used to drive cattle northward from Mexican California into Oregon in the late 1830's and in the 1840's. By 1854 a deviant wagon road circled east of Mt. Shasta into Shasta Valley, averting the Gorge. By 1860 a stagecoach route was in operation between Portland and Sacramento; it survived until arrival of the railroad in 1887. Early east-west routes included Lassen's Trail and the Emigrant Trail; the latter wound past Cinder Cone and Manzanita Lake.

GOLD SEEKERS

The volcanic Cascade has been a repellent for most mining.[1] The quest for gold

[1] However, Calaveras Cement opened a plant northeast of Redding in 1962. Commercial prospects of an iron-ore deposit in the same locality is under consideration. Both these deposits are within the sedimentary-metamorphic complex of the southeastern extension of the geologic Klamath Mountains.

brought the granitic periphery of the range into prominence briefly in 1851; most of the activity took place in the Klamath Mountains to the west. Shasta Valley was disregarded by Oregonians scurrying toward the Mother Lode Country in 1849; it was argonauts working eastward up the gravel bars along the Klamath who led the way into Shasta Valley. New finds around Yreka (then Thompson's Dry Diggings) and Hawkinsville took place in 1851; for several years gold production in Shasta Valley had moment, but it never achieved the importance of other California centers. A noteworthy development occurred in 1855—the Greenhorn "war"; rival groups contested the use of ditch water. Much later, Bully Hill, whose smelter at Kennett is now buried beneath Shasta Lake, was an important source of copper. Copper and zinc mining also took place at Ingot, east of Redding.

RANCHES AND SAWMILLS

A few gold seekers elected to remain as permanent residents of the Southern Cascade, settling down as ranchers. However widespread settlement was not effected early; the region suffered seriously from isolation in the pre-railroad era. Completion of the Shasta Line of the Southern Pacific was a major force in permitting greater utilization of the area.

Lumbering was a late occupance force, 1890-1920. Gold mining did not persist long enough to create a local market for lumber, as it did in the Sierra Nevada. Until the railroad was built, the Southern Cascade was too inaccessible to warrant extensive logging operations; good forest stands were much more available elsewhere. Thus some of the more prominent communities, with lumber orientation, were not established until the late nineteenth or early twentieth century.

UTILIZATION

The economy of the Southern Cascade has been altered during the twentieth century— lumbering, expanded commerce, use of water,

and recreation have developed or expanded. Agriculture and livestock ranching were established before the turn of the century. Population density remains low and human use is limited over much of the area.

THE SHASTA CORRIDOR

Through commerce is a primary source of livelihood in the Southern Cascade. The course of the California-Oregon Trail through the Sacramento Gorge and across Shasta Valley forms a northern segment of one of three north-south California corridors (the others are the coastal, or Redwood route, and the Intermontane passage through Susanville and Alturas). Way stations, located in the days of freight wagons and stage coaches, eventually became railroad stops; some have developed into larger towns.

The Shasta Route has formed the only through rail passage between Puget Sound and Portland and central California since 1887. The Oregon and California Railroad, constructed southward from Portland in 1866, reached Roseburg in 1872. Financial troubles and finally receivership resulted in purchase of the line by the Southern Pacific Company. Meanwhile, the Southern Pacific had extended its line northward through the Sacramento Valley. The "Shasta Route" was completed in 1887 and has been an important consideration in evolution of Southern Cascade economy. A branch line from Black Butte (near Weed) to Klamath Falls, started in 1905, was completed in 1909; it has replaced the Ashland-Medford segment as the "main line" of the Shasta Route.

U.S. 99, "main street of California," has succeeded the old trail in the twentieth century. The Sacramento Gorge was a vexatious "bottleneck" until the freeway was completed in the early 1960's (Fig. 6-7). Tremendous excavations were necessary to create the multilane highway in the vicinity of Dunsmuir. Many trucks as well as passenger vehicles utilize U.S. 99. Service for highway travelers has become an important activity in towns along the route.

Cascadian terrain has been more negotiable for east-west travel routes than topography in

Fig. 6-4. YREKA—*principal town of the Southern Cascade. This erstwhile gold camp, separated from Shasta Valley proper by Kill-dall Hills (right), has survived as a county seat, highway point, local service center, and lumbering town. (Yreka Chamber of Commerce, photo by Yreka Studio and Camera Shop)*

Fig. 6-5. LOGGING OPERATIONS EAST OF REDDING. *The motor truck, power saw, and Caterpillar Traxcavator have replaced the logging railroad, handsaw, and donkey engine. (Caterpillar Tractor Co.)*

Fig. 6-6. WEED—*lumber camp and highway junction. This growing community at the south end of Shasta Valley, long the site of a Long-Bell (International Paper) mill, benefits from its situation at the confluence of federal highways 97 and 99. (David W. Lantis)*

Fig. 6-7. DUNSMUIR AND THE SACRAMENTO GORGE. *The narrow canyon site of this railroad town long created a traffic barrier on U.S. 99. The dramatic solution is seen on the right. (California Division of Highways)*

the Sierra Nevada has been.[2] Roads can traverse the gentle tableland slopes around individual volcanoes. Several east-west highways link the Intermontane Region east of the Cascade with U.S. 99. U.S. 97 parallels the railroad between Weed and Klamath Falls. The eastern segment of U.S. 299, leading east-west highway of far northern California, crosses the range between Mt. Shasta and Lassen Peak. Farther south, California 44 and 36 from the Sacramento Valley also serve as gateways into Lassen Park; Route 36, an important year-round crossing, continues past Westwood to Susanville. California 32 as late as 1960 remained a slight modification of mid-nineteenth-century Humboldt Road, a wagon trail eventually black-topped; after continued improvement it will carry much traffic. Mechanical plows have reduced the past problems resulting from deep snow; secondary roads like Route 32 still get snowbound, usually for a few days at a time.

East of 99, California 89 is the only north-south highway through the range. It reaches from Truckee on U.S. 40 to U.S. 99 at Mt. Shasta. Its value is lessened because the section through Lassen Park ("The Lassen Loop") is snowbound in winter. Completion of a new "bypass" northward from Westwood east of the "high country" will aid local winter travel.

RANCHING

Ranching has been the most constant mainstay of the Cascadian economy since the 1850's. Farming is limited because of rugged terrain; thin, rocky soils; and extensive timberlands. Although livestock ranching is more extensive, holdings are scattered; Shasta Valley is the only sizable area. The smaller Hat Creek Valley warrants note also.

Shasta Valley, approximately 500 square miles in area, does not resemble the typical intermontane basin because of its rolling volcanic topography.[3] The "Scablands" (Pluto's Cave lava flows), which forms its eastern half, has almost no agricultural value aside from Little Shasta Valley. Besides terrain and extensive areas of poor soil, the Valley has been plagued by limited water (despite modest storage in Dwinnell reservoir), short growing season, and distance from major California markets.

Settlers found extensive grasslands in the west; much grass was plowed under and wheat was planted. Livestock, especially horses, for the mine camps had early importance. Some holdings were extensive even though some land was eventually homesteaded. Gradually sheep replaced the horses. Prior to establishment of the Forest Service (early 1900's) there was sufficient mountain range and transhumance was more significant. Even before the railroad arrived beef were trailed south to Redding. Irrigation was developed in the 1870's and alfalfa introduced; much water is still used to flood hay meadows. Transhumance is still practiced elsewhere, and cattle are trucked to mountain grasslands rather than "trailed" as in the past.

Rural land-use has not experienced widespread changes in the twentieth century although promoters established "colonies" about Grenada and Montague. Short seasons and limited markets discourage many crops found in the Central Valley. Wheat and barley yield well by dry-farming methods; about 25,000 acres are raised with alternate-year fallowing. On irrigated lands alfalfa remains important. Three cuttings are usually made; then livestock are pastured on late-season growth. Dairying achieved importance in the 1920's; milk was marketed through local creameries. Since World War II dairying has been less consequential; there is virtually no local market for Grade-A milk, and lower grades are less profitable than beef.

[2] This is true except in areas of much dissection. The country north of Highway 32, southwest of Lassen Park, contains some of the most impassable terrain in California.

[3] The traveler on U.S. 99 misses much of the Valley. The highway veers west along Yreka Creek Valley, separated from the balance of the basin by the Killdale Hills. Residents of Yreka do not regard their re-entrant Yreka Basin as a portion of the valley.

Beef cattle remains the principal product of Shasta Valley, although transhumance has almost disappeared. The "average" cattle ranch encompasses approximately 6500 acres; properties on rough land tend to be larger. Herefords (or Aberdeen Angus) are usually shipped to the Sacramento Valley for fattening before delivery to packing houses.

LUMBERING

Forestry forms the principal economic pursuit in the Southern Cascade, which ranks third to the Northwest and Sierra Nevada in lumbering. This region is one of the state's primary sources of pine lumber. During much of the nineteenth century transportation was limited and market demand modest; production generally was small scale for the limited local needs. Much land lies within three national forests, yet there are sizable private holdings. In Shasta County private forest lands are more extensive than the national forests.

Recently the future of the lumber industry, so vital to the economy of the region, has become critical. Accelerated cutting has taken place since World War II. Scores of operators have been active in the Southern Cascade and many, especially the small firms, have been more concerned with immediate return than with long-term prospects.

Extensive forest tracts have been assembled in various ways. One way was by means of the Timber and Stone Act of 1878. More recently, some nationwide wood products corporations have acquired holdings of local firms through purchase. For example, Diamond National, which processes its wood in the Sacramento Valley (Chapter 9), began accumulation of its 220,000-acre tree farms in the southwestern Southern Cascade (paralleling Highway 32) in 1907 with purchase of Sierra Lumber Company. Sierra Lumber in turn had developed in 1878 from an individual operation in eastern Butte County that originated in 1866.

Various methods of removing logs have been employed. Use of ox carts was an early-day method—obviously slow. Later in the nineteenth century much lumber was trans-

ported into the Sacramento Valley by flumes. The flumes, some as long as 25 miles, carried surprising loads; the last one was constructed to Bella Vista (east of Anderson) in 1886. Later, logging railroads were built. Diamond National completed its Butte County Railroad from the mainline of the Southern Pacific at Chico to its mill town of Stirling City in 1904. The McCloud River Railroad connects the Southern Pacific at Mt. Shasta with the Great Northern in Big Valley (Chapter 1). In recent years even more mechanized equipment has been used, including trucks and diesel tractors (Fig. 6-5). Larger firms have constructed their own logging roads.

Large-scale lumbering in the Southern Cascade commenced in the late nineteenth century. The Klamath River Lumber Company, established in 1889, operated at Klamathon until its camp was demolished by fire in 1902. The McCloud Valley Lumber Company (now McCloud Lumber Company) was incorporated in 1896 and established its company town, McCloud, east of Mt. Shasta (city); it also constructed its own railroad, as noted above. This firm has operated two sawmills, a planing mill and five bandsaws at McCloud (Fig. 6-1). Its long-term prospects were enhanced in 1954 when it gained cutting rights to a billion board feet of lumber from the Fruit Growers Supply Company at the time when that Sunkist affiliate was closing its Westwood operation. McCloud employs a thousand men and cuts a hundred million board feet annually.

Another leading operator, International Paper, had its antecedents in the Southern Cascade at the turn of the century when Abner Weed established Weed Lumber Company with seventy employees and laid out the town of Weed (Fig. 6-6). A box factory was built in 1900, a sash and door mill in 1907, and a plywood plant (the second on the West Coast) in 1911. The firm was sold in 1913; in 1924 it was acquired by Long-Bell Lumber, which was merged with International Paper in 1956. Long-Bell cut timber extensively northeast of Mt. Shasta. The one-time rail grades are still followed by dirt roads.

A Minnesota firm, the Red River Lumber

Company, obtained large holdings east of Lake Almanor and began operations at the company-owned town of Westwood in 1913. Westwood became the largest community in the Southern Cascade. Little changed through the years; it was a "typical" company town with dirt streets, unpainted frame houses, wooden plank sidewalks, and a company commissary. The Westwood operation was purchased by Fruit Growers Supply Co. (a "Sunkist" affiliate) after World War II.

Some of the largest private tracts of Cascadian timber are retained by Shasta Forests, Inc., a family holding company owned by heirs of T. H. Walker, founder of Red River Lumber Company. Operations are conducted within the Southern Cascade, in the Sacramento Valley, and in the Northeast; affiliated firms include Paul Bunyan and Ralph Smith.

More isolated stands of virgin timber remained after World War II. One of the last was the vast McCloud Country holding of the Hearst Corporation. Logging, which has been conducted by International Paper for the Weed mill, was delayed until after the death of William Randolph Hearst.

HYDROELECTRIC POWER

The Southern Cascade is an important source of hydroelectric power—it has portions of two (Sacramento and Klamath) of the state's three largest rivers and the largest single power development (at Shasta and Keswick dams) in California (Fig. 6-11). Because of small population and limited industry most of the power generated in the region is transmitted elsewhere, particularly to the Great Central Valley and the San Francisco Bay Area.

Early activity was undertaken by the California-Oregon Power Company, a consolidation of several small firms in the first decade of the twentieth century (and more recently absorbed into Pacific Power and Light of Portland). Because of the limited market within the Southern Cascade for its energy produced at plants near Lake Copco on the Klamath, the company has sold electricity to Pacific Gas and Electric since 1919. However, most

Fig. 6-8. *HYDRO PLANT ON THE PIT. P.G. and E. has constructed a chain of powerhouses along the Pit, as well as a series farther south along the Feather, the Yuba, the American, and the Kings. View shows Pit No. 5.* (Pacific Gas and Electric Company)

of the activity of this corporation is in Oregon.

Pacific Gas and Electric Company of San Francisco, chief supplier of power to central and northern California, began construction of its northeasternmost power development on the Pit River after World War I (Fig. 6-8). Hydroelectricity is developed on Hat Creek and at several plants on the Pit.[4]

Power generated at Shasta and Keswick dams by the federal government became available to metropolitan San Francisco industries in time to contribute to the war effort at the close of World War II.

[4] In mid-1962 P.G. and E. announced plans for three new plants on the McCloud; upon completion, the 733,400-kilowatt Pit-McCloud capacity will exceed Feather River production (Chapter 5).

RECREATION

The entire Southern Cascade constitutes one vast natural playground, little-frequented, which should have greater value as the population of California rises.

The California Cascade, as well as adjacent portions of the Northeast (Chapter 1) and Oregon, is known as the **Shasta-Cascade Wonderland**. This inviting land, encompassing 25 million acres, includes a national park, three national forests (with several wilderness areas), a national monument, and California's largest man-made lake. Much of the area is still accessible only by hiking or pack horse despite much highway improvement in recent years.

Lassen Volcanic National Park, smallest (163 square miles) and least frequented of California's four national parks, was created in 1916. Its establishment followed the volcanic activity that began in 1914, lifting vapor and ashes as high as 40,000 feet. Lassen Peak itself, ascended by a 2½ mile trail, provides a good view of the surrounding tableland; it is the chief attraction (Fig. 6-9). There are other volcanic features, forests and meadows and lakes. Among the other cones, Chaos Crags and Cinder Cone are best known.

The season between mid-June and Labor Day begins before snow of the previous winter is gone. The park remains cooler, greener, and less dusty than the three national parks in the Sierra Nevada. Facilities are modest—there are only three lodges; Lassen is still a "camper's choice." Most visitors follow the Lassen Peak Highway, a segment of California 89, stopping to visit Lake Helen (at the base of the peak trail) and Bumpus Hell. The latter is the most impressive of three areas with mud pots and sulphuric fumes; others are Sulphur Works and the Devil's Kitchen. The Devastated Area, down the northeast slopes of Lassen, interests most visitors. One can almost imagine the gases blasting downward from the peak, as they did nearly half a century ago.

Eastern Lassen Park, mostly accessible by trails, is a rolling land of conifer forests, meadows, and lakes. This section, not frequented by most visitors, is satisfying country for the hiker and the fisherman.

Mt. Shasta Recreation Area, part of Shasta National Forest, lacks the highways and facilities of Lassen Park. The famed naturalist John Muir considered Shasta the most impressive summit in the state; but so far his views that the peak should become a national park have not been recognized.

Shasta, a difficult climb for the "average" hiker, is much less frequented than Lassen Peak despite the fact that at least forty persons including five women had climbed it by 1856. Hikers usually depart from Mt. Shasta (city) and drive to the end of the 15-mile Everitt Memorial Highway at 7703 feet altitude. Crampons are generally recommended although ropes are not necessary. The season is generally limited to the period between July and September; Muir in *Steep Trails* describes what happens when one endeavors to climb the peak in early spring. A Ski Bowl, with lodge and ski lift to 9212 feet, was opened at the end of the highway in 1958. The winter snow supply is excellent, but the area is rather remote from population centers. A 60-mile drive surrounds the base of the Recreation Area. Most of the Area remains accessible only by foot trails.

Completion of Shasta Dam in 1944 was followed by establishment of **Shasta National Recreation Area** (Fig. 6-11). The 47-square-mile waterbody has a 365-mile shoreline. Even before construction of the reservoir the Sacramento and its tributary streams were popular with sportsmen. The valley of the lower McCloud, especially, has been used for camping and for summer cottages for many years. Much of the McCloud Country has been a longtime private preserve of the Hearst family.[5]

Shasta Dam was constructed as the first major storage unit in the Central Valley Project (Chapter 9) by a group of California contractors who called themselves Pacific Constructors, Inc. The dam is 602 feet high and

[5] In contrast to San Simeon (Chapter 8), Hearst's Wintun Lodge in the McCloud canyon is surprisingly unknown, even in northern California.

Fig. 6-9. LASSEN PEAK AND MAN-
ZANITA LAKE. *Lassen, while not the most
spectacular national park, has geologic interest and provides a satisfying area for camping, hiking, fishing, and skiing. It is less congested than Yellowstone, Yosemite, or Rocky
Mountain. Manzanita Lake, near the northern
entrance, is popular for boating and wading.*
(National Park Service)

Fig. 6-10. WINTER SPORTS IN LASSEN
PARK. *The Lassen Loop Highway becomes
snowbound, but skiing takes place near California highway 36 north of Mineral.* (National
Park Service)

Fig. 6-11. SHASTA DAM, SHASTA LAKE,
AND MT. SHASTA. *Shasta Dam, 602 feet
high and 3460 feet long, is the key unit in the
Central Valley Project. Built without widespread publicity during World War II, it provides hydroelectricity and recreation, regulates the flow of the Sacramento River, affords
irrigation storage, and has reduced flooding in
the Sacramento Valley.* (David W. Lantis)

Fig. 6-12. McARTHUR-BURNEY FALLS
MEMORIAL STATE PARK. *The beauteous
waterfall is the highlight of this 485-acre
wooded park on California highway 89.
Nearby Lake Britton, a P.G. and E. storage
reservoir, affords fishing and water sports.*
(California Division of Beaches and Parks)

3460 feet long. The structure, which contains more concrete than Hoover Dam, has created a reservoir with a capacity of 4.5 million acre-feet.

The shores of Shasta Lake provide varied facilities for outdoorsmen: campgrounds, beaches, boat landings, and cabins. Lake fishing has replaced the stream fishing of previous years; popular varieties include trout (rainbow, bass, and Kamloops), blue gill, and kokanee (landlocked) salmon.

The Southern Cascade includes two state parks. **Castle Crags**, adjacent to U.S. 99 near Castella, is a granitic mass on the border of the Klamath Mountains. It suggests a miniature Sierra Nevada and overlooks the Sacramento Gorge. It is reached by a trail; park facilities include camping and picnicking, swimming, and fishing. **McArthur-Burney Falls** is north of Burney on Route 89. Its outstanding feature is the 165-foot double falls of Burney Creek, which plunges into a pine-surrounded pool (Fig. 6-12). The park is popular with fishermen.

Two wild areas in Lassen National Forest flank Lassen Park. Both tend to be more attainable than most California wild areas. **Thousand Lakes Wild Area**, northwest of the park, is small (15,000 acres) yet seldom visited despite its accessibility from nearby highways. It affords an attractive hiking and camping setting with many little lakes. The Seven Lakes district to the northwest can be reached from Burney; somewhat desolate despite its streams and forests, it too is little known. **Caribou Peak Wild Area**, with 16,000 acres southeast of Lassen Park, is also not difficult to reach; it provides excellent sports fishing.

Lake Almanor, along the "contact zone" between the Southern Cascade and the Sierra Nevada, like some of the storage reservoirs mentioned in the previous chapter, looks deceivingly natural. With improved highways and population growth in northern California, its coniferous setting has led to construction of many summer cottages. Its shores offer appealing vistas of Lassen Peak. Considerable use is also made of the lake for fishing and water sports, although it is less accessible than

a number of larger water bodies in northern California.

TOWNS AND VILLAGES

The Southern Cascade has a few small communities, mostly old (for California) and timeworn. Except for the Northeast and the Trans-Sierra, no other region of the state has so few towns of consequence. They tend to function as local service centers, shipping points, and way points for the highway traveler; and nowhere else in the state is urban economy so dependent upon lumbering. The principal concentration of hamlets is understandably found in Shasta Valley; elsewhere, villages are scattered.

Yreka (4800), oldest town in the region and through the years generally the largest community, has never regained its gold-boom population of the 1850's (Fig. 6-4). Its several functions include seat of Siskiyou County, tourist stop, local trade, and lumber production. Its early importance is hinted by older structures on Miner Street, its principal avenue; frame cottages on locust-lined streets sometimes date from early days. Although **Montague** (782) is the leading rail station in Shasta Valley, this little dairying village has never threatened Yreka, six miles to the west.

Weed (3200) on the southern periphery of Shasta Valley, has outgrown its lumber camp origin (Fig. 6-6). At the junction of Highways 97 and 99, it has become an important transportation crossroads. It is the site of College of Siskiyou, the only junior college in the region. Lumbering remains consequential; products include the region's only plywood.

Dunsmuir (2900) has a longtime function singularly based upon its status as a Southern Pacific division point at the southern end of the volcanic uplands between the Sacramento Gorge and the Rogue River Valley of southern Oregon (Fig. 6-7). For many years its narrow canyon site created a bottleneck on U.S. 99. When the railroad shifted to diesel engines, catering to highway travelers became more important to its well-being.

Mt. Shasta (city) (1900) originated with the arrival of the railroad in 1886 and was long known as Sisson after the owner of its first inn. Recently, the town, which has lumber mills, has acquired significance as an outfitting point for sportsmen frequenting the Mount Shasta Recreation Area. **McCloud** (2100) to the east is solely a company lumber town, as has been noted.

Burney (1300) was founded in 1872, but experienced most of its growth after 1945 with expanded lumbering. It functions as a service point for a considerable area and is a northern gateway into Lassen Park (Fig. 6-3).

Since construction of Shasta Dam, some semblance of urbanization has appeared to the southeast. The largest community is **Central Valley** (2900). Many of the residents find employment in Redding (Chapter 9).

Chester (1300), attractively situated beside Lake Almanor and the North Fork of the Feather River, is a growing lumber town and highway point on California 36. It serves as a southern gateway into Lassen Park, as does **Mineral** to the west, which is the headquarters for the park and a sizable summer cottage-and-tent community.

Westwood (1200) is perhaps the most interesting town in the Southern Cascade. Founded by Red River Lumber as a company town in 1913, it became the largest community (approximately 4000) in the Southern Cascade.

After Fruit Growers Supply Company, which had purchased the mill and its dwellings in the 1940's, suspended operations in 1956 (partially because the advent of paperboard boxes for packing citrus made its box-shook production unnecessary), the physical town in its entirety was sold to two Los Angeles businessmen for dismantling. Since many residents decided to remain, the purchasers decided to sell houses individually. Many of the worn wooden cottages were purchased as vacation homes. A number of the present residents are employed in lumber mills in Chester and Susanville.

THE OUTLOOK

The Southern Cascade has been one of the least known and most sparsely populated of California regions. It seems unlikely that coming decades will witness great change in its utilization. Much of its hydroelectric potential has already been developed. Agriculture could become more intensive but is limited by shallow soils and rocky terrain. The future of the region looks more promising as a recreational land. In contrast, a marked deterioration in lumbering is apt to occur unless increased tree farming replaces the still too widespread "mining" of the forest.

PART THREE : :

THE PACIFIC
BORDERLANDS

THE PACIFIC BORDERLANDS

North America's western coast is mountain-bordered on much of its length. Sometimes the land rises abruptly, and mountain summits tower thousands of feet above offshore waters nearby. In central California the Santa Lucia Range exemplifies this, rising sheer from Pacific shores.

Geographers experience greater difficulty in delineating the California segments of western America than they do with lands to the north, for which the term "Pacific Northwest" finds wide usage. Identification of "Pacific Borderlands," including the Pacific Northwest and portions of California encompassing coastal mountains and the interior Central Valley, seems valid as a region of Anglo-America (see map, opposite).[1]

The Pacific Borderlands has much rugged topography with only a few lowlands. Where there are coastal plains, their width is generally limited. Sometimes there are narrow coastal terraces; elsewhere the mountains rise immediately from Pacific shores. Restricted though they may be, the coastal valleys and interior plains have moment in the human ecology of the Borderlands—here are concentrated most of the people of western North America. California is particularly favored, with the Los Angeles Lowlands, the fringes of San Francisco Bay, and the Great Central Valley. In its entirety the Borderlands has much empty land, and sparsely populated areas are extensive. This is more true of lands to the north than of California, however.

[1] Earl B. Shaw, *Anglo-America* (New York: John Wiley & Sons, Inc., 1959), pp. 382–446, identifies such a region. C. Langdon White and Edwin J. Foscue, *Regional Geography of Anglo America,* 2nd ed. (Englewood Cliffs, N. J.: Prentice-Hall, Inc., 1954), pp. 375–440, divide the area into two units; whereas Alfred J. Wright, *United States and Canada,* 2nd ed. (New York: Appleton-Century-Crofts, Inc., 1956), pp. 432–466, has a comparable region only within the United States. These three texts include the Sierra Nevada, which is considered separately in this book because of its unique features and greater significance to the smaller land mass that is California.

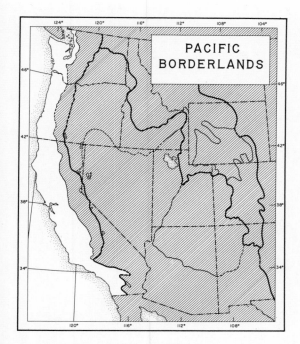

Throughout the Borderlands the ocean influences are momentous. The coastal fog belt is conspicuous, yet the effect of maritime air, a source of moisture, is more important. Most towns and cities of consequence are seaports.

Within California, examples include San Diego, Los Angeles, Santa Barbara, San Francisco, Stockton, and Eureka. Because of the Pacific with its abundant plankton, fishing has long been a principal source of livelihood—this has become less true in California with its more complex economy. Within California, some of the region's many fishing ports include San Diego, San Pedro, and San Francisco. The seacoast lures many vacationists; the Borderlands is a vast playground, whose California centers include La Jolla, Laguna Beach, Santa Monica, and Santa Cruz.

Because of its California segments, the Borderlands has newly achieved status as a "vertical frontier." Evidences of transition from simpler ways of livelihood, represented by lumbering, fishing, and farming, are apparent in the industrial establishments of such communities as Vernon, San Jose, and Emeryville.

The four subdivisions of the Pacific Borderlands identified within California are (1) Southern California, (2) the Central Coast, (3) the Great Central Valley, and (4) the Northwest. Their importance to the state is indicated by the extent of the book devoted to these areas.

Fig. 7-1. DODGER STADIUM (Chavez Ravine). *This is Southern California: the crowds, tremendous volumes of automobiles, vast parking lots, and a sun-minded and sports-enthusiastic population.* (Los Angeles Dodgers Baseball Club)

CHAPTER SEVEN:: SOUTHERN
CALIFORNIA

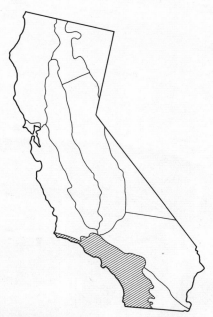

SOUTHERN CALIFORNIA

Southern California,[1] one of the world's truly unique geographical entities, lies south of the Tehachapi Mountains and west of California's southeastern deserts. This intricate land extends from Point Arguello on the northwest to the Mexican border (see map, Fig. 7-2) and includes the Transverse Ranges, Peninsular Ranges, and the Channel Islands. It has presumably approached an American dream of terrestrial paradise—a concept probably more valid before 1940 (i.e., before the fourth boom).

In area Southern California is among the smaller subdivisions of the state—only the

This chapter has been reviewed by John W. Reith, University of Southern California.

[1] Note the distinction between Southern California, a *specific* geographic subdivision, and the more ambiguous "southern California" sometimes used to describe all of California south of the Tehachapi, including the deserts, as contrasted with "northern California." Upon occasion the Los Angeles *Times* includes Fresno County and the High Sierra. Some geographers and others prefer "South Coast" to "Southern California."

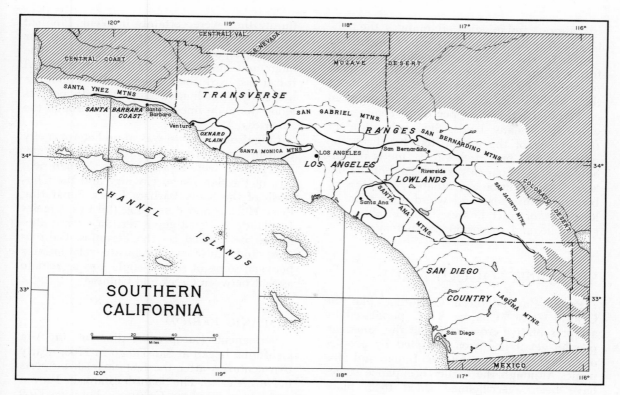

Fig. 7-2. MAP OF SOUTHERN CALIFORNIA.

Colorado Desert and the Southern Cascade have lesser extent (see Fig. 7-2). With its area of approximately 12,000 square miles, Southern California approximates Belgium in size. Although it covers only 8 percent of the state, it is the residence of over half of California's people. Southern California is crudely triangular in shape, with the Transverse Ranges forming its northern periphery. Along its eastern margin, sloping westward to the Pacific, are the Peninsular Ranges. The heart of Southern California is the Los Angeles Lowlands, a densely populated complex of coastal plain and intermontane basins (see map, Fig. 7-12).

Southern California affords many visages— miles of sandy beaches, complex granitic mountains rising abruptly along fault faces, groves of lemons and oranges, assorted Spanish missions, spots to bask in the sun or to live out one's final years under a palm tree in a winterless clime, Hollywood and its cinema heritage, sprawling Los Angeles, San Diego with its beauteous bay and its military installations. To this have been added within the past generation a vast industrial complex, traffic congestion, and the Los Angeles smog problem. Growth is so rapid and change so frequent as to suggest a temporary, unfinished landscape painting.

One ponders . . . what makes Southern California different from other parts of the United States, even from the balance of California? In measure it is the historic legacy of indolent Indians and Mexican rancheros, succeeded by the seemingly perpetual boom that commenced three quarters of a century ago. Decidedly it is the climate and the seashore topography—here is the "American Riviera." Partially it is the close proximity of ocean, coastal plain, and chaparral-covered slopes. Credence must be given to an economy dependent upon the unique combination of tourists, aircraft and missiles, oil, oranges, the military, and motion pictures. Perhaps more than anywhere else in the nation, Southern California forms a transplanted landscape—people from "almost everywhere," palms from the Middle East, groves of Australian eucalypti, Peruvian pepper trees, commercial crops from many lands. Strikingly different from much of the nation, too, has been the reliance upon imported water. One is repeatedly conscious that this is the "land of the big boom"—a condition accentuated today less by bizarre architecture and weird cults than by long files of tract houses, blatant billboards, and radio and television commercials.

SEQUENT OCCUPANCE

Present-day Southern California, like the Central Coast (Chapter 8), is populated by a representative cross section of the American people; yet it has been occupied by peoples of two other distinct cultures, Indian and Hispanic. Although the earlier occupance stages have been overwhelmed since 1848, place names, travel routes, historic sites, and the few descendants of these groups remind us that Southern California of yesteryear was radically different.

THE INDIANS

If Southern California connotes an earthly paradise, its American Indians were surely "strangers in paradise." These people and their predecessors resided here for thousands of years before the Spanish arrived, yet they were technologically unable to utilize many resources the land provided. Agriculture was unknown at the time of the Spanish conquest. The Indians depended upon hunting, fishing, and food gathering. In a winterless land, there was little incentive to store food against times of shortage.

Southern California was occupied by two Indian families, the *Hokans* and the *Shoshone*. Compared with such peoples as the Maya and the Pueblos, these Indians were backward folk. Though deemed happy and friendly, cul-

turally they were certainly indolent. Physical geography provides a partial explanation, for the environment made existence easy. The mountains and desert barriers discouraged travel eastward; their geographic isolation has helped explain limited contacts with peoples along the main lines of migration through the Americas.

Linguistically there was more heterogeneity than presence of two families might indicate. The Hokans were represented by Yuman peoples of the San Diego Country and the Chumash of the Santa Barbara Coast. Separating these Hokans and occupying the Los Angeles Lowlands and contiguous territory, were Shoshones personified by the Serranos, Gabrielinos, and Luiseños. Linguistic relationships between some of these people was as remote as that between Greek and Chinese.

HISPANIC PERIOD

Permanent European settlement in Alta California began at San Diego in 1769, nearly two centuries after the first Spanish outposts in New Mexico. The Spanish established seven missions in Southern California between 1769 and 1797. All have been preserved or restored—they serve religious needs and afford museums of a bygone time. These missions were linked by **El Camino Real**, an oxcart trail now generally followed by Highway 101—each mission was approximately a day's journey by mule from the previous one. Their sites were generally well selected with reference to water, arable land, and local Indian population. Missions encompassed the best lands in Southern California, upon which harvests expanded and herds gained in numbers.

The *presidio* (military post) constituted the governmental center in Spanish California. Political authority was maintained by the military commandant despite reluctance of the missionaries to accept army dictates. Two of Alta California's four presidios, San Diego (1769) and Santa Barbara (1782), were established in Southern California. In contrast to the more successful missions, the presidios were drab. The missions rather than the presidios formed the social and cultural centers of the colony. *Pueblos* (farm towns) were also planned as part of the settlement program. Thus was Los Angeles founded in 1781. Its settlers, recruited with difficulty among the poorest Sinaloans, were an illiterate group. However, its site was selected well and within a generation agricultural production at the pueblo compared favorably with the more flourishing of the missions.

It was the *rancho* (large land grant), however, that became the dominant element on the landscape of pre-American Southern California. The first three ranchos were granted in 1784. During the Spanish era (1769-1822) less than a score of private grants were assigned in *all* California (half were in Southern California). The choicest lands were already claimed by the missions. During the Mexican period (1822-1846) scores of land grants were distributed in Southern California upon petition to the governor. The preponderance was created after secularization of the missions began in 1834. Their boundaries, hastily ascertained with *metes and bounds,* often remain today as property lines, streets, and even city limits. The rancho, with its semi-subsistence economy, yielded grains, vegetables, meats, and other foodstuffs. Income was derived from export of hides and tallow.

Scores of Americans, beginning with Daniel Call in 1816, became residents of Southern California before the close of the Mexican period. These aliens were generally seamen from the whalers (or the hide-and-tallow schooners) or mountain men and horse traders who have traveled overland. They often married Mexican girls, accepted Catholicism, were naturalized, and adopted the life of the province. A few became some of the wealthier early day Californians, gaining their fortunes through marriage, business enterprise, or as rancheros.

THE AMERICANS: NINETEENTH CENTURY

The first two decades after statehood in 1850 did not precipitate settlement in Southern California comparable to that in central California. Relatively few Americans migrated south of the Tehachapi during this time. Few new communities were organized and existing towns grew slowly. Cattle ranching remained the way of life for a decade although the Gold Rush markedly affected the Southern California economy. Barter was supplanted by a cash system. Previously the carcass was almost worthless but demands for meat in Sierran gold camps made the beef more valuable than hides and tallow.

Wane of the mining boom less than a decade after the Gold Rush started triggered changes that did much to alter Southern California. By the middle 1850's European-type cattle and sheep were competing for the declining gold-town markets. The drought of 1856, when thousands of cattle perished, added to the difficulties of the rancheros. Many landowners were heavily indebted and interest rates caused increasing insolvency. Taxation, virtually unknown before 1847, became burdensome. Floods in December 1861, followed by the Great Drought (1862-1865) and a grasshopper plague in 1863, virtually ended ranchero days and resulted in beginnings of a new era.

Disintegration of the large estate made rural land available for occupancy by Americans in Southern California. The homestead, important in the settlement of the trans-Mississippi West, could not prevail in Southern California since arable land was already privately held by the rancheros. Bankruptcy of the cattle barons frequently prompted rancho subdivision, which permitted more landholders.

Agricultural experimentation characterized the 1860's and the 1870's in Southern California. Grapes achieved quick economic success but such other crops as citrus fruits did not bring large profits immediately. Experimentation included such items as tobacco, silkworms, cotton, and flax, none of which proved successful. The 1870's were a prelude to the boom of the 1880's. A minor rush of affluent health seekers occurred after the Southern Pacific reached Los Angeles from central California in 1876. New communities such as Pasadena were organized. Desert mine camps, especially Cerro Gordo (Chapter 2), briefly provided additional income.

A spectacular real estate boom (the first boom) followed linkage of Southern California directly with eastern United States after completion of two transcontinental rail routes in the 1880's. Straightforward refrigerated shipments allowed rapid growth of the citrus industry. More migrants began arriving from the Middle West by rail than had come from the East Coast by ship. Present-day patterns of urbanization and transportation were fashioned with the Los Angeles Lowlands the obvious economic and social center of Southern California. Petroleum, fishing, agriculture, and sunshine seekers, of course, provided the chief sources of support for over a generation.

THE AMERICANS: TWENTIETH CENTURY

The first boom barely hinted the twentieth-century migration to follow; 97 percent of Southern California's inhabitants have been added since 1900. Spectacular population increase has described the century so far except for the years 1931-1937. There have been three periods of peak growth: the second boom (1902-1914), the third boom (1920's), and the fourth boom (the current era). Population increase has been particularly large since 1937 when the Southern California economy entered a period in which military preparedness has made a momentous contribution. The region increased in population by more than 3 million during the decade of the 1950's alone.

Immigrants form a majority of the contemporary population. Primarily they are working-age persons with families. Southern California does not have an unusual proportion of older people—the 9 percent of its population over age sixty-four is nearly identical with the national figure. Migration has originated from all parts of the United States—Southern California is fittingly considered an All-American (native born) melting pot. Newcomers have represented a multitude of creeds, cultural backgrounds, racial groups, and economic strata. They have included southern Negroes, Great Plains "Dust Bowl" farmers, veterans of all conflicts since the Mexican war, poor senior citizens, and retired wealthy.

Southern California, unlike some parts of the nation, has not truly experienced a direct arrival of Europeans *en masse* to supply menial labor or create large blocs with distinct cultures. Locally, however, there are apparent ethnic distinctions within the population. Spanish-speaking people are particularly numerous, accounting for approximately three quarters of a million residents. Few represent old-line California Spanish and Mexican families—most derive from immigration from Mexico since 1900. Many are engaged in agriculture and heavily Spanish-speaking communities are commonplace in the Southern California countryside.

An impressive number with Asian ancestry are also present, particularly Japanese and Filipinos. Like the Mexicans, their immigration initially was encouraged by labor shortage in Southern California, coupled with relatively easy access from their homelands. Most present-day Japanese are native-born Americans who are now regarded more cordially than they were during World War II, when many were evicted from positions in agriculture and fishing to which they did not return.

Other ethnic groups are represented. The Jewish population comprises more than one third million (religious membership). Its numbers include many who were displaced from Europe from the middle 1930's on. The Negro population, stimulated by evacuation from the South, has been increasing faster than the over-all Southern California rate. These people, largely residents of metropolitan Los Angeles and San Diego, number over half a million.

Occupance of Southern California is confined mainly to the lowlands; the mountains are lightly peopled except for resort areas or view sites that overlook the lowlands. The Los Angeles Lowlands alone contains more than 7 million inhabitants, and the coastal terraces and western valleys of San Diego County house another million. Most of the remaining 300,000 Southern Californians live on the Oxnard Plain or the Santa Barbara Coast.

Residence is mostly urban. Even in the many localities where farmsteads prevail, towns are usually too accessible to permit a truly rural pattern of occupance. Urban dwellings consist primarily of detached single-family houses. Multiple-unit structures, likewise typically detached, are seldom more than two stories high. The result is extremely low-density urbanization; extensive areas are required to accommodate the populace.

Urban dispersal in Southern California seems partly attributable to pleasant climate, rapid adoption of the automobile in lieu of mass-transit media, and an abundance of building sites. Dispersal has been fostered by the multiplicity of attractive environments: the cooler seashores and the warmer interior basins with their orchards and mountain backdrops. Major employment sources tend to be quasi-independent, which makes far-flung urbanization almost inevitable. Facilities for long-distance rail or water transport have less concentration in Southern California than in some metropolitan areas. The widespread low-density settlement has almost endless possible social implications, ranging from effects on travel time to social organization and political behavior. Much more apparent is the tendency for urban landscapes to replace a considerable share of lately rural Southern California.

ECONOMIC BASES

The economic foundations of Southern California have been broadened appreciably since 1900. "Export" manufacturing, summer tourism, and military operations, all inconsequential in the 1890's, now rank among the leading sources of livelihood (see table below). Much of the economy, however indirectly, still relies upon the unique and abundant combination of natural resources—notably soils, climate, scenic variety, level terrain, ocean frontage, fish, and petroleum.

A measure of circumstance ("accident") attends establishment of many activities, especially certain types of manufacturing, but most export enterprises reflect Southern California's economic isolation from populous eastern United States. To overcome the handicaps of distance and late start, Southern Californians have specialized in activities oriented toward special local resources as well as those which are "foot-loose" (or relatively independent of location of materials, low-cost labor, and markets). The latter category includes motion pictures, fashion-oriented apparel, furniture, aeronautics, and military installations.

Three of the leading economic categories, agriculture, defense, and tourism, are sufficiently widespread in Southern California to merit general description here. More localized activities will be treated later within their respective subregions.

MAJOR EXPORT-ORIENTED ECONOMIC SUPPORTS OF SOUTHERN CALIFORNIA
(circa 1960)
(annual contribution in millions of dollars)

Manufacturing	8,230 (value added)
Military installations	900 (payrolls)
Agriculture	730 (value of product)
Tourist trade	700 (expenditures)
Petroleum	540 (value of refinery product)
Fish	100 (value of cannery product)

Portions of the above manufacturing, agriculture, and petroleum are consumed locally.

AGRICULTURE

Agriculture remains a major Southern California economic pursuit despite urbanization. It is the chief occupation for about 70,000 residents in addition to "imported" workers; Southern California has about 40,000 "rural" farm residents. This region produces a fourth of California's farm output, and its value of product exceeds that of any of thirty-six states. As compared with California generally, Southern California's farmland is more expensive, farms are smaller, and production is more intensive (i.e., a larger portion is irrigated and there is more emphasis upon high-value items).

Farm income is diverse (see table below) and its commodities are destined about equally to national and local markets. Distant destinations have been traditional for fruits and vegetables. Subtropical climate coupled with alluvial soils and divergent coastal and inland temperatures still permit a genuine production advantage nationally; hence orchards, truck gardens, and flower fields survive despite spiraling land values. Understandably, production of perishable items continues for local consumption. In output of market milk, Los Angeles remains the nation's leading county, and San Bernardino County ranks first in eggs. Most livestock products, and many vegetables, are destined for local consumption.

Production of foodstuffs for local use continues to expand despite urban preemption of land and water. Total farm production in Southern California, however, has declined

LEADING AGRICULTURAL PRODUCTS SOUTHERN CALIFORNIA
(circa 1960)

RANK BY VALUE	RANK BY ACREAGE
1 milk	1 oranges
2 eggs	2 hay
3 oranges	3 beans
4 flowers (& ornamentals)	4 barley
5 lemons	5 lemons
6 cattle	6 grapes
7 tomatoes	7 irrigated pasture
8 beans	8 avocados
9 avocados	9 tomatoes
10 strawberries	10 walnuts
11 chickens	11 potatoes
12 celery	12 lettuce
13 turkeys	13 wheat

markedly in acreage and employment, to a degree in volume, but only slightly in value. Citrus output, which reached its peak in the 1940's, had declined a third by 1960.

DEFENSE

Federal expenditures in Southern California related to national defense provide economic support equivalent to all other major economic bases combined. In 1960 there were over 200,-000 land-based military personnel and civilian employees of the Department of Defense in the region. At each of eight installations the number of civilian workers exceeded one thousand. Major expenditures have been made for construction and for operations; for example, the U.S. Navy in San Diego County purchases over $3 million worth of dairy products annually and reports an average yearly outlay of $24 million in new physical facilities.

Southern California military installations are commonly operated by the Navy and the Marine Corps. The earlier sites were situated mainly upon San Diego Bay and somewhat later at Los Angeles–Long Beach harbors. During World War II added facilities were developed at more spacious near-coastal locations in San Diego and Orange counties, and new harbor bases were created in Ventura County. Climatic mildness, available space, presence of the Channel Islands, and the significance of the Pacific Theater have been important Southern California attractions for military training and maintenance.

Harbor defense at fixed sites has been outmoded; hence the Army has had a smaller role locally than before World War II. Air defense, however, has been considered sufficiently important to justify important Air Force installations in Southern California. They form a semicircle around the Los Angeles Lowlands and will be noted later in the chapter.

Defense-contracted research and manufacturing have had greater economic impact than the military installations. The defense industry accounts for a third of total Southern California factory output and provides payrolls thrice those of the military bases. It includes the bulk of the aircraft, ordnance (missile), and electronics industries whose employment exceeds 300,000. Los Angeles is the chief locale but plants are widely scattered about Southern California with such major "secondary" centers as San Diego, Pomona, Riverside, and Santa Barbara. Factors in persistence of Southern California defense industries have included the early establishment of the airframe industry, available building sites, existence of research institutions, and amenable living conditions. This last factor has been an important inducement to attract the "brain-power" increasingly necessary in the airspace industries. Details in evolution of aircraft (and successor industries) will be related later.

TOURISM

Tourism, which exceeds agricultural exports in value, is surpassed only by manufacturing and military installations as a contributor to the economy of Southern California. Metropolitan Los Angeles and San Diego attract visitors from afar for entertainment, education, shopping, government, and visits with kinfolk immigrants into the region. Southern California has a poor hinterland to generate these kinds of tourism because of separation by desert and distance from most of the nation's populace.

Many Southern California visitors are attracted from distant states; hence tourism requires unusual and well-publicized attractions. A detailed survey several years ago reported that the Pacific Ocean, Los Angeles, Hollywood, and the climate constituted the four principal regional "lures." Subtropical climate and scenic shorelines are regional attributes that have particular appeal to long-term visitors and retirees. It is significant that the average tourist stay of two to three weeks in Southern California exceeds that at many American recreation centers. Such widely known man-made attractions as Hollywood and Disneyland, by contrast, appeal equally to short-term visitors. Southern California tourism has gradually shifted from its traditional winter-season emphasis. The numbers of visitors are now almost seasonally equal, although the average duration of the visit and total tourist expenditure remain greater during the winter half-year.

Economically suggestive of tourists are those Southern Californians who draw their sustenance from distance sources. Besides retirees this group includes persons who have active national or international contacts, such as investors, managers, artists, writers, and musicians. Many of these residents have settled in the region because of its appealing living qualities. Although numerically modest,

this "footloose" population provides ostentation to Southern California because of its wealth and its social prestige.

The tourist and residential attractions of Southern California are as dispersed as they are varied. Activity is focused upon urban settlements along or near the coast; it is partly coincidental to population development but is also a response to mild climate and the appeal of the ocean itself. Santa Barbara, portions of metropolitan Los Angeles, the South Coast, and San Diego constitute principal centers. Many retirees have also sought interior foothill residence sites with attention to health and lower land costs. Popular locations have included the La Crescenta Corridor, Ojai Valley, San Gorgonio Pass, San Jacinto Basin, and the San Diego Back Country. Some situations still offer semirural settings.

THE NATURAL LANDSCAPE

It is traditional in regional treatises to set the stage with a description of the physical environment. However, in Southern California man has so dramatically altered the landscape as to warrant prior attention to the above summary of human factors. It is obvious from this discussion, however, that the earth—especially the seashore, the mountains, and the weather—has much influenced man's role in regional modification.

THE CLIMATE

The dry-summer subtropical climate of Southern California is the impressive characteristic of the physical environment of this almost winterless land.[2] There are two seasons:

[2] The weather can be something less than eternally perfect. A native of northern California, visiting in Anaheim in August, wrote home: "This climate defies my comprehension. The last three days have been (1) hot, (2) hot and humid, (3) cold and clammy. All mornings are the same—grey and nicely chilled. We do Disneyland this weekend, and it will probably be No. 2 again!! Is there *any* way of predicting weather here?" (Letter from Mrs. Saud Amer to the David W. Lantises, August 1961).

the long dry period from May to November when temperatures over much of the region are considerably modified from the heat of the deserts to the east (Chapters 3 and 4) and the generally mild and hopefully moist winter half-year. Like other Mediterranean-type climes, Southern California has abundant sunshine. But its most appealing feature is the low-sun mildness, sufficiently temperate to permit year-round plant growth in most favored localities.

CONTROLS

Besides the usual statewide influence (Appendix A) there are special circumstances of terrain and location that control the fabled weather of Southern California. The latitude (32°–34° north) tends to minimize winter cyclonic activity. Often, when rain is falling in central California, impressive cirrus cloud "signs" appear over Southern California, but precipitation fails to materialize. In a "normal" year half a dozen storms bring rain; the remainder of the low-sun period tends to be clear (away from the coastal fog belt). The extraordinary rainfall of some winters has brought disastrous floods throughout Southern California—the most destructive occurred in 1938.

The condition of the ocean forms another important local control, which tends to moderate temperatures as far inland as the Transverse and Peninsular ranges. The ocean off Southern California is warmer and the northwest winds less steady than beyond Point Conception, where the coast assumes a more northerly trend. Sufficient oceanic upwelling prevails, however, to produce advection fog, especially along coastal stretches in spring and summer. The gray overcast on many a morning convinces some visitors from humid eastern United States that rain is imminent; actually, the main result of the overcast is the screening of an otherwise brilliant sunshine. Winter fog is less frequent, but it is more commonly at ground level and more disruptive of land, sea, and air travel than is the "high" summer stratus cover.

The proximity of the desert is another regional climatic influence. During the warm season, desert air seldom penetrates to the coast as the heavier cooled maritime air moves onshore. In winter, when the Hawaiian (Pacific) High (Appendix A) is displaced southward and interior air pressure increases, occasional spells of clear, dry, warm weather or even modified "polar outbursts" with subfreezing temperatures describe most of Southern California. Sometimes these desert "outbursts" are mild and welcome but upon occasion they are accompanied by violent "Santa Ana" winds with heavy sand-and-dust fall and considerable property damage.

The interior mountain wall formed by the Transverse and Peninsular ranges affects regional climate in several ways. The ranges form a shield that helps insulate coastal lowlands from extreme winter cold and summer heat of the dry interior. The northern mountain ridges are particularly important in winter when they form a major obstacle to southward-moving air masses and force them to heat by compression as they descend seaward-facing slopes. The mountains also "trap" much moisture from the winter storms.

Sometimes the mountains contribute to the complex problems of regional air pollution. Descending air from the Hawaiian High forms a warm "inversion layer" that holds pollutants near the ground and traps surface air between ocean breezes and interior mountains. Certain foothill areas, thus, are especially prone to smog conditions.

THE SEVERAL CLIMATES

Southern California has been described climatically as "desert," "near desert," "semi-arid," "Mediterranean"—all of these labels are valid, for considerable variation exists within different sections of the regions (Appendix A, Fig. A-5). Temperatures become more extreme inland from ocean littorals. There is a decided difference between the hotter summer afternoons and colder winter nights of San Bernardino (July average 76°F.), for example, and milder temperatures of coastal Santa Monica (July average 66°F.) or Ventura. Littorals are generally mild-summer subtropical and interior areas predominantly hot-summer. Many coastal localities are considered to have some of the choicest "residential climates" in continental United States, though health seekers with respiratory troubles often seek the lower humidities of interior basins.

Southern California rainfall is primarily a matter of latitude, elevation, and exposure—on lowlands there is a tendency toward more extreme drought southward. The San Diego Coast and the San Jacinto Basin, where average rainfall totals 9 to 13 inches, are often regarded as semiarid rather than Mediterranean. The Transverse and Peninsular ranges may wrest heavy precipitation from passing storms while the overcast lowlands remain nearly rain-free. Coast-facing slopes tend to be especially moist during the winter season. Above 6000 feet winter storms are likely to yield snow.

Temperatures decrease with altitude in the highlands and create a succession of vertical zones, with hot-summer conditions at the base through mild-summer elevations into more severe winters on higher peaks. Points above 3000 feet are usually above the stratus level in summer and receive long hours of sunshine with moderate temperatures.

WATER SUPPLY

All Mediterranean-type lands are confronted with water shortage and summer drought. Some aspects of water supply have been more critical in Southern California while others have been less difficult than elsewhere. The solution has tended to be more facile for Southern California—because it is part of a large nation—than for many dry-summer subtropical lands. Water importation from other climatic realms poses problems less difficult to resolve politically. Solutions have been demanded because of the population density of Southern California and because of the growth rate during the twentieth century.

Stream flow is discharged primarily by eight river basins—from northwest to southeast: Ventura, Santa Clara, Los Angeles, San Gabriel, Santa Ana, San Jacinto, San Luis Rey, and San Diego. Within the mountains, the rivers have steep gradients that naturally decrease near the coasts. There are marked variations in flow, and all of these streams frequently have dry channels (many visitors from more humid lands have been amused that the Los Angeles is called a river). A number of flood-control basins, usually on the plains, and storage reservoirs within the mountains have been constructed. Spreading grounds have been developed along some streams so that much water percolates underground and contributes toward maintenance of subterranean water levels.

Several water problems plague Southern California. Basically, this land receives far too little precipitation to supply the demand of its populace. Seasonal runoff variations are likewise serious. Even where average flow tends to be adequate and where storage facilities have been constructed, a series of dry winters can be critical locally. Underground water has formed an important resource but excessive use has often occurred so that water levels have declined. Heavy pumping of underground reserves has lowered some water tables so much that intrusion of salt (ocean) water has occurred, especially on the Oxnard Plain and the Los Angeles coastal plain. Portions of the latter area once formed a valuable artesian basin, but the pressure has been lost for decades.

A prime solution for water needs has been importation from other areas (Figs. 2-2 and 3-2). The first large-scale project was undertaken by the city of Los Angeles. During the period 1905-1913, the 250-mile-long Los Angeles Aqueduct was constructed at a cost of $23,000,000—in order to transport water from east-slope Sierran streams that had previously fed Owens Lake. In 1940, a northward extension of the aqueduct was completed, increasing the supply by 40 percent. Even in the early 1920's water authorities in Los Angeles and other Southern California communities realized the necessity of importing additional water. The Metropolitan Water District was organized in 1928; three years later a $220,-000,000 bond issue was approved. The District completed the Colorado River Aqueduct in 1939. Water is pumped from the Colorado River (Lake Havasu behind Parker Dam) and carried more than 240 miles into Lake

Mathews (near Riverside); hence it is distributed to various Southern California communities. San Diego, swollen by World War II growth, belatedly joined the District in 1946, and an aqueduct extension, the San Diego Aqueduct, was built; thus, Colorado River water flowed into San Diego's San Vicente reservoir by late 1947. The Santa Barbara Coast has twice resolved its water shortages by constructing tunnels through the San Ynez Mountains to tap the Santa Ynez River.

Two approaches are now underway toward obtaining additional water for Southern California. One is the California Water Plan, formulated in 1957 after ten years of research and investigation (see Chapters 5 and 9). Its first major project, approved by the electorate in 1960, includes the Oroville Dam on the Feather River and an aqueduct system which will transport water southward through the San Joaquin Valley and across the Transverse Ranges into Southern California. The second approach, still in the formulative stage, is seawater conversion. The Department of Interior began operating a pilot plant on San Diego Bay in 1961, employing a flash distillation process with oil as fuel. Its million gallon output of fresh water daily provides a small fraction of San Diego's needs. Costs are much higher than for the water the city has been using. A larger plant, converting sea water more inexpensively with atomic energy, was originally planned, but the government decided against location of such a plant in a metropolitan area.

TERRAIN

Three principal physiographic units of Southern California are the **Transverse Ranges** on the north and west; the **Peninsular Ranges** on the south and east; and the intricate **Los Angeles Basin**, which serves as a connective lowland between these two highland areas.[3]

[3] There has long tended to be confusion in usage between the physiographic term, Los Angeles Basin, and the more extensive geographic term, Los Angeles Lowlands, which includes intermontane basins within the Transverse Ranges as well as the Los Angeles Basin.

Southern California seems better endowed in weather than it does in topography: half the region consists of the rough hills and mountains noted above. Mile-high interior elevations are common; these almost completely separate the coastal lowlands from the rest of California. Both the Transverse and Peninsular ranges increase in height inland; fortunately for the region most of their drainage is toward the Pacific, not into the Mojave and Colorado deserts.

Flat land is particularly extensive only in the Los Angeles Lowlands and southern Ventura County. Alluvial soils, low elevation, and access to the Pacific make these areas prime sites for present-day habitation. The shoreline of Southern California is often fringed with sea cliffs backed by marine terraces, which are utilized for transport, agriculture, and urban use. San Diego Bay provides the single large natural harbor. Coastal lagoons are frequent where river valleys reach the coast; several have been converted into ports and small-craft anchorages.

The contemporary terrain of Southern California is geologically young despite some rock formations that are reportedly quite ancient. Coastal hills and plains are predominantly sedimentary and include both marine and fluvial deposits. Most of the higher surfaces east and south of Los Angeles are underlain by subterranean granitoidal masses; in the Peninsular Ranges these are considered part of a great batholith which extends into Baja California.

Highlands and lowlands alike owe their existence to major crustal movements: faulting, folding, and warping. Occasional destructive earthquakes are reminders that earth molding is continuing. The topography is aligned along major axes of crustal disturbance. Northward of Los Angeles the uplands and lowlands have a common east-west orientation; elsewhere they generally trend northwest-southeast.

The deep San Andreas Fault enters Southern California in the southeast near San Gorgonio Pass, crosses the Transverse Ranges near Cajon Pass, and continues along the northern edge of the San Gabriel Mountains, where its resultant landforms are especially evident (Appendix B, Fig. B-3). Other significant faults include the Elsinore, which bisects the Peninsular Ranges, the compound San Gabriel through the San Gabriel Range, the San Jacinto through the eastern Peninsular Ranges, the Newport-Inglewood system near the coastal margin of the Los Angeles Basin, and the Santa Ynez, which extends the length of Santa Barbara and Ventura counties. Some fault zones are bordered by magnificent scarps, while others coincide with major gaps through the mountains that have become vital transport corridors such as San Gorgonio and Tejon passes, Cajon Canyon, and Santa Ana River Canyon.

NATURAL VEGETATION

Southern California's natural vegetation reflects the long summer drought season. Almost half the region, mostly the uplands, retains its native types of cover. Principal types include coastal sage, chaparral, oak woodland, mountain forests, and grasslands.

Coastal sage, dominated by California sagebrush, white sage, purple sage, and wild buckwheat, is mistaken by strangers for chaparral, with which it commonly merges inland. The sage formation, consisting of smaller evergreen shrubs seldom more than 5 feet high, flourishes on near-coast hillsides. It is an open cover that does not discourage passage afoot as chaparral often does. It is most attractive at the end of the wintry rain period when it appears more luxuriant with sages abloom.

Chaparral represents the typical Southern California vegetation. Often a thick mass of evergreen shrubs, sometimes 10 feet tall, it has been called "elfin forest." Oft-ravaged by fire, chaparral is well adapted to long summer drought—small or leathery leaves help plants conserve moisture; individual species have sundry adaptations. Angular branches and density discourage people from cross-country hikes. Composition of the formation varies locally; scrub oak (*Quercus dumosa*) is conspicuous in different habitats. At lower elevation chamise (*Adenostoma fasciculatum*) is frequently dominant. Farther upslope manzanita (*Arctostaphylos spp.*) and various *Ceanothus* become common. Chaparral, which appears dull and drab to strangers from wetter lands, is without grazing value, but is an important asset on steep hillsides when it protects surfaces from erosion.

Oak woodland, which might be described as an oakgrove grassland, occupies north-facing hillsides away from the coast. It is dominated by the evergreen live oak (*Quercus agrifolia*), the valley oak (*Q. lobata*), and the deciduous black walnut (*Juglans californica*). Seasonal contrasts are noticeable, especially because of the change from seared to green grasslands.

Mountain forests, basically coniferous, are restricted to higher elevations and will be discussed later in the chapter. The *grasslands,* generally of a bunch-grass nature, were once characteristic of the plains, especially in the Los Angeles Lowlands and the Oxnard Plain.

SOILS

The soils of Southern California reflect varied topography and natural vegetation as well as dry-summer subtropical climate. *Lithosols* (Appendix D) are dominant in the Transverse and Peninsular Ranges. Irrespective of parent rock, they are frequently shallow and stony and associated with steep slopes.

Residual upland soils are especially prevalent on rolling sedimentary hills from Point Conception to Orange County and on rounded granitic foothills in the Peninsular Ranges. They attain moderate depth and may have considerable agricultural merit. Use, as with lowland soils, in Southern California is often more dependent upon accessibility, water supply, and intent of ownership than upon inherent soil qualities.

Lowland soils are primarily alluvial in origin. They are commonly deep and fertile, though nitrogen and other amendments may be necessary for sustained productivity. Textures become progressively finer toward coastal margins where heavy clays may prevail. Thus piedmont alluvial fans may be somewhat rocky and excessively drained, whereas coastal plains may require careful drainage preparations. Older alluvial soils, especially on the margins of the Los Angeles

Lowlands, occupy terrace sites and commonly have distinct claypans as well as darker color than floodplain soils. Marine deposits on coastal terraces, often distinctly sandy, are commonly classed with (and used similarly to) the alluvial lowlands.

Southern California, although it includes only seven of California's fifty-eight counties and 8 percent of the state's area, is the most complex geographical division of the Golden State. Accordingly six subdivisions (see map, Fig. 7-2) will be considered in succession: (1) San Diego Country, (2) the Los Angeles Lowlands, (3) the Oxnard Plain, (4) the Santa Barbara Coast, (5) the Transverse Ranges, and (6) the Channel Islands.

THE SAN DIEGO COUNTRY

The San Diego Country,[4] southernmost portion of Southern California, adjoins the Los Angeles Lowlands (see map, Fig. 7-2). Roughly rectangular in outline, the San Diego Country occupies most of San Diego County and portions of Orange and Riverside counties (see map, Fig. 7-3). It is even milder climatically, yet more drought-prone, than the balance of Southern California.

The San Diego Country remained inconsequential during most of the Spanish and Mexican periods, despite a more lengthy history than other parts of Alta California. Under American control it still languished throughout the nineteenth century, despite abortive, short-lived booms in the seventies and eighties. Many recognized even then a climatic appeal for retirement residence, if such annoyances as fleas and rattlesnakes were ignored. Around 1900 the San Diego Country wakened (though somewhat drowsily before 1940). Each succeeding decade, except the depressed 1930's, has seen accelerated growth. Stimulated by the needs of national defense and by the steadier, less sensational expansion of agriculture, retirement residence, and tourism, San Diego has become California's second most populous county.

SETTING

The physical setting of the San Diego Country, which has much influenced human utilization, affords a distinctive aspect of the area.

GRANITE KNOBS AND SEASCAPES

The San Diego Country coincides generally with the physiographic Peninsular Ranges (which extend southward into Baja California) although the San Jacinto and Santa Rosa ranges and the San Jacinto Basin have been excluded (see map, Fig. 7-3). The terrain is underlain by granitoidal rocks whose countless outcrops impart a knobby character to many slopes. Inland, faulting has produced a series of separate mountain blocks. Particularly important is the northwest-trending Elsinore Fault system, along which the Santa Ana, Palomar (Agua Tibia), and Laguna Mountains have been thrust upward so that higher summits exceed 5000 feet. Their extensive tabular uplands facilitate recreation and agriculture but partially fault-scarped slopes are often too steep even for grazing. Much of the San Diego Country is uplands, sometimes steep and rocky, elsewhere with "mesas" that are surprisingly even and deep-soiled. Downfaulting and stream erosion (commonly directed by fault zones) have created a maze of small basins, distributed widely and irregularly. The largest include San Jose (Warner-

[4] *The San Diego Country has been reviewed by Donald Eidemiller, San Diego State College.*

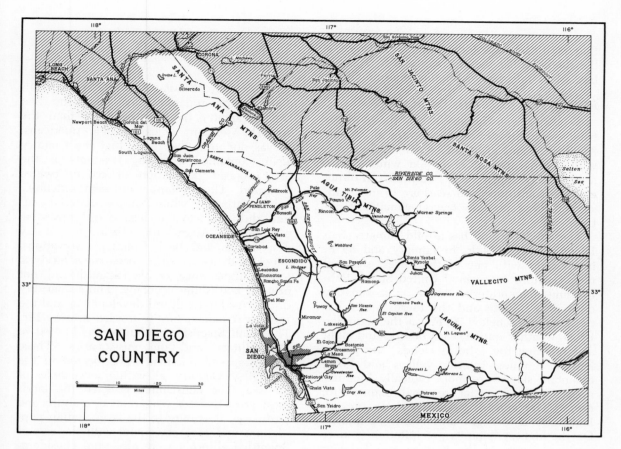

Fig. 7-3. MAP OF THE SAN DIEGO COUNTRY.

Henshaw), El Cajon, Santa Maria (Ramona), and Escondido valleys. Soils, coupled with the water supply of these generally westward-draining depressions, are precious assets amidst a somewhat forbidding countryside.

These Peninsular Ranges are suggestive of the Sierra Nevada (Chapter 5) with their eastern fault faces and west-tilted granitic blocks. But Hot Springs Mountain (6533 ft. above sea level), the highest point in the San Diego Country, indicates why the spectacular glaciated summits and U-shaped canyons of the Sierra Nevada are absent. The western peripheries of the two highlands are also different today, since the Peninsular Ranges descend to the sea.

The coastal margin of the Peninsular Ranges consists of a series of "stair-step" levels —marine terraces created by sea-level oscillations and crustal movement. Around San Diego the terraces, called "mesas," extend a dozen miles inland. Northward, the width of the terrace belt narrows irregularly to less than a mile at Corona del Mar. The oldest terraces, farthest inland and highest in elevation, are quite eroded so that the landscape has more relief than is commonly associated with coastal plains. Stream valleys have been entrenched below mesa levels and their mouths have lagoons, beach bars, and marsh vegetation. Between adjacent stream valleys the terraces commonly meet the ocean with sea cliffs, at whose bases are typically beaches of substantial width. The coastline is customarily smooth; San Diego Bay provides the only large protected anchorage. At three places—

SOUTHERN CALIFORNIA:: 167

Laguna Beach, La Jolla, and Point Loma—
the shoreline has scenic coves and headlands,
backed by hills prized for their marine vistas.

FOGBANKS AND CHAPARRAL

The San Diego Country lies on the southern
fringe of dry-summer subtropical North
America. Some of the Country is semiarid,
with warm summers and mild winters. The
area displays the typical Southern California
climatic transition from seashore to mountain
summits that provide several climatic variations.

The coastal strand has a mild climate (San
Diego averages 54°F. in January and 69°F.
in August) with one of the lowest seasonal
ranges within continental United States. Subfreezing temperatures occur approximately
once in a decade and the thermometer has
never dropped below 29°F. (at the main San
Diego weather station). Sea breezes and night
and morning fog (stratus clouds) are prevalent in summer. Interior valleys and lower
mountain slopes are more typically Mediterranean, with a wider seasonal temperature
range. The annual picture remains prevail-
ingly one of drought and relative mildness.
On the highest summits precipitation is more
copious. Crests of the Laguna and Palomar
mountains average nearly 40 inches a year.
There, winters are relatively cold and total
snowfall averages 3 to 4 feet. Summers by
contrast are comfortably warm.

Natural vegetation survives over wide areas
of the San Diego Country. Local variations
rather faithfully reflect the climatic nuances
just described. Extensive stretches of uncultivated coastal terraces are covered with
coastal sage and associated semishrubs. Inland, these formations merge with the heavier
chaparral shrubs, which blanket much of the
San Diego Country. Limited sectors support
oak groves amidst grasslands, and the highest
elevations are dotted with conifer forests of
open nature that include yellow pine, incense
cedar, and white fir as well as mesa oak
(*Quercus engelmannii*). The larger forest
stands are found upon the upper west slopes
of the Laguna and Palomar Mountains.

THE PRE-AMERICAN PERIOD

Numerically, *Shoshonean* and *Yuman* Indian groups apparently occupied the San
Diego Country more successfully than the
Spanish, Mexicans, or early Anglo-Americans.
It was not until the 1880's that the Country
again contained as many residents as the
pre-European population of six to twelve
thousand. The Indians were semi-sedentary
hunter-gatherers whose simple material culture did not leave a legacy of impressive
monuments. Apart from their present-day
descendants and Back Country reservations,
minor evidence of earlier occupance survives.

The appearance of the Spanish did not
bring a flourishing economy. The semiaridity
discouraged agricultural development and the
Indians remained hostile toward mission life.
The small Spanish population was limited to
the military and the missionaries. Three
widely spaced missions were located in the
San Diego Country, all within seven miles of
the sea. The churchmen selected the lands
most attractive for irrigation agriculture and
pasturage. Proximity to the large Indian populations and ease of contact with the rest of
Spanish California were also vital considerations in mission locations. San Diego (1769),
first of the Alta California chain, suffered from
erratic water supply so that foodstuff importation, generally from Mission San Gabriel, was
sometimes necessitated. Grazing in the Back
Country proved more successful. San Juan
Capistrano (1776) fared little better than San
Diego, especially after severe earthquake damage in 1812 (the resultant ruins are still visible
to the visitor). San Luis Rey (1798), in the
best-watered valley of the San Diego Country, proved one of the more successful missions in number of neophytes and in agricultural output. Its yields of dry-farmed grains
were often impressive.

The presidio at San Diego formed the single
nonecclesiastical establishment during Spanish times. It consisted of a few squalid adobes,
including the commandant's quarters, barracks, and storerooms. Understandably, the

English voyager Vancouver, a visitor in 1793, was not impressed.

Utilization of the San Diego Country was altered somewhat during the Mexican period. Secularization, decreed in 1834, fostered mission decay and permitted conversion of mission lands into ranchos; by the end of the era (1846) a score of ranchos had been created. In aggregate such lands encompassed more than half a million acres and included most of the suitable interior valleys as well as many of the coastal terraces. The most attractive parcels were assigned to military officers, political leaders, and their relatives. Impecunity, absence of markets, and repeated droughts frustrated irrigation agriculture; hence cattle ranching was the main pursuit, and hide and tallow were the chief exports.

The civilian community of San Diego appeared as retired servicemen began constructing adobes near the presidio in 1825. The village, now known as Old Town, was better situated to obtain river water than for ship anchorage. Indian raids discouraged rural residence; therefore most Spanish-speaking people of the Country lived in the town despite the virtual absence of retail establishments or social activity. As it did not flourish, San Diego became a "department" of Los Angeles between 1838 and 1846.

METROPOLITAN SAN DIEGO

San Diego (573,000), long regarded as the "poor southern cousin" of Los Angeles, has become California's third largest city (and the twentieth in the nation) (see map, Fig. 7-5). Its metropolitan population approximates a million. Its setting, though it has not elicited the praise lavished upon San Francisco or Rio de Janeiro, is auspicious. San Diego Bay is one of the best harbors on the Pacific Coast of the Americas. Physical advantages of the Bay include limited tidal currents and natural protection from prevailing winds. Rising gradually inland from the bay, terraces provide an ample, easily occupied urban site. The mild, sunny climate is appreciated alike by ship captain, aircraft builder, tourist, farmer, and retiree.

The recency of San Diego's emergence as a metropolis is a paradox; the urban complex is almost wholly a product of the twentieth century despite its early start as California's first mission, presidio, and seaport. The growth of San Diego has been hampered by several major disadvantages. Water shortage has been a most critical problem—its continuance was recognized with the recent selection of Point Loma as the site of an experimental federal salt-water conversion plant. Moreover, San Diego has not enjoyed the productive hinterland afforded Los Angeles by its Lowlands. The small basins and valleys of the San Diego Country are scattered. There is no direct, low (and narrow) elevation pass inland across the mountains, as is true for Los Angeles. Commercial competition from its bigger neighbor to the north has been severe since the advent of transcontinental rail linkage and harbor improvement in Los Angeles. San Diego's location in the nation's southwestern corner has also constituted a commercial detriment. Thus relatively few of the continuous flow of distinguished visitors who go to Los Angeles or San Francisco take the "side" trip to San Diego unless they specifically desire a vacation.

EVOLUTION

Metropolitan San Diego has evolved from Old Town, the somnolent village of the colonial era that was challenged by enterprising Yankee developers some years after American occupation of California commenced. Through their efforts the metropolitan center was relocated in New Town–Middletown–Horton's Addition, where it still remains, accessible to the waterfront. Several outlying nuclei of settlement had also appeared even before the Boom of the Eighties. Most important of these were **La Playa**, erstwhile seaport for Old Town, and **National City**, basically agricultural. As late as the 1870's, some regarded the San Diego area more suitable for "rattlesnakes and tarantulas."

Fig. 7-4. METROPOLITAN SAN DIEGO. This view toward the southeast shows Mission Beach, Mission Bay, Mission Valley, and the city sprawling across the terraces which rise into the knobby landscape of the Peninsular Ranges. (Historical Collection, Title Insurance and Trust Company, Union Title Office, San Diego)

The basic framework of present-day San Diego emerged during the boom of the 1880's when subdivisions, transportation facilities, and waterworks were extended across a remarkable portion of the contemporary metropolis. Settlement appeared in spots as distant from downtown San Diego as La Jolla, Coronado, Imperial Beach, Chula Vista, and La Mesa, and they were all connected by a citywide railway. Substantial growth, however, was largely confined to the periphery of the central district for several decades. The main urban "frontier" did not go around and beyond Balboa Park reserve until the early 1900's.

The contemporary metropolitan San Diego is as far-flung as its most hopeful developers of the 1880's might have dreamed (Fig. 7-4).

With recent annexations, even the political city stretches from Del Mar to the Mexican border. The contiguous urbanized complex extends inland to Bostonia and Lakeside to contain more than 200 square miles. Although considerable building space remains within the city limits, the satellites (even waterbound Coronado) have grown rapidly since 1950. Almost a third of the total population resides outside the political city.

The urban complex is greatly fragmented, partly because of an irregular shoreline, military reservations, and Balboa Park (Fig. 7-7). Another factor is terrain since terrace surfaces are deeply dissected. The steep-sided canyons that crisscross San Diego effectively preclude urban continuity, yet provide impressive view sites. Patterns of higher-income residence occur on some terrace edges, most obviously in **Mission Hills** and **Point Loma** districts. The canyon bottoms provide rail and highway passages remarkably free from competitive uses. Major examples are Pacific Highway and the Santa Fe rail line through Rose Canyon, the freeway through Mission Valley, and Cabrillo Freeway, Wabash Freeway, and Highway 94 through Chollas Valley. Such corridors thereby tend to make travel through San Diego less arduous than through many American cities of comparable size.

Another influence that has tended to fragment the urban pattern has been the preference by residents for two contrasting environments. Some persons have chosen the shoreline, which is now almost continuously urbanized except where terrain and military bases interfere. Others have preferred the interior margin, particularly the belt extending northeast from **Lemon Grove** (19,400) to **El Cajon** (38,000). This section has long been favored by farmers for its soils and water supply and by health seekers for its drier, sunnier weather. Now the small avocado and citrus groves set on low hillsides and the access to "town" provided by Highways 80 and 94 are added attractions to the suburbanite. This interior setting, like the seashore, has gained a certain residential prestige. Between the northeastern interior and the central district there is a continuous urban zone focused upon El Cajon Boulevard, the principal retail thoroughfare. Names of individual residential districts (**University Heights**, **Normal Heights**, **City Heights**, **College Heights**) and the city of **La Mesa** (30,400) bespeak the ascending terrace surface inland from Balboa Park.

Expansion of the metropolitan area southeastward has been somewhat less vigorous than northwestward to the ocean or northeastward (as noted in the previous paragraph). Only at Imperial Beach is ocean frontage immediately available for recreation. Segments of this southern zone have drainage problems although portions along the San Diego and Arizona Eastern Railroad are potential industrial sites. Agriculture has long utilized much of the bottomland from Chula Vista to the international border. **Logan**

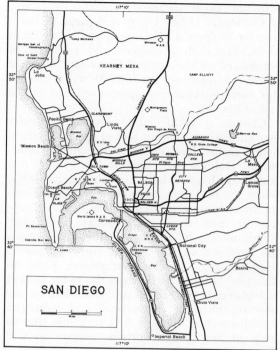

Fig. 7-5. MAP OF SAN DIEGO.

Heights, a political subdivision of San Diego, and rapidly growing **Imperial Beach** (18,-000) are predominantly low-income residential areas. The former has proximity to the canneries, rail yards, and wholesale district, which have been important neighborhood employment sources. Chula Vista–Imperial Beach provides more local employment in manufacturing and agriculture than is true in the northeastern district. Both portions of the metropolis supply many commuters to the central district.

Urban expansion northward has been slow except along the seacoast. **Linda Vista** and **Clairemont** (east of Mission Bay) were urbanized during and after World War II. Subsequently, highway improvement coupled with disappearance of "close-in" land, are stimulating urban expansion in this direction. In **Mission Valley** a major suburban shopping center and elaborate motels have appeared. General Dynamics Corporation has established extensive plants on **Kearney Mesa**, **Torrey Pines Mesa**, and in **Rose Canyon**. The

Miramar Naval Air Station and the University of California at San Diego and the Salk Institute for Biological Studies, all on Torrey Pines Mesa, are both evidences and catalysts of northward urbanization. **University City**, a planned community for 100,000, will surround the new university campus, northeast of La Jolla (Fig. 7-9).

Change is taking place too in the older central district, another fact of urban development; earlier land uses are becoming transitional. **Golden Hill**, east of the central district, has deteriorated since the early 1900's, when it was the "fashionable" residential area; its lower-income residents have a denser population than their predecessors. Lindbergh Field, although extremely accessible, seems too hemmed in for "jet-age use" despite its improvement; already Montgomery Field on Kearney Mesa is used when the older airport is fogbound. **Old Town** and **Middletown** are now occupied by commercial and industrial establishments. Perhaps it is symbolic that so little of San Diego's origins remain in Old Town.

URBAN FUNCTIONS

The visitor who is mindful of San Diego's history and its handicaps, previously listed, may not be surprised by the smallness of the downtown district aligned along Broadway eastward from the waterfront. Financial and corporate headquarters, even the number and variety of retail stores, have been modest in consideration of the recent metropolitan population. One recalls that growth of the metropolis has coincided with the suburban-oriented automotive era; it has been unnecessary to concentrate retail establishments downtown. Increasingly, though, the central business districts is gaining a third dimension.

COMMERCE

The name San Diego does not conjure a world port. In fact, port utilization has not kept pace with urban growth. The tonnage handled across San Diego docks is appreciably less than in Los Angeles or Oakland. Civilian maritime commerce is largely handled through two municipal piers and a large cargo terminal built in the 1950's (Fig. 7-8). Passenger traffic has always been minimal, even in the Hawaiian service. Primary trade items in recent years have included outgoing cotton (from Arizona, the Imperial Valley, and Mexico) and imported petroleum and lumber. Virtually all commodities for local consumption arrive by rail or truck (rather than ship), and come from metropolitan Los Angeles. Connection with the "outer world" by rail (via the Los Angeles Lowlands) was directly responsible for the population growth of the 1880's.

The drive to link San Diego directly with the rest of United States was continued between 1907 and 1919, when the San Diego and Arizona Eastern Railroad (now a Southern Pacific affiliate) was built across the Peninsular Ranges into the Imperial Valley. Its tortuous route, which required a right-of-way partially in Mexico and demanded construction of eleven tunnels along Carrizo Gorge, has been a definite handicap.

U.S. 80 (Interstate 8), between San Diego and southeastern California, ascends over 4000 feet as it negotiates some 60 miles across the Peninsular Ranges. San Diego pleas to the federal government to undertake feasibility studies for a low-level tunnel eastward have not been heeded.

"NAVY TOWN"

The term, long a commonplace appellation for San Diego, is increasingly inaccurate, although at times during World War II the city's "floating" military population nearly exceeded its civilian numbers. The Navy first arrived permanently in 1907, but San Diego did not become a major military center until World War I. Advantages as a naval base included climate, availability of the bay and its strand, and position closer to Panama Canal (than any other U.S. Pacific port).

The visitor sees unmistakable evidence that San Diego is still a "garrison" town. As one approaches from the north across Kearney Mesa on U.S. 101, he passes near a "tent city," the Marine Corps' Camp Mathews. Overhead jet aircraft, based at Miramar Naval Air Station to the east, are noisily audible.

Fig. 7-6. NORTHWESTERN SAN DIEGO. This view includes Mission Beach and La Jolla (left edge), Mission Bay (foreground), and Pacific Beach. (Historical Collection, Title Insurance and Trust Company, Union Title Office, San Diego)

Fig. 7-7. SAN DIEGO. North Island (left) and Coronado in the foreground, then the Bay. Downtown district and Balboa Park, middle right. Lindbergh Field is in the center with Old Town to the right. View to the north-east. (Official U.S. Navy photograph)

Fig. 7-8. THE PORT OF SAN DIEGO. View toward the northwest. (The Port of San Diego)

Fig. 7-9. LA JOLLA. The vertiginous coast and the wave-pounded shore have given this suburb a superlative setting. Residences rise against a slope of marine terrace known as Mt. Soledad (right). A new university campus will be developed on the terrace in middle rear. (San Diego Convention and Tourist Bureau)

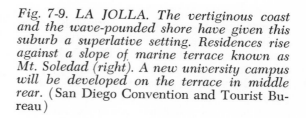

There is much evidence of military activity around San Diego Bay (Fig. 7-7). Fort Rosecrans, the Army's major harbor defense site of yesteryear, flanks the western entrance. East of the entrance is North Island Naval Air Station (at the north end of the elongated peninsula, the Silver Strand, which forms the western littoral of the bay), an important installation for Pacific Fleet aircraft carriers (Fig. 7-7). Destroyers, submarines, and tenders are conspicuously moored to buoys within the bay.

Nearly half the entire frontage along San Diego Bay is used by the military. The headquarters of the Eleventh Naval District (and its supply depot) are housed in large structures at the western edge of the central business district. At the southern limits of San Diego (with National City) is the Naval Base, which has been a major employer of civilian workers; it provides anchorage for units of the "mothball fleet." On the opposite side of the Bay, along the Silver Strand, is the Naval Amphibious Base. Along the northern fringe of the bay are the adjacent Naval Training Station and the Marine Corps Recruit Depot. Less obvious, yet significant, is the Navy Electronics Laboratory on Point Loma. Elsewhere, military facilities include the Naval Hospital in Balboa Park and Chollas Heights Naval Radio Station, whose lighted towers are nocturnal landmarks of San Diego.

MISSILES AND SEAFOODS

San Diego manufacturing, although it has never achieved a very diverse output, has rivaled the military as San Diego's leading economic activity since 1940. During the 1950's the value of product expanded tenfold (to reach a billion dollars in 1960). Manufacturing has been oriented toward the military; about 70 percent of all factory employment (circa 1960) conducts defense-related work, particularly airspace-electronics. This overreliance upon military contracts has caused severe fluctuations in payrolls and employment —a national news magazine in 1962 was prompted to label San Diego "Bust Town?"

A future in aviation for San Diego was presaged early in the century when Glenn Curtiss established a flying school on North Island. Good "flying weather" encouraged establishment of permanent Navy air installations by 1920. Soon thereafter, a "local" firm, Ryan Aeronautical Company, built Lindbergh's *Spirit of St. Louis* (the municipal airport, long the center of aircraft manufacture, honors Lindbergh). Consolidated Aircraft Corporation transferred its operations from the state of New York to San Diego in 1935, seeking an ice-free harbor and available land near the principal customer for its flying boats. During World War II the firm constructed thousands of heavier aircraft. Its successor, General Dynamics Corporation, has long been San Diego's principal civilian employer. Recently its products have included commercial aircraft, military jets, and missiles. Expansion of its production after 1950 necessitated more spacious sites (away from Lindbergh Field) on Kearney Mesa. Other airspace firms include Ryan and Rohr.

Other prominent industrial activities have included shipbuilding and the canning of seafoods. With aircraft these industries have dominated the industrial belt that extends along the eastern side of the Bay from Lindbergh Field through **National City** (33,000) into **Chula Vista** (42,000). In recent years shipbuilding (by National Steel and Shipbuilding Corporation) has been dependent upon federal contracts for civilian freighters. Seafood canning, with its ancillary fishing fleet, involves several thousand workers on a part-time basis. San Diego is the nation's fourth ranking commercial fishing port (second to San Pedro in California), and more than 100 million pounds of fish are landed annually: tuna, mackerel, and sardines are the principal varieties. Larger boats (with freezing facilities) reach 150 feet in length and sometimes operate several thousand miles from the harbor. San Diego has ranked after San Pedro nationally as a tuna-canning center. Since the early 1950's the fishing industry has been handicapped by the competition of Japanese tuna and by reduced sardine catches.

TOURISTS AND OLD FOLKS

The traditional role of San Diego as an "amenities" center is often underestimated in the bustle and problems of defense-oriented activities. The seacoast, balmy weather, and proximity to the international border, so important to development of the defense complex, are also major attractions for the visitor and the senior resident. Since military personnel became familiar with the San Diego environs, the area has been a popular retirement spot. **Coronado** (18,000) in particular has been favored for residence by retired Navy officers (Fig. 7-7). With its old landmark hotel, it has been a major sea resort for decades. Despite proximity to downtown San Diego (across the Bay), it has been fashionably removed from the mainstream of urban San Diego.

Possession of Balboa Park—site of the 1915-1916 and 1935-1936 "world fairs"—has brought justified recognition to San Diego. The expanse (over 2 square miles) is especially remarkable because the park begins a few blocks from the downtown district. Although the land was fortunately reserved before the Boom of the Eighties, it was necessary both to resist subsequent urban pressures and to landscape the unpromising iron hardpan soil. The park contains the foremost zoological garden in western United States, an art gallery, a natural history museum, a concert amphitheatre, a botanical garden, and the usual park facilities.

The attenuated shorelines of urban San Diego provide a major attraction for pleasure boating, bathing, and sports fishing. A multimillion dollar program converted the tidal flat of Mission Bay into a more attractive site during the 1950's; there are varied facilities for aquatic recreation (Fig. 7-6). Together, Mission and San Diego bays provide berths for several thousand pleasure craft. Coastal beaches include state parks at Silver Strand, Ocean Beach, and Mission Bay.

La Jolla, founded within the city limits in the 1880's, prefers to consider itself a separate community (Fig. 7-9). Its cliff-and-beach site is esteemed by artists, tourists, and upper-income residents. Quality retail shops, a little theater, and careful landscaping add charm.

THE CULTURAL SCENE

San Diego has not been renowned as a cultural center—perhaps one should not expect a Navy town, aircraft builder, and retirement city to so be. Or perhaps San Diego has not had time to crystallize as a metropolis. One local scholar has described the city as "a cultural wilderness peopled by sunworshippers." Yet Balboa Park certainly affords varied facilities.

Cultural attractions include historic sites related to San Diego's initial importance to Hispanic California. These include the mission, the remaining buildings and museum of Old Town, and Cabrillo National Monument on Point Loma.

San Diego is gaining stature as a center of higher education. San Diego State College is commonly regarded as one of the best in the California system. Other institutions include University of San Diego, California Western University, and San Diego City College. A specialized branch of the state university, Scripps Institute of Oceanography, is being converted into a full-fledged campus and is now the University of California at San Diego.

THE SOUTH COAST

The South Coast, a scenic segment of the California littoral, extends three score miles between metropolitan San Diego and the Los Angeles Lowlands. It consists of several terrace levels, as previously noted, masquerading as a coastal plain along the western flank of the Peninsular Ranges (see map, Fig. 7-3). Prevalence of level terrain, pleasant summers and mild winters, and the Pacific shoreline favor farming, recreation, and retirement residence. Such utilization, together with a large military installation and services for through travelers, support a population of over 100,-000. The Coast has become one of California's more coveted assemblages of real estate parcels, though its intensive development has been surprisingly recent. The existing cultural landscape has evolved largely since 1920 and the population has doubled in the past decade.

Many of the original rancho holdings along the South Coast remain in consolidated ownership, reserved largely for agriculture.[5] Many of these larger properties show evidence of succumbing to urbanization, but their demise has been sufficiently slow to produce urban pressures on adjacent lands.

Half of the South Coast was never awarded as land grants; hence it contains most of the present-day population. Occupance is largely urban or rurban. Apart from the old rancho lands, perennially high land and water costs have encouraged even the farmers to confine themselves to small holdings and create a type of semiurban residence.

TRANSIT CORRIDOR

The South Coast provides the transportation linkage between San Diego and Los Angeles; hence accessibility has influenced its utilization since colonial days. The original cart trail, El Camino Real, extended much the length of the Coast. It pursued the wave-cut cliff at the inner edge of the second terrace level (i.e., the head of canyon erosion by present-day streams). North of Mission San Juan Capistrano the trail reached inland away from the shore.

Rail transport has followed this route since the California Southern Railroad (Santa Fe) was constructed from the Los Angeles Lowlands to San Diego in the 1880's. The rail line parallels the old road that it superseded as the chief artery of intercity travel. After completion of the southern segment of U.S. 101 as a paved highway in 1928, road travel reasserted its primacy along this corridor. The through highway has been particularly significant to Laguna Beach, whose site had been shunned by the original El Camino Real and the railroad. Congestion resulting from vehicular traffic between Los Angeles and San Diego

[5] These estates include the Irvine Ranch, between Laguna Beach and Corona del Mar, Niguel (south of Laguna Beach), Boca de la Playa north of San Clemente, and Agua Hedionda south of Carlsbad. Santa Margarita y Las Flores, though now coincident with Camp Pendelton, is suggestive of the same category.

became apparent in Coast towns even before 1940. Local merchants long opposed freeway bypasses, which reveals the significance attached to the trade of the wayfarer. Since 1950, Oceanside, Carlsbad, San Clemente, and San Juan Capistrano have been skirted by freeway segments; however, ambulatory traffic flow still characterizes Laguna Beach, where urbanization and rough terrain pose obstacles to freeway construction.

SPECIALTY FARMING

Farming evolved belatedly along the South Coast, and water shortage remains a handicap. Rivers flow intermittently, and the underground supply for pumping is also limited. To irrigate the terraces it is necessary either to pump from the river valleys or to canalize the streams a considerable distance inland. Hence much arable land remains in pasture or is devoted to dry-farming of barley or beans (especially lima, blackeye, and garbanzo). The foggy summers, relatively cool, favor the beans but discourage crops such as grapes and olives, which could be grown without irrigation.

Irrigation farming, commenced on a significant scale in the 1920's, was stimulated by expanding California markets, by improved highways, and by use of sprinkler irrigation. It is localized primarily where there is sufficient runoff from the higher Peninsular Ranges. The largest acreage focuses upon San Dieguito Valley (between Leucadia and Solana Beach, and inland to Rancho Santa Fe), which has long had storage water from Lake Hodges. The district around Oceanside and Carlsbad has relied upon extensive pumping in the San Luis Rey Valley. The area around San Juan Capistrano, once served by part of the mission canal system, now depends largely upon pumping also. Terrace soils, often derived from sandy marine deposits, are a lesser consideration than water supply and frost-free environment.

The major irrigated products—citrus, avocados, vegetables, flowers, and nursery stock—require mild winters and bring sufficient returns to compensate for expensive land and water costs. Valencia oranges are promi-

LEADING AGRICULTURAL COMMODITIES
SAN DIEGO COUNTY, 1961
(values in millions of dollars)

Tree Crops

avocados	8.7
oranges	6.8
lemons	1.7
limes	0.48
grapefruit	0.2
tangerines	0.1

Vegetables

tomatoes	19.2
celery	1.8
cucumbers	1.3
squash	0.95
lettuce	0.64
peppers (bell)	0.51

Livestock and Poultry Products

eggs	21.6
milk, market	14.1
beef cattle	5.7
turkeys	1.1

Miscellaneous

cut flowers	3.5
nursery stock	3.1

Total Value,
All Products = 100

These figures exclude Borrego Valley but include the Back Country. The entire San Diego Country should also include a small portion of the output from Riverside and Orange counties.

Source: Agricultural Commissioner, San Diego County.

nent at San Juan Capistrano and Rancho Santa Fe, which are sufficiently inland from the coast so that summers are warmer. *Fuerte,* the most popular avocado variety, does not yield best along the coastal strand. However, summer coolness delays ripening so that growers can harvest a crop at a period of lesser competition from interior districts. Avocados are raised in all three of the leading districts, sometimes so near the sea that wooden frames are used in order to shield them from sea-breeze damage.

Vegetable growing is even more closely related to harvest schedules than the avocados. It is possible to harvest some varieties at any time of year, but competition from other sources (in California and nationally) severely curtails the "economic season." Thus

the tomato harvest extends from May through January, snap beans June through December, and lettuce in December and January. San Luis Rey Valley, with its environs, is the Coast's vegetable center.

Seasonal scheduling is also vital to flower growers (such as carnation farmers of the Oceanside-Carlsbad-Encinitas district who strive to meet the peak demands at Mother's Day and Christmas). Judicious use of lath, cloth, and plastic shelters, together with air freight shipments, permits the carnation growers to compete with flowers grown in greenhouses near larger eastern cities. The poinsettia, another major flower export, provides the traveler south of Carlsbad with whole fields of crimson flowers in December. Some of the crop is sold nationwide to hothouses as propagation stock.

CAMP PENDLETON [6]

Camp Pendleton occupies Rancho Santa Margarita y Las Flores, which was the largest Mexican rancho in the San Diego Country. It was awarded to the Pico brothers in 1841; subsequently they added land from Mission San Juan Capistrano to create a barony of 226,000 acres (more than 350 square miles—a fourth the area of Rhode Island). Much indebted by the drought years of the 1860's, the Picos "sold" the estate to their brother-in-law, John Forster. During the third of a century that Forster operated Santa Margarita it remained a vestige of the past, with vast herds and numerous Mexican and Indian retainers. Subsequently the estate was purchased by O'Neill and Flood for $250,000. Rancho Santa Margarita persisted as a vast operation, with livestock, winter grains, and irrigated fields along the Santa Margarita Valley.

The federal government purchased much of Rancho Santa Margarita in 1942 and converted it into a Marine Corps installation, Camp Pendleton. It has become one of the Corps' largest training areas with a complement that varies from 10,000 to 50,000. With its Pacific frontage for amphibious landings,

[6] *This section was reviewed by First Lieutenant Bruce Bechtol, U.S.M.C.*

rolling and rugged terrain for maneuvers, and proximity to the Recruit Depot in San Diego, the location has been ideal. Permanent installations have been erected; each of several encampments is complete with mess halls and barracks. The old rancho "casa" affords headquarters for the commandant. Several thousand acres are leased to truck farmers, who are exempt from county taxes.

Camp Pendleton, a major force in the South Coast economy, has contributed much to the growth of Oceanside and Carlsbad, and to a lesser extent, to San Clemente and more distant towns. The rural landscapes of 18 miles of ocean front within the Camp impress the traveler. This open stretch becomes more evident as competition for recreational and residential sites increases along the South Coast.

LAND OF LEISURE

The South Coast has become a regional playground, popular with residents of the San Diego Country, the Colorado Desert, the Los Angeles Lowlands, and out-of-state visitors. It remained a local vacation land until the 1920's; subsequent improvement of the Coast Highway and population growth in Southern California have afforded wider patronage.

The ocean waters along the South Coast are appreciably colder in summer than those along the nation's Gulf and South Atlantic shores. Nevertheless, swimming, skin diving, and surfboarding are commonplace. There is the general appeal of the seashore for relaxation; there are long stretches of sandy beach and a few picturesque headlands. Sports fishing is popular in the surf and at several piers. Deep-sea fishing boats operate from piers at Oceanside and San Clemente although absence of small-craft harbors has precluded extensive sailboating.

The seashore becomes progressively crowded. Much frontage is privately owned, sometimes posted with "keep out" signs. The state provides several beach parks with trailer and camping facilities. However, Doheny, San Clemente, and La Costa state parks are often jammed, especially on weekends and holidays, when the insufficiency of facilities becomes most evident.

BEACH TOWNS

South Coast towns are atypical California communities. Dependent upon resort trade and providing residences for senior citizens from "everywhere," they are neither industrial cities nor major retail centers. Hotels and motels, trailer camps, and real estate offices are much evident. Where the settlement is sufficiently old, heavy subtropical landscaping prevails and eucalyptus, avocado, ice plant, bougainvillea, and geraniums help give an illusion of lower population density.

Coast towns originated during three periods. The several founded in the Mexican period (Agua Hedionda, Santa Margarita, San Juan Capistrano, and San Luis Rey) have not grown too much. Nearly all the beach towns had their origin during the Boom of the Eighties, or in the 1920's. They have invariably had terrace sites, whereas the Mexicans restricted their hamlets to the stream valleys. Some beach towns were resorts from the start; the others were at least partially agricultural. Virtually all these communities extend in shoestring fashion parallel to the seacoast. Older (and more built-up) sections are commonly located near the highway or railroad and within half a mile of the seashore. Newer residences, which tend to extend inland, sometimes ascend steep slopes.

Oceanside (25,000), the ranking city of the South Coast, has a fine beach, an expansive terrace site, and access to water (San Luis Rey River)—these assets were important in its initial resort development and as a farm center. Oceanside, beyond the limits of normal commutation to San Diego or the Los Angeles Lowlands, has achieved a measure of commercial "independence." Branch lines extend inland from the Santa Fe "main line," which helped Oceanside to become a shipping point for interior farm products. Much growth after 1940 resulted from its function as primary service point for Camp Pendleton; the population quintupled between 1940 and 1960. Resident servicemen, their dependents, and supporting tradespeople have given Oceanside a social composition almost unique among South Coast towns. **Carlsbad** (9200) to the south shares some of these traits.

Laguna Beach (9300), the second largest city of the South Coast, is one of the more attractive resorts along the nation's Pacific Coast. It originated as a summer refuge for Orange County residents but had become an artist's colony by 1920 (its craggy coves and abrupt headlands attracted the painters). Since improvement of the Coast Highway, Laguna Beach has had increasing popularity with residents of the Los Angeles Lowlands. It strives to be a cultural center despite youthful visitors who regard it as an Atlantic City. It remains a center for arts and crafts; major "products" include ceramics as well as paintings. The ceramics industry, which relies upon California markets, has outgrown local raw materials; hence quality clay is shipped from Ohio.

Many group Laguna Beach with La Jolla, Santa Barbara, and Carmel in an elite quartet of California sea resorts. Colorful architecture and shops with appealing names lend charm. Besides artists the city houses affluent senior citizens. Actually the community is three political entities—Laguna Beach, Three Arch Bay, and South Laguna.

Rancho Santa Fe is a classic "society ranch community." In 1906 the Santa Fe Railroad purchased Rancho San Dieguito and planted eucalyptus groves—to be used for railroad ties. After 3-million trees had been planted, the railroad found other wood more suitable. The railroad then constructed Lake Hodges, to provide a water supply, and realized on its investment by selling small parcels. Rancho Santa Fe, parklike among its eucalypti, and its citrus and avocado groves, has a golf course and country properties of wealthy city dwellers including some motion-picture stars. It forms a transitional landscape between the South Coast and the Back Country.

THE BACK COUNTRY

The San Diego Back Country affords interesting contrast. Economically it is essentially the scattered pockets of irrigated land where one finds the larger towns and most of the productivity. Elsewhere more extensive surfaces suggest pre-American California of yesteryear with peaceful and sometimes lonesome landscapes which contrast strikingly with the South Coast. The transition—with respect to terrain and land-use—between these two portions of the San Diego Country is often gradual.

Paved roads have made the Back Country quite accessible despite the maze of slopes, the granitic knobs, and the canyons. Most traveled of the through routes are U.S. 395 and 80, which are San Diego's main avenues of access to the eastern Los Angeles Lowlands and Imperial Valley respectively. Even on these main roads, however, occasional long and relatively steep grades remind the traveler that the Back Country is mostly rough terrain without large interconnected lowlands.

THE PEOPLE

Back Country residents do not constitute a representative cross section of Golden State population. This area is no longer a center for Hispanic people (despite the above statement about pre-California landscapes). Most of its habitants are of northern European ancestry. Besides ranchers and tradesfolk in the towns, there are growing numbers of retired couples from all parts of the United States. This latter group includes many whose incomes are limited, and for whom climatic mildness is both healthful and economic.

A score of reservations and perhaps 2000 Indians in the Back Country testify to California's pre-European heritage. In contrast to Navaho lands in Arizona, one does not find roadside pottery or rug sellers, or hogans, or pueblos. The reservations are usually along sideroads and small "American-style" cottages prevail. **Pala**, with its restored asistencia chapel, and the area immediately to the southeast, is the major focus of Indian population. Elsewhere reservations are widely scattered over the Back Country, southward to the Mexican border, on relatively unproductive lands. Many Indians reside apart from the reservations closer to places of commercial employment.

Two thirds of the entire Back Country population (circa 90,000) is concentrated in a narrow belt that extends from **Fallbrook** (4800) southward through **Vista** (14,800) and

Fig. 7-10. BACK COUNTRY: LAKE HODGES. Water storage is vital to this land of so little rain. Lake Hodges is now used to store Colorado River water delivered by the San Diego Aqueduct. (David W. Lantis)

Escondido. Agricultural settlement here is uniquely favored by water from the San Luis Rey and Santa Margarita rivers, supplemented by import from the Colorado River. Only a few miles from the Pacific, this belt has better access to markets and milder winters than most of the Back Country. Additional employment is provided at Camp Pendleton and the adjacent Naval Ammunition Depot near Fallbrook and by rising commutation from Escondido to San Diego. Climate and landscape have attracted a number of retired people. **Escondido** (16,400), with its specialty shops and fruit-packing plants, is the leading community of the Back Country.

THIS AND THAT

The leading farm products of the Back Country (in approximate order of value) are tomatoes, poultry and eggs, citrus, market milk, avocados, and cattle. Additional "this and that," which would almost fill a grocery list, include hogs, hay and grains, grapes, honey, apples, and cut flowers. Most of the livestock and their products are consumed in Southern California, whereas citrus and avocados may reach nationwide markets.

Water is more limited than land. The multitude of reservoirs in the Back Country testifies to the importance of irrigation for nearly all major commodities. Much of the existing water is not locally available since it has been reserved for use in metropolitan San Diego and the South Coast. The Fallbrook-Vista-Escondido belt has exclusive rights to a considerable quantity. High elevation and dispersed location of many basins and mesas make import of water physically difficult. Thus the San Diego Aqueduct, although it carries Colorado River water as far south as Otay Reservoir, is best used by the lower-lying and wealthier districts toward the coast.

Tomatoes are latest in a succession of "Cinderella" crops which have enraptured San Diego County farmers. Acreage has been increasing rapidly since World War II, and recently tomatoes have been the most valuable crop in the county. They are grown almost exclusively for fresh use and production extends through much of the year. At times in late fall and early winter the Back Country and the South Coast form California's principal source of tomatoes. Cultivation is laborious; it commonly entails the placement of protective caps over each young plant and erection of poles to support the maturing tomatoes. The rolling topography from Fallbrook toward the Pacific spearheads the tomato boom.

The avocado (Fig. 7-11), indigenous to Middle America, is the most sensitive "tropical fruit" grown in California and is a distinctive Back Country crop.

The avocado tree cannot tolerate frost, aridity, or high temperature; hence locales where it can be grown in the United States are restricted to southern Florida, Hawaii, and more favored spots in Southern California. San Diego County, particularly the Back Country around Fallbrook, Vista, and Escondido, accounts for a definite majority of California output. Demand has increased with greater public acceptance, and avocado acreage has increased phenomenally since commercial production began about the time of World War I. Output is creeping closer to demand; there has been a noticeable reduction in new orchards during the past decade. Ownership of an avocado ranch has had appeal akin to what an orange

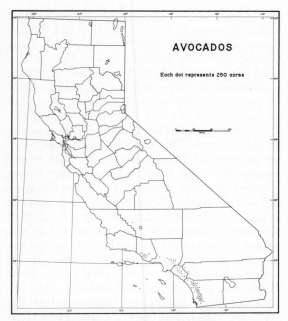

Fig. 7-11. MAP OF THE AVOCADO ACREAGE IN CALIFORNIA.

grove held for an earlier Southern California generation. Relatively few can afford to become avocado growers. Land is unbelievably expensive in the select areas that are climatically suitable. The rancher needs sufficient capital for land preparation, nursery stock, and installation of a sprinkler irrigation system, as well as for subsistence during the nonbearing period after the orchard is planted.

Citrus was an earlier "glamour" crop of the Back Country. Valencia oranges and lemons occupy comparable acreage. Navel oranges are more limited although orchards are expanding. Citrus and avocados, with broadly similar site needs, tend to coincide in areas of production. Their extent and value of output in the Back Country are comparable although with respect to profit avocados have been regarded with more enthusiasm for several decades.

Milk, eggs, chickens, and turkeys are produced in response to the rising urban population of San Diego County. Such Back Country foodstuffs should have greater consequence as farmland around San Diego is removed from cultivation. Dairying has al-ready expanded notably around Escondido, now within the San Diego "bedroom and barn belt." Poultry farming is especially widespread since its investment cost as regards land and water is minimal. The Santa Maria Valley, which surrounds Ramona, is one of California's important turkey producers. The mild, dry climate is well adapted for this fowl, which is sometimes marketed in Los Angeles. Although fresh and dressed storage turkeys are available at all seasons, the principal marketing period is between October and February. Dairy and poultry feeds are raised locally, yet a substantial import has long been necessary.

Cattle ranching provides the most widespread type of Back Country land-use. It is practiced on smoother uplands and also in many unirrigated basins, often in conjunction with cultivation of winter grain. Boundaries of a few large landholdings are still identifiable with early ranchos. Examples include the 90,000-acre Irvine Ranch (southern Orange County) and the 80,000-acre Vail Ranch near Temecula. There is an appreciable acreage of grasslands in the Back Country, but pastures are nutritious only a few months of each year. The typical summer and fall drought period endures longer than in more northerly parts of California where cattle ranching is conducted. Supplemental feeding is based upon locally grown alfalfa where water supplies permit. Attention has been given to replacement of the widespread chaparral cover by substituting grasses, and some controlled burning has been effected. Because of limited rainfall most of the year and the threat of soil erosion during winter storms, this change is probably not a solution on steeper slopes.

TOURING AND SKIING

San Diego Back Country weather and terrain blend to provide a delightful countryside and many winding roads and diverse scenery beckon the urban dweller. Landscapes vary with the season and the locale: in autumn the sycamore, cottonwood, and oak turn golden; in winter greenness remains in the lower valleys as snow laces the higher country; spring brings flowering of the chaparral and (it is hoped) flowing streams and filled reservoirs; in summer the higher forest country is sought after. Many visitors delight in the romantic legacy of Indian occupance, the Spanish period, and early mining days. As the Southern California population increases, utilization of this hill-and-mountain land as a regional playground intensifies.

Higher summits of the Back Country are largely included within the general boundaries of Cleveland National Forest, where a score of improved campgrounds are maintained. On smaller private tracts are numerous hamlets catering to vacationers or providing a second residence for lowlanders from as far away as Los Angeles and Imperial Valley. Much of the Santa Ana Mountain area is closed to public use during the long fire-hazard season, but westside canyons perennially house many older folk and commuters to the Los Angeles Lowlands. Attractions around Mount Palomar include the famous observatory, reached by ascending the Highway to the Stars, the state park, and the Agua Tibia Wild Area.

The Laguna Mountains provide the largest expanse of forest in the Back Country. Within easy access of San Diego, this is the leading highland recreation area of the San Diego Country. Snow is less common here than farther north in California, yet this is the most likely locale afforded San Diegans to toss a snowball or even to ski. Cuyamaca Lake (when it has sufficient water) and spectacular views of the Colorado Desert are among the scenic attractions. The village of **Julian** is the principal town. This one-time gold camp has no pretense of boom growth. Its false fronts suggest the "Old West" whereas white frame cottages are reminiscent of a New England hill town. Nearby **Wynola** raises just enough apples and pears to attract city folk during the spring blossoming and autumnal harvest.

Storage reservoirs in the Back Country are popular with anglers, especially since fresh-water fishing spots are so limited in Southern California. Low water level and restricted access are major handicaps, but several of the lakes are widely patronized, particularly Henshaw, Wohlford, San Vicente, and Irvine (level of the latter two now maintained with Colorado River water). Near Lake Henshaw is **Warner Springs**, Back Country "institution."

THE LOS ANGELES LOWLANDS

The Los Angeles Lowlands, heartland of Southern California and nerve center of an evolving megalopolis (Santa Barbara to San Diego), has an area extent of less than 3000 square miles, yet it contains nearly half the population of California. Its several parts extend from the Transverse Ranges across Los Angeles proper into the Peninsular Ranges (see map, Fig. 7-12).

Rows of low mountains and hills subdivide the Lowlands into five distinct units: (1) the Coastal Plain, (2) San Fernando Valley, (3) San Gabriel Valley, (4) Valley of the South, and (5) San Jacinto Basin. Each is physiographically independent, but all five are filled (or at least partially covered) with alluvium that originated in the Transverse or Penin-sular Ranges. Surfaces are generally smooth but inland margins of these lowlands have increasing slope. Immediately below the canyons of interior highlands, the surface commonly becomes coarse and rock-strewn, whereas along lower (seaward) portions of each lowland there are heavier soils and often poorly drained ground.

The strips of rough country that separate the five lowlands rise from a hundred to several thousand feet. The largest of these intervening uplands are the Santa Monica, Santa Ana, and Verdugo mountains. Each of the uplands creates an obstacle to travel and to conurbation; even some of them close to Los Angeles have been conspicuously untouched by settlement. Collectively these hills help

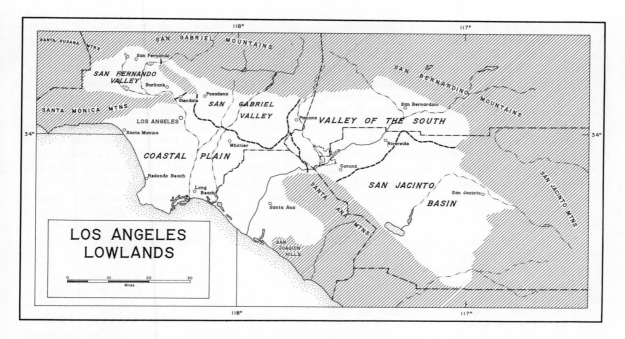

Fig. 7-12. MAP OF THE LOS ANGELES LOWLANDS.

create climatic variations among the lowlands (Appendix A, Fig. A-5) and they form barriers to water runoff (both surface and underground).

The five Lowlands are interconnected with narrow but low-level gaps (see map, Fig. 7-12). Several appear to have resulted from rivers (antecedent) that were able to maintain their courses as the intervening ridges were uplifted; others are fault-line depressions. The Los Angeles (Glendale) Narrows and Cahuenga Pass (Fig. 7-31) connect the Coastal Plain with San Fernando Valley. Between the San Fernando and San Gabriel valleys is La Crescenta (La Cañada) Corridor. Whittier Narrows, the Arroyo Seco Valley, and several others join San Gabriel Valley with the Coastal Plain. Other connective links include San Jose Valley between San Gabriel Valley and the Valley of the South, Santa Ana Canyon between Valley of the South and the Coastal Plain, and Temescal Canyon between Valley of the South and the San Jacinto Basin. These gaps have been utilized effectively for important highway and railroad routes; some

are effective sites for flood-control dams and groundwater extraction as well.

The five Lowlands are described individually later in this chapter. However the western three definitely lie within metropolitan Los Angeles; thus their geographic details are best understood if preceded by an account of the complex that has engulfed them.

METROPOLITAN LOS ANGELES

'Tis small wonder that Los Angeles is so difficult to comprehend.[7] The *political* city

[7] Professor Richard Logan of U.C.L.A., a capable field geographer, once said half-jestingly: "I took one look at Los Angeles and headed for the Mojave Desert." The first three years that he taught geography of California, Lantis approached the section of the course on the Lowlands with trepidation. Although some able local geographers have been examining the Lowlands for years, no summary study has appeared in English (see bibliography). Currently a number of geographers are engaged in a Los Angeles Geographical Society undertaking entitled *Day Tours.*

of Los Angeles sprawls over 458 square miles to form the heart of the Lowlands. It occupies much (but not all) of the western portion of the Coastal Plain and the San Fernando Valley (see map, Fig. 7-12). Within the city limits, one can drive about 60 miles in a straight line, southward from the base of the Ridge Route (U.S. 99) to San Pedro. The *geographical* city, or metropolis, encompasses virtually all of the three western lowlands and includes scores of politically independent satellites (sixteen of which exceeded 50,000 inhabitants each in 1960).

EVOLUTION [8]

The center of Los Angeles occupies the site of the Yang-Na, one of several Gabrielino Indian villages that were situated along the Los Angeles and San Gabriel rivers. Los Angeles was founded in 1781 as the second of Alta California's three original Spanish pueblos. The townsite, encompassing 28 square miles, evolved around a central square (approximately the present-day plaza) and its limits had cardinal orientation (delineated today by segments of Fountain Avenue, Hoover and Indiana Streets, and Exposition Boulevard).

The nucleus, typical of Spanish colonial villages, was half a mile west of the Los Angeles River on a terrace high enough for protection from winter floods yet irrigable by means of a *zanja* (ditch) whose intake was two miles upriver near present-day Elysian Park. There (at the Los Angeles Narrows) the river is confined by hills on the west and alluvium from Arroyo Seco on the east, thus easing diversion of irrigation water. River flow at this point was perennial (disappearing only in later years when the city began extracting water farther upstream). In contrast to the site selected by the Spanish, an American or English community might instead have been situated at a place suitable for ocean commerce (San Pedro, Santa Monica, or Newport).

The location of Los Angeles is not entirely propitious for the ranking metropolis of western United States. It does occupy the largest coastal lowland in California. And it is insulated against the interior by the loftiest coastal mountains in the state (yet which are easily penetrated through such passes as Cajon and San Gorgonio). But the city is away from the midpoint of the west coast and there is insufficient local water. Its "back country" is the sparsely populated Intermontane Region (Part One), not San Francisco's Central Valley hinterland. An initial disadvantage was the absence of a good natural harbor. Distance from the "industrial east" was also a handicap. Originally, the surrounding countryside was not productive and local mineral fuel long remained undeveloped.

THE PRE-RAILROAD PERIOD

Los Angeles did not flourish during the Spanish period; by 1800 it had only 300 residents. It grew somewhat during the Mexican era, especially after mission secularization and establishment of ranchos nearby. Upon the demise of Mission San Gabriel, Los Angeles became the economic and social center of the Lowlands and was assigned *ciudad* (city) status in 1835. Until the 1850's it was the single settlement of any substance in all Southern California and included the town houses of more prosperous *rancheros*.

Early American stewardship did not bring rapid change, though the economy was stimulated by travel and such exports as wine and beef to Sierran gold camps. The typical structure was still the flat-roofed adobe, and the earthen streets became quagmires during wintry rains. The plaza remained the focal point although the residential district expanded upslope to the west. By 1865 adjacent land was becoming too valuable for pastoral use. Orchards of citrus, figs, peaches, and apples began to suggest a "garden town." As ranchos were divided, a few outlying settlements appeared. San Pedro's roadstead remained the chief seaport.

THE FIRST BOOM

Rising regional prosperity, the start of winter tourism, and the opening of the Southern

---

[8] *This and the succeeding section have been reviewed by Gerard Foster, Long Beach State College.*

Pacific route into New Mexico and Texas helped inspire the Boom of the Eighties (the First Boom). Significant growth had commenced after rail connection with northern California was established in 1876. A land boom, with widespread subdivision, was triggered by the opening of a second direct transcontinental rail route (the Santa Fe) in the mid-1880's. Agricultural growth, as well as advertising and publicity, also helped.

Agriculture, dominated by the citrus industry which benefited from eastern markets after opening of transcontinental rail routes, remained the leading economic mainstay into the twentieth century. Small farm communities had been founded on the inner Coastal Plain and in the San Gabriel and San Fernando Valleys in the 1870's. As well-drilling became commonplace, settlement was liberated from location near springs and perennial streams. Some seaports and coastal resorts were also established, but neither the outer Coastal Plain nor most of the San Fernando Valley was favored for settlement until the twentieth century. Many localities suffered from poor drainage, excessive depth to groundwater, inadequate transportation, or climate unsatisfactory for citrus. But by 1890, Los Angeles alone had a population of 50,000.

During the 1890's Los Angeles doubled in population. Orange groves were expanded and a petroleum industry was developed. Four oil fields were producing before 1900. They were located along the inner margin of the Coastal Plain (between Elysian Park and Santa Ana Canyon) and began to supplement agriculture and tourism as supports of the Los Angeles economy. The first field, the Los Angeles City Field, "came in" in 1892.

THE SECOND BOOM

Los Angeles became a small metropolis as its population tripled during the second boom (1902-1914). Rapid growth of the city and its environs occurred as agriculture, tourism, and oil were further developed and the motion-picture industry was established. With confirmation of San Pedro as the principal seaport in 1899 and completion of a third transcontinental rail link, now part of the Union Pa-

cific, via Whittier Narrows in 1905, southeast Los Angeles with its flat terrain and maze of rail lines was assured status as the primary industrial and wholesale district. Manufacturing on a small scale, largely for local needs, was beginning, with food processing dominant. Distance prevented shipment of ordinary consumer goods east but also protected infant local industries from outside competition.

Centrally located **Bunker Hill** and **Boyle Heights** lost status as choice residential districts; affluent citizens sought the western fringes of Los Angeles apart from industry and commerce. The downtown district expanded southward from the old plaza as its importance was magnified with extension of the Pacific Electric interurban network to outlying districts on the periphery of the Lowlands.

Los Angeles finally eliminated its dependence upon its own river in 1913 when the Los Angeles Aqueduct was completed from the eastern slopes of the Sierra Nevada (Chapter 2). A surplus water supply enabled the city to absorb many outlying districts whose supplies were inadequate. The area of Los Angeles quadrupled in extent as a result of annexations in the decades that followed aqueduct construction.

Establishment of the motion-picture industry in Los Angeles was largely accidental— independent producers sought legal refuge against suits instigated by the Edison-organized "trust" in the East. After advantages of weather and landscape in Southern California became apparent, the "trust" moved west too. In 1909 the initial firm, Selig, was attracted to Edendale (two miles northwest of downtown Los Angeles) by open country with scenic diversity combined with municipal water supply and townspeople as "extras." Movie-making soon shifted westward into more spacious Hollywood, which became the focal point of centralized casting offices and other allied activities. Though many studios located elsewhere in the 1920's and 1930's, "Hollywood" has remained synonymous with the film industry.

World War I ended the second boom, with

brief curtailment of the tourist trade. The war did briefly stimulate a few industries, such as shipbuilding and steel fabrication. By 1920 Los Angeles had a population of 580,000 and was the nation's tenth city.

THE THIRD BOOM

Los Angeles experienced its third boom during the 1920's when the absolute population increase within the city limits established an all-time record. By 1930, after a decade of major economic change, it was the nation's fifth city with a population of 1.23 million. Growth was sparked by petroleum and the effects of the automobile. Fifteen new oil fields were discovered in the Los Angeles Basin between 1917 and 1929. The newly opened Panama Canal enabled petroleum export to the East Coast as nationwide consumption mounted with rising use of the automobile. Much oil revenue was reinvested around Los Angeles; many landowners, producing companies, and tool manufacturers considered their attachment to Southern California permanent. In the 1920's oil production shifted from the inner margin of the Coastal Plain to new fields along the Newport-Inglewood uplift and along the Santa Monica littoral. Huntington Beach (1920), Signal Hill (1921), and Santa Fe Springs (1919) were leading producers; more recently, the newer Wilmington field has outranked them (see Chapter 9).

Major tank farms and oil refineries were generally built on the southwestern Coastal Plain between El Segundo (Fig. 7-21) and Wilmington, convenient locations for supply of crude petroleum and ocean export; the abundance of space necessary for such sprawling facilities was then available. The oil fields themselves tended to repel residential construction but adjacent communities that housed oil workers spiraled. Impressive oil corporation office buildings arose in downtown Los Angeles and ample fuel was assured a coal-less, automobile-oriented society.

By the 1920's the population of Los Angeles was sufficiently large to stimulate new market-oriented industries. The most notable were rubber processors and automobile assembly plants, which developed rapidly during the decade. Already Los Angeles County led the nation in total number of automobiles, which assured a sizable market for cars and tires. The cost of transporting such items from eastern factories favored local production. Today all the nation's leading rubber tire and automobile manufacturers are represented in metropolitan Los Angeles. Most firms have plants in the primary industrial belt but some decentralization of auto assembly has occurred; there are now plants in Van Nuys (Chevrolet) and El Segundo (American Motors).

THE GREAT DEPRESSION

The growth of Los Angeles was slowed in the 1930's, yet the metropolitan area added over half a million new residents. Effects of nationwide depression were mollified by expansion of the motion-picture industry, which capitalized upon newly introduced sound and color techniques. Between 1933 and 1937 employment in movie-making increased by half, and total wages doubled. Urbanization was especially vigorous on the western Coastal Plain and in the southern San Fernando Valley (locations favored by the motion-picture industry). Recording and radio broadcasting achieved recognition at this time as important Hollywood enterprises. It was logical, with the talent in drama, music, and literature assembled by the motion-picture industry, that the District should have become a major program center when national radio networks materialized.

Several other Los Angeles industries based partly upon uniqueness of design gained prominence before 1940, particularly apparel and furniture. Together with ceramics, carpeting, playshoes, and cosmetics they have made Los Angeles one of the world's foremost fashion centers. Many "fashion industries" had early and humble antecedents with local service products. National acclaim has derived largely from motion-picture (and more recently television) publicity and the "Californiamania" it helped to generate. Prominent style themes have included: "outdoors," casuality, glamour, celebrity identification, and historic (Mission) attachment.

Wearing apparel is the leading fashion industry. Los Angeles is a leader in creation of playclothes and sportswear and ranks second nationally to New York in total garment output. The motion pictures exerted strong influence through attire created by Hollywood costume designers. There has also been increasing emphasis upon "styled in California" sportswear. Focal point of clothing manufacture is the downtown wholesale district with its building lofts, but there is much less concentration than in New York's famed "garment district." Establishments are scattered about the Lowlands with labor supply often an important site consideration. Lightweight woolens, synthetic fibers, and cottons form especially important fabrics.

Furniture manufacture, like garment-making and radio broadcasting, originated earlier but did not become a major "export" industry until the 1930's. Thousands of buyers now visit Los Angeles; an enlarged Furniture Mart (for display) was completed in 1957. Early growth of the industry was based upon import of foreign woods and availability of low-cost Mexican craftsmen. The distribution of furniture manufacturers is complex; many firms are located southeast of downtown Los Angeles in the primary wholesale-industrial district.

THE FOURTH BOOM

The continuing fourth boom began during World War II with much industrial expansion, particularly aircraft. After 1945 population increase continued at an accelerated rate so that by 1950 the city had replaced Philadelphia as the nation's third city—now its metropolitan population has exceeded Chicago and ranks second to New York City. The boom has seen vast housing tracts and new suburban shopping centers on former agricultural lands. After 1950 the population of Orange County became explosive. Such growth has justified a multitude of new service industries and an influx of young "working" families.

The airspace industries have been a major economic contributor to the fourth boom. Evolution of aircraft manufacture was affected by early popularity of flying in Southern California (doubtless encouraged by superior flying weather). One of the first motion pictures filmed in Los Angeles concerned Knabenshue's pioneer dirigible in 1904. Glenn Martin built California's first airplane in Santa Ana in 1906, and the air show at Dominguez Field four years later was one of the first in the nation. Donald Douglas, who had been Martin's chief engineer, formed his own company in Santa Monica in 1920, whereas the Lockheed organization had been founded even earlier in Santa Barbara.

The expansion of aircraft manufacture was aided by a nucleus of experienced personnel (such as Gerard Vultee and John Northrop from Lockheed and James H. Kindelberger of North American from Douglas). The industry is highly flexible, from the standpoint of location, and has depended upon residence of skilled designers, availability of financing, and early start more than upon labor, market, or raw materials. As western terminus of commercial transcontinental air service in the late 1920's, Los Angeles was an ideal location for airplane builders. Government military and airmail contracts were major incentives from the first.

The aircraft industry, heretofore scattered, began to concentrate in Southern California, which became the major assembly center of the United States. Climate, which allowed year-round work outdoors, reduced plant maintenance costs. The mighty expansion during World War II was facilitated in the Lowlands by availability of land in proximity to parts manufacturers and labor supply. The larger plants were situated apart from the primary industrial belt; many were originally on the urban fringe where ample airport space was available. Los Angeles International Airport became the chief focus; other major facilities were located around airports in Burbank, Santa Monica, Hawthorne, and Long Beach. Lesser assembly plants and parts makers have been scattered widely through the metropolis.

Some major military installations, which continue to operate, were established in the Los Angeles area during World War II. The Naval base at Long Beach and Fort Mac-Arthur (Army) in San Pedro had been the major installations before 1940. Newer establishments were concentrated on "empty land" of the southern Coastal Plain, most as close to Los Angeles Harbor as space and safety permitted. Facilities included: shipyards, veterans' hospital, storage depots (ammunition, petroleum, and nets), and air stations. An important Air Force supply center was constructed in the primary industrial district.

CONTEMPORARY ECONOMIC DEVELOPMENTS

Manufacturing has become increasingly dominant as the leading supporting function of metropolitan Los Angeles. It employs almost a third of the labor force, a proportion comparable to many eastern industrial cities. The majority of Los Angeles factory output is destined for nearby consumers, but export production alone exceeds other basic sources of income.

The table below ignores the tremendous moment of service industries (professional services, food processing, etc.) that are con-cerned with supplying the needs of the 7 million people of the Los Angeles Lowlands. These activities employ hundreds of thousands. Although there is sometimes jesting about "taking in one another's washing," service industries are monumental in total scope. This market now permits the manufacture of everything from adzes to zithers. Significant industrial activities important to the American economy that are underdeveloped in metropolitan Los Angeles include the manufacture of textiles (especially cotton), window glass, and certain appliances.

Such long-established resource-oriented industries as citrus packing, petroleum refining, and fish canning have become relatively less important as the economy has matured. The petroleum fields of the Los Angeles area can no longer supply local needs entirely. Huge imports (and exports) are made presently on the basis of long-established refinery location.

Many film studios have converted to television-film manufacture. Television broadcasting was initiated by radio stations around 1950, but as larger facilities became necessary, separate network television facilities were constructed (notably in Burbank and the Wilshire District). Space and climate no longer provide the advantages they did for motion pictures, but Los Angeles has become

BASIC ECONOMIC ACTIVITIES, LOS ANGELES METROPOLITAN AREA
(in millions of dollars, circa 1960, estimated)

ACTIVITY	EMPLOYMENT	CONTRIBUTION
Export Industries		
Aircraft	161,000	$1,587
Electronics	80,000	736
Motion pictures and television	22,000	260
Petroleum and refining	21,000	188
Apparel	22,000	131
Fishing and fish canning	5,000	72
Furniture	7,000	53
Citrus	—	40
Tourism	—	500
Military Installations	48,000	202

Data for apparel and furniture consist only of the export portion of those industries. Contribution for aircraft, electronics, apparel, and furniture equals value added in manufacturing. For petroleum and fishing, figures equal value of raw material plus value added in manufacturing; for motion pictures, total production expenses shown; for citrus, FOB value; for tourism, total expenditures; for military, payrolls of Armed Forces and civilians.

the nation's television center, which is a testimony to local talent accumulation and its reluctance to relocate in New York City. Another factor in declining local motion-picture production has been the increased use of foreign settings with their realistic, exotic landscapes, the financial advantages implicit in production outside the United States, and the competition of movie-makers in other lands.

Aircraft employment has declined with reduced output of military aircraft. Federal defense expenditures have not created jobs for all displaced aircraft workers—some have forsaken Los Angeles entirely (there is an obvious secondary migration within California, to points north of the Tehachapi Mountains). Aircraft plants have partially converted to production of missiles and various electronic goods.

The burgeoning electronics industry comprises portions of the electrical machinery, instruments, ordnance, aircraft, and nonelectrical machinery industries. Los Angeles has become one of the world's principal centers of electronics production, supported by its aircraft industry and facilities in education and research. Products include radio and television sets, industrial controls, and X-ray apparatus, but the industry depends largely upon federal contracts (thus like aircraft, it is vulnerable to defense changes). Because of shipping costs, many of its consumer products cannot successfully be marketed east of the Rocky Mountains. Electronics research and manufacturing is rapidly decentralizing around Los Angeles; the spacious "campus-style" plant on the urban fringe is typical. The smokeless, noiseless, airportless nature of much electronics manufacturing gives it much freedom in location—communities are happy to receive its tax revenue and welcome its educated and skilled personnel. The industry is heavily dependent upon much-sought scientists, planners, and other professional personnel; hence location near attractive residential sectors is a decided advantage. The western San Fernando Valley and Orange County are the leading new electronics centers, with other important development around South Bay and Palos Verdes Hills.

PRESENT URBAN PATTERNS

The dispersal of the electronics industry noted above merits a review of industrial location in metropolitan Los Angeles (Fig. 7-13). There are over 15,000 factories and 900,000 industrial workers. Although the large establishment (oil refinery or electronics plant) is dramatic on the landscape, the vast number of small factories is less easily discerned. The primary industrial belt extends southward from Burbank, generally parallel to the Los Angeles River toward the Los Angeles Harbor. After World War II marked eastward expansion into the San Gabriel Valley (along railroad rights of way) and southeastward into Orange County took place. The scattered locations of oil refineries, motion-picture studios, aircraft factories, and electronics plants have been noted. They mirror in part available land at the time of construction.

There has been a continuing outward spread of low-density urbanization across the Coastal Plain and into the San Fernando and San Gabriel valleys. The contiguous built-up metropolis now extends more than 20 miles from downtown Los Angeles wherever level land prevails. Freeway development (almost entirely since 1950) has facilitated and seemingly accelerated centrifugal movement. The urban fringe now lies more than 25 miles from the central district along the Ventura, San Bernardino, and Santa Ana freeways.

Metropolitan Los Angeles has nearly attained its physical limits at the base of the San Gabriel Mountains where slopes and federal land ownership have been unyielding. To the southwest it has contiguity along 30 of the 50 miles of seashore. Greatest expansion is now directed into the northwest-southeast corridor between the ocean and mountain barriers. At present rates, complete urbanization of the Coastal Plain and San Fernando and San Gabriel valleys is anticipated soon.

The "city" of Los Angeles, which contained almost 60 percent of the metropolitan population in 1910, now has less than 40 percent (2,500,000 in 1960) as outlying localities have rapidly filled. Since Colorado River water be-

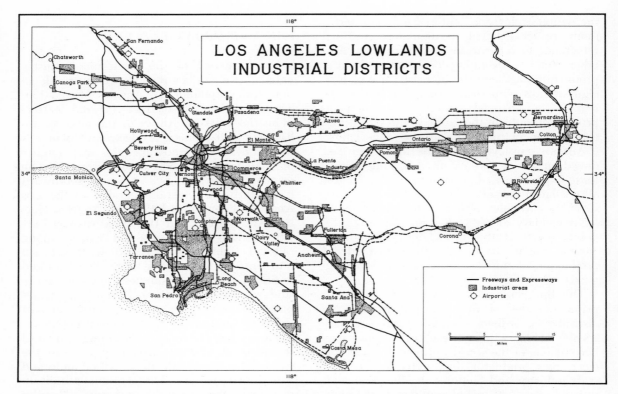

Fig. 7-13. MAP OF THE INDUSTRIAL DISTRICTS OF METROPOLITAN LOS ANGELES.

came available through the Metropolitan Water District, surrounding cities have not been forced to merge into Los Angeles to obtain water; the last major annexation into the city took place before World War II. Thus the metropolis has marked municipal fragmentation. The residents of scores of independent satellites in Los Angeles and Orange counties commonly do not look upon themselves as Angelenos and many resent being so labeled. Incorporation of new political units, in lieu of annexation, is favored in Los Angeles County by the so-called "Lakewood Plan" whereby county government effectively provides many municipal services under contract. In Orange County (and elsewhere in California generally), annexation of newly settled areas into existing cities still prevails. In both counties several communities have incorporated to preserve special functions

such as high-quality residence, agriculture (especially dairying), and industry.

Within the urban complex sizable tracts of semirural land persist. These include the aforementioned uplands, oil fields, and surfaces reserved for flood control as well as several communities zoned for agriculture. "Dead land" is still apparent, especially in potential industrial zones. Some of it finds temporary use for intensive truck farming, as do extensive flood-control lands and the rights-of-way for power transmission lines. Such lands permitted Los Angeles to remain the nation's sixth agricultural county in 1961 (leading commodities included market milk, vegetables, nursery stock, cut flowers, and citrus).

THE CULTURAL SCENE

Metropolitan Los Angeles has become the cultural center of western North America (although this fact does not yet find wide acceptance north of the Tehachapi Mountains). Although urban dispersal and rapid expansion have not permitted sufficient cohesion, there is some evidence that Los Angeles will eventually be regarded with New York, London, and Paris as a cultural center. Its "major-league" status in virtually all types of athletics (Fig. 7-1) is now accepted, but the metropolis already warrants more recognition in architecture, art, engineering, journalism, law, literature, medicine, and music than it is generally given. For half a century its theatrical arts (including motion pictures, radio, and television) have much influenced American (and worldwide) customs, tastes, and mores. An influx of educated and cultured individuals continues, attracted by the opportunities in this spiraling money market, but their cultural tastes tend to be obscured by the fascination with casual living that the climate permits.

Los Angeles and its Lowlands are rapidly acquiring educational recognition. The University of California at Los Angeles is becoming a great university, and the California Institute of Technology already has international recognition in its more restricted fields. The University of Southern California is also advancing, though it has been plagued by the financial problems of a private school. There is already a new campus of the state university at Riverside and another is being established in Orange County. Six new state colleges have been opened since 1948 and are already gaining recognition. There are well-known private colleges, including Occidental, the Claremont Colleges, Loyola, and Whittier, and several dozen two-year (junior) colleges.

PHYSICAL PROBLEMS

All conurbations have multiple problems—those of Los Angeles have been compounded by the rambling and disjointed growth of its metropolis. With suburban movement "old" Los Angeles has experienced rapid blight of residential districts around its downtown core. Submarginal neighborhoods tend to differ physically from those of Eastern cities: the "slums" often consist of single frame houses on 30- to 50-foot lots, not tightly packed multistory brick tenements. With upkeep and better landscaping many of these dwellings would be attractive; they resemble houses in "good" sections of many stable Middlewestern towns—some are of near-palatial dimensions. Some older houses are being replaced by multifamily apartments or nonresidential land uses, but peripheral blighting continues. Some fear that many vast housing tracts, hastily erected since World War II, will become the slum prototype of the future.

Public transportation has deteriorated from earlier years of the excellent Pacific Electric interurban system. Low population density and heavy traffic flow discourage use of public buses. An extensive freeway program is easing vehicular movement except during rush hours when these multilane routes are jammed (Fig. 7-31). A rapid transit system is projected, but low population density makes its economic feasibility questionable, and one wonders if a "motor-minded" public will accept it.

Los Angeles has been more fortunate than some of its outlying neighbors in acquiring a water supply. Importation of Sierra Nevada and Colorado River water (Chapters 2 and 3) provides for present needs; northern California's Feather River is an anticipated future source (Chapters 5 and 9). Still, delivery systems are expensive and the specter of water famine seems ever imminent. Storm runoff has posed difficulties too in low-lying localities despite many dams, levees, and storm drains constructed since the great flood of 1938. A long-range Los Angeles County program affords hopes of minimizing this problem. Rapid growth has placed heavy loads upon the sewage system despite the proximity of the open ocean (sewage must be treated so as to avert beach contamination). Although garbage-disposal units and automatic washers discharge additional water per family, little attempt is yet made to reclaim such waste despite its apparent feasibility.

Air pollution, a major problem since World War II, has evoked worldwide interest. *Fortune* once described the Lowlands as "The Valley of Smoke." Although weather is a prized Southern California asset, it is inherently smog-prone when sufficient industrial and domestic gases are present. Sunshine reacts with such gases to create complex chemicals and produce a "dirty yellow haze." Accumulation of pollutants in the Los Angeles Lowlands is fostered by sea breezes, creation of an "inversion layer" in settling marine air (from the Hawaiian High), and presence of the interior mountain wall. Backyard incinerators have been banned, and rigid controls are exerted over smoke emission from factories. The automobile exhaust is still a major source of pollutants, and the rapid influx of new motorists and industries tends to counteract abatement progress.

THE LOS ANGELES COASTAL PLAIN

The Los Angeles Coastal Plain (see map, Fig. 7-12) is the most intensively utilized of the five Lowlands even though the San Gabriel Valley was the site of original European occupance. The degree to which man has urbanized the Coastal Plain is impressive. From a promontory in the Santa Monica Mountains one senses that the metropolis encompasses the entire surface despite ephemeral agricultural patches.

The Coastal Plain includes large portions of Los Angeles and Orange counties. It is bounded along its inner margin by the Santa Monica Mountains, San Rafael Hills, Montebello Hills, Puente Hills, Santa Ana Mountains, and San Joaquin Hills (map, Fig. 7-12). It faces the sea from Malibu to Newport Bay, with miles of sandy beaches interrupted only by the Palos Verdes Hills and the Harbor Area.

Sedimentary rocks extend to a depth of 20,000 feet beneath the extensive alluvial cover; deeper still are old hardrock blocks. Faulting of these blocks has been responsible for rippling of the sediments to form the anticlinal Newport-Inglewood Uplift with its line of low hills and domes. The Palos Verdes Hills, one-time island that now forms the

southwestern edge of the Plain, has been uplifted, faulted, and folded; they rise to 1500 feet, with marine terraces and cliffs along their seaward side.

The Coastal Plain contains the southern half of the city of Los Angeles and a dozen other municipalities of over 50,000 people each. It is crisscrossed by a network of rectangular streets; many have cardinal orientation to section lines, whereas others were laid out irregularly according to old rancho boundaries. Selected arteries that radiate from central Los Angeles follow old Indian paths, oxcart trails, and former lines of the Pacific Electric interurban. Many older major thoroughfares are lined for miles with miscellaneous retail shops. Such "string streets," along with the newer suburban shopping centers and miles of housing tracts, reflect the influence of the automobile. Streetcars were used in central Los Angeles until 1963; the final interurban rail service had been discontinued in 1961.

Urban skylines are still low; across much of the Plain trees (sometimes rows of palms) vie with buildings for the visitor's attention. Oil fields add a distinctive touch to the scene along the inner and coastal edges of the Plain. Sizable agricultural tracts, despite decimation, remain in Orange County. Elsewhere, farming occurs in many small patches skipped over by urbanization. Relict chicken farms and dairies are pressed closely by busy streets and even new apartment houses, and factories appear amidst cabbage fields.

Urbanization and level terrain give the Coastal Plain certain uniformity; its many localities, with their differences in natural setting, age of occupance, and economic evolution, create a bewildering mosaic. It is for this reason that the following description of the Coastal Plain has been further subdivided into these parts: the **Northwest** (which includes central Los Angeles), the **Santa Monica Littoral**, the **Central Section**, the **Harbor Area**, and the **Southeast**.

THE NORTHWEST

The Northwest section of the Coastal Plain, with the possible exception of the city of San

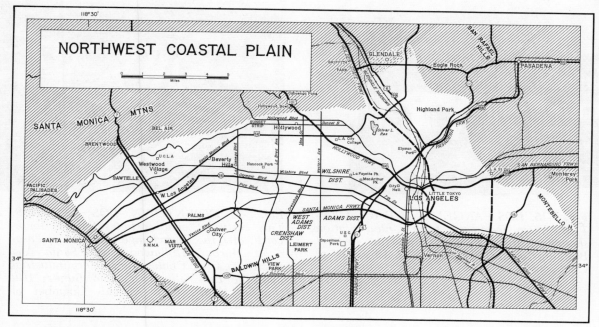

Fig. 7-14. MAP OF THE NORTHWEST COASTAL PLAIN.

Francisco, contains the greatest cultural complexity in western North America. It has scores of neighborhoods, with poverty and wealth, shanties and mansions, some of the oldest dwellings in California, and some of the newest, and it includes central Los Angeles.

CENTRAL LOS ANGELES

Downtown Los Angeles occupies the site of the Spanish pueblo near the emergence of the Los Angeles River upon the Coastal Plain. Its street grid has northeast-southwest alignment (an orientation related to terrain and colonial flow of irrigation water). Its older portions (east of Main Street) display the imperfectly rectangular city blocks laid out before 1848. Few vestiges of the original community remain; the much-altered plaza is a tiny park with adjacent Olvera Street "restored" as a tourist attraction. "Old" Chinatown too has largely disappeared as has the early Mexican settlement (Sonora Town). Business blocks of the late nineteenth century have been replaced by the Civic Center, whose buildings, most

of contemporary design, are flanked by multi-acre parking lots (Fig. 7-15). The Civic Center has encroached westward upon **Bunker Hill** (Fig. 7-16), once occupied by the city's wealthier residents and now experiencing impressive urban renewal.

The **Central Business District** ("C.B.D."), whose pivotal point was once the plaza, has migrated southwestward since the boom of the 1880's, so that Broadway and Seventh are now its main shopping arteries. Since construction of the Harbor Freeway, new office buildings have arisen toward the west.

This downtown core, small for the area of Los Angeles and its metropolitan population, contains scarcely 200 city blocks (roughly bounded by Sunset, San Pedro, Venice, and Figueroa streets). Since Los Angeles is so completely the product of the automobile age, rapid vehicular movement has permitted much dispersal of urban facilities. The erstwhile 150-foot limitation on building height, combined with small area, has given the "C.B.D." a distinctively low skyline among larger Amer-

SOUTHERN CALIFORNIA : : 193

Fig. 7-15. LOS ANGELES CIVIC CENTER. View westward from Union Station showing City Hall (left) and the Federal Building (center). (Los Angeles Chamber of Commerce)

Fig. 7-16. DOWNTOWN LOS ANGELES. This eastward view includes Sunset Boulevard (left), the Interchange (junction of Pasadena, Harbor, Hollywood, and Santa Ana freeways), Civic Center, the primary industrial belt, the East Side (rear), and Bunker Hill (middle right). (Los Angeles Chamber of Commerce)

ican cities. It is now completely ringed by freeways and more of the "C.B.D." is devoted to parking spaces than in most cities, which affords an openness unusual in great cities.

Office workers constitute a rising proportion of the daytime population. Besides the Civic Center, with its adjacent concentration of law firms, various federal and county agencies occupy temporary quarters in the "C.B.D." The downtown district is also an important financial center, with central banks, brokerage houses, and insurance companies along Spring Street and elsewhere, though numerous firms are now located outside the District, especially along Wilshire Boulevard.[9] A distinguishing aspect, reflecting historic development of the Lowlands, is created by corporate offices of petroleum corporations, which occupy some of the most conspicuous downtown buildings.

The District has importance as a transportation hub. Passenger rail service (via Southern Pacific, Santa Fe, and Union Pacific) is con-

centrated at Union Station; bus terminals are also located on the eastern fringe of the area. Helicopter service is provided to the principal airports, Los Angeles International (southwest of Inglewood) and Lockheed Air Terminal (in the San Fernando Valley). The "C.B.D." contains a number of airline ticket offices, travel agencies, and offices of major ocean shippers. Freight terminals (both rail and freight) are largely situated east of the District in the primary industrial-wholesale belt.

Retail trade and services remain important, though diminishing in dollar volume and importance as additional establishments arise in outlying areas. There are few first-class hotels (these are scattered from Santa Monica to Pasadena), and metropolitan dispersal is also reflected in the absence of night club, theater, and quality restaurant concentration.[10] Although metropolitan Los Angeles ranks after New York nationally as a focal point for the legitimate theater, few theaters are downtown.

[9] Los Angeles far outranks San Francisco as a financial center, although this is obscured by the clearing house functions of the Twelfth Federal Reserve District Bank in San Francisco. Per capita personal income and investment are higher in San Francisco.

[10] The metropolis has more hotels and motels and more service stations than are found in any other city, including New York City.

Fig. 7-17. DOWNTOWN LOS ANGELES. View northward showing the Harbor Freeway (left) and Civic Center (upper right). (Los Angeles Chamber of Commerce)

There is a marked nocturnal difference between the District and Midtown Manhattan or the Chicago Loop.

The central district and its periphery still have residential importance, especially in the form of cheaper hotels, apartments, and other multiple-unit dwellings. Population density, higher than in most of the city, is declining because of commercial and industrial encroachment. Permanent downtown residents tend to be single persons or elderly couples in lower-income categories. The core itself houses 16,000, with a much larger number on its submarginal periphery.

THE EAST SIDE

East of the Los Angeles River, but still within the city of Los Angeles, is an area of small plains, terraces, and valleys backed by a broad belt of low hills that separates the Coastal Plain and the San Gabriel Valley. This is the **East Side**, crossed by main-line railroads and containing their classification yards. Along the railroad ways are warehouses and factories that represent several eastward extensions of the primary (north-south) industrial belt. The factories, of small to medium size, have diversified products (mainly for local use) that include flour, beer, pottery, machinery, and furniture.

Some East Side residential districts once represented prestige addresses; proximity to industry has generally favored their transition into workers' neighborhoods, especially **Lincoln Heights**, **Boyle Heights**, and **East Los Angeles** (pop. 104,270 and politically independent). Low- to middle-income population predominates with much admixture of distinct ethnic groups, particularly Mexican and other foreign-born. Densely populated, with some depressed quarters, this area brought Los Angeles notoriety in the 1940's with its "Zoot-Suiters" and more recently, its teen-age gangs. Social workers grapple with its many problems.

Early settlement and central location in the metropolis encouraged location here of such community institutions as the County Hospital and White Memorial Hospital, Juvenile Hall, City Jail, and the Home for the Aged. Its major cultural institutions include Southwest Museum, three medical colleges (University of Southern California, Osteopathic Physicians and Surgeons, and Medical Evangelists College), Occidental College, Los Angeles State College, and East Los Angeles Junior College. Founded in 1948, Los Angeles State College was established on its present small campus after much controversy over a location; in less than fifteen years it had become the largest state college, and was erecting multistory buildings.

SOUTHWESTERN LOS ANGELES

Southwest of its central district the city of Los Angeles has an extensive area south of Pico Boulevard and extending westward from the Harbor Freeway into the Baldwin Hills (map, Fig. 7-14). Land-use is almost wholly residential with recency of construction (and often of size) increasing westward. It includes a series of distinctive neighborhoods. The **Adams District** on the east was the fashionable part of the city around 1900. Many of its mansions, now multiple residences, have deteriorated badly. It houses many elderly people on limited incomes and is a cultural hodgepodge that includes Mexicans, Orientals, and Jews. The **West Adams District** reflects a notable ethnic change since 1950. As the Negro moves into Los Angeles at the rate of 2000 monthly, increasing heterogeneity is developing in various parts of the Lowlands. This area, focal point of the westside Negro concentration, is popular with middle-income migrants; there are many professional people and white-collar workers.

The major cultural concentration in the southwest occurs around Shrine Auditorium, the University of Southern California, and Exposition Park. The park, rather small for its diverse uses, has many athletic events—it contains the Coliseum and the Sports Arena, also the County Museum and the State Exposition Building. Belatedly the University of Southern California, a private institution, discovered that its campus was too small; it is being enlarged slowly by destruction of surrounding residential blocks.

The **Baldwin Hills**, along the Inglewood-Newport Uplift (see map, Fig. 7-14), remained largely agricultural until the 1950's; this "close-in" countryside had been held in anticipation of rising land values. The Inglewood oil field, on its western side, developed in the early 1900's. Much of the Hills, outside city limits in county territory, is now covered with expensive "view-lot" residences.

THE WESTERN DISTRICTS

Between downtown Los Angeles and the Santa Monica Littoral is an intricate, almost completely urbanized landscape. It includes portions of Los Angeles and the politically independent cities of Beverly Hills and Culver City. It is primarily residential, with heavy commutation to downtown Los Angeles. Higher-income districts extend along the base of the Santa Monica Mountains from Silver Lake and Los Feliz Hills to the Pacific. Except for Beverly Hills, these western districts are within the limits of Los Angeles. Country clubs, hospitals, entertainment places, and specialty stores north of Pico Boulevard partially reflect the presence of a large affluent population. On the east, toward downtown Los Angeles, older houses and higher population density prevails with a lower-income occupance. Motion pictures and allied products constitute the chief industries. Oil deposits have been exploited for many years, but with the advent of urbanization production has been carefully restricted. The districts are important for educational and recreational attractions. It includes the University of California at Los Angeles and a variety of theaters and auditoriums.

The **Hollywood District** is separated from downtown Los Angeles by miles of older residential neighborhoods, yet is easily reached by the Hollywood Freeway, one of the world's most heavily traveled city streets.

Hollywood, a temperance center of the 1880's and an orange-grove community, acquired its first motion-picture studio in 1911, a year after water shortage forced its merger with Los Angeles. By the 1920's this city district had 50,000 residents and was the center of a billion-dollar industry whose "stars" were world famous. Many picture companies estab-

Fig. 7-18. THE HOLLYWOOD DISTRICT.
View northward with the Santa Monica Mountains and the San Fernando Valley in the distance. Paramount Studios and Hollywood Cemetery (lower left) are also visible. (Hollywood Chamber of Commerce)

lished (or relocated) their lots and ranches elsewhere, but the District remains the headquarters for several major producers and scores of smaller firms who make advertising, religious, and specialty films. There are also many allied activities (casting offices, photographic equipment—also cosmetics, costume, and lingerie houses).

Functions of present-day Hollywood include entertainment, tourism, retail trade, sports, higher education, and residence (Fig. 7-18). The District is a tourist mecca, the first spot in the Lowlands visited by many strangers. It has a much higher proportion of courts and apartments than is typical in the metropolis. Hollywood residence for many means convenience; for others (particularly newcomers from the American "midlands") it implies glamour. Hollywood business enterprises stress "prestige." The District affords a "good" location for divorce lawyers, psychiatrists, beauty specialists, and travel agents.

Hollywood has significance overlooked by many tourists. Away from its main thorough-

fares it is a tranquil residential community (Fig. 7-18). On its eastern margin is Los Angeles City College, long the nation's largest two-year college. Its small campus was the ancestral site of U.C.L.A. (once Los Angeles Normal School). At the edge of the Santa Monica Mountains are the Pilgrimage Theatre, Hollywood Bowl, and Griffith Park (the nation's largest city park) with its planetarium, Greek theater, and zoological garden.

The **Sunset Strip**, a small enclave of county territory between Hollywood and Beverly Hills along Sunset Boulevard, contains smart specialty shops, expensive restaurants, and widely known night spots. Another "restaurant row," along La Cienega Boulevard (a north-south street), also has a number of art galleries.

The **Wilshire District**, south of Hollywood, focuses upon Wilshire Boulevard, the counterpart of Michigan Boulevard in Chicago and the Champs Élysées in Paris. This "fabulous boulevard" extends from downtown Los Angeles westward through Beverly Hills and

Santa Monica to the sea. Younger than many of the world's great avenues, Wilshire looks surprisingly "mature" for Los Angeles. Palm trees lend a tropical atmosphere and building construction seems interminable. The District is a fashionable residential locale characterized by expensive apartment buildings, large churches, office buildings, hotels, restaurants, and several shopping centers. West of downtown Los Angeles the boulevard bisects MacArthur Park, an old and stable neighborhood; business blocks include offices of many physicians, fraternal lodges, and the Los Angeles County Art Institute. Farther west, beyond Lafayette Park, are some of the smartest department stores and specialty shops in the nation and several first-class hotels. Westward still is Fremont Place, an older, conservative mansion neighborhood.

The "Miracle Mile," product of post-World War II growth, was one of the first shopping centers with huge off-street parking lots. On its western edge Wilshire passes the converted La Brea tarpits, where Los Angeles has created Hancock Park. North of the park rises the luxury skyscraper apartment development, Park La Brea. A nearby outlier of Hollywood includes Farmer's Market and Television City (C.B.S.).

Beverly Hills (30,800), a sumptuous residential satellite, is the costliest city in the nation for median-house purchase. Despite its municipal independence and village government, the city is largely supported by employment outside its limits. This slum-free community reflects careful planning and strict zoning. Thousands of curbside trees are city-planted, and utility poles are placed unobtrusively along alleys. In the "golden twenties," high-salaried movie stars began building mansions on the slopes of the Santa Monica Mountains. Beverly Hills experienced another population spurt in the 1940's, and there are few vacant lots. Apartment houses and business blocks along the principal thoroughfares help muffle traffic from individual homes.

The triangular Beverly Hills business district includes three internationally known hotels, department stores, and expensive specialty shops. There is a residential transition (south to north) with smaller homes (south of Santa Monica Boulevard), to pretentious homes (between Wilshire and Sunset along curved drives), to palatial estates (north of Sunset Boulevard on the slopes of the Santa Monica Mountains).

West of Beverly Hills, beyond the Los Angeles Country Club, is a larger area (Westwood, Brentwood, Bel Air, and Cheviot Hills) within the city limits of Los Angeles that also has large homes (including those of many celebrities and business executives), hilly terrain, and winding streets. **Westwood Village** became the site of a donated 400-acre campus for the University of California at Los Angeles. As the institution has grown, it has added professional schools (architecture, medicine, law, engineering) and has achieved academic excellence. Westwood's shopping center caters more to high-income residents of the surrounding districts, including Bel Air, than to the university community.[11] Tall office and apartment buildings have been erected along its section of Wilshire Boulevard.

Exclusive **Bel Air**, in the Santa Monica Mountains northwest of Beverly Hills, has developed since the 1920's. It has no shopping district—Westwood and Beverly Hills supply its retail needs. Social focus of the community is a small hostelry opened in 1945; this inn, inconspicuous from the street, was carefully merged into its canyon setting and is surrounded by gardens. The luxury of Bel Air cannot be fully appreciated from the streets. The chaparral-covered slopes, especially during the long drought season, do not have the beauty of exclusive suburbs in more humid lands.[12] Low rambling structures with walls of glass provide impressive views of the Coastal Plain and the Pacific; some are surrounded by ornate gardens obscured from

[11] U.C.L.A., U.S.C., and most of the colleges in the metropolitan area tend to be commuter institutions—student and staff parking has become a difficult problem.

[12] And the threat of disastrous fire is markedly greater. On November 6, 1961, fire, bellowed by high winds, destroyed 447 homes valued at $24,000,000.

public view, and most have private swimming pools.

South and west of the districts just described the land becomes flatter, streets follow the ordinary grid pattern, and houses are decidedly smaller and more modest. This portion of the Northwest includes West Los Angeles, Mar Vista, Palms, and Culver City. There is also **Sawtelle**, a county enclave west of Westwood, which contains the Veterans Administration's "Sawtelle Hospital," one of the largest institutions of its type. **West Los Angeles**, between Santa Monica and Beverly Hills (but south of Westwood), has an old business district and homes that vary from expensive (northeast near Los Angeles Country Club) to modest. One of the largest motion-picture studios, Twentieth Century Fox, is being converted into an apartment "city." **Culver City** (32,000), the other independent community of the Western districts, is an industrial-residential city whose economy has been much influenced by motion-picture studios (especially M.G.M.) and aircraft and electronics (particularly Hughes). Its low tax rates helped entice several studios from Hollywood in the 1920's; now it also has miscellaneous industrial plants scattered along Exposition and Sepulveda boulevards.

THE SANTA MONICA LITTORAL

Miles of sandy beaches, surf-spanked by the Pacific, broadside Santa Monica Bay from Point Dume southeastward to the Palos Verdes Hills. Despite its cool swells, the Littoral has been an aquatic frolic place for decades— some communities were founded by the 1880's. Thousands of homes, usually of pastel stucco, have been constructed since 1945 to produce a nearly continuous urban landscape from Santa Monica southward. Despite occasional fog and cooler summers, the virtually smog-free Bay towns experience the narrowest temperature range of the Lowlands, which has enhanced residential appeal.

The **Malibu Coast**, which extends westward from Santa Monica for 22 miles, was once occupied by three Mexican ranchos. Much of this foreshore and its mountainous back coun-

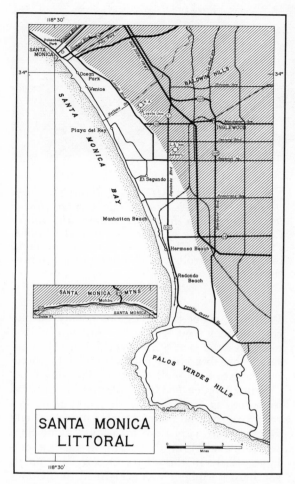

Fig. 7-19. MAP OF THE SANTA MONICA LITTORAL.

try was purchased by Frederick Rindge in 1887. The wealthy Bostonian died before he could convert it into an American Riviera. His widow stubbornly kept the property intact and thus prevented the Southern Pacific from following the shore with its Coast Line. The state, by obtaining court approval in 1925, was able to construct a segment of Coast Highway (U.S. 101A). Now the strand is cluttered with rows of beach cottages, private clubs, public beaches (including Will Rogers State Beach Park), motels, and restaurants. At sheltered Malibu Beach Colony affluent Angelenos maintain "beach cottages" (mansions). **Pacific**

Fig. 7-20. SANTA MONICA. Rand Corporation, beach hotels, and Civic Center (lower
left). Downtown district (center) with Malibu
Coast along base of Santa Monica Mountains.
(Santa Monica Chamber of Commerce, photo
by Tom Carroll of Photographic International)

Fig. 7-21. OIL REFINERY, EL SEGUNDO.
Southern California's largest refinery. (Standard Oil Company of California)

Palisades, a one-time religious colony on marine terraces (but within Los Angeles limits),
overlooks the sea. Since World War II "Palisades" has become a community of harmoni-
ous houses and well-selected plantings.

Santa Monica (83,000), platted in 1875 and
intended as a seaport, is a combination sea
resort, residential bedroom, and industrial city
whose homes vary from mansions (along Sunset Boulevard) in the north to modest cottages. Early in the 1900's Ocean Park on its
southern periphery was acclaimed the "Coney
Island of the Pacific." Santa Monica grew considerably in the 1920's, a time when movie
stars built beach estates (which became clubs
after Malibu Colony became more fashionable). Establishment of Douglas Aircraft
adjacent to the municipal airport stimulated
industrial growth. In the late 1940's most remaining "vacant" land (especially truck
patches) was converted into housing tracts.
Santa Monica is one of California's more attractive beach towns, with an assembly of
seaside hotels, a fishing pier, and a yacht
basin. Municipal pride is demonstrated in
Santa Monica City College, Palisades Park,
and the Civic Center (public library, city hall,
and auditorium, site of annual Academy
Award presentations) (Fig. 7-20). Nearby is

a "think" factory, the Rand Corporation research center that employs 150 Ph.D.'s.

Venice, founded in 1904 as an intended center of Western culture, was patterned after its
Italian namesake even to canals and gondolas.
Visitors preferred the beach and muscle-build-
ing, so its designer erected an amusement
park. Water shortage forced its merger with
Los Angeles in 1925 and the original image
vanished entirely with an oil boom in 1930 and
"town-lot" drilling, which brought a forest of
derricks. Instead of being a west-coast Fort
Lauderdale, Venice is occupied by a sizable
low-income population. Playa del Rey, established to the south as a beach resort in 1903,
was annexed to Venice in 1911 but has remained a more attractive residential area than
the remainder of Venice. Loyola University, a
sectarian college on its eastern periphery, originated as St. Vincent's College in downtown
Los Angeles in 1865. The new $100 million
Marina del Rey, a residential community aris-
ing (in county territory) around a small-boat
harbor (with space for 10,000 pleasure craft)
at the mouth of Ballona Creek, will change the
district considerably; it occupies a former
marshland.

El Segundo (14,000), the industrial
"orphan" of this residential-recreational coast,

was open ranch land when Standard Oil Company established its 1000-acre refinery (now the largest in Southern California) in 1910 to process oil from nearby fields (Fig. 7-21). The bay afforded tanker anchorage and cheap sea water for cooling, the dunes a good storage location from which gravity flow into tankers was possible. Vacant land, long leased from the oil company for beans and truck crops, has been converted into an industrial district adjacent to Los Angeles International Airport.

The southern Littoral, locally known as **South Bay** (a term sometimes generously extended inland) includes Manhattan Beach, Hermosa Beach, and Redondo Beach. There is rolling topography with semiconsolidated sand dunes that make popular housing sites. Earlier in the century the beaches became accessible but were too distant for much residential use. Since 1945 thousands of homes have replaced fields of gardenstuffs (strawberries, cut flowers, and vegetables). Large shopping centers have been erected and a new state college established. Middle-income residence is predicated upon shore and mild weather; hence there is much commutation to work. **Manhattan Beach** (34,000), a picturesque residential town founded by a religious group in 1897, has been spared the usual beach concessions; contiguous **Hermosa Beach** (16,000) has been less finicky. **Redondo Beach** (47,000), once considered a potential site for Los Angeles harbor, was for decades one of the most popular beaches of the Lowlands. Following breakwater construction in 1938, much beach erosion took place. Despite its new marina (berthage for 1000 boats), Redondo Beach is more residential than recreational in orientation.

Isolation (and court litigation) long delayed occupance of the **Palos Verdes Hills**, where extensive marine terraces were used to raise grain, truck crops, and cut flowers. Since 1950, numerous long, low dwellings have been erected on large lots (some with facilities to keep riding horses). Elevation provides vistas of the Pacific (and Catalina Island in good weather) as well as the impressive nocturnal sight of the well-lighted Coastal Plain. Marineland of the Pacific, with its whales and seals, has been a major tourist attraction.

THE CENTRAL COASTAL PLAIN

The central Coastal Plain extends eastward from the Santa Monica Littoral to the Orange County line and northward from the outskirts of San Pedro Bay cities to the Montebello and Puente hills (see map, Fig. 7-22). From 1910 to 1950 Los Angeles County was the nation's agricultural leader, and during those years much of its farm output came from the central Coastal Plain. As late as World War II this area still possessed broad expanses of rurban landscape with small farm towns, politically independent of Los Angeles and surrounded by "ranches" (usually small irrigated farms, intensively tilled). Flood problems, a scattering of oil fields and some heavy industries tended to make the central Plain less popular for subdivision until sites closer-in to Los Angeles had been occupied. Since 1940 the gargantuan metropolis has encroached upon the farmlands—vast housing tracts, shopping centers, and numerous industrial plants have replaced the fields to produce a complex urban mosaic. The stranger to the metropolis is usually cognizant of passing from one "political city" to another along a boulevard or freeway only because of "city limits" signs.

To clarify description of this bewildering landscape, the central Coastal Plain here is divided into three somewhat arbitrary units: (1) a western "block" (between the Santa Monica Littoral and the Los Angeles "Shoestring"), (2) a middle "block" (between the Shoestring and the Los Angeles River), and (3) an eastern "block" (from the Los Angeles River to the border of Orange County).

THE WESTERN BLOCK

This portion of the Coastal Plain (see map, Fig. 7-22) includes a segment of Los Angeles, eight incorporated cities, and considerable "county" land (unincorporated fringes). It was utilized primarily for grainfields and truck gardens before the 1920's. Subsequent oil discoveries, development of Los Angeles International Airport, and establishment of aircraft

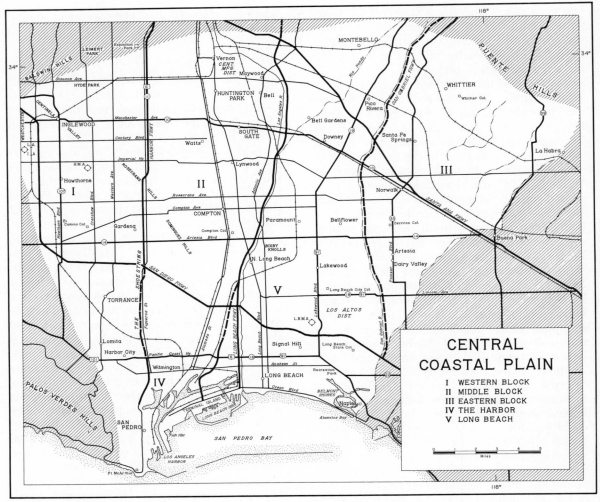

Fig. 7-22. MAP OF THE CENTRAL COASTAL PLAIN.

factories and a host of other manufacturing plants have diversified its economy and contributed to rapid urbanization. South of Inglewood much farmland remained into the 1950's. Much of the area, which includes the Westchester district of Los Angeles and the cities of Inglewood, Hawthorne, Gardena, Lawndale, and Torrance, consists chiefly of middle-income residences with numerous large housing tracts.

Westchester, which had been bean and grain fields, was one of the fastest growing districts of Los Angeles in the 1940's and early

1950's. Its middle-income families include numerous employees—many in the managerial category—of aircraft, electronics, and engineering firms adjacent to Los Angeles International Airport.

Los Angeles International Airport is the leading air terminal of western United States. It originated with the purchase of a site for a municipal field west of Inglewood in 1938. The airport handles upwards of 20 million passengers annually and has numerous airline connections to all continents. There is also a large volume of feeder traffic within California and helicopter service to outlying portions of the Lowlands. The volume of air freight has continued to increase rapidly. The land had served as a flying field even before it was purchased by the city, and in 1936 North American Aviation opened a plant on its southern periphery. Now 100 industrial establishments, concerned principally with airspace and electronics, fringe the airport and provide employment for 55,000 (in addition to the 4500 airline employees). Timely establishment of the field while much open country was available has permitted the construction of 8500-foot runways to handle jet flights. For many years passenger services were located in barracks that suggested a military base. In 1962 the city completed elaborate passenger terminals.

Inglewood (63,000), a boom town of the 1880's, remained a farm supply center for the surrounding Centinela Valley ranchers through the 1930's. Subsequently its growth has been based upon industrial firms in the city and around International Airport. Hollywood Park, a prominent horse-race concourse, is in the eastern portion of the city. Northrop Institute of Technology, founded in 1942 to train aircraft workers, is gaining status as an engineering college.

Hawthorne (33,000), another ex-farm village, grew rapidly after industrial development took place around Los Angeles International and Hawthorne airports. There are a number of modest bungalows in the city. Evolution of **Gardena** (36,000) to the southeast has been somewhat comparable although it is less industrial and more of a surburban bedroom. Tolerance of burlesque shows and "poker palaces" has given the city local notoriety.

Torrance (101,000) began as a planned industrial city in 1911; from the first it had railroad facilities, adequate water and fuel, and accessibility to Los Angeles Harbor. It was laid out with workers' bungalows around a central business district and with a peripheral industrial zone. Manufacturing has been related to the Torrance oil field and has also included steel and aluminum processing and aircraft assembly. On its northern periphery is two-year El Camino College, whose spiral-ing enrollment reflects population growth in the environs.

THE SHOESTRING

The "Shoestring" (see map, Fig. 7-22), only half a mile wide, extends for a north-south distance of nine miles along Figueroa Street (and now Harbor Freeway). It was created in 1906 to provide political linkage between Los Angeles and its harbor satellites, San Pedro and Wilmington. Its motley array of dairy farms, a pet cemetery, chicken farms, cattle ranches, motels, the Rosecrans oil field, and assorted industrial plants (including synthetic rubber) has given many tourists approaching the metropolis from the south an inadequate impression of Los Angeles.

THE MIDDLE BLOCK

A row of manufacturing towns and industrial suburbs has grown athwart rail lines between downtown Los Angeles and the harbor (see map, Fig. 7-22): Vernon, Huntington Park, Maywood, Bell, South Gate, Lynwood, and Compton. Industrial output is of a diversified, locally oriented nature: food processing and metal working are leading categories, with automobiles and tires among the major products. Although factories dominate zones along rail routes, most of the area is solidly residential, and many inhabitants commute to other places on the Coastal Plain. Economic status is predominantly lower to middle income, with large lower-income populations residing in unincorporated districts west of Alameda Street.

Vernon (200) is the industrial core of the primary industrial belt of metropolitan Los Angeles. This independent village, with limited municipal services besides those demanded by industrial plants (which provide their own fire protection), has the lowest tax rates of any incorporated California "city." [13]

[13] Wesley Marx, in "As If Los Angeles Didn't Have Enough Trouble," *The Reporter* (October 25, 1962), reviewed the effect upon the metropolitan area of communities incorporated for industrial use. Besides Vernon, the first, others include Commerce, Irwindale, Industry, and Santa Fe Springs.

Fig. 7-23. *CENTRAL MANUFACTURING DISTRICT, VERNON. View eastward across the center of the 3800-acre C.M.D. complex, with the Terminal Warehouse Tower Building in the center. The C.M.D. houses 750 industrial establishments which employ 75,000. The Los Angeles River runs diagonally across the picture.* (Central Manufacturing District, Inc., photo by Howard Kelly)

Its generally dilapidated dwellings, occupying 1 percent of the corporate area, are surrounded by scores of factories that employ some 80,-000; there is no shopping center. The rail and truck-line facilities are excellent. They include the Santa Fe classification yards and sixteen spur lines of the Southern Pacific plus the Los Angeles Junction lines, specifically constructed to serve the district. There is marked concentration of meat-packing plants and other food-processing establishments. Steel fabrication, auto assembly, lumber yard, and a wide variety of other industrial types are represented. A major growth factor has been the **Central Manufacturing District,** a 3800-acre tract (Fig. 7-23).

Huntington Park (30,000) is a well-planned residential community established adjacent to Vernon in 1903. Early start as a retail center affords its business district a larger retail volume than in Compton and South Gate, both larger cities. **Maywood** (14,600) and **Bell** (19,500) are industrial suburbs.

South Gate (54,000), established in 1918, contrasts with Huntington Park. Besides its

residential function it has diversified industrial output that includes auto assembly, rubber processing, machinery, and furniture. The **Watts** district to the west is a political subdivision of Los Angeles that lies athwart the north-south "minority belt" (Mexican-Negro) extending southward for many miles along the eastern side of Los Angeles. This belt, with a large number of unskilled workers, has a high population density for metropolitan Los Angeles, and its schools have sometimes been overcrowded. However, half of the workers of Watts are classified as white-collar or skilled. **Lynwood** (32,000) is another industrial bedroom.

Compton (72,000), one of the oldest American towns in the Lowlands, began as a religious colony and was long a farm center. Rapid growth as a residence town for industrial workers after 1940 has caused some social unrest. Two-year Compton College is supported by several cities.

THE EASTERN BLOCK

This portion of the Coastal Plain extends southward from the Montebello Hills to the outskirts of Long Beach (map, Fig. 7-22). This long prosperous agricultural countryside experienced quite a tremendous urban growth after 1950 with construction of the Santa Ana and Long Beach freeways. Major agricultural usage had included citrus (Whittier and Downey), dairies (Paramount and Artesia), truck gardens and poultry farms, and bean and grain fields. Many of its communities long remained small "crossroads" villages. Long before the Fourth Boom, there had been a pronounced contrast between the *northern* districts with a physical environment that favored orchards and cultural assets for industry (rail lines, oil fields, and closer proximity to Los Angeles) and the *south*, with heavier soils, which still retains some agricultural aspects. Major cities, in order of approximate size, include Norwalk, Downey, Lakewood, Pico-Rivera, Bellflower, Whittier, Montebello, Paramount, Bell Gardens, and Santa Fe Springs.

Whittier (34,000), founded in the 1880's, has been a tranquil Quaker colony, despite discovery of the Whittier-Coyote oil field in 1912. Avocado orchards remain on the south slopes of the Puente Hills, but the orange groves were replaced by housing tracts in the 1950's. The city is the home of Whittier College, a sectarian liberal-arts institution, and Whittier Junior College.

Montebello (32,000), another product of the First Boom, had an important nursery stock output before 1950 (favored by air drainage off the Montebello Hills). Rise of the Montebello oil field (1916) reduced acreage of flowers and nursery stock somewhat. Industry, warehouses, truck terminals, and housing tracts reflect eastward expansion of the primary industrial belt during the Fourth Boom.

Downey (82,500) was established in 1873 and eventually became the center of a citrus and dairying district. Its character changed rapidly after 1940 with aircraft production, tract housing, and eventually incorporation. Many of its dwellings are more costly than is typical in this area.

Santa Fe Springs (16,300), lately a scattering of houses in an oil field, is still more interested in attracting industry than people.

Norwalk (88,800) long depended upon its truck gardens and dairies. As the metropolis stretched southeastward along the Santa Ana Freeway, Norwalk's population quadrupled in a decade. A shopping center exceeds the original downtown district in size. The payroll of Metropolitan State Hospital is an economic stimulant.

The *dairy belt* of Los Angeles County remains the national leader in production of market milk (100 percent is Grade A) despite its spiraling urbanization (Fig. 7-24). Dairies have already been replaced by housing in **Paramount** (27,000) and **Bellflower** (45,000); more than 100 dairies have been relocated around Ontario, and metropolitan dairymen have much interest in Stanislaus County (Chapter 9). Despite the determination of many dairymen and the efforts of the Regional Planning Commission, it seems problematic that the dairying can continue in the Eastern Block. Already land is quoted (in 1962) at $5000 to $50,000 an acre. The county has 430 dairies and an average herd of about

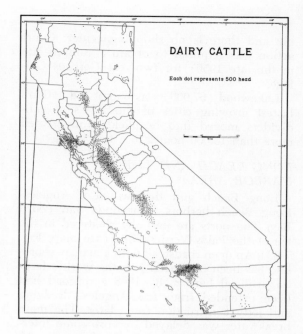

Fig. 7-24. MAP OF THE DISTRIBUTION OF DAIRY COWS IN CALIFORNIA.

240 animals. The dairy "farms" are small lots (average size about 15 acres; see Fig. 7-38). The absence of pastures and the employment of unionized dairy hands contrast with the eastern "American Dairy Belt." Alfalfa is trucked from Imperial, Antelope, and San Joaquin valleys. Other feeds, as well as replacement cows, are largely imported. It takes an average annual replacement of 50,000 animals to maintain twice the national milk production per cow. Most dairymen are of Dutch or Portuguese ancestry. Despite the highest costs (in wages, taxes, replacement cows, and feed) of any dairy belt in the United States, this $75 million (annual production) operation retails milk about as inexpensively as in any American city.

Artesia (10,000) is the center of the dairy belt, which also includes two towns incorporated in 1956 exclusively for dairying, Dairy Valley and Dairyland (in adjacent Orange County). Both have far more cows than people and there is no shopping center. Court action was required to obtain a campus site in the late 1950's for two-year Cerritos College.

Lakewood (67,000) was one of the nation's fastest growing cities of the 1950's as subdividers moved into beanfields and erected more than 15,000 homes in a few years.

LONG BEACH AND THE HARBOR AREA [14]

Long Beach and the twin Los Angeles-Long Beach harbors front upon San Pedro Bay. The ports are partially sheltered in the lee of the Palos Verdes Hills (see map, Fig. 7-22). An open roadstead with a marshy shoreline has been converted into the world's largest artificial harbor. By 1868 a railroad had been extended from Los Angeles; dredging and jetty construction came later. The main breakwater was delayed because some interests (especially the Southern Pacific Company) favored Santa Monica as the chief harbor. Breakwater construction began in 1899 after the controversy was settled and federal funds were allocated.

Los Angeles then extended its boundaries to the sea by absorbing San Pedro and Wilmington, which were attached to the city by the Shoestring cited earlier. In 1911 state tidelands were ceded to Los Angeles and Long Beach. The waterfront, including docks and buildings, is largely municipally owned.

The harbor has two units (Fig. 7-25): Outer Harbor (San Pedro Bay) provides Navy and commercial anchorage 46 to 52 feet deep; Inner Harbor, dredged to create a 35-foot channel, has entrances at San Pedro and Long Beach. Between these entrances is Terminal Island, bridge-connected to the mainland. Earlier docks were concentrated in Inner Harbor. Newer facilities (as the Navy Base and supertanker terminals) have been formed through fill into Outer Harbor. The federal government and the two cities have expended some $200 million on facilities. Despite 40

[14] *This section has been reviewed by Gerard Foster, Long Beach State College.*

miles of waterfront, much space for expansion remains.

Los Angeles–Long Beach ranks second on the Pacific Coast to the collective ports of San Francisco Bay in annual cargo tonnage and value. Among individual West Coast ports, Los Angeles is the tonnage leader. Commerce is rising despite competitive transport media. Ship clearances are fewer than in 1930 (the peak year), but tonnage volume has increased. Southern California is the primary hinterland. Imports are largely consumed in the metropolis; exports also tend to be local in origin.

The five Pacific Basin states form the leading trade area (largely for petroleum and lumber). Foreign-trade tonnage now almost equals the traditionally dominant domestic commerce. Especially significant is such high-value cargo as perishable foods, vehicles, glass, and porcelain. Japan is an outstanding customer (scrap metal, potash, iron ore, cotton, and tallow).

Major commodities include heavy bulk-transport items (see list). Petroleum accounts for almost three quarters of all tonnage. After the opening of Panama Canal and discovery of local fields, heavy oil exports moved to the East Coast. Foreign oil imports now form a quarter of all petroleum traffic.

Lumber, long the second-ranking commodity by weight (until superseded by scrap metal), was imported from the Pacific Northwest and northern California, but this has declined as overland hauls by truck and rail have increased. Specialized lumber-carrying ships still call, and there is large dockside lumber storage.

Besides lumber and other building materials, inbound cargoes include volumes of tropical products (copra, bananas, rubber, and coffee). Leading outbound items include minerals and farm products. Commodities shown in the list scarcely reveal the export diversity. Passengers and military cargoes add significantly to harbor traffic.

Los Angeles has long been the nation's leading fishing port. Fresh fish for local markets are landed at Fisherman's Dock in San Pedro,

LEADING COMMODITIES
LOS ANGELES–LONG BEACH HARBOR
(in order of tonnage, circa 1960)

INBOUND	OUTBOUND
petroleum	petroleum
lumber	scrap metal
steel-mill products	potash
newsprint	iron ore
gypsum	borax
copra	pig iron
fish	cotton
bananas	tallow, hides, and skins
molasses	citrus fruit

but most of the catch is unloaded at Fish Harbor canneries (western Terminal Island). Canning commenced at San Pedro before 1900. Fish Harbor, constructed in 1915-1916, is the site of a dozen canneries employing about 4000 workers. Output has been primarily for national and international markets.

Larger fishing vessels with refrigerated holds operate southward beyond the equator in search of tuna (leading species). Some tuna, as albacore and bluefin, are caught in the colder nearby waters. Other species canned include mackerel and sardines.

Supply and market fluctuations have been pronounced. Sardines have diminished greatly since the late 1940's. International competitors, with better techniques and improved equipment (since World War II economic recovery), have absorbed much of the world market for canned sardines and mackerel; even Terminal Island canneries consume increasing volumes of foreign-caught fish.

Tuna supplies are not yet dramatically depleted as have been sardines, and American consumption is rising. Canneries rely heavily upon Japanese and Peruvian tuna in partial preference to more expensive fish landed locally. Establishment of American-owned canneries in Puerto Rico, Peru, and Samoa causes San Pedro fishermen concern.

Los Angeles–Long Beach Harbor, at the south end of the primary industrial belt, is a major manufacturing center of the Lowlands. Port-type industries are characteristic. Wood processing and petroleum refining are important. Lumber milling occurs at tidewater but oil refining, with its vast tank farms, is more scattered.

Copra from Pacific islands is converted into supplemental dairy feeds, margarine, and soap. Borax from Searles Lake (Chapter 3) is processed for international export. Gypsum from Mexico is manufactured into wallboard and other building materials at shipside.

Shipbuilding and repair, a vital harbor industry, depends heavily upon federal contracts. Several private yards and a Navy shipyard are represented. Since the late 1950's the industry has been stimulated by contracts for cargo-passenger ships; employment exceeds 10,000. To foster shipbuilding here for strategic reasons the government has permitted higher costs (labor and steel are more expensive) than along the Atlantic seaboard.

The Wilmington oil field, discovered in the vicinity in 1934, is presently California's leading producer. Land subsidence accompanied petroleum withdrawal until 1959; subsequent salt-water injection proved remedial. Subsidence had already reached depths of 25 feet and has necessitated widespread rebuilding in the Long Beach sector. Oil-field revenue has helped Long Beach to construct fine waterfront facilities, and the Long Beach share of total harbor commerce has been increasing since 1930.

San Pedro (approximately 50,000), a political subdivision of Los Angeles between the harbor and Palos Verdes Hills (Fig. 7-25), was California's chief colonial center in the hide and tallow trade. After Wilmington was established, San Pedro languished until railroad service opened in 1868. Port functions are documented by nautical equipage establishments along the waterfront; located here are Los Angeles Harbor Commission offices. The nearby Civic Center has a sub-City Hall. Farther south are Fort MacArthur and Cabrillo Beach Park. Residential districts ascend marine terraces overlooking the harbor.

Wilmington, originally New San Pedro, was established in the 1850's and flourished in pre-railroad days because it was closer to Los Angeles than San Pedro; San Pedro, with more

Fig. 7-25. THE PORT OF LOS ANGELES. This 7000-acre man-made harbor handles 5000 ships and 24-million tons of cargo annually. Note the main channel (middle), San Pedro (left), and Terminal Island (middle right). (Port of Los Angeles)

Fig. 7-26. THE CITY AND PORT OF LONG BEACH. Harbor facilities in the foreground have been partially financed with oil revenues. This view includes the central district and Rainbow Pier (middle left). (Long Beach Chamber of Commerce)

appealing residential sites, is now larger. Wilmington's harbor segments contain various passenger and cargo terminals, oil wells, industrial plants, and sundry activities related to the port such as the shippers' association and the longshoremen's dispatch hall. The community has one of seven Los Angeles municipal two-year colleges, Los Angeles Harbor College.

Long Beach (344,000) is the third city of Southern California (and the nation's thirty-sixth largest). It was founded in the Boom of the Eighties, and was known for decades principally as a beach town popular with midwesterners. Its economy has gradually broadened: seaport, Navy base and shipyard, oil town, and, since 1940, industrial center.

Balmy weather helped make Long Beach a favorite West Coast center for retired middlewesterners, for decades the leading segment of its population. Reputedly there are more ex-Iowans in Long Beach than in any Iowa city except Des Moines.[15] These people have tended to be conservative Protestant church-goers. Often gregarious, they made the city renowned for a multitude of organizations supported by "joiners"; picnics were characteristic. After establishment of the Navy base

[15] It is appropriate that a local supermarket chain was called "Iowa Pork Shops."

in 1925, social stratification began to change. This process was accelerated during the depressed 1930's, World War II, and subsequently during the Fourth Boom, which has brought numerous younger working families.

The downtown district, like central Los Angeles and San Diego, is small for the city population (Fig. 7-26). There are fewer department stores and specialty shops than should exist if Long Beach were a dominant regional center (this factor suggests the relationship between San Francisco and Oakland; see Chapter 8). A compact Civic Center flanks the western edge of the business district adjacent to Lincoln Park. The Pike, an amusement center with roller coaster and other rides, novelty shops, and the adjoining Rainbow Pier, denotes moment as a Navy base and resort city. Within the semicircle of Rainbow Pier are the municipal auditorium and Arena. These serve the needs of this convention city. These facilities, like the harbor and other shoreline improvements, have been partially financed with oil revenues. A file of waterfront hotels further reflects the resort nature of the city.

East of the central district are numerous apartment houses, hotels, and motels near the beach; this locality has been popular with Navy families. Here are Bixby and Recreation parks, sites for some of the long-famed "state picnics." Contiguous Marine Stadium was constructed for rowing races of the 1932 Olympic games. Alamitos Bay has a state beach park and pleasure-craft anchorages. **Naples** is a seaside residential district amidst canals. Northeastward from Alamitos Bay are Long Beach State College, the Veterans' Administration Hospital, and miles of tract housing erected in the 1950's.

Western Long Beach was urbanized largely during the 1930's and during World War II. Much of it consists of middle- to low-income residence districts that are rather extensive near the Los Angeles–Long Beach harbors. There have also been "temporary" federal housing tracts, light industrial plants, and warehouses.

North Long Beach, although largely an area of modest homes, includes the city's most exclusive residential sector, Bixby Knolls, suggestive of a small Beverly Hills. The shopping center along Atlantic Boulevard contains attractive retail stores. Reminiscent of the Mexican era is Adobe los Cerritos, a remodeled Monterey-style mansion that is now a city museum. To the east is Long Beach City College and the Municipal Airport with a Douglas Aircraft plant that has been the city's leading employer.

Signal Hill (4600), surrounded by Long Beach, is suggestive of Beverly Hills and San Fernando (both surrounded by Los Angeles) —it is a "city within a city." Prior to 1921, Signal Hill was an attractive village whose view lots offered promise of exclusive residence. Between 1921 and 1923 came the world-famed oil boom with its wasteful "town-lot" drilling and a subsequent forest of derricks. This event much influenced the growth of Long Beach as thousands of oil-field workers arrived. An almost unbelievable wealth in petroleum has been removed from the 1400 acres beneath Signal Hill. Although not primarily a refining place, the town possesses numerous oil-tool and other service establishments. Recent plans indicate that Signal Hill may yet become a choice residential area. However, industrial encroachment may result from its low tax rates.

THE SOUTHEAST

The southeastern Coastal Plain has long been regarded as a separate lowland—it is popularly referred to as "Orange County." [16] The Southeast reaches inland to the Santa Ana Mountains and the lower-elevation continuations of that range known as the China and Puente hills (see map, Fig. 7-27); in the south it abuts against the San Joaquin Hills.

Before the 1950's the southeast Plain remained primarily an agrarian land without the rapid urbanization occurring in Los Angeles. After 1950 the Southeast experienced rapid metamorphosis, and it tended to merge into the urban complex like pieces of a jigsaw puzzle after construction of the Santa Ana Freeway. As "closer-in" residential acreage disappeared elsewhere on the Coastal Plain, vast new housing tracts were created on the southeast Plain. The airspace industry and diversified service manufacturing for metropolitan markets, seeking "free land," have become important stimulants of urbanization here, supplemented by petroleum, recreation enterprises, and military bases. There is also much commutation to Los Angeles and Long Beach.

THE LAND

The Southeast, an alluvial surface built mainly by the Santa Ana River, seems featureless. Before construction of Prado flood-control basin (in the Inland Valleys upriver) and dikes downstream, the Santa Ana River wandered excessively during flood stages. The alluvial soils of the interior tend to be well-drained loamy sands with poorly drained clays along the coastal margin. North of Fullerton is a belt of low, oil-bearing hills, which separate the Plain from a higher basin in which are located La Habra, Brea, and Yorba Linda. Along the coast the Newport-Inglewood Uplift is evidenced by low mesas and rich petroleum deposits.

AGRICULTURAL OCCUPANCE

The Spanish made limited use of the Southeast, rather remote from Mission San Gabriel

[16] *This section has been reviewed by Arthur Earick and Gertrude Reith, Orange State College.*

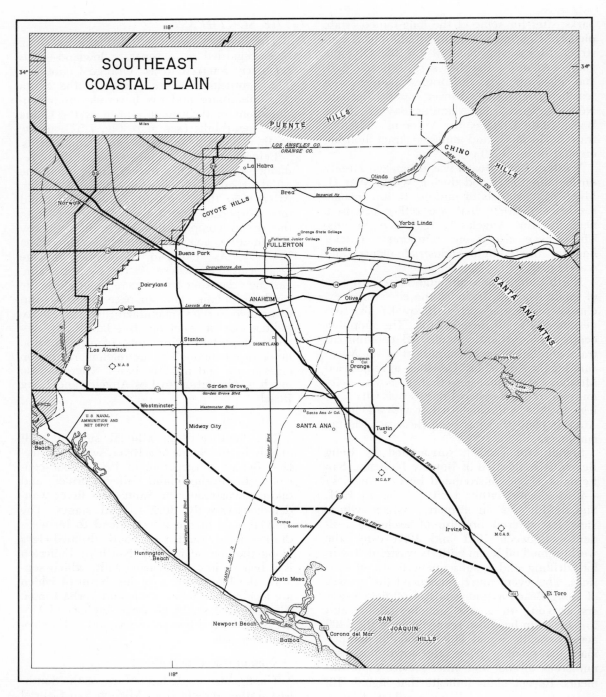

Fig. 7-27. MAP OF THE SOUTHEAST COASTAL PLAIN.

210 : : CHAPTER SEVEN

LEADING AGRICULTURAL
COMMODITIES, ORANGE COUNTY, 1961
(values in millions of dollars)

Fruits and Nuts	
oranges, Valencia	28.9
strawberries	6.45
avocados	1.2
lemons	1.1
oranges, navel	0.6
walnuts	0.16
Livestock and Products	
milk, market	18.9
eggs	16.2
cows, milk	2.4
baby chicks	2.3
cattle, beef	1.4
chickens	0.91
turkeys	0.78
Field Crops	
dry beans	3.8
sugar beets	0.25
Vegetables	
celery	3.67
tomatoes	2.85
peppers	1.98
green beans	1.35
carrots	1.15
asparagus	1.1
sweet corn	1.0
cauliflower	1.0
lettuce	0.69
cabbage	0.56
squash	0.4
mushrooms	0.39
parsley	0.33
Nursery Stock	5.4
Total Output	110.2

Source: Agricultural Commissioner, Orange County.

and Los Angeles. Ten ranchos, some with limits extending beyond the Coastal Plain, were awarded during the Mexican period. Activity was centered along the Santa Ana River, especially on the eastern portion of the lowland. Here there was water for garden irrigation as well as the typical cattle grazing.

Grazing and grain farming were the basic activities in the last half of the nineteenth century. Anaheim, first post-Mexican "colony" in the entire Lowlands, was established in 1857 by the Los Angeles Vineyard Society (a group of Germans from San Francisco). It

became the Lowlands' principal wine producer; output reached a zenith in 1885 when there were 500,000 vines. Drought and floods hampered production, but it was disease that ended viticulture.

A new agricultural phase began in the middle 1880's with the sudden shift from vines to walnuts and Valencia oranges. In the 1930's avocados and lemons were planted on the southern slopes of the Chino and Puente hills, where air drainage minimized frost damage. Alfalfa, beans, sugar beets, and truck crops were grown extensively on lands west of the citrus groves, where soils were heavier and the water table high.

Farm products reached peak value in 1959; the acreage of Valencia oranges had attained its maximum (66,000 acres) a decade earlier. Contrariwise, dairying increased for a decade after World War II as the Los Angeles dairy belt migrated eastward into Orange County. Recently, major commodities have included Valencia oranges, milk, eggs, strawberries, and truck crops (see chart).

URBANIZATION AND INDUSTRY

An urban landscape and a defense-oriented economy began to dominate the Southeast in the 1950's. The census of 1960 included most of the Plain for the first time within the Los Angeles urbanized area. Population now exceeds three quarters of a million and annual increment recently has averaged more than 50,000. Most of the Plain northwest of the Irvine Ranch is encompassed within more than 20 municipalities, almost half of which were incorporated in the 1950's.

Recent urbanization of the Southeast is supported in the main by two activities: local manufacturing and commuter employment elsewhere within the Los Angeles complex. Both have been motivated by general growth of Los Angeles and improved highway links with the metropolitan core. Roughly 15 percent of all workers commute to Los Angeles County, a major explanation for heavy residential development close to the Santa Ana and Riverside Freeways and along other major arteries leading westward, such as Whittier Boulevard in La Habra and Garden

Grove Boulevard (Highway 22) in West-minster and Garden Grove.

Manufacturing accounts for nearly 30 per-cent of Southeast local employment. Many new establishments are of miscellaneous urban-service types, whose output includes such diverse items as foods, machinery, chem-icals, containers, and automobile parts. There are also the "old-line" industries based on handling of local farm output or catering to petroleum production. Petroleum, especially significant since the early 1920's, helped to diversify the economy of the Plain. Produc-tion has been centered in two areas. The *coastal* zone from Newport to Seal Beach in-cludes Huntington Beach, one of the state's leading producers (see Chapter 9). *Inland,* oil is produced around Brea, Olinda, and Fuller-ton, where there are two large oil-company research laboratories and a related synthetic fertilizer plant.

Recently more fundamental industrializa-tion has been based upon airspace develop-ments. Although the Southeast has lacked traditional aircraft plants, its open spaces have proved irresistible to parent firms in Los An-geles County as the electronics era began and additional factories became necessary. Hughes, Northrop, Lockheed, North Ameri-can, and Douglas—for example—have estab-lished plants in Orange County. Some smaller firms have transferred their entire operations from Los Angeles as new facilities were needed. Other major electronics concerns are essentially indigenous to the Southeast, or, like Ford Motor Company's Aeroneutronics, represent the influx of eastern manufacturers.

Most of these new airspace developments are not attached to airports. Those that em-phasize heavy production have been located on level tracts beside railroad spurs. Where research and lighter production dominates, however, site qualities are less restricted; hence rougher lands around Fullerton and Newport Beach are utilized. Industrial zones are widely dispersed on the Southeast Plain. Generally they form ribbons parallel to estab-lished rail lines or around oil fields.

Most of the larger airspace plants so far have been located in the Anaheim-Fullerton area, particularly along an east-west belt aligned with the Santa Fe Railroad main line between Hughes Aircraft in west Fullerton and the gigantic Autonetics complex on the northeast fringe of Anaheim. South Santa Ana and Buena Park are also important indus-trial centers; still others, as Seal Beach, are beginning to evolve as urbanization continues.

Shoreline recreation has had increased im-portance since the early 1920's; improvement of the Coast Highway (U.S. 101 Alternate) and continued population growth of the Low-lands have been significant. Activity at **New-port Bay**, erstwhile mouth of the Santa Ana River, has converted this locality into a popu-lar aquatic playground and yachting center. **Disneyland**, erected near the Santa Ana Free-way in the early 1950's, has become one of the world's best-known amusement parks (Fig. 7-28).

ORANGE BELT TOWNS

The "orange-belt towns" evolved in the American period, yet they are among the old-est post-Mexican communities. As late as 1950, they gave the suggestion of having been placed amidst the citrus groves along main rail lines with much care, so as not to dis-turb a single orchard. For several decades these clean and conservative little cities, eco-nomically independent of Los Angeles, re-mained chiefly residential communities serv-ing as trade centers and shipping points for the surrounding farmers. Social stratification was rather rigid. Change came quickly after 1950 with the rapid construction of housing tracts, shopping centers, and industrial plants. Now Buena Park, Fullerton, Anaheim, Orange, Santa Ana, and Garden Grove are merging into the continuous urban fabric of metropoli-tan Los Angeles.

Anaheim (104,000), largest city of Orange County (and twelfth city of California), has lost most evidences of its German colony origin (Fig. 7-29). Before 1950 it had been stable and growing relatively slowly. Then it was engulfed by the outward expansion of metropolitan Los Angeles along the Santa Ana Freeway. Closer to downtown Los Angeles than Santa Ana, it benefited sooner from con-

Fig. 7-28. DISNEYLAND. Sleeping Beauty Castle and Fantasyland. (Disneyland)

struction of housing tracts adjacent to Santa Ana Freeway. Its business community has long been receptive to in-migration of industry. Electronics firms are most conspicuous among the many new industrial plants, though Disneyland is perhaps its best-known institution.

Santa Ana (100,000), seat of Orange County, was the largest city of the southeast Plain for half a century. Growth, accelerated in the 1940's, quickened in the 1950's. During World War II Santa Ana Air Base and El Toro Marine Corps Air Station influenced its growth; the latter remains a major installation. The imposing city-county civic center and multitude of specialty shops and services reflect countywide population increase. Special cultural attractions include Santa Ana College and Bowers Museum.

Fullerton (56,000), another product of the Boom of the Eighties (there are many in the Lowlands), grew less rapidly than Santa Ana or Anaheim despite an oil boom in 1922. Now extensive areas of higher-income residence are appearing on the slopes north of the city, and industrial growth is augmenting the important food-processing industries. Orange State College and Fullerton College are here.

Orange (26,000) like Fullerton was eclipsed by its proximity to Anaheim and especially to Santa Ana. One of the county's older towns, it was known as Richland before citrus groves became important in the 1880's. Despite surrounding orange orchards, the town has had a smaller service area than other Orange Belt cities. Chapman College moved here from Los Angeles in 1954.

Garden Grove (84,000) was an inconsequential farm village before the 1950's. Now it has miles of tract housing.

Buena Park (46,000), on the western fringe of the citrus belt, was another small village

Fig. 7-29. ANAHEIM. View of the central district, the Santa Ana Freeway, and many blocks of new housing. (Anaheim Chamber of Commerce, photo by Pacific Air Industries)

before 1950. The farmlands were used for truck crops, dairies, poultry farms, and sugar beets. For several decades the city has been known for Knott's Berry Farm, one of the tourist attractions of the Lowlands.

THE BEACH TOWNS

The Orange County strand provides a continuation of the Coastal Plain shore with its miles of sandy beaches (previously noted along Santa Monica Bay); it continues from Seal Beach to Newport Bay. To the south the San Joaquin Hills reach the Pacific, and there are abrupt headlands and sea cliffs. Oil wells, public beaches, sports-fishing piers, steam-generator plants, sewage-disposal units, a surprising extent of open tidal marshland, increasing numbers of dwellings, and Newport Bay with its yacht basin characterize this coast.

Seal Beach (7000), erstwhile site of Anaheim Landing (roadstead serving Anaheim's wine growers in the nineteenth century), is a growing seashore suburb of Long Beach. Many Lowlanders come here during the grunion runs between March and August, when these little fish spawn on the sand in the moonlight. Adjacent to Seal Beach is the Naval Ammunition and Net Depot and, farther to the north, Los Alamitos Naval Air Station. Both bases were established during World War II as an outgrowth of Naval activity in Los Angeles–Long Beach harbors. The environs of Seal Beach Depot are becoming significant for development and assemblage of craft for outer space.

Despite its sports pier and sandy seacoast, **Huntington Beach** (11,500) has been known for its productive oil field. Adjacent to the town is much frequented Huntington Beach State Park. The oil boom began in 1923; later, "whipstocking" (directional drilling) permitted tapping of offshore tideland pools. Another (onshore) pool located in 1955 prompted town-lot drilling. The metropolitan fringe reached the city during the 1950's, and residential development and annexation took place. Within two years after the 1960 census, the population had doubled.

NEWPORT BAY COMMUNITIES

A quartet (Corona del Mar, Costa Mesa, Newport Beach, and Balboa) of towns around Newport Bay are the chief "watering spots" of the Lowlands. The Bay naturally was a silt-clogged water body at the mouth of the Santa Ana River. The lower course of the river was straightened when it was diked, and a new mouth was created northwest of the bay. Plans for resort development were inaugurated in the 1890's, but little activity materialized until construction of the Pacific Electric system in the following decade. More transition has taken place since the 1920's, when the bay was dredged. The summer population of this resort area is much swollen, yet, increasingly, permanent residents are either employed in local industries or commute to other parts of the metropolitan area. There are also a substantial number of older, retired residents.

Newport Beach (26,500) constituted the original town on the bay—it was merged with Balboa as a single political unit in 1902. Today it includes three man-made islands and an elevated residential sector known as Corona del Mar. Newport Beach itself serves as the political and retail center. The islands, where land values are high, are covered with dwellings, and numerous pleasure craft are anchored in the bay, self-styled as "yacht capital of the Pacific." **Costa Mesa** (37,600), established on terraces north of the bay in 1915, long remained unincorporated. Its rapid growth has resulted from light industry, Fairview State Hospital, and residence by many commuters. Two-year Orange Coast College is here.

IRVINE RANCH

The Irvine Ranch, occupying the southeast portion of the Plain and adjacent hillsides, evolved from accumulation of Mexican ranchos by James Irvine and partners in the 1860's; later it became an Irvine family patrimony. Recently, products of this 90,000-acre barony have included citrus, grains, sugar beets, beef cattle, and lima beans.

For many years urbanization of the Lowlands stopped abruptly at the ranch boundary near Newport Avenue (California Route 55) but increasingly agriculture is retreating southward. The civic-minded landowners have built a water system for Laguna Beach and have presented Irvine Bowl, where the Art Festival is held. Much corporate land around Newport Bay has been converted into residential tracts with long-term leases. Cur-

rently a planned city is being developed around the new University of California campus intended for 27,500 students. Large-scale airspace industry has also appeared on ranch land near Newport Bay.

THE SAN FERNANDO VALLEY

The San Fernando Valley,[17] northwesternmost of the Los Angeles Lowlands (map, Fig. 7-30), has experienced a tremendous population growth since 1945—much of the gain within the city limits of Los Angeles has occurred here. In 1940 its population approximated 230,000; by the early 1960's only the nation's six largest cities exceeded its population of approximately a million, including Glendale (at the entrance to the Valley from the Coastal Plain and sometimes considered apart from the Valley). As has been noted, much of the Valley is within the city limits of Los Angeles.

The Valley, the geographical center of population in California in 1960, contains four independent communities (Burbank, Glendale, San Fernando, and Universal City) and a score of communities (such as Van Nuys, Sherman Oaks, and North Hollywood) that are political districts of Los Angeles. It forms a suburban complex with superior living standards—in few places in the nation do so many people live quite so well materially.[18] This affluence is reflected in dwellings, swimming pools, educational attainment, and per capita ownership of automobiles. At least two cars per family are virtually essential in the San Fernando Valley, where public transportation is almost nonexistent.

[17] *This section has been reviewed by Louis Guzman, San Fernando Valley State College.*

[18] Pacoima, San Fernando, and large sections of Burbank, Glendale, and other communities have median incomes below the countywide average; hence the reader should recognize that there is cultural complexity in occupance of the Valley.

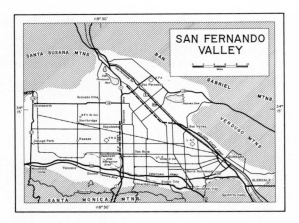

Fig. 7-30. MAP OF THE SAN FERNANDO VALLEY.

PHYSICAL REALM

The Valley is mountain-girt, with the Santa Monica Mountains separating it from the Los Angeles Coastal Plain (map, Fig. 7-12). To the west rise the Simi Hills and to the north the Santa Susana Mountains. On the east are the San Rafael and Verdugo Hills, backed by the loftier San Gabriel Range beyond the rift known as La Crescenta Valley (La Cañada Corridor).

The Valley is an intermontane basin of more than 200 square miles, covered with alluvial debris transported by streams flowing out of surrounding highlands. Its surface, a southward-sloping plain without apparent local relief, increases from 500 feet along the Los Angeles River to 1500 feet elevation in the north. Alluvial fans flare out from surrounding uplands, especially in the northeast.

External drainage of the Valley has a single exit, the Los Angeles River. During some winter storms excessive runoff from surrounding canyons has created serious drainage problems. The shallow washes (channels of intermittent streams) are alluvium-choked. The channel of the Los Angeles River, with considerable subterranean flow, is heavily pumped by Los Angeles in the vicinity of the Glendale Narrows. A high water table has prevailed in the Valley since development of irrigation. Despite Sepulveda and Hansen

flood-control basins, the water table is sometimes raised by winter storms.

Climatically the Valley is more variable than the Coastal Plain. It approaches semiarid modification of dry-summer subtropical climate that is characterized by hot summer days with pleasant nocturnal temperatures (San Fernando has an average July temperature of 73.5°F., in contrast to 66°F. for Santa Monica). Though winters tend to be mild for the latitude, temperatures are often lower than on the Coastal Plain (although January averages are about the same, circa 53°–55°). Thick banks of advection fog drift over the summits of the low Santa Monica Mountains, especially in summer, to create a high overcast that usually "burns off" before noon. The Valley gains limited benefit from sea breezes although sometimes cooler ocean air flows inland across Cahuenga Pass. Seasonally, particularly in spring and fall, hot, dry (and sometimes dusty) winds from the Mojave Desert blow into the Valley via the Santa Clara River Valley and San Fernando Pass.

Soils and natural vegetation have been suitable for development of irrigation agriculture. The soils tend to be sandy loams, gravelly toward marginal uplands but well drained and responsive to cultivation. Natural vegetation includes grasses and cacti, and floodplain groves of willows, sycamores, and scattered stands of oak.

TRANSIT CORRIDOR

The Valley affords an important gateway into central Los Angeles from the north and west (Fig. 7-31). In the recent past the three most important highway routes across the Valley have been Ventura Boulevard, San Fernando Road, and Sepulveda Boulevard. Now the heavy vehicular flow utilizes new freeways, Ventura (U.S. 101) and Golden State (U.S. 99). Of increasing importance is San Diego Freeway (California 7), which extends southward from U.S. 99 at the base of San Fernando Pass and then across the Santa Monica Mountains and over the Coastal Plain. In spite of the freeways and a system of intersecting boulevards, rush-hour traffic becomes congested at many points.

Rail service in the San Fernando Valley is provided by the Southern Pacific Railroad; the "S.P." tracks come into the basin along a single right-of-way through Glendale Narrows from central Los Angeles. At Burbank routes bifurcate (see map, Fig. 7-30); the Coast Line crosses the Lowland northwestward through Chatsworth, then continues to the Oxnard Plain via tunnels beneath Santa Susana Pass, whereas the Valley Line (i.e., Central Valley) continues northward and leaves the San Fernando Valley through a tunnel underneath San Fernando Pass and on into the Mojave Desert. Spur lines of the Southern Pacific and trackage of its affiliated Pacific Electric (no longer used for passenger interurban service) allow freight movement to industrial zones within the basin.

The Valley also has an important airline terminal; numerous flights operate to and from the Lockheed Air Terminal in Burbank. Also, there is San Fernando Valley Airport in Van Nuys as well as smaller fields for private aircraft.

Fig. 7-31. CAHUENGA PASS. Note the morning concentration of "inbound" traffic from the San Fernando Valley toward downtown Los Angeles. (California Division of Highways)

TRANSFORMATION

The San Fernando Valley has been much altered from its pristine landscape. Little evidence of San Fernando Indian occupance remains, except for a few modified place names, some romantic lore, and a few settlement "sites." The Indian villages were located along perennial streams or near springs around the Valley margin. The basin served as a hunting ground: acorns, berries, game, fowl, and fish provided food for these sedentary hunter-gatherers.

Two grants in this lowland were awarded early in the Spanish period. Captain José Verdugo received Rancho San Rafael, in the eastern portion of the basin, in 1784. In 1795 Francisco Reyes, alcalde of Los Angeles, was granted extensive Rancho Encino encompassing most of the Valley; two years later Reyes relinquished his land to San Fernando Mission in exchange for other property.

Mission San Fernando Rey, established in 1797, was among the more prosperous California missions—known for its wheat and grapes. In the 1820's it had irrigated fields and pasturage for thousands of sheep and cattle. Hides and tallow were hauled to San Pedro in oxcarts.

Secularization in 1834 did not cause immediate decline in mission productivity, probably because of the efforts of major-domo (superintendent) Pedro Lopez. Gradually the Indian converts drifted away. Before the Mexican era ended, the mission had become five ranchos: El Escorpion to the southwest, Providencia to the southeast, El Encino in the south, Tujunga to the northeast, and Ex-Mission San Fernando. Far largest was Ex-Mission, sold to Eulogio de Celis in 1846 for $14,000; the money was used to defend the province against the Americans.

The early American decades were similar to those elsewhere in California where there had been a rancho economy. In 1869 the southern portion of Ex-Mission became the property of a San Francisco group headed by Isaac Lankershim and I. N. Van Nuys, who formed

Fig. 7-32. SAN FERNANDO GRAIN HARVEST CIRCA 1900. This century
has brought much change to the Valley. (Historical Collection, Title Insurance
and Trust Company, Los Angeles)

the San Fernando Homestead Association,
which was soon reorganized as the San Fernando Sheep Company. By 1873 the company's lands were supporting 40,000 sheep.
After drought in 1877, the firm shifted to
grain, dividing its property into a series of
large wheat farms (Fig. 7-32). So successful
was the operation that the company was reorganized as Los Angeles Farm and Milling
Company and constructed a flour mill. In
1888, the record year, 510,000 bushels of wheat
were harvested.

Meanwhile the northern portion of Ex-Mission lands was acquired by Americans in 1874.
Three San Francisco Bay Area residents, Senator Charles Maclay and the Porter brothers,
purchased 56,000 acres from De Celis heirs.
The town of San Fernando was founded along
the new trackage of the Southern Pacific near
the southern approach to San Fernando Pass.
The remaining Maclay-Porter land was
planted in wheat and barley. Disagreement on
farm policy resulted in a three-way division,
with each partner receiving about 20,000
acres: Maclay, the eastern third around San
Fernando; George Porter, the central portion;
Benjamin Porter, the western third.

Grains remained the chief products until
construction of the Los Angeles Aqueduct.
Subirrigation of fruit was attempted around
North Hollywood without great success. The
city of Los Angeles with prior Los Angeles
River water rights prevented widespread
pump irrigation through court action. Until
1913 the static Valley towns remained farm
centers. In anticipation of Owens River water,
a Los Angeles syndicate began purchasing
Valley properties in 1905. The G. K. Porter
estate sold 16,000 acres for $500,000 to Mis-
sion Land and Water Company in 1905. The
Los Angeles Farm and Milling Company sold
47,000 acres to Los Angeles Suburban Homes
Company in 1910 for $2,500,000. Four towns
were established: Zelzah (Northridge),
Marian (Reseda), Owensmouth (Canoga
Park), and Van Nuys; they were located along
the Coast line of the Southern Pacific
Railroad.

Los Angeles absorbed 170 square miles of
the Valley into its corporate limits in 1915.
Since the city did not consume all the aqueduct water this expansion permitted it to sell
the surplus to Valley irrigators and still re-
cover a third to a fourth through return flow

from irrigation seepage into the Los Angeles River. Most Valley communities did not elect to join Los Angeles immediately. Within a decade water shortage forced most of them to merge into the city: Canoga Park (1917), Chatsworth (1920), and North Hollywood (1923). Now only Glendale, Burbank, Universal City, and San Fernando remain politically independent.

The sudden availability of irrigation water favored a rapid shift in land-use from grains and cattle to truck gardens, vineyards, and orchards. In 1917 only 30,000 acres were irrigated; three years later, 50,000 acres.

Towns in the southern San Fernando Valley rapidly gained in population during the boom of the 1920's. With automotive transportation, the lure of a "country home" was inviting; rurban advance swept westward from Glendale through Van Nuys.

Population growth in San Fernando Valley was retarded by depression years in the early 1930's. Yet in North Hollywood, for example, only 140 legitimate farms remained; the 2000 acres under cultivation were devoted mostly to truck gardens operated by Japanese. Agricultural decline in the southeast resulted in disappearance of dairies, poultry farms, fruit-packing plants, and nurseries. In the 1930's local motion-picture studios, which migrated from congested Hollywood, contributed more to the economy of the southeast Valley than did agriculture. Toward the northwest, however, the bulk of the Valley remained agricultural. In the northwestern corner a new trend developed. On the B. F. Porter estate, 10,000 acres in the Northridge district along Devonshire Road were converted into gentleman ranches as Hollywood stars and other affluent Angelenos established residence. Such development inspired the 1941 popular song "San Fernando Valley." Meanwhile, with industrial expansion underway late in the 1930's, population of Glendale and Burbank was accelerated more than elsewhere in the Valley.

After World War II the San Fernando Valley became a major center of population growth. Scores of housing tracts were created, varying from modest dwellings (as in Kaiser's Panorama City) to luxurious hillside homes along the north slopes of the Santa Monica Mountains.

THE SATELLITES

The cities of San Fernando, Burbank, and Glendale—politically independent of Los Angeles—stretch along the eastern periphery of the San Fernando Valley and straddle California's "main street" (U.S. 99, locally the "Golden State Freeway") and the Valley line of the Southern Pacific Railroad. Only the traveler who observes city-limit signs is apt to denote the separation of these three communities from the city of Los Angeles, for the cultural montage that characterizes the Valley crosses city limits with scant regard for political delineation.

Glendale (119,500), ninth city of California and third city of the Lowlands, originated as a citrus town athwart the Southern Pacific Valley line during the boom of the 1880's; it remained a tranquil agricultural village for a generation. After construction of its Pacific Electric interurban link in 1904, Glendale flourished as a suburb of Los Angeles. "Close-in" to downtown Los Angeles, it experienced much growth during the Third Boom (1920's). By 1940 much of the land within its corporate limits was urbanized. Although the growth rate has declined, its population has doubled since 1930; annexations have extended Glendale limits through wooded Verdugo Canyon and into the La Crescenta Valley.

Glendale is an attractive residential community, especially its northeastern periphery nestled along canyons within the San Rafael Hills. Most residences are modest frame or stucco bungalows; however, a significant number of apartment units have already replaced single dwellings. Cultural elements include Glendale City College, hillside Brand Park, and Forest Lawn Memorial Park. Forest Lawn, without tombstones, differs from the typical American cemetery. It is renowned for its several churches, and especially for its Memorial Court with the stained glass reproduction of Da Vinci's "The Last Supper"; part of the cemetery is within Los Angeles city limits.

Even many residents of the Lowlands are

not cognizant that Glendale is also a major industrial city. Along its western fringe, paralleling the railroad line and San Fernando Road, is a continuation of the principal industrial belt of metropolitan Los Angeles. Glendale's 300 industrial plants produce such varied items as foodstuffs (including pet foods), aircraft parts, house trailers, and pharmaceuticals. Grand Central Air Terminal, chief airport of Los Angeles (in the 1930's) before construction of International Airport, now consists of industrial sites.

Burbank (90,000) is another legacy of the boom of the 1880's. A group of Angelenos including Dr. David Burbank founded the city on lands of Rancho Providencia in 1887. More distant from Los Angeles than Glendale, Burbank remained a slow-growing village until the 1920's; even in 1940 Burbank was scarcely half as large as Glendale.

Transformation from an agricultural village into an industrial center and residential suburb began in the 1920's, quickened during World War II, and reached a crest in Valley urbanization after 1945. The city is a major center for television (N.B.C.) and motion pictures (studios of Disney, Columbia, and Warner Brothers–First National). It is also the home of Lockheed Aircraft, whose tremendous expansion during World War II abetted city growth. Many firms allied to airspace industries have developed here. Adjacent to the aircraft plants is Lockheed Air Terminal.

As late as 1948 northern Burbank still contained many acres of vineyards and other cropped land. Continuing growth of the city, however, led to rapid replacement of fields by thousands of tract houses. Today Burbank, like Glendale, has little vacant land exclusive of steep hillside slopes.

San Fernando (16,000), original American settlement in the Valley, was sufficiently distant from Los Angeles to develop an independent economy as an agricultural trade center, with packing and shipping plants for citrus, olives, and truck crops. It has been an important pass city since its founding, at the southern approach to San Fernando Pass and "the Ridge Route." It grew somewhat after surrounding farmlands within Los Angeles limits received water from Owens Valley. Yet the Third Boom (1920's) affected San Fernando slightly.

Functions of San Fernando changed quickly during the 1950's as the mushrooming suburban growth of metropolitan Los Angeles finally reached this community. Tract homes replaced orange and olive groves; packing plants closed down. With population growth in the north Valley, San Fernando has increased in importance as a local shopping center. In the foothills north of the city are a well-known sanitorium and a Veterans' Administration Hospital.

LOS ANGELES DISTRICT

Most of the San Fernando Valley is a political division of Los Angeles—in recent years farmlands throughout the Valley have become residential tracts. Urban encroachment in the southern Valley radiates from principal boulevards paralleling abandoned Pacific Electric interurban lines: Lankershim, Chandler, Van Nuys, and Sherman. Ventura Boulevard and San Fernando Road have been other conurbation axes. Communities that were once distinct villages have coalesced so that a single conurbation is evolving (Fig. 7-33). Nevertheless, a score of districts retain the identifying nomenclature of individual communities.

North Hollywood (100,000) was the small farm town of Lankershim in 1920; it grew appreciably during the Third Boom, but much of its population gain was achieved after 1940. Its northern and western portions were urbanized after World War II. Provision for industry was not made in the original zoning; it is principally residential. The southwestern sector known as "Studio City" contains Republic Studios. Farther east, the "ranch" of Universal Studios retains political independence as **Universal City**. Between these studios along Ventura Boulevard is a strip with restaurants, night clubs, and motels. On the Burbank boundary is the superior residential district, **Toluca Lake**, developed in the 1930's as a residence of film personalities. Lankershim Boulevard early became the commercial street

Fig. 7-33. HOUSING TRACTS, RESEDA DISTRICT. There were still large alfalfa fields in 1953 when this picture was taken. (David W. Lantis)

of North Hollywood; the district's elongated "shoestring" shopping belt has remained along this thoroughfare.

Van Nuys (112,000), west of North Hollywood, has evolved from a post office established in 1912. After most of the Valley fused with Los Angeles, Van Nuys was selected as an outlying "city" administrative center. Additional services commonly provided at the neighborhood level (police, fire, library, water, and power) are available within each Valley district of the city. Los Angeles Valley College, one of two Los Angeles public two-year colleges in this Lowland, is located in eastern Van Nuys. The other, Los Angeles Pierce College, is in Woodland Hills. Retail activity in Van Nuys suggests North Hollywood—the principal retail street is Van Nuys Boulevard. As in North Hollywood, the downtown district has an attenuated "shoestring" extent. Southern Van Nuys, known as **Sherman Oaks** (28,000), is linked with the Coastal Plain by two canyon boulevards across the Santa Monica Mountains, Sepulveda (San Diego Freeway) and Beverly Glen. The northern slopes of the Santa Monica Mountains in Sherman Oaks afford a "spill-over" of luxury-level dwellings of Beverly Hills and West-

wood. The belt of expensive homes reaching along the entire southern slopes of the Hollywood Hills (east end of Santa Monica Mountains) has been noted. Portions of north Van Nuys along the Southern Pacific tracks and around Van Nuys Airport have much industrial activity: several large breweries, an automobile assembly plant, missile and electronics firms.

The once small farm villages (pre-1950's) in the western Valley—**Reseda** (66,000), **Canoga Park** (56,000), **Encino-Tarzana** (32,000), and **Woodland Hills** (24,000)—became foci of much tract housing during the 1950's after "closer-in" sections of the Valley had been urbanized. Completion of Ventura Freeway in 1961 made these districts more accessible to other parts of the metropolis. Large new electronics plants have caused much of the growth. **Chatsworth** (22,000) in the northwest remained essentially rurban until the middle 1950's. Within five years, following establishment of the nearby North American Aviation facilities in the Santa Susana Mountains, much new housing appeared in Chatsworth.

Despite the zoning study completed in 1944, the tremendous population growth of the Valley has made achievement of a "planned" basin almost impossible in the 1960's. The City Planning Commission zoned portions of the Valley for industrial use, but Valley residents have been unenthusiastic about many types of manufacturing plants. Also, speculation has sometimes made land too expensive for some industrial use. Some of the earlier, more hastily constructed tracts may become "bungalow slums." A public rapid-transit system has been suggested, but it is doubtful that dispersed settlement would allow economic service. Public recreational facilities in the Valley have been limited, but much use has been made of Hansen and Sepulveda flood-control basins. Valley determination succeeded in locating fast-growing San Fernando Valley State College in **Northridge** (17,000) in 1956 when adequate land for a campus was still available; this situation contrasts with the problems noted earlier in obtaining a campus for Los Angeles State College, from which San Fernando State evolved by division.

THE SAN GABRIEL VALLEY

The San Gabriel Valley,[19] nucleus of original European settlement in the Los Angeles Lowlands, was well known for decades as a garden spot. Like much of the Coastal Plain and San Fernando Valley, it has experienced almost complete urbanization. Unlike the two lowlands already discussed, the San Gabriel Valley is politically independent of Los Angeles. Economically, however, it is closely linked with Los Angeles, partly because there is somewhat less employment in manufacturing within San Gabriel Valley than in San Fernando Valley or Orange County (and hence much commutation).

The San Gabriel, like the San Fernando Valley, is an intermont basin of structural origin (see map, Fig. 7-34). The two basins are separated by the hilly uplands of the Verdugo Mountains and San Rafael Hills. The low Montebello, Puente, and Chino hills rise between the San Gabriel and the Coastal Plain to the south, whereas on the east the San Jose Hills provides separation from the Valley of the South. The abrupt-rising southern block (Sierra Madre) of the San Gabriel Mountains makes a definitive northern boundary.

The Valley floor has been filled to considerable depth with aluvium transported by the Arroyo Seco, the San Gabriel River, and smaller streams flowing out of the San Gabriel Mountains. Subsequently the Arroyo Seco has been entrenched into its own floodplain, well below the main surface of the San Gabriel Valley. The alluvial fans slope upward more steeply northward from Foothill Boulevard. Within this lowland, Santa Fe and Whittier Narrows flood-control basins have been constructed across the San Gabriel River.

[19] *This section has been reviewed by Delmas Bugelli, Pasadena City College.*

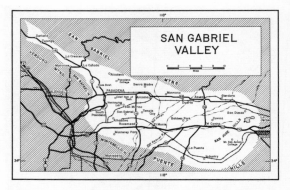

Fig. 7-34. MAP OF THE SAN GABRIEL VALLEY.

SEQUENT OCCUPANCE

Mission San Gabriel, founded in 1771, was the fourth mission in Alta California; until secularization it dominated much of the Los Angeles Lowlands—a million and a half acres from the San Gabriel Mountains to the sea. The present location was selected in 1776, when the original site proved susceptible to flooding. One of the more prosperous missions, it was the first on whose lands oranges and grapes were planted. At its zenith the mission had 1700 Indian converts and 40,000 head of cattle.

After secularization in the early 1830's, seven ranchos and a number of lesser tracts near the mission were parceled out by the Mexican government. The three largest ranchos were San Pasqual (site of present-day Pasadena and Alhambra), Santa Anita (now locale of Monrovia), and San Francisquito (site of El Monte). These ranchos experienced the customary rise of cattle herds and eventual subdivision.

The Valley became an early site of irrigation advances in the Lowlands; agricultural colonies were founded in the 1880's. It was the first major source of oranges in Southern California and remained an important agricultural area through the 1930's. Its citrus belt extended eastward from Pasadena along the foothills through Glendora into the Valley of the South. In the southern Valley, where drainage of cold air downslope caused more

Fig. 7-35. DOWNTOWN PASADENA. (Pasadena Chamber of Commerce, photo by J. Allen Hawkins)

serious frost problems, extensive acreages were devoted to dairying and poultry, alfalfa, walnuts, flowers, and truck crops. Urbanization tended to move eastward from Los Angeles relatively slowly for a while. During the Fourth Boom, after 1945, a surge of housing tracts transformed the basin, focusing particularly on the San Bernardino Freeway.

THE WEST VALLEY

The western San Gabriel Valley (Pasadena, South Pasadena, San Gabriel, and Alhambra) experienced urbanization many years before eastern portions of the lowland. The Pasadena (then Arroyo Seco) Freeway was the only expressway in the metropolitan area before 1950.

Pasadena (116,400), principal manufactural and residential center of the Valley, was long esteemed for its high-income "gracious living" (Fig. 7-35). It has changed considerably since 1940, especially with development of precision industries and aging of its famed Orange Grove Avenue district with "millionaire's row."

Pasadena had its inception in the California Colony of Indiana in 1872 on lands of Rancho San Pasqual. Like Riverside a few years sooner, it developed as an orange grove town populated by prosperous, often conservative business and professional people. "Millionaire's Row" was established along Orange Grove Avenue before 1900, and large resort hotels were built. The famed Tournament of Roses was inaugurated in 1890.

The city acquired international renown as a winter playground and the home of wealthy senior citizens. It was known for its resort hotels, especially the Green and the Huntington. Retired industrialists sometimes joined the Chamber of Commerce to oppose industrial development. Not all residents were wealthy, however; a large number of permanent and temporary residents lived in many blocks of small frame cottages apart from the exclusive residential district. Like most cities, even Pasadena had acquired a depressed section by the 1940's.

Pasadena has long been acknowledged as a cultural center. The Huntington Art Gallery and Library are in nearby San Marino. The California Institute of Technology has a justified reputation, and Pasadena City College is well regarded among two-year colleges. Pasadena Art Institute, the Community Playhouse, and the public library contribute to the cultural atmosphere. The attractive Civic Center has buildings with Mediterranean-style architecture.

After World War II Pasadena has become more of a middle-income suburban community: industrialization, smog, and high costs of mansion maintenance prompted some wealthy citizens to abandon Orange Grove

Avenue; many large houses were converted into apartments or replaced by multifamily units. The large downtown district, which is concentrated along Colorado Boulevard and Lake Avenue, has quality specialty shops and branches of better-quality Los Angeles department stores (Fig. 7-35). Presence of the California Institute of Technology is partly responsible for location of precision instrument plants (to supply Southern California's airspace industry). "Cal-Tech" supervises operation of the large Jet Propulsion Laboratory next to the Arroyo Seco.

San Marino (13,700), conservative and restricted southeastern outlier of Pasadena, suggests a smaller, less flamboyant Beverly Hills without its shopping district. It was founded in 1903 by Henry Huntington, whose mansion has become Huntington Art Gallery with its adjacent Library. The city's spacious homes and beautifully landscaped gardens suggest the high per capita incomes of its residents. The diminutive shopping district reflects affinity to Pasadena.

South Pasadena (20,000) was established in the 1880's but remained politically aloof from Pasadena—the two have long had close contacts, but South Pasadena has remained less affluent. Once chiefly residential, it still houses many workers employed in Pasadena and Los Angeles. Limited growth since 1940 indicates land shortage. Crossed by routes of three transcontinental railroads, the city has a modest portion of the primary industrial complex of the Lowlands.

Alhambra (55,000), another of the older American towns of the Lowlands, was founded in 1874. Once agricultural, it is only 6 miles from downtown Los Angeles and is bisected by rail lines. As the Los Angeles manufacturing belt pushed eastward, Alhambra became an industrial community in the 1920's. It still houses many commuters, however. Absence of open land for housing tracts has restricted its growth since 1940. Adjacent **Monterey Park** (38,000) lies mostly to the south of the expanded industrial belt along the rail lines. Newer than most Valley towns, it was established during the Second Boom in 1906. Some lower-income families have resided here (the

city tends to be a continuation of Eastside Los Angeles). There were long truck gardens and poultry farms, but they were replaced by tract houses in the post-World War II years.

San Gabriel (22,500) evolved haphazardly, beginning with adobe huts around the mission. Distribution of small "lot-size" ranchos around the mission explains its unusual urban pattern. The village languished for decades but gradually its mission brought tourists. Since 1940 it has also become the residence of many Los Angeles commuters. Development of industrial plants has reflected the continued eastward expansion of the primary industrial belt of the metropolis along rail lines.

FOOTHILL TOWNS

A strand of suburban communities extends eastward along the northern fringe of the San Gabriel Valley at the base of the Sierra Madre. Most of these towns began as orange-grove colonies during the Boom of the Eighties. In their earlier days they tended to be especially conservative, with elderly, affluent residents. These staunch Protestants contributed to well-maintained church properties; still, the towns were strongly segregated—housing ill-paid Mexican citrus workers and business and professional people. After World War II citrus groves were uprooted to accommodate housing, and the cultural composition of the communities changed.

Altadena (40,600), a residential satellite upslope from Pasadena, was still a quiet orange grove and residential area in the 1940's. After 1945 hundreds of homes were erected and this unincorporated community became more heterogeneous. **Sierra Madre** (10,000) to the east remains small, although its orange groves have also succumbed to post-1945 urbanization.

Arcadia (41,000) was founded on "Lucky" Baldwin's Rancho Santa Anita. Another former citrus town, it experienced some growth during the Second Boom (early 1900's). Gradually it gained importance as a retail center and citrus shipping point. In the late 1940's metropolitan expansion prompted widespread replacement of orange groves by residential tracts. Because of attractive landscaping Santa Anita race track does not mar community appearance, and revenues from horse racing keep municipal taxes lower. Adjacent **Monrovia** (27,000) has grown less dramatically. It combines residential and industrial functions; commodities include chemicals, foods, and pottery. Toward the southeast is **Duarte** (14,000), another erstwhile citrus village, which did not experience rapid growth until the late 1950's.

Azusa (20,500) long remained an important orange-shipping point. On its western margin the extensive gravel-covered floodplain of the San Gabriel River has become a major source of Southern California sand and gravel quarrying. This barren surface, unsuitable for citrus orchards but favorably situated with regard to highway and railroad transportation, has also become an industrial district. Thus Azusa has gained importance as a manufacturing city—producing beer, chemicals, and missile motors. Housing tracts have replaced its citrus orchards. **Irwindale,** south of Azusa, has been incorporated exclusively to facilitate extraction of sand and gravel.

Glendora (20,800), on the eastern edge of the Valley, long acclaimed itself "the citrus city." Situated on the well-drained fans of two washes, it was a tidy farm village with six packing plants. After 1950 urbanization finally overtook Glendora too—tract homes have replaced the orchards and the citrus groves of the San Gabriel Valley have all but vanished.

THE EAST CENTRAL TOWNS

South of the citrus belt the lower portions of the San Gabriel Valley remained a rurban landscape with diversified agriculture and small farm cities until the 1950's. Completion of San Bernardino Freeway (U.S. 60-70-99) and urbanization of more accessible (to central Los Angeles) or more physically attractive portions of the Valley have been followed by rapid growth in recent years. Industrial growth has also taken place, particularly along rail lines.

El Monte (13,000), one of Southern California's first American towns, was founded in 1852. It was once called the western terminus of the Santa Fe Trail, and served as a way station between Los Angeles and the interior of western America. Since 1945 rail lines and land availability have attracted a wide variety of industrial establishments, and El Monte has lost its previous importance as a center for walnut shipping.

Covina (20,000) and **West Covina** (50,-000), established in the 1880's, remained small villages in the east central San Gabriel Valley, surrounded by thousands of acres of citrus and diversified agriculture, until about 1950. With freeway access, they grew rapidly during the 1950's as centers of sprawling housing tracts. For a time West Covina almost became a byword for rapid urbanization in the Lowlands.

PUENTE VALLEY

The southeastern San Gabriel Valley, drained by intermittent San Jose Creek, is known as Puente Valley. The San Jose Hills have given it some separation from the remainder of the San Gabriel. A "frost pocket," its fertile bottomlands formerly produced walnuts, nursery stock, cut flowers, and truck crops. The Puente Valley is traversed by tracks of the Union Pacific and Southern Pacific. In advance of urbanization, the Regional Planning Commission zoned considerable acreage for industry to provide local employment for a segment of the San Gabriel populace and thus reduce rush-hour commutation. **City of Industry,** twelve miles long and a mile wide, has been incorporated for manufactural activity. Mount San Antonio College is located in the east not far from the Pomona Valley.

LA CAÑADA CORRIDOR

The La Cañada Corridor (or La Crescenta Valley), a rift between the San Gabriel Mountains and the Verdugo Hills, links the San Gabriel and San Fernando valleys. Flat terrain is limited along the Corridor, which formerly had citrus and olive groves and vineyards. With expansion of the metropolis and highway improvement, the Corridor has gained popularity as a residence area with many custom-built homes. About half of it remains in unincorporated county territory. Sloping terrain permits imaginative landscaping as well as views, and its higher elevation has appealed to many health seekers, just as has the northern edge of the San Gabriel Valley. Corridor communities include **La Cañada** (18,400), **Montrose, Tujunga,** and **Sunland.**

VALLEY OF THE SOUTH
(The Inland Valleys)

The Valley of the South,[20] referred to locally as "The Inland Valleys" or "The Inland Empire," is another intermontane basin, triangular in shape.[21] It is bounded on the southwest by the San Jose and Chino hills, on the north (and northeast) by the San Gabriel and San Bernardino mountains, and on the southeast by the ill-defined hilly uplands that separate it from the San Jacinto Basin (see map, Fig. 7-36).

The Valley remains more rural than the Lowlands discussed previously; however, its complete urbanization seems imminent. Despite the spectacular population growth in the Pomona-Ontario and Riverside-San Bernardino metropolitan areas, many communities still function as important agricultural centers. Already, however, this lowland has a population of about a million.

THE LAND

The Valley of the South is physiographically one of the more complex of the Los Angeles Lowlands despite the fact that alluvial surfaces obscure underlying structures. Topo-

20 *This section has been reviewed by Homer Aschmann and William L. Thomas, Jr., University of California at Riverside.*

21 The term Valley of the South does not have local cognizance. Lantis borrowed it from D. E. Willard's *Adventures in Scenery* for want of an accepted name. Aschmann and Thomas report local custom accepts "Inland Valleys," "Inland Empire," or "San Bernardino Lowland." Terms such as Pomona Valley, San Bernardino Valley, or Riverside Basin describe segments of this lowland.

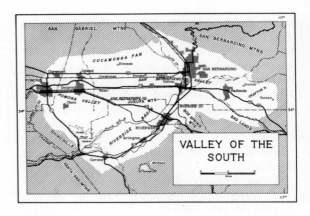

Fig. 7-36. MAP OF THE VALLEY OF THE SOUTH.

graphically this intermontane basin is filled to considerable depth with alluvium from the San Gabriel and San Bernardino mountains. This debris has partially buried several low granitic uplands. Alluvial fans, especially prominent along its northern flanks, include the great Cucamonga Fan. Prior to irrigation, low spots in the Pomona Valley contained marshes. External drainage of the entire basin is limited to the Santa Ana River Canyon west of Corona. The San Andreas Fault, at the base of the San Bernardino Mountains between San Gorgonio and Cajon passes, adds another complicating aspect.

The hot (interior) summer phase of dry-summer subtropical climate (considerable areas are even semiarid) has afforded less residence appeal than some parts of the Lowlands. Polar outbursts sometimes bring subfreezing temperatures as interior air flows seaward from the Mojave Desert. The desiccating *Santa Ana wind*, resulting from higher pressure over the Mojave, sometimes stirs up much dust and brings enervating heat across the Valley.

Marshland, chaparral, and native grasses (and sage shrub) provided the common vegetation cover in the early nineteenth century. Today slight evidence of such cover remains.

SETTLEMENT

The Valley was inhabited by small numbers of hunter-gatherer Indians (*Serrano, Cahuilla,* and *Gabrielino*). Not much is known of these people, who utilized the basin floor and the surrounding slopes.

The Valley remained on the fringe of Spanish settlement, a condition that continued during much of the Mexican era. For decades it formed part of Mission San Gabriel and afforded pasturage. Rancho San Jose was finally awarded in 1837. The Serrano Indians, who lingered in the nearby highlands, raided cattle even after the Mexican War.

American occupance commenced early in the Interior Valleys. Mormons and others soon began settling, sometimes as squatters, along the Spanish Trail westward from San Bernardino through Pomona. Significant agricultural settlement was delayed until the 1870's, when the arrival of the railroad and the irrigation work of Chaffey and others prompted citrus colonies and appreciable settlement in the 1880's.

CITRUS, EGGS, AND MILK

Portions of the Valley may retain their agricultural importance for several decades longer despite urban encroachment. With disappearance of farmlands in the Lowlands discussed previously, the Valley is the leading agricultural area of Southern California. Its several agricultural zones are related to such factors as climatic variations (as frost threat) and soil conditions. They include: (1) citrus; (2) vineyards; (3) pastoral; (4) truck crops, poultry, and dairying.

THE ORANGE BELT

Southern California's major "orange empire," which often impressed visitors whisked through the belt on guided tours via Pacific Electric interurban coaches, once extended from Hollywood (Cahuenga Valley) into the Interior Valleys, where it formed a crescent around the upper Santa Ana floodplain—from Claremont east to Redlands. It then continued southwestward through Riverside to Corona and thence into Orange County. The orange was the most valuable commodity of the Lowlands between 1890 and 1938—it was a major factor in permitting Los Angeles County to rank first nationally in agricultural output for

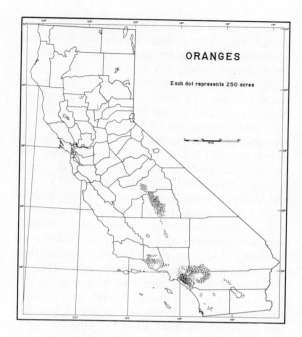

Fig. 7-37. MAP OF THE ORANGE ACREAGE IN CALIFORNIA.

forty years. Cahuenga Valley orchards were eliminated early with the growth of Hollywood. After World War II most of the orchards disappeared from the San Gabriel Valley and the Pomona Valley. More isolated districts, such as Corona and Redlands, have remained major orange producers (Fig. 7-37).

Portions of the orange belt have also produced lemons and grapefruit, both of which are still important in the Inland Valleys. Lemons, which cannot tolerate much frost, tend to be grown upslope from the oranges where there is better air drainage. Grapefruit likes the summer heat of this lowland, but again is frost-sensitive. This area is the second-ranking California source of grapefruit (after the Colorado Desert).

Orange production began with a small grove planted at Mission San Gabriel in 1804. But commercial production was long delayed, pending market development. During the 1860's Los Angeles oranges had to compete against Mexican imports even in San Francisco. By the 1880's changed circumstances resulted from transcontinental rail lines, reduced freight rates, local feeder rail lines, new varieties, refrigerator cars, and enthusiasm engendered by eastern visitors.

The Riverside colony of 1870 was based upon oranges; so were colonies at Pasadena, Santa Ana, and many other towns. Colonies followed subdivision of Mexican ranchos after the drought of the 1860's. Mutual irrigation districts, established in conjunction with the colonies, assured a water supply. The navel orange, introduced from Brazil (in 1873), and the Valencia from the Azores (in 1876) proved tastier and more juicy than older varieties. The winter-marketed navel can tolerate warmer summers and more frost (after fruit harvest) than can the Valencia. Accordingly the navel has been grown more extensively in the Inland Valleys and the Valencia on the Coastal Plain. The easily peeled navel, sometimes called the "lunch-box orange," has had less competition from Florida "juice oranges" as a dessert fruit.

The Los Angeles Lowlands have constituted one of the world's most concentrated major areas of orange production: groves covered approximately 140,000 acres before the decline commenced. Production has been sharply delineated—principally by micro-climates, soils, and drainage. Customary sites have included the higher portions of inner basins (San Fernando, San Gabriel, and Inland valleys) and inner (well-drained) portions of the Coastal Plain. Higher middle portions of alluvial fans have afforded air drainage and fertile granitic loams.

Orange groves have been most widespread on small individually owned tracts, with groves averaging 10 to 25 acres. Although there have been relatively few large corporate properties, the larger groves have tended to produce a disproportionate share of the crop. Many earlier growers were elderly and conservative—business and professional people who came to California with sufficient funds to "retire to an orange grove." For several generations, visions of owning such a property, fragrant with the scent of blossoms, and where the money actually grew on trees, remained an American dream.

Producing a tropical crop in a dry subtropical land poses problems. Citrus in the Lowlands has been restricted by water availability, but a high water table was not favorable. Water, a valuable California commodity, has been distributed by the mutual companies through steel or concrete pipes underground —one sees surface ditches only in a few older localities. Water in good districts has amounted to 8 to 10 percent of total production costs.[22] Soil moisture has needed careful regulation—orchards have been irrigated five to twelve times annually. Even the more favored localities have required "protection" on some winter nights. As many as seventy-five to a hundred orchard heaters are employed per acre. Powerful wind machines are sometimes used today instead of heaters to "stir up" inverted near-surface air. For several decades an efficient frost-warning service has been provided over commercial radio stations. Yet invasion of interior polar air masses wrought damage of millions during cold spells in 1922, 1938, and 1949. The drying "Santa Ana" winds from the deserts, especially hot in summer and autumn, have been second to frost as agents of destruction. Fortunately, through much of the interior citrus belt the San Gabriel and San Bernardino ranges reduce the force of such winds. Windbreaks generally of cypress or eucalyptus have also been used. Another source of damage has been biologic agents, such as gophers and "quick decline."

CITRUS IN SAN BERNARDINO COUNTY

YEAR	ACREAGE	VALUATION (GROSS RECEIPTS)
1940	48,073	$17,170,000
1945	50,615	50,364,000
1950	43,239	24,057,000
1955	33,528	22,946,000
1960	27,739	21,787,000

Source: Agricultural Commissioner, San Bernardino County.

[22] With the evolution of frozen orange juice, artificially colored and sweetened Florida oranges, grown much closer to large eastern cities than Southern California without the cost of irrigation and with cheaper labor and land, obviously has had a marketing advantage.

Marketing in the past has been possible because of what has been described as "postage stamp" freight rates east of Denver, coupled with cooperative organization. A poor season in 1892-1893 at a time of rising output led to formation of the Southern California Fruit Exchange; it became California Fruit Growers Exchange and later Sunkist Growers, Inc. Not all oranges are marketed through this organization although expenditure of millions of dollars has made the cooperative brand name "Sunkist" the accepted national trademark for quality fresh oranges. The organization eventually included twenty-seven "district exchanges" and more than 200 local packing associations. Membership has indeed permitted "leisure farming"; the Exchange upon request (for a price, of course) has handled all phases of production—irrigation, spraying, picking, packing, and shipping. It has operated by-products plants and has even prepared box shooks at its northern California mills (at Westwood, Susanville, and Hilts).

VINEYARDS

Southern California's principal grape-growing district occupies a triangular area on the Cucamonga alluvial fan. This sandy surface, bordered by Guasti (southwest), Etiwanda (north), and Fontana (southeast), has not been suitable for citrus because of soils, lack of irrigation, wind-blown sand, and seasonally hot or cold air blowing down from Cajon Pass; it forms a "frost zone" break in the citrus belt. The 6000-acre Garrett vineyard, founded by immigrant Secundo Guasti in 1902, is one of the nation's largest wine producers. More than twenty varieties of grapes are grown commercially on the farm—this district produces nearly all of Southern California's wine, which has been shipped east "bulk" in tank cars. Summer heat and abundant sunshine favor the high-sugar "sweet-wine" varieties: Zinfandel, Alicante, Mataro, Mission, and Muscat.

TRUCK CROPS AND LIVESTOCK

"Inside" of the encirling horseshoe of citrus on the alluvial fans, much of the remaining

MAJOR AGRICULTURAL COMMODITIES
SAN BERNARDINO AND RIVERSIDE
COUNTIES, 1961
(values in millions of dollars)

Fruits and Nuts	
oranges, navel	23.6
lemons	6.2
wine grapes	5.9
oranges, Valencia	5.7
walnuts	0.7
apricots	0.6
peaches	0.6
apples	0.25
Livestock and Products	
eggs, market	53.7
milk, market	39.2
beef cattle	8.4
turkeys	5.4
dairy cattle	3.25
baby chicks	1.0
rabbits	0.55
Vegetables	
potatoes	8.4
melons (misc.)	1.5
sweet potatoes	1.4
onions, dry	1.2
asparagus	0.75
bell peppers	0.7
sweet corn	0.7
eggplant	0.5
Nursery Stock	7.0
Field Crops	
alfalfa	6.7
irrig. pasture	2.3
barley	1.6
corn (ensilage)	0.6

Desert production is excluded, but statistics include the San Jacinto Basin.

Source: Agricultural Commissioners, Riverside and San Bernardino Counties.

rurban bulk of the Valley forms a complex of farming districts occupying a triangle bounded by Chino, Corona, and Rialto. The production from this area appreciably exceeds the value of the more conspicuous citrus groves. The Chino-Ontario dairy belt has had increased significance as dairymen have forsaken the urbanized Coastal Plain. In the past much milk was processed in Ontario creameries, but today it is sold as fresh Grade-A milk. The district suggests the countryside around

Fig. 7-38. DAIRY FARM, CHINO. This dairy district, unlike the one in southeast Los Angeles County, still has sufficient space for some pasturage! Note the bales of alfalfa. (Dairy Council of California)

Artesia on the Coastal Plain, although individual holdings of land tend to be appreciably larger (see Fig. 7-38). The dairymen commonly are of Danish, Dutch, or Portuguese ancestry.

Farther east the Fontana-Rialto district has long been an important center for production of chickens and rabbits. When "Fontana Farms" was originally established as a series of small tracts, essentially for retired couples, small-scale poultry farms prevailed. More recently, the demand of Los Angeles markets has made this the leading poultry area in western United States and large-scale production is characteristic. Eggs are now the leading agricultural commodity of the Inland Valleys.

Several districts have an important production of nursery stock, which again reflects urbanization on the Coastal Plain and continuation of a high demand for trees and shrubs for residential use.

Yucaipa Valley is a small but distinctive agricultural site and the only area of apple production in the Lowlands. The little basin along the San Andreas Fault, separated from the San Bernardino Valley by the Crafton Hills, enjoys popularity with retired couples on limited incomes; there are many small cottages. Along the eastern side of the Yucaipa are a few hundred acres of apple orchards around Oak Glen. The fruit is sold directly from the orchards; motorists drive out from Lowlands cities by the thousands each fall.

TRANSIT CORRIDOR

Millions of Americans have been introduced to the "real" (legendary Mediterranean) California as they descended from Cajon or San Gorgonio Pass. Position athwart the eastern gateways into Los Angeles has given the Valley of the South importance as a transportation corridor. Most Valley communities have stations on one of the three major rail lines. Santa Fe trackage, entering the Lowlands from Cajon Pass into San Bernardino, extends westward through Claremont into the San Gabriel Valley. After descending from San Gorgonio Pass, the main (Los Angeles–New Orleans) line of the Southern Pacific's "Sunset Route" continues westward through Colton to Pomona. The Union Pacific, which leases Santa Fe trackage through Cajon Pass, extends from San Bernardino to Riverside, and on westward through Pomona. A deviation of the "original" Santa Fe route to San Diego follows the Santa Ana River into the Coastal Plain. Santa Fe shops at San Bernardino and Southern Pacific yards at Colton have given the Valley a significant industrial payroll.

Three major east-west highway routes, U.S. 66 (Interstate 15), the San Bernardino Freeway (U.S. 70 and 90), and U.S. 60, cross the Valley. Vehicular traffic supports numerous motels, cafes, and filling stations. One of California's important north-south routes, U.S. 395, shares a segment of Riverside Freeway with U.S. 91. These highways bifurcate at

Fig. 7-39. KAISER STEEL MILL AND THE SAN BERNARDINO VALLEY. View of Fontana (middle) and Colton (right) with the San Bernardino Mountains in the rear. (Kaiser Steel Company)

Riverside, and U.S. 91 carries the freeway designation westward along the Santa Ana River.

INDUSTRIAL EVOLUTION

Industrial expansion is anticipated in the Inland Valleys. This lowland has favorable transportation facilities and available land. Before World War II manufacturing was principally of a processing nature, especially citrus by-products and dairy foods. There are still important cement plants at Colton and Crestmore. Manufacture of pumps in Pomona reflected the development of irrigation agriculture. Before 1940 the electrical-appliance plant in Ontario afforded a unique industrial firm.

The Kaiser Steel mill at Fontana was constructed during World War II and provided plate and structural steel for West Coast shipyards; it was converted to production of civilian goods after 1945 (Fig. 7-39). Despite the cost of constructing the plant, steel markets in California have permitted repeated expansion of the state's first integrated steel mill. Inland location away from the seaboard was felt

necessary for wartime safety; the specific site was determined by such considerations as land, water, labor supply, and transportation facilities (rail lines especially). A unique feature has been its extreme economy in water consumption. Postwar expansion has emphasized such products as structural members, sheet, tinplate, wire, and concrete reinforcements. Raw materials are brought from scattered sources, with coal (from Utah and Oklahoma) traveling the greatest distance and limestone coming from the nearby Mojave. Iron ore originally came from the Providence Mountains in the Mojave. After construction of a feeder line extended from the Southern Pacific right-of-way, ore has come from a captive open-pit mine (Chapter 3) at Eagle Mountain (Fig. 3-11). The steel plant has prompted rise of allied industries (such as coal-tar products and oxygen) in the vicinity.

Industrial growth has been evidenced especially in Pomona, San Bernardino, and Riverside since 1945. As yet output is relatively small in contrast to metropolitan Los Angeles. Sufficiently dispersed as to obscure total out-

Fig. 7-40. *POMONA AND THE POMONA VALLEY. This view includes downtown Pomona (central foreground), the San Bernardino Freeway (across middle), Claremont, citrus groves, and the San Gabriel Mountains; Mt. San Antonio is on the right.* (United States National Bank of San Diego)

put has been the "overflow" of the airspace industry from San Diego and Los Angeles.

POMONA VALLEY CITIES

Most larger cities of Pomona Valley originated as nineteenth-century orange colonies. These citrus towns tended to be clean, staid, and conservative. Industry was limited; functions included agricultural shipment, local trade, and farm-labor residence. In the early 1950's the population surge of the Lowlands prompted extensive housing tracts, and freeways improved automotive transportation into downtown Los Angeles. Recent growth has occasioned coalescence into an almost continuous metropolis (Fig. 7-40).

Pomona (67,000), appropriately named for the Roman goddess of fruits, originated in

1874 after the Southern Pacific acquired a right-of-way across Rancho San Jose. A land syndicate laid out the townsite. After establishment of a water company in 1882 citrus groves were planted. Before 1940 Pomona was an attractive city whose prosperity depended upon the thousands of acres of surrounding orange groves. It is also the site of the Los Angeles County Fair. One of two California State Polytechnic College campuses and a state hospital are located west of the city. Since 1945 Pomona has experienced considerable change as orange groves have been replaced by housing tracts. Industrial growth has included an airspace plant in 1952 (the nation's first integrated guided missile producer), paper, plastics, brick and tile, shoes, glass containers, bicycles, and soap.

Claremont (12,600), founded during the Boom of the Eighties, has been another citrus town, partially eclipsed by proximity to Pomona. This pleasant foothill town has been distinguished by the presence of Claremont Colleges, an Oxonian association of small private institutions, well endowed and noted for scholarship. More recently Southern California School of Theology was moved here from Los Angeles. Nearby is Rancho Santa Ana Botanic Garden with its 80 acres of native California plants. The academic atmosphere has given Claremont residential preference for senior citizens, a trait shared with some middlewestern college towns. Padua Hills Theatre, presenting Mexican players, is located north of town.

Upland (16,000) and **Ontario** (47,000) are actually one continuous city. Originally they were one political unit, and they remain linked by broad Euclid Avenue with its rows of pepper trees. Upland has been principally residential and a citrus-packing center. Ontario, long the second city of the Pomona Valley, began as an agricultural colony in 1882. Its longtime functions as residential city and orange-belt trade center have been widened with industrial development. Aircraft repair service maintained at its International Airport gives employment to many.

Chino (10,300) differs considerably from the above towns. Bypassed by rail lines and long plagued by water shortage, it provides residence for agricultural workers in the surrounding dairy, truck, and nursery farms. Incomes tend to be lower than for orange-grove owners; proximity to Pomona helps explain absence of quality specialty shops. Payrolls at the Chino State Correctional Institution provide an additional support.

Diamond Bar, a planned city occupying 8000 acres of Rancho Los Nogales, is evolving in the Chino Hills west of the Valley. The ranch had been one of the best reminders of pastoral California left in the Lowlands in the late 1950's.

SAN BERNARDINO VALLEY CITIES

Urbanization has lately much altered the appearance of the San Bernardino Valley. Most of its communities were founded early in the American period, but they long remained apart from the sprawl of metropolitan Los Angeles. Now intervening fill-in (as West Covina and Pomona) indicates that eventually there will be a continuous conurbation from the Pacific to the San Bernardino Mountains.

San Bernardino (92,000), seat of the nation's largest county, is one of the oldest American towns in the Lowlands. In 1851 a Mormon group purchased Rancho San Bernardino for $77,000 and patterned a townsite after Salt Lake with broad streets. After Brigham Young recalled his people to Utah in 1857, the city experienced a "wild period" as gateway to Mojave mines (Chapter 3). Then the city gained importance as a "pass city" with construction of rail and highway lines through Cajon Pass. Despite orange groves and the annual National Orange Show, it is not a typical orange-belt town. Location of the western shops of the Santa Fe Railroad here has long provided a sizable working populace. Other industrial activity includes metal fabrication. In recent years many employees of Kaiser Steel have resided in the city as have many civilians employed at Norton Air Force Base (supply, repair, and missile defense for the Lowlands) and at Patton State Hospital. There is a significant downtown retail district, increasingly eccentric as the city expands northward. San Bernardino College and the new California State College are located here.

Colton (18,700), an agricultural colony of the 1870's, has owed much growth to its Southern Pacific Railroad facilities. Its large laboring population includes many employees of the cement plant. Many residences are modest and the small downtown district reflects retail trade conducted in either Riverside or San Bernardino.

Redlands (27,000), perhaps more than any community in the Lowlands, still exemplifies the "prim and proper" orange-belt town. It is the leading Southern California center for packing and shipping navel oranges and has 15,000 acres of surrounding groves. As yet it has been less affected by the Fourth Boom than most Lowlands cities. Redlands has long been known for its homes and gardens; the newer district, Sunset Drive, has impressive views of the San Bernardino Mountains, as does the appealing campus of the University of Redlands. Loma Linda, a Seventh Day Adventist community nearby, also has a college (Medical Evangelists).

RIVERSIDE BASIN CITIES

A string of citrus towns has extended along the southeastern side of the Santa Ana River. River water, developed here early for irrigation, has provided the largest canal system within the Lowlands. In the Fourth Boom (post-1940) Riverside has experienced much more growth than its smaller neighbors.

Riverside (84,000), the agricultural colony where the navel orange industry started, was long a "jewel" of the citrus belt—a trim residential community with well-kept homes and gardens and a downtown district whose specialty shops reflected the prosperity of the surrounding countryside. Mission Inn, a legendary Southern California hotel, once popular with visitors who took the orange-belt circuit in the "red cars" of the "P.E.," survives. As an eastern gateway into the Lowlands on U.S. 60, the city has been an important tourist center. It is also a county seat and one of the important centers of higher education in the Lowlands: University of California at Riverside, Riverside College, La Sierra College, Southern Baptist College, and Sherman Institute. It provides a service center for March Air Force Base.

The Fourth Boom has affected Riverside as it has Pomona. Orange groves have been replaced by housing tracts, and in 1960 the city purchased for urban use two of the old irrigation canals built to supply orchards. Per capita incomes have tended to decline relative to purchasing power. Land, transportation facilities, and community appeal have encouraged industrial growth (including airspace industries), and the city has much extended its limits, absorbing suburban Arlington.

Corona (13,000), founded as South Riverside during the 1880's, has like Redlands retained some of its citrus-belt atmosphere. The slopes to the south are the leading producer of lemons in Riverside County, and the city has a large by-products plant. Despite several industrial establishments, it remains basically an agricultural supply center.

THE SAN JACINTO BASIN

The San Jacinto Basin is associated with the Los Angeles Lowlands almost by default —geologically this structural depression is part of the Peninsular Ranges.[23] This essentially rural land is the most isolated and least visited of the five Lowlands. It lies south of the Valley of the South with the Santa Ana Mountains to the west and the San Jacinto Mountains to the east (see map, Fig. 7-41).

THE LAND

The San Jacinto Basin, more rugged than the other Lowlands, is a granitic block. Marginal faults, the San Jacinto to the northeast and the Elsinore to the southwest, are two of the most impressive cracks on the face of Southern California—activity along these ruptures explains hot springs that have been used commercially. The irregular terrain results from an earlier period of mountain building —the Basin was not uplifted when the Peninsular Ranges were most recently elevated. Scattered about the Basin are small granitic knobs whose rocky outcrops and thin soils minimize agricultural use. One of the most prominent of these uplands is known as the Lakeview Mountains.

The area is about equally divided between the knobby hills, which rise to elevations around 2500 feet sea level, and small valleys. The valleys, about a thousand feet lower than the knobs, are relatively smooth and generally have alluvial surfaces.

Most of the little intermittent streams drain into Lake Elsinore. A number of them are tributary to the San Jacinto River, which rises

[23] The term San Jacinto Basin, like Valley of the South, does not have common local meaning. It is used in absence of a widely accepted proper name.

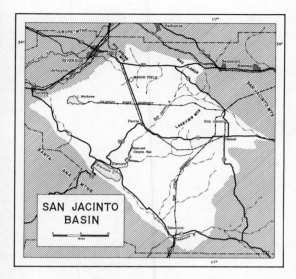

Fig. 7-41. MAP OF THE SAN JACINTO BASIN.

on the upper slopes of the San Jacinto Range. Since irrigation development, its channel is generally dry. Historically Lake Elsinore has spilled over northwestward into the Santa Ana River, but generally drainage must be considered internal.

The Basin is farther south than the other Lowlands and also lies in the lee of the Santa Ana Mountains—precipitation is insufficient to warrant classification as a Mediterranean type; it must be considered semiarid. Because of interior location, without the benefit of sea breezes, summer afternoons are often quite warm. Winter temperatures are significantly lower than elsewhere in the Lowlands, and the eight-month growing season is short by Southern California standards.

OCCUPANCE

The San Jacinto Basin has lacked the attractiveness of many portions of Southern California. This characteristic was reflected in its modest Indian population—the residents were *Luiseños*, hill-dwelling Shoshones. These hunter-gatherers, perhaps totaling several thousand, focused their activity on the periphery of the Lowland where their usual diet (small game, acorns, and seeds) was more readily obtained. As their land held slight appeal for the Spanish, the Luiseño have persisted into the twentieth century.

The Basin provided neither sufficient water nor Indian neophytes to encourage the Spanish to establish a mission. An interior route connecting missions San Diego and San Gabriel, known as the **Canyon Road,** traversed the western periphery. Later it became a link in the Old Emigrant Trail from Ft. Yuma to Los Angeles, followed by many gold seekers; it also formed part of the route of the Butterfield stages.

Four land grants were awarded in the Basin at the close of the Mexican period—they encompassed only marginal eastern and western lands where water was available. The typical patterns of livestock and then grains were developed. Land was still available for homesteading in the 1870's. During the boom of the 1880's several hot springs became the sites of thermal resorts, particularly around Lake Elsinore. Modest irrigation development came rather late.

LAND-USE

Extensive irrigation agriculture, so widespread in the Los Angeles Lowlands in the half of this century, has been limited in the San Jacinto Basin by the double curse of thin rocky slopes and limited water. Thousands of acres of grain, usually barley, are dry-farmed, but many steeper slopes are covered with chaparral. Livestock, both beef and dairy cattle, have become increasingly important since 1945. By 1950 the irrigation situation had become especially critical in the Perris Valley where there was a perilous decline in the water table.

Partial solution to water problems came with establishment of Eastern Municipal Water District in 1950. Colorado River water, obtained through affiliation with the Metropolitan Water District, became available in 1952. Although Lake Mathews, largest M.W.D. reservoir in Southern California, is located on the northern edge of the Basin, water delivery awaited construction of San Diego Aqueduct across the lowland. With

Fig. 7-42. *HEMET VALLEY. This vertical view shows Hemet (upper left) and its surrounding patchwork of fields and orchards.* (Soil Conservation Service)

aqueduct water many wells are no longer used. The Colorado River supply is sufficiently expensive to restrict some uses; only larger barley fields are given supplemental sprinkler irrigation. For alfalfa, too, the imported water is economic only on larger fields.

The **Perris Valley**, west of the Lakeview Mountains, has benefited especially from imported water. Its products include potatoes, deciduous fruits, truck crops, winter barley, and milk, largely consumed in the Lowlands. **March Air Force Base**, established as a training field during World War I, occupies a sizable tract in the northwestern portion of the Valley. During World War II it was a staging center for the heavy bombers that participated in the raids on Japan (from bases in the Mariana Islands), and more recently has accommodated Strategic Air Command craft.

The **San Jacinto Valley**, especially east of the Lakeview Mountains, is the principal agricultural section of the Basin. It receives water chiefly from the San Jacinto River, much of it groundwater; there is also storage in Hemet Lake in the San Jacinto Mountains. In the foothills around Valley Vista, where there is good air drainage, oranges and even lemons are grown. Downvalley, Hemet is the center of a district known for its tomatoes, apricots and peaches, olives and walnuts, poultry and rabbits. Farther north there is an important and expanding dairy belt west of San Jacinto. Race-horse breeding has suggested to several writers an improbable image of the Kentucky Bluegrass.

Agricultural development of the **Elsinore Valley** followed division of Rancho Laguna in the 1880's. Water shortage has always hampered productivity. Grain farming succeeded early cattle ranching; in turn, suitable tracts were converted into orchards. Much land, especially around Temecula, is still used for dry-farmed grains. Irrigated orchards are limited to sites with favorable soils and water, especially northwest of Lake Elsinore.

Despite its physical handicap, continuing population growth elsewhere in the Lowlands, leading to curtailed farming, suggests that the San Jacinto Basin will have a more important future in agriculture than it had in the past. It can be assumed, for instance, that a significant expansion of dairying will take place. Its hot springs early encouraged retirement residence, which has increasing significance (especially around Hemet and Elsinore). A considerable housing development for retired persons, Sun City, has been constructed near Perris.

THE VILLAGES

The little towns of the San Jacinto Basin, although they were founded in the nineteenth century, have not experienced the recent growth characteristic of so many cities in the Lowlands. A suggestion of a quiet yesterday tends to prevail.

Perris (2900), a boomtown of the 1880's, developed along a branch line of the Santa Fe Railroad. With increased irrigation agri-culture in its valley, this local trade center appears more prosperous than it did in 1950. It serves as an agricultural shipping point.

San Jacinto (2500) is a somnolent village serving the dairy belt along the San Jacinto River. It developed slowly around a general store established in 1872.

Hemet (5400), largest town in the Basin, is the center for the more extensive agricultural district along the upper San Jacinto River (Fig. 7-42). It is also a pass town at the base of the Pines-to-Palms Highway, serving recreational areas in the San Jacinto Mountains. The town has packing houses and shipping sheds. Each spring the Ramona Pageant is re-enacted in nearby Ramona Bowl.

The economy of **Elsinore** (2400) has been allied with its intermittent lake, with agriculture and, lately, retired residents. The town had its origin in hot-spring resorts in the 1880's. Recreational use of the lake increased with Southern California population growth and the rise of automotive transportation. Fluctuations in lake level determined usage. The lake filled in 1937-38, and was popular during World War II when sports boating was curtailed in the nearby Pacific Ocean. The lake dried up during the early 1950's. A state park has been established, in hopes of maintaining a small lake of imported water.

THE OXNARD PLAIN

The Oxnard Plain,[24] a fertile coastal lowland, lies northwest of the Santa Monica Mountains beyond the Malibu Coast (see map, Fig. 7-43). The Plain, "economic heart" of Ventura County, faces the Pacific Ocean at the mouth of the Santa Clara River. On its interior edges it is bounded by units of the Transverse Ranges: Sulphur Mountain (part of the Topatopa "complex") to the north, South Mountain to the northeast, and the Santa Monica Moun-tains to the southeast (Fig. 7-46). Although the Plain is appreciably smaller than the Los Angeles Coastal Plain, it constitutes one of California's more important coastal lowlands.

THE LAND

The Oxnard Plain, a delta-like surface, is underlain by several hundred feet of horizontal-strata alluvium, deposited at its mouth by the Santa Clara River (and from other sources). Surface irregularities are slight, and the shoreline is straight, despite a few marshy

[24] *This section has been reviewed by Rex Brittingham, Ventura College.*

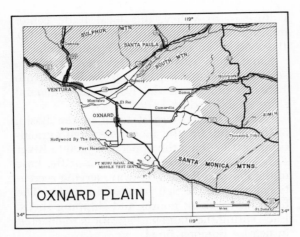

Fig. 7-43. MAP OF THE OXNARD PLAIN.

areas such as the lagoon west of Point Mugu.

The Plain has a mild-summer modification of the dry-summer subtropical climate (see Appendix A). Except for occasional outflow of continental air from the Mojave Desert down the Santa Clara River Valley, the Plain is well insulated against interior heat or cold.

Soils and water resources are related to the Santa Clara River. Groundwater is carried by the Santa Clara and other streams from interior mountains. Soils are generally rather fine alluvium, sandy to loamy, with patches of clay near the coast and gravelly soils adjacent to the mountains.

LAND UTILIZATION

There is limited knowledge of pre-Spanish utilization of the Oxnard Plain, a habitat of the *Chumash* Indians. Despite available water, these Indians did not practice agriculture—like most California Indians, they were hunters-fishers-gatherers.

Mission San Buenaventura was established by Father Serra near the mouth of the Ventura River on the western edge of the Oxnard Plain in 1782. Local Chumash were recruited as neophytes; for several decades the mission prospered—at one time it held more cattle than any other mission. As the church possessed the Plain through the Spanish period, no ranchos were granted. After secularization

in 1837, mission properties were administered for the Mexican government.

The Plain was carved into eight ranchos during the final decade of Mexican control. Most of its surface became a part of Rancho El Rio de Santa Clara o La Colonia, a 45,000-acre tract awarded in 1837. An even larger holding, Ex-Mission Rancho, included a portion of the Plain east of the mission besides considerable mountainous terrain—it was awarded in 1846.

Subdivision of ranchos followed the customary Southern California pattern after the drought of 1862. Large grain farms were established and remained here much longer than in most arable portions of Southern California. Construction of the Southern Pacific "Coast Line" from Los Angeles through Ventura to Santa Barbara in 1887 encouraged some town growth, although the scale was not comparable to boom activity around Los Angeles.

Transformation of the Oxnard Plain into a landscape characterized by irrigation agriculture has occurred almost wholly since 1900. At the turn of the century, sugar-beet cultivation was established and a sugar factory constructed. A generation later, lima beans became an important crop; then citrus orchards were planted.

Much change in agricultural activity has taken place during the twentieth century. Widespread irrigation agriculture was long delayed by a water table too deep for primitive drilling machinery and by the marshy coastal fringe. Population growth in California coupled with changing dietary habits of the American people created a demand for more vegetables—the Plain gradually shifted from cattle and grain ranching to specialized agriculture. Between 1917 and 1950 irrigated acreage tripled to encompass 100,000 acres.

THE FERTILE LAND

Present-day agriculture on the Oxnard Plain is of an intensive nature and brings a high return per acre, so that Ventura County ranks eleventh in the state in agricultural output. There is much mechanization and still much use of Mexican field labor. The mild climate

LEADING AGRICULTURAL COMMODITIES
VENTURA COUNTY, 1961
(values in millions of dollars)

Fruits and Nuts	56.5
lemons	30.1
oranges, Valencia	18.4
oranges, navel	2.8
strawberries	1.8
avocados	1.7
walnuts	1.1
Field Crops	7.2
beans, lima	4.3
vegetable seeds	0.97
sugar beets	0.28
Livestock and Products	16.8
cattle, feed lot	5.4
chicken eggs	5.2
milk	3.6
cattle, range	1.2
turkeys	0.9
Vegetables	27.0
tomatoes	9.2
beans, green	4.3
lettuce, all types	3.5
celery	3.5
broccoli	1.0
cabbage	0.97
cucumbers	0.58
peppers, chili	0.56
mushrooms	0.54
peppers, bell	0.45
carrots	0.43
peppers, pimiento	0.41
Cut Flowers	1.5
Nursery Stock	1.5
All Commodities	110.6

Source: Agricultural Commissioner, Ventura County.

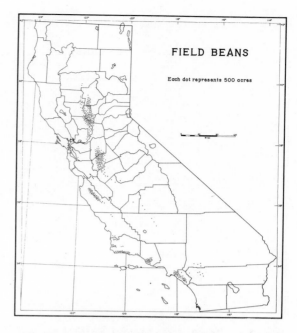

FIELD BEANS

Each dot represents 500 acres

Fig. 7-44. MAP OF THE FIELD BEAN ACREAGE IN CALIFORNIA.

(although acreage has declined). Many of the crops—including tomatoes, lettuce, strawberries, cabbage, carrots, and bell peppers—are cultivated carefully for off-season harvest in spring or fall, so as to reduce market competition. Celery is marketed much of the year (except in summer), whereas the year-round harvest includes alfalfa, livestock products, and lemons. Several specialty crops merit note, especially large lima beans and lemons.

LARGE LIMA BEANS

The Oxnard Plain has been the world's chief commercial producer of large lima beans, which are more sensitive to summer heat and drought than baby lima beans (Fig. 7-44). Hence they tend to be grown in Southern California only along the fog-belt coast. The Ventura Lima Bean Association was established in 1916; during the developmental period most beans were dry-farmed. Yields have more than tripled since the late 1920's under irrigation agriculture. For some years much of the crop has been fresh-frozen.

permits some commodities to be marketed every month of the year. Citrus and avocados have importance in the interior portions of the Plain; lemons especially can tolerate the cool summer weather. Much of the Plain tends to be too cool in summer or too poorly drained for optimum orchard production. Shallow-rooted plants adapted to mild temperatures tend to be more widespread than tree crops. Walnuts, which have been retained here longer than in the Los Angeles Lowlands, are now declining rapidly. Midwinter products include celery, cut flowers, broccoli, Brussels sprouts, and avocados. Midsummer crops include tomatoes, lima beans, and sugar beets

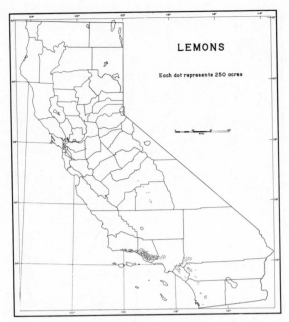

Fig. 7-45. MAP OF THE LEMON ACRE-AGE IN CALIFORNIA.

THE LEMON

Southern California has a national near monopoly on lemon production and benefits through tariff against foreign imports (Fig. 7-45). The lemon, an evergreen that bears repeatedly throughout the year, demands almost frost-free conditions but does not demand as much summer warmth as some citrus. The Oxnard Plain, together with the contiguous Santa Clara River Valley, is the nation's leading producer.[25] However, a rapid decrease in acreage commenced in the late 1950's with urban expansion.

THE WATER PROBLEM

The seriousness of water depletion on the Oxnard Plain dramatizes the limitation of

[25] In a sense the Santa Clara River Valley and the Ojai Valley might best be considered extensions of the Oxnard Plain. Because of their intermont position, these two areas are considered later in the chapter as part of the Transverse Ranges.

local water supply in Southern California even better than do the Los Angeles Lowlands and the San Diego Country—the Plain did not receive Colorado River water until the 1960's. The water supply became acute as a result of the marked expansion of pump irrigation coupled with urban growth. Ventura, which formerly depended upon the Ventura River, now has pump wells near the mouth of the Santa Clara River. Increased pumping has lowered the water table so much around the outer edge of the Oxnard Plain that salt-water intrusion has occurred.

Local drainage basins for decades were not used with maximum effectiveness. However, spreading grounds have been constructed along the tributary streams at the apex of alluvial fans, and a storage reservoir has been constructed on Piru Creek. Insufficient accord between water users in the various parts of the Santa Clara drainage basin was resolved and a water conservancy district established.

PETROLEUM

Ventura County has been a longtime Southern California petroleum producer. Most of the output has not actually come from the Oxnard Plain but from surrounding mountainsides. **South Mountain**, along the south side of the Santa Clara River Valley, and **Sulphur Mountain**, south of Ojai, have produced oil since the nineteenth century. South Mountain production stimulated the establishment of Union Oil Company. More recently three oil fields have been developed northeast of Oxnard.

The **Ventura Avenue** oil field on the northwestern periphery of Ventura was discovered in 1916; important additional strikes were made in 1923 and 1925. This field, one of the richest in the state, has made Ventura County one of California's three ranking petroleum sources (see chart, Chapter 9). High production has been allowed by a repetition of oil-bearing sands resulting from multiple faulting within an elongated anticlinal ridge with east-west orientation.

TRANSPORTATION

Transportation makes an important contribution to the economy of the Oxnard Plain, athwart the coastal corridor between Los Angeles and San Francisco, and with its agricultural production and adjacent oil fields. Railroad, highway, and ocean commerce are all significant.

Ocean transportation focuses upon Ventura and Port Hueneme. Ventura does not have a harbor, but oil shipping gives it moment as a port. Tankers lie at anchor and receive their cargo by flexible pipeline. **Port Hueneme** was founded in 1870; eventually a citrus-packing plant and a fish cannery were located beside this swampy natural harbor. Then in the late 1930's the harbor was dredged;- an offshore submarine canyon eases entry of large vessels. During World War II Port Hueneme became the site of the major Naval Construction Battalion ("Seabee") base on the Pacific coast—it was an important supply depot for shipment of materiel to Pacific bases.

The Oxnard Plain is the focus of highways radiating outward to the west, north, and east. U.S. 101 crosses the width of the Plain; at El Rio there is a junction with the coastal link to Los Angeles (U.S. 101 alternate). California 126 connects the Plain with U.S. 99 via the Santa Clara River Valley, and U.S. 399 extends northward from Ventura across the Transverse Ranges in the San Joaquin Valley.

The Plain has good rail and airline facilities. Rail service is provided by the Coast Line of the Southern Pacific from Santa Barbara to Los Angeles via Ventura and the freight line extension to Oxnard and Port Hueneme. "Feeder" airline service is provided by Pacific Air Lines.

THE STRAND

Military installations and seaside towns partially occupy the littoral of the Oxnard Plain; however, much of the straight coastline long had no consequence. The two military installations along this coast are operated by the Navy: Camp Rosseau at Port Hueneme and the Naval Air Missile Test Center (allied with the Pacific Missile Range; see Chapter 8). The **Point Mugu Test Center** was created after World War II with the evolution of the military missile (Fig. 7-46). Missiles are fired southwestward across the Pacific; observation stations are maintained in the Santa Monica Mountains and Channel Islands. Evolution of Port Hueneme as a seabee base and supply depot has been noted. A sizable reservation has developed north of the harbor.

The strand had little recreational consequence until the 1960's. Although the coast is often foggy, distance from metropolitan Los Angeies was the principal handicap. More recently, as the population of the Plain has increased and Southern California seashore facilities taxed, this coast has assumed importance. Pierpont Bay at Ventura and San Buenaventura State Beach Park have been much improved, and two small-boat harbors have been constructed. Part of the program included groin construction and beach rebuilding. Three seaside villages adjacent to Port Hueneme—Mandalay Beach, Hollywood Beach, Hollywood-by-the-Sea—have served chiefly as housing centers for military personnel. A steam plant at Mandalay has curtailed local beach use.

OXNARD AND VENTURA

Oxnard and Ventura, principal cities of the Plain, have had differing histories. Ventura evolved as the small settlement around a Spanish mission. Oxnard was established as a farm village a century later.

Ventura (29,000) was known during its first century as San Buenaventura. It remained a small hamlet, albeit the seat of county government, until the oil boom of the 1920's; in a decade its population doubled to surpass Oxnard, which for a short time had been larger. The unusual elongated pattern of the city results from its topographic constriction (Fig. 7-47); Ventura occupies a narrow shelf between the Pacific and the outer wall of the Transverse Ranges. Situation has hampered

Fig. 7-46. POINT MUGU. *The southeastern edge of the Oxnard Plain, with Headquarters, Pacific Missile Range, and the west end of the Santa Monica Mountains. View eastward.* (Official U.S. Navy photograph)

Fig. 7-47. *VENTURA AND OXNARD PLAIN. Note the constricted site of Ventura and Junction of U.S. 101 and 101A in the foreground. Observe the north-south windbreaks.* (California Division of Highways)

its downtown district, which is characterized by narrow streets and congestion. Suburban growth, with a new shopping center, appeared after 1950 on the widening Oxnard Plain to the east. Here the new campus of Ventura College was located in 1955. Many suburbanites commute from inland residences along the Ventura Valley and in Ojai Valley. Ventura's role as an oil center is especially evident along Ventura Avenue, where oil-field equipment firms are found. The open roadstead has necessitated the delivery of oil to tankers at anchor by flexible pipe.

The founding of **Oxnard** (40,000) in 1898 followed rise of a sugar-beet industry and construction of a refinery (now abandoned). The city is centrally located to serve sur-

rounding farmlands. In recent years it has received considerable trade from military personnel at Port Hueneme, Point Mugu, and Oxnard Air Force Base. The city trebled in population during the 1940's to become again the largest city of the Plain; growth since 1945 has witnessed much tract housing. There is social demarcation between the portion of the city west of the railroad right-of-way and the "Little Mexico" to the east, inhabited by field workers. Besides agricultural shipment, Oxnard has gained importance in vegetable packing, with citrus and vegetable fresh freezing plants. Eventual coalescence of Oxnard and Ventura as part of the Southern California (San Diego to Santa Barbara) megalopolis seems inevitable.

THE SANTA BARBARA COAST

The Santa Barbara Coast is the North American counterpart of France's Cote d'Azure, the famed Riviera. This narrow lowland, with dull hues of the swiftly rising wall of the Santa

Ynez Mountains as a backdrop, the richer blue of the Pacific, and the charm of imaginatively landscaped dwellings, is an inviting part of Southern California. The east-west trend of

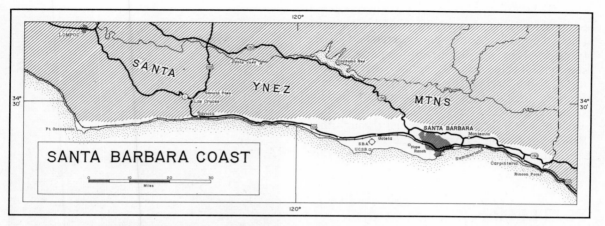

Fig. 7-48. MAP OF THE SANTA BARBARA COAST.

the coast, and its inland mountain wall, produces more equable weather than most of California. Yet it does not quite duplicate the Riviera—the cool Pacific is less attractive for surf bathing than the warmer Mediterranean.

SETTING

The attenuated plain, never as wide as 10 miles, extends for more than 50 miles from Point Conception eastward to Point Rincon (see map, Fig. 7-48). Between Ventura and Point Rincon, the mountains rise from the sea, thus separating the Coast from the Oxnard Plain. In days bygone, before Coast Highway and automobiles, the wagon trail in places followed the narrow sandy beach, and a trip by horses and coach demanded timing of tide and sea.

This narrow alluvial lowland has extensive terrace remnants and the foreslopes of the Santa Ynez Mountains. There has been much faulting; the city of Santa Barbara, for example, lies in a small graben between parallel faults with northwest-southeast trend. Movements along these ruptures have produced the several disastrous earthquakes that have plagued the city. The Carpinteria Plain east of Santa Barbara is also fault-bound on its inner edge. The Plain, however, has more abrupt sides and is more oriented east-west than Goleta Valley to the west.

There is considerable climatic similarity between the Coast and the Oxnard Plain; both have a mild-summer phase of dry-summer subtropical climate. But the Coast does not suffer from outbursts of interior air. North-south windbreaks of trees have been planted instead as protection against eastward flow of maritime breezes. The offshore waters coupled with the Santa Ynez barrier contribute to the ameliorating effect—'tis small wonder this Coast is so well regarded for residence.

WATER SUPPLY

Water resources are understandably limited —the Coast has no rivers such as the Santa Clara, Los Angeles, or Santa Ana. Hence irrigation agriculture was long dependent upon pump wells and, like the Oxnard Plain, long had no access to imported water. Urban growth and increasing rural demands had caused serious depletion of underground supplies by the 1940's. In 1947 severe water rationing was necessitated in Santa Barbara, and there was the threat of salt-water intrusion. The Cachuma Project, authorized by Congress the next year, has provided the needed supplemental water for the Goleta Valley, Carpinteria Plain, Santa Barbara, and Montecito.

The small arable acreage within the drainage basin of the Santa Ynez River north of the

SOUTHERN CALIFORNIA : : 243

Santa Ynez Range has a better supply of water (see Chapter 8). Santa Ynez water had been transferred by an older transmontane diversion but its value was largely lost with the silting of Santa Barbara Reservoir. The Cachuma Project included a larger storage body (Cachuma Reservoir), downriver from the older unit, 6-mile Tecolote Tunnel through the Santa Ynez Mountains, and the South Coast Aqueduct, which distributes water along the Coast.

SETTLEMENT

The Coast was a favored area for primitive peoples even as it is a choice spot for contemporary Americans. Before Spanish settlement it was occupied by the *Chumash*, and supported perhaps the densest population in Southern California. The Chumash, considered superior to other Southern California Indians by the Spanish, were skilled mariners as well as food gatherers. They utilized both the mainland and the adjacent Channel Islands, where they were known to the Spanish as Canaliños.

Like most of the Southern California littoral, the Coast became known to the Spanish early. It was visited by Cabrillo in 1542. The region acquired its name, however, from the visit of Viscaíno on St. Barbara's Day in 1602. Mission Santa Barbara was established in 1782 by Father Serra. Acclaimed "the queen of the missions," it has been maintained by the Franciscans continuously since its founding. The mission flourished for some decades and its pastures supported many cattle. With secularization, however, its lands were taken from the church and the era of ranchos began. The rancho period was similar to that elsewhere in Southern California. Changing economic conditions and the drought of the early 1860's caused the loss of many cattle and led to division of the ranchos and the evolution of American farming.

Changes in rural land-use came more slowly to the Coast than to portions of the Los Angeles Lowlands adjacent to Los Angeles. Transportation facilities were meager until

Fig. 7-49. LEMON GROVES, CARPINTERIA VALLEY. Lemon production here approaches monoculture. (David W. Lantis)

the Coast Line of the Southern Pacific reached Santa Barbara in 1887. The Coast Highway and the through railroad to San Francisco did not evolve until the twentieth century. Walnut groves were established late in the nineteenth century and flourished for two generations.

Lemons have virtually replaced the walnuts. Whereas the Coast had only 4 percent of California's lemon crop in 1930, today it ranks third (after the Oxnard Plain and Santa Clara River Valley). This locale has "almost perfect" frost protection and lemon yields are high. The orchards add to the aesthetic appeal of the Coast (Fig. 7-49). Many groves are maintained by "gentlemen farmers," as in the estate areas of Hope Ranch and Montecito.

THE CARPINTERIA PLAIN

The Carpinteria Plain, east of Santa Barbara, is the most fertile portion of the Coast. Today its rural economy is almost completely dominated by lemons (Fig. 7-49). The extent of the groves is seldom appreciated by the motorist speeding along U.S. 101, despite the fact that groves extend along both sides of the highway.

Fig. 7-50. GOLETA VALLEY. View of Hope Ranch (upper left), the University of California at Santa Barbara (upper middle), and U.S. 101. (Mark Hurd Aerial Surveys, Goleta)

Fig. 7-51. POINT ARGUELLO. Sudden Ranch area is pictured here with Coast Line of the Southern Pacific Railroad. (Official U.S. Navy photograph)

LEADING AGRICULTURAL COMMODITIES, CARPINTERIA VALLEY, 1961
(in millions of dollars)

lemons	3.88
avocados	0.78
cut flowers	0.145
vegetables, miscellaneous	0.14

Source: Agricultural Commissioner, Santa Barbara County.

Petroleum has been produced for many years around Summerland, with some wells rising from the tidal flats. In late years a new and much-expanded tidelands source has been tapped near Santa Barbara.

Carpinteria (5000), a town dating from 1868, is the local farm center. This unincorporated community, within the trade area of Santa Barbara, functions chiefly as a shipping point and a home for farm workers. Some growth results from its function as a residential town.

THE GOLETA VALLEY

The Goleta Valley west of Santa Barbara has more diversified land-use than the Carpinteria Plain (see tables). The gentler slope of the Santa Ynez foothills permits cattle grazing that is not possible on the steeper land behind Carpinteria. Variation in soils and drainage conditions partially accounts for the varied crop patterns, which include orchards, field crops, lemons and avocados, and nursery stock as well as small plots of vegetables (Fig. 7-50). Already however, industrial plants are rising beside the new freeway (U.S. 101), and there are implications that transformation into the Southern California megalopolis has started here too.

Fig. 7-52. SANTA BARBARA. (Eldon Tatsch-Graymar Aviation)

LEADING AGRICULTURAL COMMODITIES,
GOLETA VALLEY, 1961
(in millions of dollars)

lemons	4.4
nursery stock	1.19
cut flowers	0.77
beef cattle	0.55
avocados	0.5
eggs	0.32
field crops	0.26
vegetables	0.13
walnuts	0.11

Source: Agricultural Commissioner, Santa Barbara County.

Goleta (2000), long much smaller than Carpinteria, has had virtually no retail trade in the past. This once unattractive town was occupied principally by field workers. But since establishment of the new campus of the University of California at Santa Barbara upon a seaside site, the town has experienced an almost Cinderella-like transformation and promises to become an inviting community. The Santa Barbara airport here provides feeder service to Los Angeles and San Francisco.

THE WESTERN TERRACES

West of the Goleta Valley the width of the Coast narrows to a series of dissected terraces cut by a succession of small parallel streams flowing southward out of the Santa Ynez Range in gullies (Fig. 7-51). Because of water limitation, much land is devoted to beef-cattle pasturage or dry-farmed grains. A large orchid "ranch" forms a contrary use.

SANTA BARBARA

Santa Barbara (59,000) is one of California's select seaside communities (see Fig. 7-52). Its appeals include scenic setting, romantic history, pleasant climate, and well-maintained homes with landscaped gardens. Santa Barbara, where industry has been discouraged, has been described as the home of the wealthy and those who serve the monied. Smog and congestion in the Los Angeles Lowlands has prompted some affluent business executives to reside in Santa Barbara and commute to their offices by private planes.

Evidences of the Spanish colonial legacy are widespread in Santa Barbara. Some, like the mission (despite its new façade) and such street names as Cabrillo, Laguna, Arrellaga, and Micheltorena, are genuine. Others, such as the widespread use of the synthetic mission architecture, blend with the landscape and the historic tradition. Santa Barbara County courthouse is an outstanding example. Damage caused by the earthquake of 1925 prompted restoration in the mission style. State Street, the principal business thoroughfare, seems an incongruous name here. The spirit of the Spanish heritage is revived each August with a fiesta.

Economic bases of Santa Barbara vary somewhat from those of other California cities of comparable size: tourism, investment income, attendance upon a leisure group, pensions, county government, higher education, regional trade, and limited manufacturing. Winter brings fewer visitors who tend to remain longer and spend more per capita. This group frequents the exclusive hotels; motels advertise "off-season rates" (i.e., in winter). Summer brings the "great American public" by family automobile. Santa Barbara's monied "coupon clippers" include representatives of some of the nation's most prominent families. The city houses a surprising number of retired couples on modest pensions—many reside in the southwestern section of the city. Although Santa Barbara serves as the retail center of the Coast, the luxury items in its specialty shops are found in quantity unusual for its population. The number of brokerage offices is another reflection of high per capita incomes.

The city is understandably one of California's important cultural centers. Besides activities related to the state university, there is a community playhouse, a museum, parks, and organizations related to the arts. The city has crafts shops as well as designers' studios. Many artists, musicians, and writers make the city their home: clubs related to music, drama, and art flourish.

Santa Barbara is fringed by attractive suburban residential districts. To the east is Montecito and to the west Hope Ranch; on the north homes ascend the lower slopes of the Santa Ynez Mountains.

Montecito, politically separate, has been called the "home of American trademarks"— residents represent families of American industrialists whose products are widely known. Center of this millionaires' retreat is not the diminutive shopping district along Coast Highway, which does not divulge the nature of the community, but the Montecito Country Club. Homes are sequested by lemon groves, and signposts, marked "private" or "no trespassing," are found along the winding lanes.

Hope Ranch, west of Santa Barbara, is an exclusive residential area of 2000 acres developed on rolling terrain amidst lemon groves. The Ranch has no retail stores—its center is La Cumbre Country Club. It has the appeals of a private beach (Laguna Blanca), 25 miles of bridle paths, view lots affording vistas of the Santa Ynez Mountains and the Pacific, and an absence of commercialism.

THE TRANSVERSE RANGES

The Transverse Ranges have been publicized and frequented unduly because of their proximity to the millions who inhabit the Los Angeles Lowlands. They are not spectacular nor are they of breath-taking beauty, but they are accessible—and they are cooler in summer and provide appealing vistas. But they lack the hardwood forests of the Appalachians, the

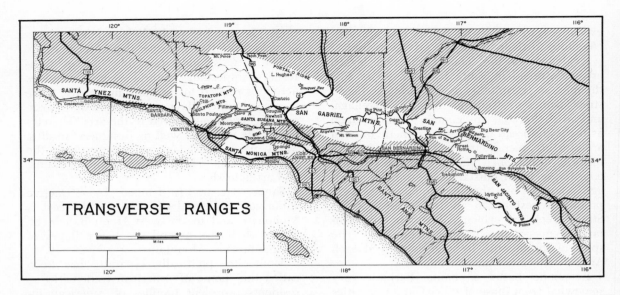

Fig. 7-53. MAP OF THE TRANSVERSE RANGES.

snowy crowns of the Cascade, the serrated summits of the Rockies, and the glaciated canyons of the Sierra Nevada.

Some have called these ranges the Los Angeles Ranges; others refer to them as the Southern California Mountains or less accurately as the Coast Range. Whereas the Coast Ranges trend north-south, the Transverse Ranges have an east-west orientation. From west to east they include the Santa Ynez, Topatopa, "The Knot," Santa Susana, Santa Monica, Verdugo, San Gabriel, and San Bernardino (see map, Fig. 7-53).[26] Because of location and utilization (by residents of the Los Angeles Lowlands), the San Jacinto and the Santa Rosa are herein discussed with the Transverse Ranges, although physiographically they belong to the Peninsular Ranges.

These ranges provide an important physical function in utilization of Southern California —they "shut out" most of the desert heat of summer and the interior cold in winter. But they also contribute to floods and are ravaged by fire. They ensnare considerable moisture from Pacific maritime air masses. The barrier function has not been restricted to air movement alone—the ranges have tended to curtail plant migrations as well. And until this century these mountains also hampered the movements of man.

PHYSICAL ASPECTS

BLOCK MOUNTAINS

The Transverse Ranges vary considerably in elevation, structure, size, and surface expression. Generally the eastern ranges (especially the San Gabriel, San Bernardino, and San Jacinto) are much higher. Highest summits include Mt. San Antonio (10,089 ft.), San Gorgonio (11,485 ft.), and San Jacinto (10,-805 ft.). Farther west the local relief is sometimes insufficient to classify the ranges accurately as true mountains. It is fitting that the segment of the Santa Monica Mountains between the Los Angeles Coastal Plain and the San Fernando Valley be called "Hollywood Hills." Within these ranges are a num-

---

[26] The term "The Knot" is suggested for the area crossed by the Ridge Route (U.S. 99) where the Sierra Nevada, the Coast Ranges, and the Transverse Ranges converge.

ber of intermont basins, of which the Santa Clara River Valley is the most prominent.

The ranges represent several periods of mountain building. The contemporary topography largely results from diastrophism during the Pleistocene—recent earthquakes suggest that some development continues. Between periods of uplift, erosion has been dominant and deep narrow canyons are commonplace. In the west, where slopes rise from the Pacific, narrow marine terraces are characteristic, as has been noted in connection with other subdivisions of Southern California.

The Transverse Ranges might be described as a group of "uplifted" blocks, bordered and bisected by great faults such as the San Andreas and much dissected by erosion. More westerly ranges show tilted and folded sedimentary structures. These include the Santa Ynez, Santa Monica, and Santa Susana ranges. The San Gabriel (a compound horst), San Bernardino, and San Jacinto are conspicuous for their granitic cores and impressively steep fault-scarp faces. They possess many flattish summit areas where erosion has not yet worked its way back from the mountain margins.

VERTICAL ZONES

The Transverse Ranges show the greatest climatic variation within Southern California. The general rhythm follows the usual regional pattern of hot, dry summers and mild winters with occasional cyclonic storms. Elevation differences, distinctions between shady (north-facing) and sunny (south-facing) slopes, and location with respect to the ocean all combine to create a multitude of diverse "micro-climates."

Coastal slopes below about 3000 feet are exposed to considerable maritime air and stratus cloud. The Santa Ynez and Santa Monica Mountains and the Santa Clara River Valley thus tend to have milder temperatures than the more eastern ranges. Interior slopes (particularly eastward from the Ridge Route on U.S. 99) are more exposed to dry continental air and their summer and winter temperatures are somewhat extreme.

Because of temperature decrease with altitude, hot-summer Mediterranean aspects do not prevail much higher than a mile above sea level. A milder-summer Mediterranean phase (too small to be shown on Fig. A-5, Appendix A) occurs still higher, which is suggestive of the cool coastline localities. Higher summits display middle-latitude, severe winter conditions not typical of the subtropics at lower elevation. Extreme interior slopes are classified as semiarid. Winter precipitation tends to increase with altitude. Coastal margins receive about 15 inches of precipitation annually, although some highland stations in the San Gabriel and San Bernardino Mountains receive in excess of 40 inches. Precipitation around higher summits often falls as snow.

CONIFERS AND CHAPARRAL

Natural vegetation has understandable variations with semblance of vertical zonation. Chaparral forms the most widespread association—stands tend to be less dense on south-facing coastal slopes. Its shrubs are evergreen but hues vary seasonally. It consists of numerous species adapted to the long rainless season—leaves are often small and sometimes leathery. Near the coast the chamise (*Adenostoma fasciculatum*) subdivision prevails. Chaparral clothes steep slopes and checks erosion, but it generally has no grazing value and is fire-susceptible during the drought season.

Desert-facing slopes of the eastern ranges reflect arid influence and support a piñon-juniper woodland in which yucca is sometimes prominent.

A yellow pine (*P. ponderosa*) association, prevalent above 6000 feet, has thicker stands on north slopes and best development around 8000-9500 feet. There is Coulter pine in this forest. Along streams a canyon-floodplain assemblage of sycamore, oak, alder, willow, and maple is common—it usually forms groves rather than true forests. Oak forest typically forms the transition between chaparral and conifers. It is widespread on south-facing slopes at 4000 to 6000 feet and reaches much lower elevations on shady slopes where evaporation is lessened.

UTILIZATION

Utilization of the "subtropical" Transverse Ranges differs appreciably from that of most middle-latitude highlands. Location has particular significance—proximity to large lowland populations. The principal uses of these uplands include watershed, transportation, recreation, mining, residence, and ranching.

WATERSHED

Southern California, a water-short land, must conserve as much of its highland precipitation as possible. Steep stream gradients and the slope of canyon walls accelerates runoff. Chaparral helps check runoff, but its value in this respect is sometimes debated. Snowpack, although appreciably less than in some parts of the Sierra-Cascade (Part Two), is still relatively heavy and important (Big Bear Dam averages 124 inches—over 20 inches monthly, December through March).

Storage reservoirs have been constructed in a few localities: the nature of the precipitation, sometimes torrential, and the stream gradients and dangerously faulted rock structures do not favor large units. Important storage reservoirs for local runoff include Gibraltar and Cachuma on the Santa Ynez River; Matilija, Casitas, and Santa Felicia in Ventura County; and Big Bear on the Santa Ana River. Canyons of the Transverse Ranges are also used to store "imported" water, as at Morris and Bouquet reservoirs in the San Gabriel Range and Franklin Reservoir (for Beverly Hills) in the Santa Monica.

Runoff from the Transverse Ranges is accelerated by precipitous terrain and many barren surfaces, which explains why the lowly chaparral is so highly regarded as ground cover. Protection is particularly vital to densely populated lowlands that adjoin the Transverse Ranges—this was evidenced by the tragic flood of 1934 in La Cañada Corridor.

Yet chaparral is a voracious consumer of moisture; canyon-bottom forests also absorb great volumes of streamflow that is badly needed for human use. Thus removal of riparian forest has been practiced in selected

Fig. 7-54. GRAPEVINE CANYON. This portion of the Ridge Route (U.S. 99), with its six percent grades, is now an eight-lane thoroughfare. The divided construction has reduced the accident rate on this heavily traveled highway. (California Division of Highways)

locations and efforts are underway to find satisfactory substitutes for chaparral. The "brush problem" is intensified by flammability of this vegetation most of the year—a menace increasingly serious the longer chaparral is "saved" from fire. Large sums are allocated annually to prevent and extinguish fires in the Transverse Ranges. To reduce the hazard, extensive tracts within the national forests are withdrawn from public entry during the long "fire season."

PASSAGEWAYS

All land routes into Southern California from the north and east must cross or skirt the Transverse Ranges. In the 1960's these afford relatively easy passage—this was not always true in the past. Important passes (from west to east) include **Gaviota** (950 ft.), pursued by an important Coast Highway (U.S. 101) freeway link, and **San Marcos** (2224 ft.) in the Santa Ynez Range. To the east U.S. 399 crosses Pine Mountain Summit north of Ojai, and U.S. 99 uses **Tejon Pass** (4239 ft.) on the Ridge Route. This limited-access highway with some eight-lane stretches is indeed a different road from what it was originally (Fig. 7-54). Slow

Fig. 7-55. CAJON PASS. Union Pacific's City of St. Louis. (Union Pacific Railroad)

movement of heavy trucks reflect six percent grades, the maximum allowed on federal highways.[27] Brief closures due to winter icing or snow are sometimes necessary. To the south the Coast Line of the South Pacific uses long tunnels beneath low **Santa Susana Pass** between the San Fernando Valley and Oxnard and then skirts the west end of the Santa Ynez Mountains. **San Fernando** (or Fremont) **Pass** at the northeast edge of the San Fernando Valley and **Soledad Pass** to the northeast provide the Valley Line of the Southern Pacific egress from the Los Angeles Lowlands. The railroad must later cross the Tehachapi Mountains to reach the San Joaquin Valley (Fig. 5-14). **Cajon Pass** (4301 ft.), between the San Gabriel and San Bernardino ranges, is an important crossing. A freeway (designated U.S. 66 and 395) is vastly different from the crude trail that was followed by early traders in the late Mexican period. The Santa Fe trackage across this pass is also used by the Union Pacific Railroad (Fig. 7-55). In

the southeast is another extremely important entry way into Southern California, **San Gorgonio Pass** (2559 ft.), between the San Bernardino and San Jacinto mountains. The freeway has a triple designation, U.S. 60, 70, and 99. This crossing is also used by the main line of the Southern Pacific Railroad eastward.

Utilities must also cross the Transverse Ranges to deliver water, oil, natural gas, electricity, and telephone service to Southern California. Often the above passes provide crossings for them too. However, power lines especially are less restricted by terrain and tend to follow shortest paths.

RECREATION

To many outlanders the Transverse Ranges may seem to be a "desperation fringe," where recreational congestion is extreme in relation to the limited attractions. For one thing there is only modest scenic appeal—the Ranges are too dry and too barren. Moreover, vistas from the eastern ranges are often blurred by the smog layer over the Los Angeles Lowlands. Such handicaps, however, are offset by proximity to large populations; the San Bernardino Mountains alone have twice as many visitors

[27] Because of some tragic accidents, several escape roads have been built away from the highway with sandy surfaces and upgrades, so that trucks whose brakes have "burned up" will eventually stop.

SOUTHERN CALIFORNIA : : 251

Fig. 7-56. LAKE ARROWHEAD. A much-frequented mountain playground. (U.S. Forest Service photo)

annually as the most popular of the national parks. Visits of a few hours, a day, or a week-end are typical. Habitués are primarily Southern Californians rather than out-of-staters.

Drives, some with inviting names, which afford spectacular views, lead across several of the highlands. Major examples are Mulholland Drive in the Santa Monica Mountains, Angeles Crest Highway (California 2) in the San Gabriel, Rim of the World (California 18) in the San Bernardino, and Pines-to-Palms Highway (California 74) in the San Jacinto. On weekends such roads may become more congested than many city streets; on the other hand they are extremely well built for such rough terrain—construction is often justified by the need for fire-fighting access alone.

Much of the mountain country is included within three national forests: Los Padres in Santa Barbara and Ventura counties, Angeles in Los Angeles County, and San Bernardino in San Bernardino and Riverside counties. Campsites, "recreation areas," and hiking trails have been provided. Sites for cabins and even ski lifts are leased, though these are at a premium. Hunting and fishing, also, are too popular for the limited resources. In five locations within the national forests are **Wild Areas** (see Chapter 5); these permit the limited number willing to abandon their automobiles for long hikes to visit some of the most rugged terrain in Southern California.

Major resort centers with substantial year-around residence occur in the western Santa Monica Mountains, the San Bernardino Mountains, and around Idyllwild in the San Jacinto. The Santa Monica is much favored by proximity to both Los Angeles and the seacoast. The San Bernardino Range has the largest resorts, which enjoy a unique combination of fairly level topography and higher elevation. Here is Southern California's greatest extent of forest, lake, and winter snow country, which has long been familiar to millions of movie-goers as the Rocky Mountains and the Canadian North Woods (Fig. 7-56). Permanent population, including the communities of **Crestline**, **Lake Arrowhead**, and **Big Bear**, exceeds 8000.

MINING

Mining has had slight consequence in the Transverse Ranges except for petroleum. Small amounts of gold were recovered from Placerita Canyon north of San Fernando Valley even before the Gold Rush commenced. As late as the 1930's gold panning took place along San Gabriel Canyon and near Baldwin Lake (San Bernardino Mountains). Holcombe Valley (same range) was sufficiently important in the "early days" that the seat of San Bernardino County was almost located there.

An extensive oil zone extends along both sides of the Santa Clara River Valley from

Newhall to the sea and thence westward parallel to the shore past Santa Barbara. This belt, generally called the **Ventura Basin**, has ranked after the San Joaquin Basin and the Los Angeles Basin as a California source of petroleum. Production around Sulphur Mountain south of Ojai commenced in 1866; the Newhall district was developed shortly thereafter. The most important field, opened in 1916, has been the Ventura Avenue field, mentioned previously with the Oxnard Plain. Production comes from sands at depths of 800 to 12,000 feet, most in anticlinal and fault-trap structures. Elsewhere several fields began producing after 1949: Castaic Junction, Placerita Canyon, and Honor Rancho–Castaic Hills; all are near the Ridge Route (U.S. 99).

VIEW LOTS

Sections of the Transverse Ranges, particularly within and adjacent to metropolitan Los Angeles, have much residential utilization. Development has taken place largely since 1920, with evolution of automotive travel. "View lots" in the San Jose Hills near Pomona, the San Rafael Hills west of Pasadena, and the eastern Santa Monica Mountains ("Hollywood Hills") have become quite expensive— by 1963 a choice relatively flat half-acre lot might cost from $25,000 to $100,000 in the most "exclusive" settings. Some of the most luxurious homes around Los Angeles are found on such hillsides. More prominent localities include Flintridge (between Pasadena and Glendale), northern Beverly Hills, southern Sherman Oaks, Bel Air, and Brentwood. Mountain Park, an 11,000-acre project along Mulholland Drive west of Bel Air, is under development now. This one district, half the size of San Francisco, had been the largest tract of "raw land" left within the Los Angeles city limits.

RANCHING

Stream valleys and intermont basins within the Ranges provide many small pockets of arable land. Although chaparral-covered hillsides have not been used for grazing, some unirrigated lands afford seasonal pasturage, whereas others yield dry-farmed winter barley. The most extensive ranchlands are found within the western ranges where slopes tend to be gentler and soils deeper. Here too are the Santa Clara River Valley, the Simi Valley, the Ojai Valley, and several lesser areas where farming is conducted.

THE SANTA CLARA RIVER VALLEY

The Santa Clara River Valley [28] affords an excellent transect of Southern California agriculture—only a low divide separates its upper end from the Mojave Desert, and on the west it debouches into the Oxnard Plain near the ocean. A series of Mexican ranchos were awarded along the Valley, several relatively early. Their history repeats the typical Southern California pattern: rise of large cattle herds, drought in the 1860's, rancho subdivision, sheep ranching, grain farming, and eventually specialized agriculture. Several large properties remain: the Newhall, the Sespe, the Camulos, and the Limoneira. The vast Limoneira Ranch near Santa Paula contains California's largest single lemon acreage.[29]

Upriver around Saugus and Newhall, winter frost negates production of many sensitive crops. However, alfalfa, carrots, and various other crops are grown on irrigated bottomlands. Cattle and hogs (fed on Los Angeles garbage) are other specialties. Westward around Piru there are walnut orchards, and on adjacent lower slopes orange groves appear. From Fillmore westward citrus groves are more widespread. Below Santa Paula, well-drained slopes are almost frost-free. There is an interesting crop stratification: lemons and avocados on lower foothills and the tops of alluvial fans, with oranges and then walnuts on lower (and more frost-prone) portions of fans. Seed flowers, lima beans, and

[28] This is often called the Santa Clara Valley or the Santa Clara Valley of the South. To distinguish it from the better-known basin south of San Francisco Bay it is referred to here as the Santa Clara *River* Valley.

[29] The diversity of a large operation like this is impressive. It maintains its own soil laboratory, packing houses, residences for workers, railroad spur, and irrigation system.

Fig. 7-58. OJAI VALLEY. (David W. Lantis)

Fig. 7-57. ASCENDING MT. SAN ANTONIO. This narrow ridge, the Devil's Backbone, leads to the summit of "Old Baldy" (10,064 ft.). (David W. Lantis)

other field crops are raised at the base of the fans, where the water table may be high. Grazing takes place in the bed of the Santa Clara River.

Towns of the Santa Clara provide residence for agricultural and petroleum workers and serve as retail and shipping points. Santa Paula, Fillmore, and Newhall are the largest communities. **Santa Paula** (13,000) serves as principal farm center and shipping point of the Valley. It has been an oil town since its founding (Union Oil Company originated here). Modest farm workers' cottages are conspicuous near the Santa Clara River. **Fillmore** (4800) is smaller than Santa Paula but is also growing. Well-maintained shipping sheds suggest the output of the surrounding citrus groves. It is a gateway into the Sespe Wild Area for fishermen and deer hunters. **Newhall** (4700) is now on the urban fringe of Los Angeles. There is growing commuter residence

and diversified manufacturing in addition to farming and petroleum.

THE OJAI VALLEY

When viewed from Denison Grade, the picturesque Ojai Valley, inland from the Oxnard Plain, presents one of Southern California's most pleasant rural scenes—orchards, ranches, groves of oak, and sycamore (Fig. 7-58). Citrus and deciduous fruit are important products.

Ojai (4500) and neighboring towns have a combination of agricultural, retirement, tourist, and commuter residence. The Valley is noted for its private schools, several resorts, annual music festival, and spring tennis tournament.

LESSER INTERMONT BASINS

Within the folds of the Santa Monica and Santa Susana Mountains are several little basins whose agricultural value has been enhanced by pump-well irrigation and market expansion within metropolitan Los Angeles. These include Russell Valley, Conejo Valley, and Hidden Valley adjacent to U.S. 101; and the Simi, Little Simi, and Santa Rosa valleys to the north. Where terrain or water resources do not permit irrigation, winter grains are raised. The Simi Valley has deciduous fruits and grapes, the Santa Rosa citrus. Communities like **Moorpark, Simi,** and **Thousand Oaks** have some trade but have also functioned as residences for farm workers. On the eastern edge of the Simi is Corrigan's Ranch, used for filming western movies and television films. In the 1960's urbanization is spreading westward into some of these valleys from the San Fernando.

SAN GORGONIO PASS

San Gorgonio Pass is another of the commercial corridors into the Los Angeles Lowlands where agriculture has significance. Farming commenced during the boom of the 1880's. Elevation of half a mile, coupled with winds that seem to blow almost constantly, has discouraged cultivation of some subtropi-

cal plants. However, deciduous orchards were established quite early. Peaches (especially late Rio Oso) have become the leading crop, followed by plums. Cherries, however, are the best-known fruit in the Pass; their spring-time blossoms and summer "pick-your-own" harvest arrangements attract many city dwellers.

Beaumont (4300) and **Banning** (10,300) are residential towns that serve as highway gateways into Southern California. Both rely considerably upon trade from highway travelers as well as upon local agriculture. Both communities have large retirement populations, which have been attracted by the higher, drier weather and magnificent mountain scenery on both sides of San Gorgonio Pass.

THE CHANNEL ISLANDS

The least visited and most sparsely populated portions of Southern California are the two groups of Channel Islands: [30] Santa Barbara and Santa Catalina. Few Californians have ever been ashore on any of these islands except for much-frequented Santa Catalina (see map, Fig. 7-59).

Although these islands are all within seventy miles of the mainland, public transportation is available only to Catalina, and to a lesser extent, Anacapa. The other islands might as well be in the Indian Ocean—except to yachtsmen and governmental personnel, they are virtually inaccessible.

The **Santa Barbara** group, consisting of Anacapa, Santa Cruz, Santa Rosa, and San Miguel, forms a string of islands separated from the mainland by the Santa Barbara Channel. The **Catalina** group is more scattered. Santa Catalina is separated from the coast by San Pedro Channel; the other three,

San Clemente, Santa Barbara, and San Nicolas, are beyond Outer Santa Barbara Channel (southwest of Catalina).

SETTING

LANDFORMS

The sea floor between the Southern California coastline and the continental slope has an area of over 30,000 square miles. The islands rising from this surface appear to be of two general types. The Santa Barbara group seems a continuation of the Santa Monica Mountains: a granitic ridge capped by complex anticlinal structures. The Catalina group perhaps is a continuation of the Peninsular Ranges; however, it is apparently nongranitic. South of the Santa Barbara group, the structure seems to be a series of parallel horsts and grabens. The grabens form sea troughs reaching depths of as much as 6000 feet below sea level. The higher horsts form the Catalina islands; those that do not reach above sea level form "banks."

The Channel Islands have much rough terrain and their narrow stream-dissected val-

[30] Authorities differ in use of the term "Channel Islands." Gudde, in *California Place Names,* uses the term to describe only the Santa Barbara group. Drury, in *California, An Intimate Guide,* includes both groups but suggests they should be called Cabrillo Islands after the early Spanish explorer.

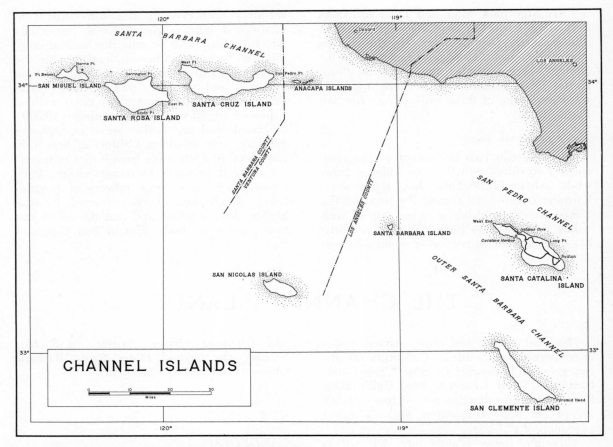

Fig. 7-59. MAP OF THE CHANNEL ISLANDS.

leys have steep gradients. Lower portions of some valleys are drowned. Wave-cut terraces extend as high as 1500 feet above sea level. Some islands, such as Catalina and Anacapa, have surprisingly level summit uplands. There are prominent fault scarps, such as the southwestern face of Catalina.

FOGS AND COOL AIR

The climate of the Channel Islands represents a cool-summer, drier phase of the Mediterranean type. Elevations are insufficient to produce much orographic effect during winter storms. Water deficiency has been a major deterrent of greater utilization. Because of oceanic location, seasonal temperature ranges are low for the latitude. The outer islands tend to be windy and chilly, particularly in winter, and experience considerably more summer fog than Catalina or Santa Cruz.

CHAMISE AND GRASS

Chamise chaparral and coast sage form the characteristic vegetation on these dry, rocky isles. In some instances flattish summit uplands are covered with wild grasses. Santa Cruz, with pines and some excellent stands of manzanita, is the best wooded. Eucalyptus and other types of trees have been planted on Catalina and Santa Cruz.

WILD SHEEP AND ALBACORE

Despite their rocky slopes and their dryness the islands support a rich fauna. Some animals, such as Catalina's bison herd, the wild goats of San Clemente, the wild boars, Santa Rosa's deer and elk, and the rabbits and wild sheep on several islands, were brought from the mainland by man. Other species, such as fox and skunk, are indigenous. There are numerous birds, including eagles, hawks, ravens, meadowlarks, and sea gulls. Sea life is abundant; sea lions are found along several coasts, particularly Santa Barbara and San Nicolas, which also has a sea elephant colony. The cool waters contain numerous fish, such as sea bass, albacore, mackerel, bonita, whitefish, perch, swordfish—and also sharks.

THE PAST

Utilization of the Channel Islands has followed the characteristic Southern California "pattern" with certain modifications. The Islands supported *Canaliño* Indians in pre-European times. They were discovered during the first Spanish explorations of California. After establishment of mainland missions, the Indians were taken from the islands to become neophytes. Ranchos were created on some islands. American utilization has tended to differ from that on the mainland—insular ranchos did not become cities, as often happened in the Los Angeles Lowlands.

The Islands apparently supported some hundreds of Canaliños prior to the Spanish period. Doubtless the largest populations subsisted upon Santa Catalina and Santa Cruz. Like coastal Indians, these people were hunter-gatherers and, especially, fishermen. They were adept navigators and builders of planked canoes. The sea provided them with food; they also fashioned shells and bone into tools and implements.

Juan Cabrillo discovered the Channel Islands just half a century after the first voyage of Columbus. Cabrillo was injured while landing on San Miguel and was buried in the islands. Crews of his two small ships explored northward along the California coast; no riches were found and California was forgotten for a time. Even after Sebastian Vizcaíno,

merchant turned pearl fisher, visited the Islands in 1602, the area was neglected until the arrival of Portolá in 1769.

The Spanish weighed establishment of a mission on Catalina; investigations indicated that there was insufficient water for irrigation. Thus many of the Canaliños were removed to mainland missions. Presumably, most of the rest were killed by Russian seal hunters. Under Mexican rule three islands became land grants: Santa Rosa, Santa Cruz, and Santa Catalina. Throughout the Mexican period, however, the islands had slight economic value.

THE PRESENT

The Channel Islands still have relatively little economic importance and remain sparsely populated. The single incorporated town is **Avalon** on Catalina. Utilization is restricted because of private ownership, governmental use, and environmental restrictions. Coasts are rocky and arable land is limited. Perhaps the greatest handicap is limited water. Fog, kelp beds, rough seas, shoals, and absence of suitable landings hamper navigation.

There are several modes of utilization. Of the eight islands only Santa Catalina has any recreational consequence, except for the activities of local yachtsmen and fishermen. Insular waters have considerable importance as commercial fishing grounds and for sports fishing. Livestock ranching has significance only on Santa Cruz, Santa Rosa, and Catalina. Military activities are conducted on several of the islands.

THE CATALINA GROUP

Santa Catalina has greater utilization than the other seven islands. Except for the town of Avalon, the island has been the property of the Wrigley family since 1919. Although the Wrigleys have expended several million dollars to construct reservoirs and develop a water system, much of the island remains useless. Most of the remaining land affords pasturage for Wrigley's Black Jack Ranch.

Fig. 7-60. SANTA CATALINA ISLAND. (Lane Magazine Company, photo by Litton)

Several hundred acres of uplands grain are grown for feed.

Catalina is the weekend destination of numerous Southern California yachtsmen. The surrounding waters are also popular with sports fishermen, and skin diving has become popular near the shore.

Avalon (1500) is the center of public activity, and its small beach becomes extremely congested in summer. The waterfront Boardwalk, inspection of marine life through glass-bottom boats, and the Aviary are popular. Despite narrow streets, there is no traffic congestion since visitors cannot bring their automobiles. Many homes are nestled on hillsides.

Attenuated **San Clemente**, south of Catalina, is quite dry and lacks all-weather harbors. The island was formerly used for sheep ranching; today the sheep are gone, but grass provides forage for thousands of wild goats. Clemente has been military property since World War II. The Navy maintains an airfield and major naval vessels have used the south end of the island for a target range. More recently the Air Force has established a radar station at the north end of San Clemente as part of its aerial protection of Southern California. Navy missile testing has been another recent activity.

Santa Barbara, smallest of the group, is sometimes called "Santa Barbara Rock"—with Anacapa it forms a national monument. Its characteristic vegetation, coreopsis, attains surprising size here. The island is uninhabited; its only use is the two flashing navigation lights, unattended, at either end of the island.

San Nicolas is the most remote of the Catalina group. It was inhabited by Canaliños, some of whom were killed by Russian sea-otter hunters; the remainder were removed to Mission Santa Barbara. In the American period sheep have been raised here. During the boom of the 1880's even a townsite was laid out. The island is a naval installation with several million dollars worth of electronic equipment for use in testing of missiles from Point Mugu.

THE SANTA BARBARA GROUP

Barren windswept **San Miguel** is the most westerly of the Islands. A marker indicates, presumably, the grave of explorer Juan Cabrillo. At times the island has been used as a sheep ranch although it has been unoccupied since 1942. During the Korean conflict the Navy used it as a bombing range. It is a habitat for the once almost extinct sea elephant.

Santa Rosa, one of the larger (17 miles long) and better watered islands, has long afforded pasturage; it is also a military base. Here as on San Clemente the Air Force maintains a link in the aerial defense designed to protect Southern California from surprise attack. Continuous and careful surveillance is made by radar of planes operating in surrounding skies.

Santa Rosa was once a rancho owned by the Carrillo brothers of Santa Barbara. It is now the 53,000-acre Hereford ranch of Vail and Vickers Cattle Company. Cattle are shipped to market on barges from the wharf at Beechers Bay on the northeast coast. Grass is carefully conserved; trespassing is discouraged.

Santa Cruz, comparable in size to Catalina, is perhaps the most favored of the eight islands. Summer launch schedules once brought visitors from Santa Barbara, but the island is less favorably located than Catalina for recreational use. Because of damage inflicted by careless yachtsmen, the island is now closed to the public. As one of the larger cattle ranches in California the island has had a colorful history. For a time it served as a penal colony. Later it was granted to Andre Castellero who sold it to Justinian Caire in 1869. Caire, who died in 1898, had a hundred retainers and maintained an Old World barony in the central valley, Arroyo Principal. Before Prohibition the ranch was renowned for its excellent wines. Besides the 8000 acres retained by the Gherini family (relatives of Caire), Santa Cruz has been since 1937 the 54,000-acre property of Angeleno businessman E. L. Stanton, who commutes to his insular estate by airplane. Since 1949 a high summit has been used by the Navy as part of the missile-testing program at Point Mugu.

Anacapa actually consists of three separate blocks whose steep walls rise from the sea. It is unpopulated except for Coast Guard personnel, who maintain the lighthouse at the east end of the island. Because of sheer cliffs lighthouse supplies are landed by hoist. The Coast Guard acts as custodian of this remote national monument, established in 1938 to preserve wild life and geological features. Visits are restricted to scientists conducting approved research.

REGIONAL PROSPECTS

Southern California has been occupied by people of European ancestry for two centuries, yet there is a suggestion of the frontier in the rawness of the new treeless housing tract reaching outward on the periphery of most communities. An added frontier flavor is cast by the Pacific shore and the wild, brush-covered mountain backdrop. In half-hidden inland corners are new orchard plantings and dairy parlors.

It seems difficult to visualize a cessation of the migration that brings a thousand new residents to Southern California daily. Economic opportunity, bolstered by federal preparations for defense and space exploration, shows little likelihood of subsiding.

Regional assets for military preparedness, particularly production and research facilities and amiable climate, outweigh such liabilities as congestion, strategic vulnerability, and isolation from nationwide launching sites. Growth rate in defense industries may be slowed, however, with demise of the airplane and emergence of such competitive airspace centers as the San Francisco Bay Area. Nonetheless the immediate future seems to be hitched to the vicissitudes of world affairs and related technological developments.

The national urge to live "in the sun," increasing population mobility, and the pursuit of newly arrived residents by consumer-oriented industries generated much Southern California growth after World War II. Possibly these still provide sufficient cushion against sudden upheaval in the defense-oriented economy. Predictions have been voiced that Californians in this decade will conduct a rising share of their own manufacturing. As the West's largest market, Southern California should be in the vanguard of such a trend.

Depletion of natural resources has been much-lamented. Petroleum extraction, fishing, and agriculture have probably seen their zenith—although they should contribute to the diversity and distinctiveness of the region for some decades. Fuel and water deficits are also mounting, but Southern Californians have acquired justifiable self-confidence in their ability to find new supplies when necessary.

Of much concern is shrinkage of open spaces and pollution of the atmosphere. The specter of high land costs, crowded transportation routes and outdoor vacation places, and the health menace of smog hardly seems balanced by multistory residence, freeways, manmade tourist attractions, and indoor weather control. It is these conditions that may make Southern California most vulnerable; but the day when vacant land entirely vanishes, traffic becomes impossibly jammed, and smog becomes omnipresent, still seems distant.

Southern California hardly presents a mellowed, stable, or quietly attractive milieu. Its urban prospects, probably as a single megalopolis stretching 200 miles from San Diego to Santa Barbara, are anathemas to some. To others there is excitement and opportunity in the pattern of expanding cities, highways, industries, recreation places, and cultural institutions that characterize the region. Along with employment, the backyards, the sunshine, the nearby deserts, mountains, and beaches promise to them more attractive living than anything offered "back East." Why should they not continue to emigrate? Compared to such incentives, what matter a few smoggy days, occasional freeway tie-ups, or the dim possibility of cataclysmic earthquake?

Fig. 8-1. THE CENTRAL COAST—a land of fertile valleys. The intensively farmed lowlands produce numerous fruits and vegetables. Collective values of such commodities annually total scores of millions of dollars. Mexican braceros, seen here, are transplanting celery in the Arroyo Grande Valley in April; the crop will be harvested in July. (David W. Lantis)

CHAPTER EIGHT:: THE CENTRAL
COAST

THE CENTRAL COAST

Lights of San Francisco from an apartment on Buena Vista Hill, a stroll beneath the redwoods of Big Basin, a July dip in Big Sur River, acres of blooms at Lompoc, ripening grain in the Carrizo, fruit canning at Santa Clara, a classroom lecture in Berkeley—all this is California's Central Coast. So is Mt. Diablo, the beach at Santa Cruz, Morro Bay, Carmel, and Monterey, Mission San Antonio de Padua, San Simeon, Marin County with Sausalito and Muir Woods, Pebble Beach, Cambria Pines, and Pinnacles Monument. Who can deny the appeal of this delightful land that extends along the Pacific for 300 miles from Point Arguello to Tomales Bay?

The Central Coast seems transitional—between the palms of Southern California and the redwoods of the Northwest, and between the cool foggy Pacific and the dry summer heat of the Great Central Valley (Fig. 8-2). With Southern California and the Central Valley it forms a triumvirate of California

This chapter has been reviewed by Richard Ellefsen, Michael McIntyre, and Raymond Stanley, all of San Jose State College.

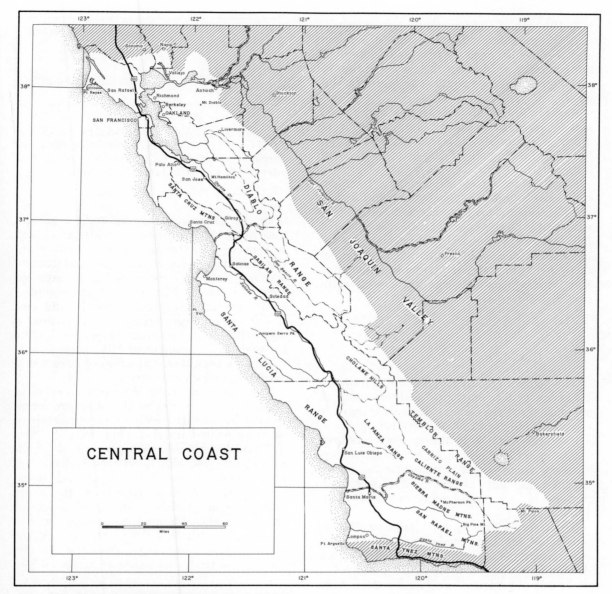

Fig. 8-2. MAP OF THE CENTRAL COAST.

population concentration and human activity. There is contrast within the Central Coast too —between metropolis and crossroads, or San Francisco and Simmler. There is the variation afforded by irrigated lowlands, pastured hillsides, and forested summits.

This land between Los Angeles and San Francisco, whose northern margin is in fact the San Francisco Bay Area, is a fourth larger than Southern California (approximately 15,-000 square miles). Because of its position it is a major transportation corridor. The old Spanish cart trail **El Camino Real** is approximated by the Southern Pacific's "Coast Route" and

U.S. 101, one of California's two major north-south thoroughfares. The influence of tourism and of travel between the two great metropolitan centers is evident in the concentration of motels, restaurants, garages, and service stations.

Basically the Central Coast is a hilly region and as such, its dominant use (in terms of area) is pastoral. It is significant that San Francisco, metropolis of the area, is a city of hills.

San Francisco does not dominate the Central Coast as Los Angeles overwhelms Southern California. This fact reflects the transitory nature of the region and also the fact that the Bay Area is peripheral rather than central in location. One might ponder what differences there would be today if Monterey rather than San Francisco had become the metropolis of central California.

THE LAND

The Southern Coast Ranges, which form the backbone of this portion of California, lie en echelon, three tiers deep. Summits commonly rise to elevations of 2000 to 4000 feet; however, a few higher peaks in the extreme southeast exceed 8000 feet elevation. Yet almost everywhere the local relief is such that the region qualifies as hilly rather than mountainous terrain—in fact, considerable upland is cultivated.

The trend of the ranges, relative to air-mass movement, imparts a marked contrast between seacoast, exposed summits, and interior basins. Accordingly the Central Coast possesses a multitude of intricate "small landscapes," more suggestive of New England than most parts of California.

LAND OF HILLS

The Southern Coast Ranges, northward from the Santa Ynez Valley into Marin County, are California's counterpart of the folded Appalachians of eastern America. Geologically, however, they are much newer, consisting of Jurassic or younger sediments, which arose

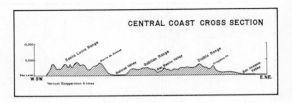

Fig. 8-3. EAST-WEST CROSS SECTION OF THE CENTRAL COAST—revealing the three parallel groups of ranges and the outer and interior files of structural depressions.

from the geosyncline to the east of ancient Cascadia. Metamorphism is widespread and is especially noticeable in the Franciscan-Knoxville group (in which shales, sandstones, and conglomerates are conspicuous sedimentaries). Geologic history has been complex, with repeated submergence, uplift, and erosion. Contemporary terrain is the product of uplift that has occurred since the middle Pleistocene, accompanied by considerable folding and faulting; formation of stream and marine terraces occurred late.

There are three rows of ranges, en echelon, separated by two parallel files of narrow longitudinal basins.[1] The whole area is suggestive of a corrugated tin roof (Fig. 8-3). Folding and faulting have been prominent; these diastrophic forces, plus rapid erosion, have created the numerous sharp ridges and steep-sloped canyons. Most famous of the many faults, the **San Andreas**, extends the length of the region; this rupture has been estimated to extend 20 miles into the crust. The surface often rises immediately from the Pacific; coastal lowlands are narrow except where

[1] The three groups do not form straight-line rows; verily each range seems offset from its neighbors; thus there are really no continuous ridges or valleys as the Great Appalachian Valley of eastern America. Hence, there are "low" passes between lowlands: La Cuesta Grade, with its famed Southern Pacific horseshoe curve and the now gentler gradient of U.S. 101; Pacheco and Panoche passes in the Diablo Range and La Panza Summit. The wayfarer who travels the main highways cannot truly grasp the nature of the Southern Coast Ranges! Two other major gaps are the Golden Gate and Carquinez Strait.

valleys meet the sea. At these places one finds small harbors like Tomales Bay and Moss Landing. Marine terraces, often rising like stair steps, are prominent as are sand dunes (around Pt. Reyes, Fort Ord, Pismo Beach).

The outer group of ranges consists of the Santa Lucia and San Rafael. The Santa Lucia ascends abruptly from the ocean edge and reaches its climax elevation in Junipero Serra Peak (5844 ft.). It contains some of the genuine wilderness country of the Central Coast. The San Rafael forms a series of southwest-facing cuestas; Big Pine Mountain rises to 6828 feet. The middle group includes the Marin, Santa Cruz, and Gabilan ranges. The Marin and Santa Cruz, originally a continuous mass, are separated by the submerged water gap of the Sacramento River (the Golden Gate). The Gabilan contains Pinnacles, an ancient volcanic area now a national monument. Again the high summit is in the south; McPherson Peak reaches 5763 feet. The inner group, which begins in the north with the Diablo complex, includes the Hamilton, Call, and Temblor ranges and culminates in "The Knot" where the Sierra Nevada (Tehachapi), Southern Coast Ranges, and Transverse Ranges converge. Mt. Pinos (8826 ft.) is the highest peak in this area.

The two parallel rows of basins of course have much more consequence for man than do the ranges. Although they are called valleys, these lowlands are the products of diastrophism, both faulting and folding. Their alluvial fill, often of considerable depth, afforded parent material for the fertile soils. Often too the alluvium provides a storage reservoir for quantities of groundwater; the Salinas Valley is an outstanding example.

The outer line of lowlands includes San Francisco Bay, Santa Clara, Salinas, Pajaro, Santa Maria, and Lompoc. By far the largest are the San Francisco Bay (the product of local submergence), which continues as the Santa Clara Valley, and the Salinas Valley. Irrigation agriculture is noteworthy in the outer basins. The interior basins include the San Ramon–Livermore, San Benito, Carrizo, Cuyama, and Santa Ynez. Because of their rain-shadow position and lesser supply of moisture, they are

generally used for winter grains and livestock pasturage.

FOG AND SUMMER HEAT

Topographic complexity, especially, leads to climatic variation in the Central Coast; types include "fog-belt," "mild-summer," and "hot-summer" dry-summer subtropical (Mediterranean) phases, as well as considerable interior areas with semiarid subtropical, and even middle-latitude desert (see Appendix A). Coupled with mountain barriers, the direction of air flow and the cool ocean waters offshore are especially significant considerations.

Much of the coastal strand, west of the first summits, is characterized by "fog-belt" climate. Effects of maritime air are visible on agriculture as far inland as Santa Maria, San Luis Obispo, and Hollister. Fog appears frequently during the year—but especially in summer. Banks, which often reach depths of 1500 feet, are prone to move against the coast during late afternoon and evening hours; ofttimes the fog deck "burns off" during the forenoon so that afternoon periods are ordinarily clear. Because of summer fog, highest temperatures are commonly recorded in August and September.

The influence of the Hawaiian (Pacific) High diminishes northward so that much of the Central Coast receives heavier precipitation than does Southern California. Rainfall amounts at Santa Maria and Lompoc are comparable to Los Angeles, but at San Francisco the annual total (22 inches) averages about 50 percent higher. Rain-shadow areas like the San Benito Valley and the Carrizo Plain, however, are markedly drier.

Much of the San Francisco Bay Area, the Santa Clara Valley, and an appreciably smaller area toward the south is "mild-summer Mediterranean." In this environment maritime influence remains strong with some fog and with afternoon sea breezes often prevailing. The low interior ranges, usually not affected too much by such conditions, are described as "hot-summer" phases.

Much of the Central Coast south of the Santa Clara Valley and inland from the outer ranges, is described as dry climate. Over much

of this surface a classification of semiarid subtropics is indicated. In the southeast interior,
Cuyama Valley and Carrizo Plain have
weather conditions that approximate the southwestern San Joaquin Valley and are thus designated as arid subtropics.

Precipitation is appreciably higher in the
upper portions of exposed ranges, particularly
the Santa Lucia and the Santa Cruz. This fact
is reflected in forest cover, including redwood
groves in canyons, in contrast to types of vegetation characteristic elsewhere.

PARKLAND AND CHAPARRAL

The natural vegetation of the Central Coast
reflects variations in terrain and climate. As
elsewhere in California, seasonal change is significant—spring is the season of wildflowers,
with entire hillsides of California poppies and
lupines, a time when even the chaparral bursts
into bloom.

A parklike cover, with groves of oaks set
in grasslands, is the "trademark" of the Central
Coast countryside. Such woodland association
typifies interior valleys and many of the
slopes. The deciduous valley oak (*Quercus
lobàta*), a graceful tree known to early Spanish as "roble" is widespread on many basin
floors, whereas the more stumpy coast live oak
(*Q. agrifòlia*), or "encina," is more typical of
the slopes. Soils occupied by these formations
tend to be moderately deep and rich. Grasses,
which perhaps have the highest carrying capacity of all the major vegetation types within
California, warrant praise.

The dominant vegetation over more southerly ranges and drier leeward slopes is chaparral, the elfin forest so difficult to penetrate
and sometimes too tall to be considered really
shrubs. This intricate flora, an important watershed protector, changes aspects with the
season. In spring when ceanothus and other
species are abloom, it is especially attractive.

The Central Coast has the southern limits
of the coast redwood in the northern portion
of the Santa Lucia Mountains. More extensive
stands remain in the Santa Cruz Range, but
in Marin County much of this magnificent
tree has been cut off.

SETTLEMENT

The Central Coast has been an important
portion of the state since its American Indian
occupance. The Spanish padres located thirteen of their twenty-one missions in this region. Monterey and San Jose ranked among
the five leading communities of the province
in Mexican days; Monterey served as capital
of Alta California. The fertile fields of Central
Coast valleys have provided some of the major
foci of irrigation agriculture under American
domination. Today the Central Coast contains
one of the state's three great population conurbations.

HOKANS AND PENUTIANS

Two American Indian families resided in
the Central Coast—the Penutians and the
Hokans. Their habitats included half of California: portions of Southern California, the
Sierra Nevada, and the Great Central Valley.
In the Central Coast the Penutians were represented by a single group (Costanoans) and
the Hokans by three.

The *Costanoans* (Spanish for "coastal folk")
lived in scattered villages. Kroeber has estimated that their numbers may have reached
7000. Their culture was rude even for California—men went naked when the weather
allowed and women wore short skin aprons.
Their dwellings, of tule or brush over poles,
were simple. Seemingly they braved both tide-
torn San Francisco Bay and the open ocean
in tule rafts. Salmon, especially in winter, and
mussels were important in their diet; acorns
(or other seeds in oakless areas) were also a
staple.

The *Hokans* were represented by three
groups (Esselen, Salinan, and Chumash). The
Esselen lived south of the Costanoans in limited numbers. Hill folk of the Santa Lucia
Mountains, they apparently focused their activity on Carmel Valley. These were the first
California Indians to become extinct. The
Salinans of the upper Salinas Valley and adjacent Coast Ranges, including the Santa
Lucia coast south of Big Sur, did not occupy
an ideal habitat. They ate about everything

that their land afforded, including fish, reptiles, acorns, berries, and bulbs. The *Chumash* (Chapter 7) were apparently limited in numbers north of the Santa Ynez Mountains in Lompoc and Santa Maria valleys. Their imprint has been left in such place names as Cuyama, Lompoc, and Sisquoc.

THE COLONIAL PERIOD

Considerable Spanish effort was expended along the Central Coast. Activity began early with discovery of Monterey Bay by Vizcaíno in 1602. His enthusiasm for this water body much influenced eighteenth-century activity. In 1769 Gaspar de Portolá led a party overland in quest of the bay. En route northward he failed to recognize it and continued onward to San Francisco Bay, then retraced his path to San Diego. The following year Portolá again traveled overland and guided the clerics and settlers; a presidio was established at Monterey and Mission San Carlos founded (it was moved to Carmel a few years later).

Captain Juan Anza "opened" between San Diego and Monterey the route that in 1776 became "El Camino Real" and selected the site of San Francisco. His aide, Lt. José Moraga, accompanied by fathers Palou and Cambon, conducted settlers thence in the fall of that year.

Three cultural features so significant in colonial New Spain (presidio, mission, and pueblo) were all part of the Spanish program along the Central Coast. Two of Alta California's four presidios, Monterey (1770) and San Francisco (1776), were established in the region, and two of the three pueblos, San José (1777) and Branciforte (now Santa Cruz), in 1797. The Franciscan fathers located these thirteen missions along the Central Coast: San Carlos (1770); San Antonio (1771); San Luis Obispo (1772); San Francisco (1776); Santa Clara (1777); La Purisima Concepción (1787); Santa Cruz and Soledad (1791); San José, San Juan Bautista, and San Miguel (all 1797); Santa Ynez (1804); and San Rafael (1817).

The Spanish never achieved more than a thin hold on the Central Coast. Much activity was devoted to Christianizing the Indians.

Most of the secular Spanish were located at the presidios and the pueblos. The few land awards included a small rancho near Mission San Carlos to Manuel Butron in 1775; this was the first such grant in California. Several small ranchos near Monterey did not prove permanent. Rancho San Ysidro, containing the present city of Gilroy, was given to Ygnacio Ortega in 1810. At the close of the Spanish era Governor Pablo Sala made several awards, including Rancho San Antonio (along the eastern strand of San Francisco Bay) in 1820, and in 1822 the two earliest ranchos in the Salinas Valley, Rancho Bolsa del Potrero and Rancho Buena Vista.

At the end of Spanish rule Alta California was virtually self-sufficient. American fur traders, anchoring in San Francisco Bay and at Monterey, provided inhabitants of the Central Coast with outside needs. The final mission, San Francisco Solano, was established on the site of Sonoma in 1823. It was originally intended to replace San Francisco de Asís (Dolores) but the older mission was not abandoned.

The first decade of Mexican rule brought little change to the Central Coast; major modification of land-use was delayed until secularization of the missions (1834-36). This action followed years of rising demands for land by the expanding Mexican populace.

Secularization precipitated a small-scale "land boom" along the Central Coast; scores of grants were awarded between 1834-1846. The choicest land had been mission properties. Stocking of these new estates was facilitated through acquisition of mission herds. With a rash of grants awarded at the close of the period, the rancheros held the best lands around San Francisco Bay and southward through the lowlands to Lompoc Valley. As in Southern California, this period was a somewhat idyllic time in California. Lands remained unfenced, the cattle roamed widely, and the rancheros and their retainers indulged in numerous fiestas.

Urban growth was inconsequential in the Mexican era; nonetheless, the pueblos of Sonoma and San Francisco were established in 1835. Withering of the missions resulted in evolution of nearby villages without pueblo "status": San Juan Bautista, San Luis Obispo, and Carmel.

THE AMERICAN PERIOD

The Central Coast, with exception of San Francisco, was not greatly altered during the decade that followed the transition to American sovereignty. With statehood, San Jose, Benicia, and Vallejo briefly served as capitals. The Gold Rush created a market for rancho beef even as in Southern California.

Changes in land utilization along the Central Coast began in the mid-1850's. As the Gold Rush slackened, many miners elected to become farmers. Their numbers were augmented by new arrivals moving westward, unaware that much of California's good land was not "free" as had been true farther east. Without too much regard for rights of Mexican rancheros, many Americans squatted on lands that impressed them. Their actions were eased because of unsettled rancho titles, following passage of the congressional act of 1851 that required Mexicans to prove ownership. Oakland was established by squatters on Rancho San Antonio in 1850.

Circumstances that contributed to rancho deterioration in Southern California likewise operated along the Central Coast. The brief beef market in the Sierran Mother Lode Country encouraged some *paisanos* to live beyond their means, and then borrow from Americans at ruinous rates. More significant factors included the drought of 1863, delinquent taxes, and legal costs engendered in attempts to prove rightful land title. In any event the breakup of most ranchos had been completed before 1870. Much land became property of Anglo-Americans, many of whom had been at the gold camps.

Sheep ranching, first encouraged by wool demands during the Civil War, became widespread in the 1870's and remained important for a generation. During this time many Basque herders came to the Central Coast. In the 1880's Monterey County was the state's third ranking producer of livestock.

Grain farming was the next major development, and by the 1880's fields of winter wheat stretched for miles along coastal valleys. This was large-scale farming, employing eight-horse gangs of plows, harrows, and seeders. Monterey, Moss Landing, and San Francisco were major ports; inland, accessibility to railheads was important. The Central Coast, whose El Camino Real had been the principal roadway before statehood, lapsed into a backwash after the Southern Pacific completed its "Valley Line" between Los Angeles and San Francisco through the San Joaquin in 1876. Construction of the "Coast Route" southward from San Jose to Soledad took place between 1868-1873. Soledad remained the railhead until 1886 when southward construction was resumed. Finally, in 1901, the Coast Route was open between San Francisco and Los Angeles. Meanwhile, wheat had been declining in importance, and barley acreage remained more stable; by 1900 barley had become the chief grain crop of the region.

Major agricultural changes along the Central Coast took place after the turn of the century. The through railroad improved marketing from many districts. Meantime irrigation agriculture was developed. Early attempts at small-scale stream diversion were replaced by pump irrigation, at first with steam-powered pumps. Many immigrants, including Scotch, Swiss, Danes, Italians, and Portuguese, began settling in the valleys and commenced farming on a share-crop basis. Sugar beets and alfalfa were earlier crops; the beets depended upon construction of refineries. In the twentieth century the Central Coast has become an important producer of dairy products, fruits, nuts, and vegetables. In some instances reliance was placed upon national markets, but California's growing urban centers also have provided enlarged outlets.

THE CONTEMPORARY SCENE

Before essaying a more detailed review of specific subdivisions, let us examine some overall aspects of the Central Coast today. Population is concentrated in the outer lowlands (including the Bay Area); there are evident affinities between irrigation agriculture, the Los Angeles–San Francisco coastal corridor (the Southern Pacific's Coast Route and U.S. 101), and population distribution (Appendix E, Fig. E-2). Away from the metropolitan Bay Area smaller cities along U.S. 101 serve as local agricultural centers (residence for ranch owners and full-time personnel, processing, and shipment), and tourist stops; a few are county seats. Nonagricultural manufacturing is limited. Fruit and vegetable farming is big business, land values are high, and returns per acre among the best in the nation. Permissive factors include fertile alluvium, moderately good water supplies, access to market, long growing season, limited frost threat, and ameliorating influence of maritime air.

The coastal strand remained isolated generally until 1940 (Santa Cruz and the Monterey Peninsula were exceptions); more extensive use in many instances has been achieved since 1950. Population remains modest with scattered small clusters and long "open stretches." The coast has increasing appeal for residence, particularly for moneyed senior citizens. Recreation is becoming a dominant function of many coastal towns.

The inner lowlands, water deficient and with less climatic appeal than the coast, remain sparsely populated with extensive properties producing livestock and dry-farmed grains. In general these basins have not experienced the rapid change affecting some portions of the region. Uplands (the Coast Ranges) are also devoted to livestock and grains; population is dispersed and there are no towns of consequence.

Such functions as military bases and mining also localize population. In some cases, there is overlap between these and other economic supports. The major development of military installations began with World War II and continued through the Korean emergency into the "Cold War missile age." The Central Coast has had obvious advantages: mild climate, proximity to harbors, good surface transportation, an abundance of land without highly competitive alternative uses.

The functions of the Bay Area conurbation differ considerably from the remainder of the region. Yet reciprocal relations between the Bay Area and outlying portions of the Central Coast have been strengthened with improved transportation and population growth. The Bay Area, especially San Francisco, relies upon a hinterland that extends into the Northwest, the Great Central Valley, the Sierra-Cascade, and even into adjacent states, as well as the Central Coast. The Bay Area provides many manufactured goods and wholesale services for the region and affords urban recreation and shopping facilities. In turn, Bay Area residents support outlying resorts and provide a significant market for agricultural commodities.

Detailed discussion of the Central Coast as a single regional entity is difficult because of physical variations, history, land-use, and population density. Hence five subdivisions will be reviewed successively: (1) the Outer Lowlands, distinguished principally by specialized agriculture; (2) the Interior Basins, used for cattle ranching and grain farming; (3) the Coast, used particularly for recreation and residence; (4) the Ranges, economically restricted by slope; (5) the Bay Area, unique as a regional conurbation.

THE OUTER LOWLANDS

The Outer Lowlands,[2] favored by modifying influences of Pacific air and good transportation facilities, is one of the nation's chief summer producers of cool-season vegetables and deciduous fruits, valued at scores of millions of dollars annually. These structural depressions with their fertile alluvium have more physical appeal for the wayfarer than the Great Central Valley or most agricultural areas: (1) they are relatively narrow—hence their mountain backgrounds are more conspicuous; and (2) in summer they are more likely to be relatively cool.

The following lowlands will be included in this section: Lompoc–Santa Ynez, Santa Maria, Arroyo Grande, San Luis, Salinas, Pajaro, Santa Clara, and Northern San Benito Valley.

THE LOMPOC– SANTA YNEZ VALLEYS

The east-west trending Lompoc–Santa Ynez valleys together compose the southernmost Central Coast lowlands (see map, Fig. 8-7). To the south they are flanked by the Santa Ynez Mountains, northwestern outlier of Southern California (Chapter 7). The Santa Ynez River drains the south slopes of the San Rafael Mountains, whose 6000-foot summits are sufficiently high and extensive to provide adequate water for the lowlands as well as some for export to the Santa Barbara Coast.[3]

From a narrow upriver canyon, the Santa Ynez widens into a circular basin centered on the hamlet of Santa Ynez. Farther west the canyon is again narrow where the river cuts through Miocene volcanics and dissected marine terraces (the Santa Rita Hills). About 12 miles before the river enters the Pacific, the lowland again widens into the Lompoc Valley.

Through the nineteenth century, utilization of the two valleys remained comparable: Chumash Indian rancherias, missions (La Purisima Concepción and Santa Ynez), Mexican ranchos, cattle (decline with drought of 1863-1864), sheep (decline with drought of 1863-1864), general livestock, and grain farming (until after the Southern Pacific coast line was completed in 1901).

Whereas irrigation agriculture has developed since 1900, Lompoc farming previously included establishment of one of California's earliest agricultural colonies in 1874. Since the 1920's the small Lompoc farms have generally flourished. Land is leveled to grade, fields are fenceless, land values high; Santa Barbara County has effected careful zoning, thus protecting farmland against wanton urban encroachment. Cropping patterns have gradually changed; walnut groves, once widespread, have disappeared as have cherries. In the 1920's the entire valley sometimes suggested a carpet of yellow until competition from the Great Plains curtailed mustard-seed acreage. Since 1929 the Lompoc has become the nation's chief source of flower seeds; during the summer, its floor becomes a patchwork of all possible floral hues (Fig. 8-4).

Southern France long provided flower seeds for the United States. As appreciation of coastal California materialized, seed flowers were grown from the Salinas Valley to El Monte (Los Angeles Lowlands). Increasingly production has been focused on the Lompoc with about 1500 acres under cultivation. Flower growers usually

---

[2] *This section has been reviewed by Charles Taylor of Allan Hancock College and Curtis Wilson of Hartnell College.*

[3] Normally the water table in the Lompoc Valley remains within 20 to 30 feet of the surface even at the end of a drier season. After three unusually dry years in succession, there was some salt-water intrusion in 1962.

Fig 8-4. PLANT GENETICIST, LOMPOC VALLEY. The Lompoc Valley is the nation's ranking producer of commercial flower seeds. The geneticist, responsible for selection of new varieties, is a key figure in this specialized agriculture. A section of W. Atlee Burpee's Floradale Farms is shown. (David W. Lantis)

lease their lands. Cultivation also occurs in the Santa Maria, Arroyo Grande, and San Benito valleys. Seed-flower production is highly specialized. A key figure is the plant geneticist, responsible for new varieties.

Flowers are also shipped fresh to California's metropolitan markets. Other crops include beans and a variety of vegetables.

The hilly surfaces between the Lompoc and Santa Ynez valleys around Buellton are devoted to livestock ranching. A modest increase in poultry farming in the 1950's reflected elimination of farmlands in the Los Angeles Lowlands and rising California demands for fresh eggs.

LEADING SANTA YNEZ–LOMPOC FARM
PRODUCTS, 1961
(all figures in millions of dollars)

beef cattle	4.12	poultry (eggs)	0.75
dairy goods	1.8	alfalfa hay	0.6
flower seeds	1.4	celery	0.6
beans (dry)	0.8	bean seed	0.5

Source: Santa Barbara County Farm Advisor.

Two plants near Lompoc process diatomaceous earth; the large diatomite deposits here, residues of billions of single-celled Miocene sea plants, are among the purest in the world. Diatomite has been mined since 1893; it is estimated that a 75-year reserve remains. Diatomite has scores of uses, particularly for filters.

The rural landscape of the Santa Ynez Valley has experienced less twentieth-century change than has the Lompoc, especially east of Santa Ynez (village) where livestock ranching remains dominant. Cattle ranching is indeed a way of life; farmhouses are well appointed, and sleek herds of Herefords and Aberdeen Angus graze behind painted fenceposts. Partially because of its proximity to Santa Barbara, which retains a tradition of the Spanish-Mexican eras, the upper Santa Ynez is widely known for raising of fine Palomino horses.

The western Santa Ynez with its alluvial bottomlands is devoted to irrigation agriculture although interior location does not provide the climatic advantages of the Lompoc. The Danish-American Corporation obtained erstwhile rancho lands in 1911, and a Danish colony was established at Solvang ("sunny meadow"). Colonists experienced difficulty in adjusting to dry-summer irrigation agriculture; nonetheless, lands around Solvang are quite productive—a few windmills lend an exotic note to the landscape. Besides winter grains and hillside grazing, the valley floor produces such crops as alfalfa, legumes, and sugar beets. Increased output of vegetables since 1940 has led to expanded pump irrigation.

Nearness to Santa Barbara has enhanced recreational use of the Santa Ynez Valley. Construction of Cachuma Dam has provided a new aquatic playground since 1950; the lake is trout-stocked (Chapter 7). Since World War II the Santa Ynez has become a major California center for dude ranches; especially well known is Alisal Guest Ranch.

THE PACIFIC MISSILE RANGE

The periphery of Lompoc Valley makes a signal contribution to the nation's military defenses. In 1941 the Army established Camp Cooke with artillery ranges on marine terraces north of the Valley; after the Korean emergency the camp was deactivated. The Pacific Missile Range, which includes Point Mugu (Chapter 7), also encompasses *impact areas* around the Hawaiian Islands and in the Pacific Trust Territories. Adjacent to Lompoc are 20,000-acre **Naval Missile Facility** at Point Arguello, and 65,000-acre **Vandenberg Air Force Base**. Factors in establishment of the two missile bases in 1956 included: curvature of the coast around Point Arguello, vast ocean areas to the west-southwest, prior government land title (Camp Cooke), transportation facilities, isolation from metropolitan areas, and accessibility to California's missile-making establishments. Hundreds of millions of dollars have been expended at the two facilities; personnel includes military, civilian employees, and contractors' crews—approximately 50,000 persons. The impact of these numbers and their payrolls has been felt in communities as distant as Santa Barbara and San Luis Obispo.

TOWNS

What happens to a tranquil agricultural community with local orientation when missile bases are established nearby? **Lompoc** (14,400) grew from approximately 6000 in 1958 to around 20,000 within five years. Changes in the town make a fascinating sociological study. Heavy burdens were placed on all public services; school enrollment increased from 1900 to 9000 in four years. Suddenly the town, with its new world-minded citizens (many college graduates in engineering, mathematics, and physics), lost its conservatism. Property values increased, and a new suburban shopping center was erected.

Towns in the Santa Ynez have not much reflected the effects of the missile bases. **Santa Ynez** remains a somnolent farm village. **Solvang** (1300), intentionally made picturesque, caters to an expanding tourist trade with its gift shops and restaurants. Mission Santa Ynez probably has the finest paintings of any California mission. Mission La Purísima Concepción near Lompoc, in ruins before restoration in the 1930's, is a state historical monument intended to depict a mission as it was in colonial times. **Buellton**, long known for its split-pea soup, has grown as a crossroads stop at the junction of California 150 and U.S. 101.

THE SANTA MARIA VALLEY

The Santa Maria Valley, a deltaic plain, is surrounded by sand dunes and marine terraces (map, Fig. 8-7).[4] It has impressive agricultural output despite a mere 20,000 acres under irrigation cropping. The lowland, approximately 20 miles long and 6 miles wide (north-south), did not have a Spanish mission, but late in the Mexican era it was divided among three ranchos. The 38,000-acre Nipomo grant, awarded to Captain William Dana (cousin of author Richard Henry Dana) was especially prominent. The Valley experienced California's usual nineteenth-century transitions: cattle before the drought of 1863-64, American settlement, sheep in the 1870's, then grains and also beans. Access to harbor facilities at Port Harford (Port San Luis) was fortunate.

Contemporary agricultural patterns have evolved since 1900. Sugar beets became important early in the century after construction of a refinery at Betteravia; sugar beets have subsequently declined in acreage.[5] Pump wells, power lines, and standpipes suggest irrigation practices. Shabby appearance of many farm houses reflects land consolidation and owner residence in Santa Maria; weathered barns dramatize the former significance

[4] The Santa Maria Valley shares a coastal lowland with the Lompoc Valley and the Arroyo Grande Valley. Dissected marine terraces, locally called *mesas*, serve as dividing uplands.

[5] Union Sugar Company, which built the refinery, sold its processing plant to Consolidated Food Corporation about 1960 but retained 11,300 acres of land in the Lompoc and Santa Maria valleys and contiguous terraces. The value of this holding has subsequently increased with the land boom since the Pacific Missile Range was established.

of draft horses. Since 1940 output of vegetables has expanded; fluctuation in acreage of different varieties is in response to market conditions. Artichokes are conspicuous only near the coast and alfalfa on the inner edge of the lowland. Important vegetables include lettuce, broccoli (spring and fall crops), celery (mostly fall crop), cauliflower (year-round), and potatoes. Winter mildness permits leaving the Netted Gem (Russet Burbank) potatoes in the ground until shipment; hence potato cellars are unnecessary. Strawberry production has expanded markedly since introduction of fresh freezing; sandy soils afford good berry land, and the climate allows a longer harvest season than anywhere else in California. A typical scene during most of the year is provided by groups of Mexican braceros, who perform the "stoop labor."

The Santa Maria, like the Santa Ynez–Lompoc, has had a fair water supply. But, with more intensive truck farming, pump wells steadily depleted the water table until the $17-million Vaquero Dam (Twitchell Reservoir) was constructed on the Cuyama River in the late 1950's. Water stored in the reservoir during the rainy season percolates underground during the summer.

Fig. 8-5. *OIL REFINERY IN SANTA MARIA VALLEY. One of two Santa Maria Valley refineries lies in the foreground. There is also a coking plant in the valley. Note the vegetable fields.* (Union Oil Company of California, photo by Stonehart Studio)

LEADING SANTA MARIA VALLEY
FARM PRODUCTS, 1961
(all figures in millions of dollars)

beef cattle	3.7	celery	1.5
strawberries	3.4	cauliflower	1.2
dairy goods	3.0	beans (dry)	0.8
potatoes	2.25	alfalfa hay	0.8
lettuce	2.0	flower seeds	0.7

Source: Agricultural Commissioner, Santa Barbara County.

Nipomo Mesa, an undulating marine terrace separating the Santa Maria from Arroyo Grande Valley to the north, was long used for grazing and winter grains. Of late there has been a marked expansion of poultry farms, many owned by senior citizens residing on modest properties. This activity culminated in establishment of the western breeding ranch of Arbor Acres (one of the world's largest breeders of meat chickens) in 1958. Farther

east on hillsides adjacent to Twitchell Reservoir, trial groves of Valencia oranges have been planted on the old Suey Rancho; enthusiasts insist the climate is as mild as in the Oxnard Plain (Chapter 7).

The Santa Maria Valley and the mesas (terraces) to the south around Orcutt have long yielded petroleum. The Santa Maria and inland Cuyama Valley (see section on Interior Basins) make Santa Barbara County the principal oil producer of the Central Coast. Union Oil Company, the major firm in the area, built a new coking plant and refinery on Nipomo Mesa north of Guadalupe in the middle 1950's; there are also two small oil refineries near Santa Maria (see Fig. 8-5).

Santa Maria (20,000), a city of wide streets, serves as trade center for the Valley and residence for many ranch employees. It was founded in 1874 and is not on the main route of the Southern Pacific Coast Line; its growth, buoyed by oil, expanded truck crops, and service to highway travelers, has largely occurred since 1920. Produce sheds and processing plants are prominent along railroad spurs. Since establishment of Pacific Missile Range there has been much population growth, with new eastside tracts; Santa Maria now extends southward almost to Orcutt. Motels and restaurants along the principal thoroughfare, built before completion of the freeway bypass (U.S. 101), reflect the city's significance as a stop for wayfarers. Hancock College (formerly Santa Maria Junior College) has a new eastside campus on the former site of defunct University of Southern California School of Aeronautics. **Guadalupe** (2600) on California Route 1 and the Coast Line of the Southern Pacific is the Valley's principal vegetable packing and shipping point. It has significance as a farm workers' residence town with much evidence of Oriental and Mexican population. **Betteravia** is a company (sugar refinery) town with prominent livestock feed lots.

THE ARROYO GRANDE VALLEY

The little Arroyo Grande Valley (map, Fig. 8-7), watered by Arroyo Grande Creek, was part of Mission San Luis Obispo's grazing lands; portions remained unused until brush was removed in the 1870's. Formation of an irrigation company in 1882 encouraged agricultural development. Its 2000 acres, intensively cultivated, are double- or even triple-cropped and produce such truck crops as broccoli, strawberries, cauliflower, peas, bell peppers, and Brussels sprouts (Fig. 8-1). Urban growth (see section on The Coast) has almost eliminated globe artichokes. Recent efforts have been made to reduce recurrent problems of floods and drifting sand dunes.

THE SAN LUIS AREA

Emphasis upon dairying in the San Luis Area (which focuses on the San Luis Valley) contrasts with land-use in the lowlands previously discussed. There is no surface irrigation source of consequence, and level land is restricted to the small San Luis Valley and coastal terraces. Hilly uplands include low San Luis Range, which separates the Area from Arroyo Grande Valley, and fringes of the Santa Lucia Range (map, Fig. 8-7).

Good grass and cattle herds made San Luis Obispo one of the more prosperous missions; by the late 1830's its land had been divided into a group of Mexican ranchos. Later there was the usual California history of Gold Rush prosperity followed by drought in the 1860's.

Contemporary land-use patterns were established early. Wealthy dairyman E. W. Steele and his brothers purchased four ranchos in 1866, brought in hundreds of dairy cows and began selling cheese in San Francisco. Other dairymen followed and several cheese factories were operating by the 1870's. Since the 1880's Swiss, Italian, and Portuguese immigrants and their descendants have conducted the dairy farms.

For a generation the San Luis Area has been an important secondary source of California market milk. During World War II milk consumption at Camp Roberts and other Army installations permitted dairymen to shift from manufactured dairy products (cheese, butter, condensed milk). More recently fluid milk has been shipped to Los Angeles and the San Francisco Bay Area. Although the number of milch cows has been stable for many years, in the 1960's virtually all milk is marketed as Grade A. Farmers indisposed toward Grade A production, either from insufficient capital or disinterest, have tended to shift to beef cattle. Herds of Holsteins are large and dairy farms well equipped (Fig. 8-6). Significant dairy centers include Los Osos Valley, Cambria, Cayucos, and Harmony.

San Luis Obispo (20,500), which dates from 1850, lies in the San Luis Valley; for decades it has been the principal city between Santa Barbara and Salinas.[6] Surrounding hills, which shut out sufficient Pacific air so that summer afternoons are sometimes warm, provide a distinctive setting; newer residential districts on slopes include many view lots. The city, a county seat and Southern Pacific division point, retains some of its Spanish-Mexican heritage in street names. The number of downtown specialty shops reflects the city's

[6] Professor Charles Taylor of Allan Hancock College points out that residents of Santa Maria would challenge the validity of this statement!

Fig. 8-6. DAIRY FARM NEAR SAN LUIS OBISPO. The San Luis Area provides some of California's best pasturage. Dairying has been important in this locality for a century. (David W. Lantis)

longtime importance as trading center for an extensive, though sparsely populated, portion of the Central Coast. As a "half-way point" between San Francisco and Los Angeles, San Luis Obispo obtains considerable travelers' trade. It is also a gateway to coastal recreation areas along California 1, and its mission makes it a tourist town. It is the site of California State Polytechnic College, a growing institution with emphasis in engineering and agriculture. Contiguous Camp San Luis Obispo, a World War II Army base, more recently has been the home of California National Guard; a portion of the inactive base, which is largely leased for grazing, has become California's Men's Colony, a state correctional institution.

THE SALINAS VALLEY

The Salinas Valley, self-acclaimed "Salad Bowl of the World," is the ranking agricultural section of the Central Coast; its prodigious output places Monterey among the nation's ranking farm counties. The Valley, vividly described by Steinbeck in *East of Eden,* is one of the two largest lowlands in the region.[7] A portion of Steinbeck's description is as follows:

[7] The other principal depression is occupied by the San Francisco Bay Area and extends southward into the Santa Clara and San Benito valleys.

The Salinas Valley . . . is a long narrow swale between ranges of mountains . . . I remember that the Gabilan Mountains to the east of the valley were light gay mountains full of sun and loveliness and a kind of invitation . . . The Santa Lucias stood up against the sky to the west and kept the valley from the open sea, and they were dark and brooding . . . I always found myself in a dread of west and a love of east. . . .

On the wide level acres of the valley the topsoil lay deep and fertile. . . . I have spoken of the rich years when the rainfall was plentiful. But there were dry years too, and they put a terror in the valley. . . .

First there were the Indians . . . Then the hard, dry Spaniards came exploring through . . . they collected souls as they collected jewels. . . .

Then the Americans came—more greedy because there were more of them. They took the lands, remade the laws to make their titles good. . . .[8]

This attenuated syncline extends southeastward between the Santa Lucia and Gabilan ranges for more than 120 miles from Moss Landing to Santa Margarita (map, Fig. 8-7). Its width exceeds 12 miles along Monterey Bay but inland it becomes quite constricted.

[8] John Steinbeck, *East of Eden* (New York: Viking Press, 1952), pp. 3–7. Reprinted by permission of the publishers.

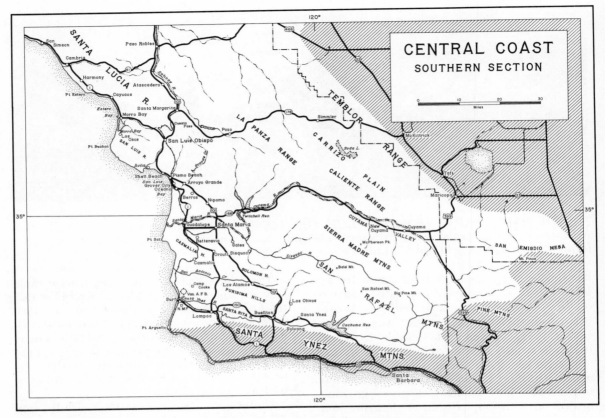

Fig. 8-7. MAP OF THE SOUTHERN SECTION OF THE CENTRAL COAST.

The Salinas *looks* prosperous; there is an air of rural substance exemplified by well-maintained farmhouses and carefully tilled earth. The discerning traveler occasionally glimpses labor camps for the Mexican braceros, who perform stoop labor throughout the year. Fields are leveled to grade although irrigation methods have changed—instead of field ditches one increasingly notes sprinklers and long aluminum tubes. There is widespread absence of fences, especially in the lower valley; windbreaks (generally eucalyptus) are conspicuous. From the air the Valley rolls out like an elongated hall runner woven in many shades of green.

AGRICULTURAL DIVERSITY

Agricultural fecundity of the Salinas received early recognition; the Franciscans

established two missions, Soledad and San Miguel Arcangel, in the valley. During the Mexican era thirty-two land grants were awarded with eight in excess of 10,000 acres. Among the best known was El Alisal, acquired by patriarch W. E. P. Hartnell. The Valley —with Monterey as its port—became a leading California source of hides and tallow.

The Salinas experienced the usual Central Coast sequence of cattle expansion during the Gold Rush; then decimation of herds during the drought of 1862-64 (cattle in Monterey County numbered 90,000 in 1862; 14,000 in 1865), followed by an influx of Americans. Although some ranchos remained large properties into the twentieth century, most estates were divided. Anne Fisher provides a breezy account of rancho expiration in *The Salinas*. Grain farming increased in the lower valley following creation of shipping facilities at Moss Landing in 1866. Sheep tended to replace cattle, especially in southern portions of the valley distant from the Pacific or a railhead. Transition from sheep to wheat and barley proceeded with southward construction of the Southern Pacific's Coast Line. Although machinery permitted vast grainfields, crop rotation was not practiced; by the late 1880's barley was replacing wheat.

Some evidences of present-day agricultural diversity appeared relatively early. Dairying started in the lower valley after the drought of 1862-64, with butter and cheese the principal nineteenth-century products. Swiss, Portuguese, and Danish dairymen moved into the valley, sometimes leasing from large landholders. By the early twentieth century evaporated milk plants were operating in Gonzales and Coburn; after 1920 shipment of fresh milk to San Francisco increasingly replaced local manufacturing. Alfalfa, grown for feed in the 1880's, became more important after 1900. Dry-farmed beans were grown early; acreage expanded during World War I, then again in the middle 1920's after temporary decline. The Tariff Acts of 1894 and 1897 favored sugar beets in western United States. After construction of the state's largest beet factory at Spreckels in 1897 there was a rapid shift from grains to sugar beets; beets achieved their maximum acreage within three years. Meanwhile, irrigation replaced dry-farming. Vegetable growing became significant after 1920; now the Salinas has multifarious varieties whose annual output returns scores of millions of dollars.

Irrigation has been a major force in agricultural development in the Salinas. Stream diversion was attempted by the mission fathers, but irrigation was not practiced between 1830 and 1877. It seems ironic that the drought of 1862 decimated herds in a basin with a relatively high water table. The deep alluvial fill of the lower Salinas affords an excellent underground water basin. Although stream diversion was tried again in the late nineteenth century, the Salinas River does not have much surface flow in summer; much of the runoff from its 4330-square mile watershed flows underground. Pump irrigation, at first utilizing steam engines, was developed in conjunction with sugar beets.

Expanded irrigation consumption created a serious depletion of the underground basin as early as 1930 despite a mean annual runoff of 520,000 acre-feet above San Lucas. In years of heavier runoff, the basin recharges itself during the winter. In drier years water-table decline has allowed salt intrusion three miles inland from Moss Landing. Like most California lowlands the Valley has also experienced floods; damage has been serious about one year in seven. Particularly disastrous floods occurred in 1911, 1914, and 1938. Hence a countywide flood-control and conservation district was established; it completed 350,000 acre-foot Nacimiento Dam in the eastern San Lucia Range in 1957.[9] An additional 500,000 acre-foot reservoir is planned on San Antonio River.

Contemporary crop patterns in the Salinas Valley can be described by tripartite land-use division into lower valley, middle valley, and upper valley. Such physical variations as topography, fog cover, summer heat, length of growing season, and frost threat have contributed to evolution of present-day crop distribution.

The *lower* Salinas from Moss Landing to Soledad is favored with deep alluvium, long growing season, and cool summers (nocturnal inflow of fog reduces morning temperatures before the fog "burns off"). Globe artichokes and Brussels sprouts have been major crops on heavy peaty soils around Castroville since the 1920's (Fig. 8-8).

The artichoke, introduced from Mediterranean Europe by Italians, cannot tolerate either frost or summer heat, which restricts its habitat even in California. The artichoke has been difficult to "popularize"; it finds its best markets with people of southern European extraction in New York, Los Angeles, and San Francisco. The plant is a perennial, planted every four to seven years; the

[9] There are virtually no irrigation districts in the Central Coast, and this fact makes a distinct difference between this region and the Great Central Valley (see Chapter 9).

Fig. 8-8. ARTICHOKES AT CASTRO-
VILLE. *Production of this vegetable is largely
restricted to the "fog belt" along the littoral of
the northern Central Coast.* (David W.
Lantis)

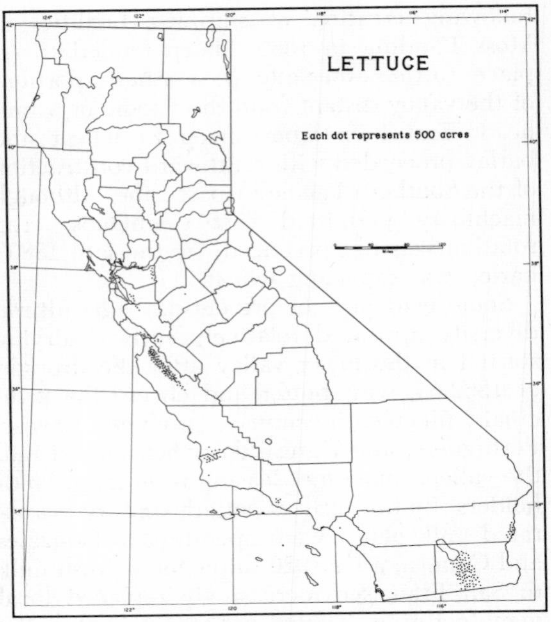

Fig. 8-9. *MAP OF THE LETTUCE PRO-
DUCTION IN CALIFORNIA.*

harvest season can be regulated through irrigation
and pruning—winter marketing has been preferred because of less competition. Canned mari-
nated artichokes are gaining popularity for salads.

Farther inland some 55,000 acres of head
lettuce are grown around Salinas (Fig. 8-9);
the Valley has been the nation's leading warm-
season producer since the 1920's.

The Salinas has produced between a third and
a half of the nation's warmer season head lettuce
since the 1920's, dominating the national market
from late April to November. Declining sugar-
beet yields occurred about the time that urbanization was encroaching upon lettuce fields in Los
Angeles County and the American people were
changing their diets to include salads. Originally
Salinas fields were small, but they have become
larger.

The long season and cool summers gave the
Salinas an advantage over most eastern districts
as long as the crisp Boston and New York varieties
were grown. However the American housewife
preferred firmer heads, which suggested a better
buy. The firmer Great Lakes variety is less demanding than older varieties; hence the Salinas
has had increasing competition from more northerly parts of eastern United States—it has a near
monopoly in California.

Acreage has been stabilized for many years; although a single field will yield only one crop of
lettuce annually, double and triple cropping is

practiced, rotating lettuce with other vegetables.

Lettuce is shipped almost continuously from
May through November (in winter Imperial Valley lettuce is commercially dominant).

Production is speculative. The market depends
not only upon local growth rate and the amount
ready to harvest but also on temperatures east of
the Rocky Mountains, which influence salad consumption. Salinas lettuce men joke half-seriously
about "millionaire yesterday, pauper today."

Production is highly specialized and mechanized although there is still much hand labor.
Since 1946 lettuce has been cut by "assembly-
line" methods. In the middle 1950's the practice
of field packing in cardboard developed; boxes
were rushed to packing houses and the lettuce
shipped in dry ice to avoid the spoilage resulting
from the older wet pack (in ice). The practice of
"wrap pack" (sealing in plastic) by hand in the
field was devised in 1961. Because of the long
season, laborers can reside in Salinas, moving to
the Imperial Valley briefly in winter but leaving
their children at home in school.

The lower valley "fog belt" also yields crops
such as onions, strawberries, carrots, broccoli,
celery, tomatoes, cauliflower, and sugar beets

LEADING MONTEREY COUNTY
FARM PRODUCTS, 1961
(all figures in millions of dollars)

lettuce	29.3	artichokes	3.2
tomatoes	15.0	milk	3.0
strawberries	12.3	potatoes	2.9
celery	10.7	chicken eggs	2.6
beef	9.8	alfalfa hay	2.3
carrots	9.7	barley	1.5
broccoli	4.4	cabbage	1.2
beans (white)	3.6	onions	1.1
cauliflower	3.4	garlic	0.9

Figures do not include upper Salinas Valley within San Luis Obispo County—data from Monterey County Agricultural Commissioner.

—verily this is a salad bowl! Since 1935 sugar beets have regained significance with government acreage controls, rotation, better tilthing, mechanical thinning, and elimination of Cuban sugar imports (in the 1960's)—beet acreage has doubled since 1930. Dairying has particular importance on westside terraces between Salinas and Gonzales, where whitewashed barns and large Holstein herds are conspicuous. Use of feed lots is more reminiscent of the Los Angeles Coastal Plain than most California dairy belts; it reflects value of floodplain land for truck crops. In fact many dairymen with bottomland who did not elect to convert to Grade A milk during the 1950's sold their lands to vegetable growers. Acreage of strawberries, which replaced grains on gravelly soils northeast of Salinas in the 1950's, has tended to stabilize; the valley has experienced much competition from Southern California. Carrots, originally grown as livestock feed, have become a million-dollar crop although the Salinas faces competition from the lower Rio Grande Valley of Texas, where fields are as large as 1000 acres. Carrot production in the Salinas originally expanded in the 1950's when carrots in plastic bags gained popularity in supermarkets. Celery was a "new" crop in the Salinas in the 1950's; discovery that superior quality stalks could be grown there over a longer harvest season (late June until January) led to reduced acreage in the Delta Lands, previously the leading California producer (Chapter 9). Also dietary habits have increased the sales of this low-calorie vege-

table. Onions, a late-season crop, are usually shipped to eastern Asia. Broccoli, which can be grown throughout the year, is planted in fields previously in lettuce—thus averting seasonal idleness. Expanded output of cauliflower reflects decline in production in the Santa Clara Valley.

The *middle* Salinas Valley between Soledad and San Ardo forms a transition zone between the coastal fog belt and interior conditions (see Interior Basins). Summers tend to be appreciably warmer than around Castroville, and the growing season is shorter. North of King City the valley remains relatively broad with several terrace levels; it narrows noticeably toward the south. Lower terraces are cropped and sprinkler-irrigated, whereas higher terraces produce winter grains and adjoining hillsides are grazed. Fields of alfalfa, sugar beets, and beans (small white, large lima, pink, and garbanza) are conspicuous. The supplemental feeding of livestock pastured seasonally on adjacent uplands forms the chief use of alfalfa. Sugar beets have replaced some bean fields since elimination of imported Cuban sugar. Early spring and late fall crops of lettuce now are grown even south of King City, a reflection of reduced competition from other areas at these seasons. Acreage of tomatoes also has expanded around King City at the expense of bean fields; if prices are favorable, the crop is shipped fresh; otherwise, it goes to canneries. Two crops of spinach, spring and fall, are also grown; most of the output is either fresh frozen or canned. Beans, which acquired more acreage during World War II, prefer the hotter summers of the mid-valley; as legumes they make good rotation crops.

The San Ardo oil field, one of the northernmost in California, was opened in 1947 and has consistently yielded $12–$20 million annually (see chart, page 410). Its low pumping units are less conspicuous than the derricks of older fields. This reserve was long known, but because of its low gravity its recovery awaited new cracking processes and rising California consumption.

South of San Ardo the topographic character of the Salinas changes; the Valley is narrow and surfaces are rolling rather than flat. Fog is uncommon and some summer afternoons feel "oven-hot." Sea breezes, when they penetrate this far inland, tend to be desiccating winds that stir up dust. Many servicemen of World War II and Korean emergency years recall the upper valley without enthusiasm— the Army maintained one of its larger western training stations at **Camp Roberts** (now inactive). The deep alluvial layer of the lower valley is absent, and irrigation agriculture limited. Winter grains, livestock pastures, as well as almond orchards around Paso Robles and poultry farms around Atascadero, are representative.

California produces virtually all of the nation's almonds. Around Paso Robles there are over 6000 acres of orchards, and some new trees have been set out to replace older trees. Almonds are uneconomic and must be tariff-protected. Competition from the Mediterranean countries is strong, especially for shelled nuts. Almonds were planted around Paso Robles as a land-promotion scheme; some orchards are on steep slopes.

Much hilly land in and around the upper valley has been seriously eroded by overgrazing. There are many senior citizens and considerable semi-retirement around Atascadero; income from poultry farms totals more than a million dollars annually.

FARM TOWNS

Many Salinas communities function as small farm villages, providing residence for farm personnel and ofttimes providing produce shipping facilities. Agricultural processing has some consequence in most towns.

Salinas (29,000), largest and most important city in the valley, is seat of Monterey County, site of Hartnell College, and an important tourist stop. It began as an early American cattle town; memories of its formative years are renewed through the Salinas Rodeo in July. Its consequence as the valley service center increased after arrival of the Southern Pacific in 1872. Salinas is a prosperous trade center, shipping point, and residential community. There is much attractive new housing in the south and southwest, which reflects considerable wealth. Downtown Salinas has a number of specialty shops. The commercial zone along railroad tracks is characterized by packing houses, machine shops, and industrial plants. Expanding industry includes foods (jams, milk products, and frozen foods) and shipping containers (paper and plastics). Metropolitan Salinas is considerably larger than city statistics reveal. Contiguous **Alisal** (unincorp.) to the northeast is nearly as large as Salinas; it is a residential community with modest workers' cottages.

Other lower valley communities include Moss Landing, Castroville, Gonzales, and Soledad. **Moss Landing** (unincorp.), erstwhile grain port, whaling station, and sardine packer, is a picturesque assemblage of weathered canneries, fishing boats, and shanties. More recently Kaiser has established a plant to extract magnesium from sea water; there is also a large Pacific Gas and Electric steam plant. **Castroville** (2800) is a residential town with conspicuous artichoke shipping sheds. **Gonzales** (2100) is a farm village, as is **Soledad** (2800), which has a state Correctional Training Facility.

Middle valley towns are likewise small. **King City** (3000), the principal center since its founding in 1868, is a shipping point and residential place with attractive ranchers' homes and caters to highway travelers. Smaller **Greenfield** (1200) provides farm residence.

The upper valley towns of Paso Robles and Atascadero are slightly larger than most Salinas communities; both are highway junctions. **Paso Robles** (6700) was founded in 1886 and was long known for its hot sulphur springs, which Indians used in pre-Spanish times. It has long acted as center for an extensive, sparsely populated ranching area including the Santa Lucia Range and interior basins to the east; some aspects of tourist trade have declined since construction of a freeway bypass. **Atascadero** (6000) is surrounded by poultry farms and garden patches; this retirement town has grown since establishment of a state hospital.

PAJARO VALLEY

The little Pajaro Valley (120 square miles) affords one of California's most aesthetically pleasing agricultural landscapes; it has spurs of the Santa Cruz Mountains (north and east) and Monterey Hills (south) on its interior sides (map, Fig. 8-7). Once used as grazing lands of Mission Santa Cruz, this deltaic lowland was divided into Mexican ranchos. The Pajaro experienced a period of grain farming but later land-use was anticipated with successful planting of an apple orchard in 1853. Arrival of the Southern Pacific in 1870 facilitated marketing in San Francisco. With establishment of a refinery (later moved to Spreckles) at Watsonville, sugar beets were grown on rich muck soils. Later vineyards and then lettuce (in the 1920's) replaced the beets.

The Pajaro has long been known for its *apples*. Orchard expansion took place in the 1890's with strawberries (for central California markets) as a cover crop. Briefly in the early twentieth century before large-scale production in Washington state, the Pajaro was the leading producer west of the Rockies. Orchards on the valley floor were pulled out to provide lettuce land in the 1920's. The Pajaro now vies with the Goldridge (Chapter 10) as the leading California producer; it has about 8000 acres, returning $10–12 million annually (Fig. 8-10). With 20-inch precipitation, irrigation is generally unnecessary; the apples are grown on well-drained fringes of the valley—orchards range from 10 to 100 acres. The climate unfortunately does not favor good "market" color; hence yellow varieties were long favored, especially the Newtown and Bellflower, picked in September. Before World War II drying and canning were important. More recently with the greater demand for fresh fruit within California, small-size Delicious, marketed in small Cello-packs, has tended to replace the Bellflower.

The Pajaro has varied agricultural output despite its limited size. Products include strawberries and apricots, milk, poultry,

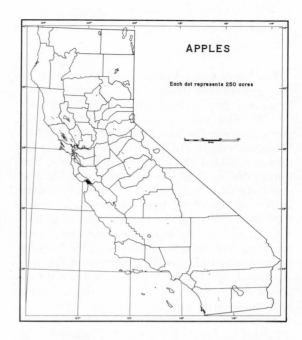

Fig. 8-10. *MAP OF THE CALIFORNIA APPLE ACREAGE.*

alfalfa, and vegetables (tomatoes, Brussels sprouts, and broccoli) in addition to the apples, sugar beets, and lettuce previously noted. Little land is available for sale; on the valley floor it would probably require $5000 an acre to make a purchase. A dramatic Valley development has been that of string beans for freezing since invention of hydraulic pole-setting and stringing machines; about 2700 acres were grown in 1962.

Watsonville (13,300), with older downtown business blocks, has long been the trade and shipping point of the Pajaro. It was laid out in 1852. Attempts in 1902 to develop a port proved short-lived, as did premature development of the sea-resort suburb of Palm Beach. Newer homes are being constructed in the northwest toward **Freedom**. Packing sheds, cold storage plants, and processing plants are located along the railroad tracks in south Watsonville and in satellite **Pajaro**, residential town for farm laborers.

THE SANTA CLARA VALLEY

The Santa Clara Valley, southern portion of the graben-like trough that contains San Francisco Bay, extends inland from the Bay for 70 miles with a maximum width of 25 miles between the Santa Cruz (west) and Mt. Hamilton ranges (east) (map, Fig. 8-7). Farther southward the depression becomes San Benito Valley (in San Benito County). For some decades the Santa Clara was widely known as "the fruit bowl of America"; since 1950 this agricultural paradise has been rapidly changing into a rurban landscape with leapfrog replacement of orchards by housing tracts. Industrial growth is converting the section north of Coyote Narrows into the urban South Bay section of the Bay Area; urban aspects as such will be discussed later.

The Santa Clara has been favored geographically; location near San Francisco and tidewater afforded it early marketing advantages—by 1864 it had rail connection with San Francisco. The climate is characterized by a long mild season; the Santa Cruz Range shuts out sea fog, and the Mt. Hamilton Range provides a partial barrier against continental air masses that sometimes plague the Great Central Valley in winter. Originally the Santa Clara was blessed with an adequate supply of groundwater. The underlying alluvium includes extensive areas of loam as well as coarser soils and peat immediately south of the Bay.

The Spanish recognized the potential of the Santa Clara and established Mission Santa Clara and California's first pueblo, San Jose, in 1777. By 1835 Richard Henry Dana could note that the Valley produced more hides than any other portion of Alta California; during the Mexican era practically the entire valley was divided into ranchos and became a vast pasture.

The early American period, however, witnessed speedier modification of colonial land-use patterns than occurred farther south in the Central Coast. In the 1850's the northern Santa Clara was producing fruits and vegetables for the gold camps; Brewer (in *Up and Down California in 1861-1862*) commented on the beauty of the oaks and observed that although the southern Valley is

. . . all covered with Spanish (Mexican) grants, so is not cultivated but near San Jose, where it is divided into farms, it is in high cultivation; farmhouses have sprung up and rich fields of grain and growing orchards everywhere (pp. 169-170).

Louis Pellier, who had visualized the Valley's merits for orchards previously, brought workers from France in 1856 and introduced the prune plum known as *Agen*. The Spanish had previously introduced the fig, grape, and apricot. Meanwhile, wheat acreage increased to reach its peak in the middle 1870's and was extensively replaced by barley. Cattle regained importance (decline during the drought of 1862-64) in the southern Valley where "cattle king" Henry Miller (Chapter 9) acquired his home ranch, Bloomfield Farm (formerly Rancho Las Animas) in 1858.

Fruit production gained greater importance in the 1870's; a few years earlier, before the Central Pacific was built, the Valley suffered from overproduction. But after Dr. James W. Dawson first canned pears and peaches on a kitchen range in a backyard shed, the future of the orchards was assured. Soon after the transcontinental railroad was completed, Santa Clara pears were shipped east in iced refrigerator cars. By 1900 there were thousands of acres of bearing orchards valued at $400 to $500 an acre.

In this century agriculture has become more complex and increasingly specialized. Truck crops, grown earlier by Chinese and Japanese, have long been significant. By the late 1930's there were some 120,000 acres of orchards and 25,000 acres of vegetables in Santa Clara County, besides vineyards, walnut groves, berry patches, alfalfa fields, dairies, and poultry farms. The Valley helped make "Del Monte" and "Sunsweet" international brand names. Towns became prosperous centers for residence, processing, and shipping.

We noted above that originally the Santa Clara was fortunate with regard to its groundwater.[10] California's first artesian wells were dug as early as 1854. State attempts to regulate artesian flow in the Valley in 1876 came too late; by 1900 most wells were failing. As irrigation expanded, pumping increased, partly because the Valley has no sizable streams. Eventually much of the hundreds of thousands of acre-feet stored underground was depleted. Belatedly a water-conservation district was created in 1934; many small reservoirs have been developed in the Mt. Hamilton Range, including Anderson Dam on Coyote Creek, and also Lexington Dam on Los Gatos Creek in the Santa Cruz Range. Released storage water percolates downward into the gravelly substrata and thus raises the long-critical water table in years of adequate rainfall. The California Water Plan (Chapter 9) envisages importation of water from Oroville Dam as well as additional local development including recovery of purified waste water.

AGRICULTURAL PATTERNS

Brief discussion of agricultural patterns in the Santa Clara is difficult—the Valley has yielded prodigious quantities of fruits and berries, vegetables, nuts, alfalfa, poultry, and dairy products. Distribution has tended to reflect terrain, water availability (needs and cost), soils, land values, and urban encroachment. Between 1947 and 1961 cultivated land declined by a third, from 99,000 to 63,000 acres. Fruit farms have tended to be small; production of a single type of fruit has favored labor efficiency and has reduced fixed costs but in poor years has had the disadvantage of "all one's fruit in one bowl." Livestock and field crops are conspicuously absent on fruit farms; in the past the pump-well house and the water tank were ubiquitous. Labor has long been a critical factor; much use of migra-

---

[10] The Valley has been fortunate, too, that its great subsurface reservoir of sands and gravels has been protected against incursion of salt water from San Francisco Bay by an impervious clay layer. Subsidence here, as in the western San Joaquin Valley, and in Long Beach (with removal of oil instead of water) has been a problem.

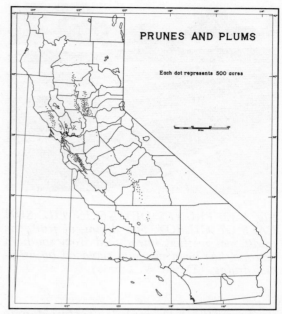

Fig. 8-11. MAP OF THE PLUM AND PRUNE ACREAGE IN CALIFORNIA.

LEADING SANTA CLARA COUNTY
FARM PRODUCTS, 1961
(all figures in millions of dollars)

prunes	15.0	nursery stock	3.5
cut flowers	9.3	cherries	3.3
vegetables	9.2	walnuts	2.0
pears	6.9	sugar beets	0.97
apricots	4.8	grapes	0.97
strawberries	3.6	irrigated pasture	0.5

Source: *Agricultural Crop Report,* Santa Clara County, 1961.

tory workers occurs during harvest periods. In the past Filipinos and migratory American-born "fruit tramps" were employed; since 1950 the Mexican bracero has done much of the field work.

Prunes and apricots are the most important Santa Clara fruit trees, occupying as much as 80 percent of the orchard area. *Prunes,* varieties of plums that can be dried (Fig. 8-12), were once California's third-ranking fruit crop (after oranges and grapes); they have been supplanted by peaches (Chapter 9). The Santa Clara has been the world's leading prune

Fig. 8-12. PRUNES DRYING IN THE SUN
EAST OF GILROY. Sun drying of fruit, the
traditional method introduced from southern
Europe, has been partially replaced by artificial drying. (David W. Lantis)

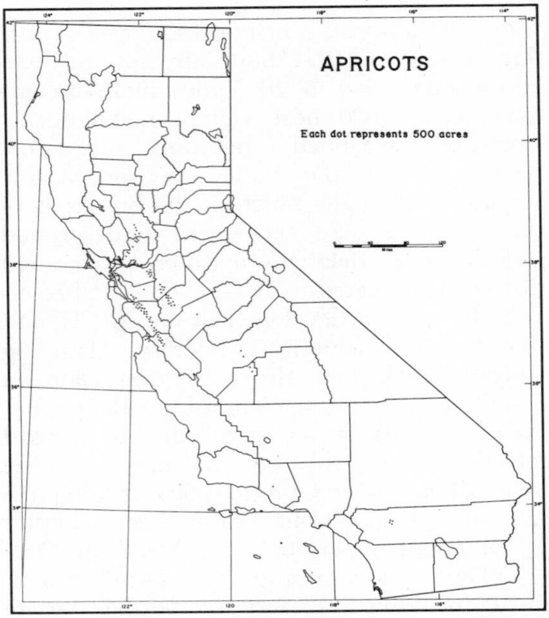

APRICOTS

Each dot represents 500 acres

Fig. 8-13. MAP OF THE CALIFORNIA
APRICOT ACREAGE.

producer (Fig. 8-11) for half a century despite
marked acreage decline.

The prune, any variety of plum whose sugar
content and firm flesh permit drying without seed
removal, was introduced from France in 1856.
California raises about 90 percent of the U.S. output. The tree prefers warm, clear, dry summers,
but does not flower well unless winters are cool.
Production has been centered around the San
Francisco Bay. Expansion of orchards took place
during the 1920's when foreign markets for dried
fruit were good. Bearing acreage declined after
1932; since 1950, however, new orchards have
been planted in the Sacramento Valley. Acreage
in the Santa Clara has declined by 50 percent
since 1941. Orchards have been scattered throughout the Santa Clara, but especially on well-drained
loamy soils from Almaden through Los Gatos and
north to San Jose. Urbanization has been pronounced here.

Apricots, an East Asian fruit, have been
grown chiefly on the lower slopes of Mt.
Hamilton Range (Fig. 8-13).

The apricot has about the same climatic tolerances as the peach. World production tends to be
concentrated within the subtropics. The Santa
Clara remains the leading California producer
despite a 50 percent decrease in acreage, 1941-
1961; other important counties include San Benito,

Stanislaus, and Contra Costa. Bearing acreage has
been declining in California since 1928. Some
Santa Clara orchardists have been setting out new
trees south of Tracy (Chapter 9), although the
Central Valley generally may have late frost. The
Santa Clara fruit was largely dried in the past,
but now the bulk is canned or marketed fresh;
Royal and Blenheim are the leading varieties.

Pears and apples, more typically middle-
latitude crops, were long raised on the valley
floor north of San Jose, where frosts would
have been critical for prunes and apricots.
The Valley was a secondary California producer of apples; orchards have nearly vanished. The *pears* (mostly Bartlett plus winter varieties) have wide tolerances and grow
well under irrigation on dense clay soils and
benefit from cooling breezes off the Bay and
the Pacific.

The pear ranks after the apple as a middle-latitude fruit tree. California has long been the leading producer in the United States, but distance
from eastern markets has encouraged canning of
much of the crop. Bearing acreage has stabilized

since 1940. The Santa Clara has long been the leading producer but with its continued decline Lake County (Chapter 10) should soon rank first. Pears in the Santa Clara had been less affected through the early 1960's by urbanization than some fruits.

Cherries, which prefer well-drained soils, are grown in the western Santa Clara, northeast of San Jose and south of Coyote Narrows. This latter location suggests that cherries may persist as a major crop longer than some of the other fruits. The white-fleshed Royal Annes are canned, whereas red bings and Black Tartarians are often consumed fresh.

Strawberry acreage increased rapidly after 1950 with the advent of fresh freezing; California has become the national leader. In the early 1950's strawberries ranked after prunes in value among all Santa Clara crops; the Valley still ranks second to the Salinas. However, the berries have been grown on the valley floor around San Jose, and acreage has already been partially replaced by housing tracts. The Santa Clara has also long been known for its quality wine grapes although acreage has been halved in recent years.

The grapes have generally been grown on eastern slopes of the Santa Cruz Range. The Pinot Chardenay and Pinot Noir varieties, modifications of French imports, have been used for pink champagne. The Novitiate monastic vineyards at Los Gatos have been renowned for their port, the nearby Montevello for good red wines, Almaden for Riesling, and the Evergreen district south of San Jose for sauterne. The Valley, like the Livermore and lowlands north of San Francisco Bay, has been concerned with better-quality wines.

Vegetables have also had an important place in the Valley's agricultural scheme, especially since the 1920's with continued population growth in the Bay Area. Some vegetables, like tomatoes and cucumbers, have been grown largely for cannery sale. Important truck crops have included tomatoes, sweet corn, and garden peas. The peas and corn for spring markets were once found on the sunny lower slopes of the Mt. Hamilton Range; tomatoes are widely scattered around the Valley with significant acreages south of Coyote Narrows.

AGRICULTURAL CHANGE IN SANTA CLARA COUNTY

CROP	1941 ACREAGE	1961 ACREAGE	RANK AMONG CALIFORNIA COUNTIES IN 1961	1941-1961 ACREAGE DECREASE
apples	300	130	—	170
apricots	18,630	10,980	1	9,650
cherries	2,600	3,140	2	—
grapes	7,175	3,140	14	3,725
pears	6,332	5,997	1	335
prunes	56,810	30,890	1	25,920
raspberries	312	84	—	228
strawberries	307	965	2	—
walnuts	7,291	8,090	7	—
beans (lima)	450	1,320	6	—
beans (snap)	750	880	2	—
cauliflower	800	805	—	—
celery	500	800	—	—
cucumbers	790	630	4	—
lettuce	200	1,860	—	—
onions	100	315	—	—
peas	2,500	300	—	2,200
tomatoes	4,300	5,175	—	—
barley	800	2,000	—	—
sugar beets	5,600	4,865	—	735

Source: Agricultural Crop Reports, Santa Clara County, 1941 and 1961.

Cut flowers (especially chrysanthemums and carnations), dependent upon adjacent metropolitan markets, now ranks second only to prunes among Santa Clara products. As in the Los Angeles Lowlands, production of nursery stock expanded tremendously after 1945 in response to development of new subdivisions in the Bay Area. Some nurserymen from the East Bay have relocated in the Valley.

The poorly drained marshy areas and alkaline soils in the northern end of the Valley between Sunnyvale and Alviso, well-located relative to metropolitan markets, long had significance as a *dairying* area and also for production of hay and winter grains. The dairy products once ranked after fruits and nuts in value, but much encroachment by new subdivisions and industrial plants took place after 1950. Dairying persists south of Coyote Narrows.

The chart on page 285, showing agricultural change in the Santa Clara Valley, suggests (through lack of acreage decline) the crops that are grown in southern Santa Clara Valley apart from the urban expansion around San Jose. It would seem that truck crops, market milk, walnuts, cherries, and cut flowers, among others, may remain important after some of the long dominant fruits have virtually disappeared.

COMMUNITIES

Until the 1950's virtually all towns of the Santa Clara Valley were agricultural centers affording residence for farm personnel, processing plants, and shipping facilities. They tended to be clean, prosperous, and conservative. That image has partially disappeared north of Coyote Narrows.[11] Farther south the functions of Morgan Hill and Gilroy have changed less. **Morgan Hill** (3200) serves as a local farming center. **Gilroy** (7400), leading city of the southern valley, has agricultural-processing industries as well as shipping; it is partially supported by livestock ranchers to the southeast.

[11] The northern Santa Clara Valley cities will be considered later as The South Bay subsection of the San Francisco Bay Area.

THE NORTHERN SAN BENITO VALLEY

The San Benito Valley tends to have a dual land-use personality. Its northern portion, a southward continuation of the Santa Clara, merges into the better-known lowland to the north so that any geographical division must be arbitrary; its narrow southern portion is dry and rolling and is used for livestock and grains (see Interior Basins—map, Fig. 8-7).

Evolution of land-use tended to follow the usual Central Coast pattern. The Spanish located Mission San Juan Bautista in 1797; before secularization in 1835 the mission was relatively prosperous with some irrigated fields as well as cattle herds. Later there were several Mexican ranchos in the northern Valley. In the early American period two groups, W. W. Hollister and the Flint, Bixby and Company, maintained large flocks of sheep in the San Benito. The Bixby firm acquired much grazing land elsewhere in California, eventually including the present site of Long Beach. Wheat raising was important before barley became the principal grain. Development of irrigation agriculture has become significant in the present century.

Agricultural production in the northern Valley is appreciably less than that of some Central Coast lowlands. However, the San Benito contains only 40,000 acres of irrigated land, which is rather intensively farmed. On heavier soils in the northwest, subject to repeated flooding, pastureland and sugar beets are especially prominent south of Coyote Creek. Rainfall averages around 13 inches and is supplemented by pump wells. The Hollister Irrigation District stores a limited amount of water in Paicines reservoir. The California Water Plan anticipates additional reservoirs and spreading grounds to maintain the water table; the water situation is not extremely critical yet.

The northern Valley has considerable agricultural diversity; fruit orchards are prominent around Hollister where there are loamy soils and good air drainage. The lower Valley ranks second to the Santa Clara in apricots, and the county ranks eighth within California in prune production. Several hundred acres of winter pears are found on heavier soils near San Juan Bautista; walnut groves are also significant, and acreage has increased. Grapes are conspicuous, yet production is inconsequential in comparison with leading San Joaquin Valley districts. The warm, sunny summers seem favorable for seed maturation; the Valley is an important producer of such vegetable seeds as lettuce, radishes, and onions—Ferry-Morse Seed Company maintains a large ranch east of San Juan Bautista. Besides seeds, a variety of vegetables is grown, including fall potatoes, lettuce, tomatoes, and garlic (the lower Valley and adjacent Santa Clara forms the nation's leading producer of this crop).

The San Benito has a relationship to the San Francisco Bay Area suggestive of that of the San Jacinto Basin on the fringe of metropolitan Los Angeles (Chapter 7). It would seem that with loss of good orchard land to urbanization closer to the Bay the Valley should gain additional significance in production of deciduous fruits. Poultry (eggs and broilers), already consequential, should also expand in the future.

Hollister (6100), trading center, county seat, and shipping point, is the only community of consequence. The town has had slow steady growth since its founding in 1868. Packing houses are conspicuous along railroad spurs. San Benito Junior College is located on the southern edge of the town.

San Juan Bautista (1100) seems the epitome of the midnineteenth-century mission village. Before the Southern Pacific extended a branch line to Hollister in 1870, San Juan had briefly been a stopping point on the Los Angeles–San Francisco stagecoach route. The old earthen plaza with its mission, Castro House, and picturesque Plaza Hotel, became a state monument in 1935. Many residents of San Juan are employed at the nearby Ideal Cement plant, one of a number on the margins of the Bay Area.

INTERIOR BASINS

The Interior Basins are *terrae incognitae* for most Californians—they form a land apart from the more favored Outer Lowlands just discussed. There is neither a through rail line nor a good north-south highway passage through this portion of California. Physically the Interior Basins are hampered by rain-shadow location east of two rows of southern Coast Ranges. They suffer from aridity and experience slight influence from maritime air and coastal fog, and thus are hotter in summer and colder in winter. There are no large towns—hamlets are little-known crossroads, perhaps with a schoolhouse, a service station and a few residences, and possibly a general store. This sparsely populated portion of the Central Coast has three principal depressions: upper San Benito Valley, Cuyama Valley, and Carrizo Plain. Lesser basins include Cholame, Shandon, and Peachtree (map, Fig. 8-7).

THE UPPER SAN BENITO VALLEY

The upper San Benito Valley extends southward along the San Andreas Fault from Tres Pinos for a distance of 40 miles. Residents know it by such local names as Bear, Dry Lake, and Little Rabbit valleys. The trough is frequently less than a mile wide, with marginal fault facets and stream terraces, some severely dissected. As gateway to Pinnacles Monument (see Ranges) and traversed by California 198, the upper San Benito is more frequented and better known than other Interior Basins.

The characteristic use remains winter grains and beef cattle despite apricot orchards and walnut groves around Paicines. Harbinger of the future could be the new 1200-acre Almaden vineyard. Properties tend to be large and

Fig. 8-14. OIL TOWN IN THE DESERT. New Cuyama is a "company town" in the arid Cuyama Valley. Note bed of the Cuyama River in the foreground and contrast the irrigated fields in the distance with the barren slopes beyond. (Richfield Oil Corporation)

ranch headquarters are often well appointed; barbed wire and windmills, like grasslands and oak groves, are characteristic features of the landscape. Undulating terrain, as much as dryness, hampers more intensive land-use. **Tres Pinos** (unincorp.) is a sleepy ranch village without evidence of growth.

CUYAMA VALLEY

The mountain-girt Cuyama Valley, with an area of 300 square miles, is a synclinal basin between the San Rafael and Sierra Madre mountains (southwest) and Caliente Range (northeast) (map, Fig. 8-7). Since folding and faulting in the Tertiary, erosion (i.e., gullying and canyon cutting) has frayed surrounding slopes; there is an impressive badlands, San Emigdio Mesa, north of Pine Mountain Summit, and the barren Caliente Range is also much dissected. The upper valley is narrow but the middle valley, underlain by thick alluvium, widens into an aggraded surface with a broad floodplain.

The Cuyama was ignored until the end of the Mexican era when two grants, Cuyama

No. 1 and Cuyama No. 2, were awarded. By the 1880's about 3000 cattle ranged over 72,-000 acres. Around 1900 a few Anglo-Americans settled in the Valley, homesteading along peripheral canyons with small streams and constructing roads. Additional homesteading took place about the time of World War I. Utilization was dependent upon dry-farming (barley and wheat) on alluvial fans and grazing (sheep and cattle) on the uplands. The Cuyama is the driest portion of the Central Coast and grain farming is risky. The Valley produces a good yield of grain and hay once in three to five years. Normally it affords fair grazing land with its surface cover of annual grasses (Brome and fescue), rabbit brush, and sagebrush. Rainfall averages around 5 inches on the valley floor. Homesteaders eked out a precarious livelihood—the distance to railhead (Maricopa) was far for many ranchers.

Land-use was altered locally with successful drilling of pump wells in 1939; in the following decades about 10,000 acres were placed under cultivation; water is drawn from depths of 100 to 850 feet. However, the water table is declining and there are too few landholders

Fig. 8-15. SHEEP BROWSING ON STUBBLE, CARRIZO PLAIN. This isolated basin suggests the western Great Plains to some people. Its extensive properties are devoted to winter grains and seasonal pasturage. (David W. Lantis)

to develop surface storage. Peas, potatoes, onions, and tomatoes have been grown as well as sugar beets (trucked to the refinery at Betteravia). Feed (alfalfa) and irrigated pasture have been dominant, enhancing livestock production in the Valley.

Another transition commenced in 1948 when the Richfield Oil Corporation discovered petroleum; isolation had hampered earlier drilling. Within two years Richfield, Superior, and Hancock had opened three fields with hundreds of producing wells; by mid-1951 the Cuyama was the fourth-ranking producer in California (see chart, page 410). Richfield extended pipelines from the Cuyama to their San Joaquin Valley system and then built a 125-mile pipeline from Wheeler Ridge pump station to their refinery at Watson (near Wilmington).

There were no consequential towns before discovery of oil; since 1950 Richfield has created **New Cuyama**, a "model" company town with community hall, shopping center, and $1.5 million high school (Fig. 8-14). However, as in other arid lands: what will happen when the oil is depleted?

THE CARRIZO PLAIN

The Carrizo Plain, located half a mile above sea level in eastern San Obispo County, is more suggestive of the Great Plains east of the Rocky Mountains than of California's Central Coast (Fig. 8-15). This remote and little-known (to most Californians) basin along the San Andreas Fault actually has internal drainage, with a playa known as Soda Lake (map, Fig. 8-7). It was considered worthless by the Spanish; it is one of the drier portions (precipitation averages about 8 inches) of the region and has been designated as middle-latitude desert, suggestive of the

Tulare Basin of the southern San Joaquin Valley across the Temblor Range to the east (see Appendix A).

Today much of the Plain belongs to the Kern County Land Company and other large corporations; utilization is based upon winter grains and grazing of sheep and cattle. Strip farming is practiced; with fallowing, there is almost always enough moisture for a satisfactory harvest of Baart wheat, which brings a good price for flour making (Fig. 8-16).

The Carrizo is sparsely populated. There have been no towns; **Simmler** on California 178 consists of a few houses and a school. In 1960 a Beverly Hills firm announced plans for a 25,000-acre community, **California Valley**, in anticipation of receiving water under the California Water Plan following construction of San Luis Reservoir to the northeast. A number of lots have been sold; as one enthusiastic retired wheat farmer from Montana noted: "It looks just like the Great Plains but without those miserable winters."

WHEAT

Each dot represents 500 acres

Fig. 8-16. MAP OF THE CALIFORNIA WHEAT ACREAGE.

THE COAST

The littoral of the Central Coast has been much less accessible than the coast of Southern California. Yet in recent years that isolation has disappeared, and a momentous change is beginning to transpire.

The principal business of the Coast is recreational and residence, even as that of the Outer Lowlands is irrigation agriculture and through commerce and that of the Interior Basins is livestock ranching. So far there is little evidence that the littoral will become a heavily frequented corridor for rapid surface travel between Los Angeles and San Francisco. The physical impediments to speedier highway travel have been terrain, fog, and winter storms. The problem of terrain has been somewhat lessened, but fog and storms pose continuing hazards along this Coast. The Santa Lucia Range, rising steeply from the Pacific over considerable distance, forms the chief topographic barrier.

Localization of activity in specific portions of the littoral is partially a matter of human barriers too. Since the days of the Spanish, large landholdings have reached to the shore. Because of limited value of much of the land for intensive use, some large parcels have persisted into the 1960's. Another land factor has been governmental ownership: national forest, military reservation, and state parks.

The several mountain ranges that rise from Pacific shores of the Central Coast have helped restrict human activity to places of more favorable terrain. It warrants reiteration that the Outer Lowlands reach the Pacific, but their larger size, inland penetration, and emphasis upon agriculture rather than residence and recreation seems sufficient reason for ignoring them here. Accordingly these foci of activity will be discussed: San Luis Obispo Bay, Morro Bay, Route 1 (i.e., the Big Sur Country segment), the Monterey Peninsula, the Santa Cruz Coast, and the western flanks of the Santa Cruz Range (i.e., the Half Moon Bay Country) (maps, Figs. 8-7 and 8-19).

SAN LUIS OBISPO BAY

San Luis Obispo Bay was discovered by Cabrillo in 1542. It does not provide the finest anchorages on the Pacific Coast; yet Point San Luis and the San Luis Range to the northwest afford some protection against prevailing winds (map, Fig. 8-7). Despite its hilly hinterland, the Bay provided a point for shipment of hides and tallow from Mission San Luis Obispo and later from Mexican ranchos of the area. Before the Southern Pacific arrived, a narrow-gauge line, the Pacific Coast Railroad, was extended from Port San Luis (then known as Port Harford) to Los Olivos in the Santa Ynez Valley. Such items as lumber were unloaded, and wheat was shipped out. Today the pier lies in a state of semi-decay. Union Oil has a dock a short distance to the south for shipment of petroleum from the Santa Maria and San Joaquin valleys. Crude oil has been shipped from Avila for half a century.

Recreational use of San Luis Bay began in the 1880's when the cool summers of Pismo Beach began luring residents of the southern San Joaquin. With arrival of the Southern Pacific in 1891 additional communities, including Grover City and Oceano, were organized. Plans in 1906 for a major resort city, Le Grande Beach, came to naught. In 1935 the state established **Pismo Beach State Park**, which extends along the ocean for 6 miles. The popularity with thousands of visitors of the delicate Pismo clam has long necessitated a limit on size and number of clams that can be dug in a day.

The popularity of resort communities along San Luis Bay has been increased by accessibility. This is the single place between the Santa Barbara Coast and the Golden Gate where U.S. 101 reaches the Pacific. Improvement of California 178 has also made the area more available to residents of the Southern San Joaquin Valley.

Towns along San Luis Bay serve differing functions. **Arroyo Grande** (3300) and **Grover City** (5200) are principally residence towns with significant numbers of senior citizens. A number of lower-middle income persons from around Bakersfield have built modest cottages and maintain small garden patches. **Oceano** (1300) is the packing and shipping center for Arroyo Grande Valley produce and houses farm workers. **Pismo Beach** (1800) is obviously a sea resort, whereas adjacent **Shell Beach** (1800), whose terrace site affords good marine views, is the preferred residential community (Fig. 8-17). **Avila Beach** enjoys popularity with residents of the San Luis Valley; it is a local center for sports fishing.

MORRO BAY

Morro Bay, a segment of Estero Bay sheltered by the 576-foot high volcanic mass of Morro Rock (sometimes called "Gibraltar of the Pacific"), would probably be an important commercial harbor if it had a productive hinterland. As a recreation area, the Bay is favored by position approximately halfway between San Francisco and Los Angeles. As late as 1950 **Morro Bay** (3700) was a reluctant seaside town with modest facilities. More recently it has become the most urbane resort between Santa Barbara and the Monterey Peninsula, although its many senior citizens (especially from the San Joaquin Valley) tend to be conservative and oppose careful planning and incorporation. Nevertheless, the rock, the bay, the eucalyptus groves, and the state park with its golf course lend appeal to the environs. Small wonder that it becomes congested with sports fishermen and other visitors from southern and central California in summer. Pacific Gas and Electric's generating

Fig. 8-17. PISMO. BEACH AND THE COAST HIGHWAY. The towns along the strand of San Luis Obispo Bay have rising recreational importance. This is the only place along the Central Coast, from Santa Barbara to San Francisco Bay, where U.S. 101 approaches the ocean. (California Division of Highways)

Fig. 8-18. HEARST—SAN SIMEON STATE PARK. This baronial estate of the newspaper publisher is located along the western slopes of the Santa Lucia Range. Its opening to the public in 1958 has quickened traffic along California Route 1. (California Division of Highways)

plant, which utilizes sea water, was considered an innovation at the time of its construction.

BIG SUR COUNTRY

The coastal fringe of the Santa Lucia Range, northward from Morro Bay to Carmel, is sometimes called "Big Sur Country" after the promontory of that name (map, Fig. 8-19). This wild country, with long empty stretches resulting from rugged terrain, government ownership, and large private holdings, is much appreciated by vacationists, artists and writers, and travelers along the Central Coast who can tarry longer than is demanded by driving U.S. 101.

The Big Sur Country long remained one of the most isolated portions of the Central Coast. It was not until 1852 that the first settler of European descent, retired sea captain John R. Cooper, established Rancho El Sur. In the 1870's George Hearst began to acquire the barony that eventually totaled tens of thousands of acres. Before 1900 a horse-and-wagon physician, Dr. John Roberts, envisaged a true coast highway as he rode the tedious miles between homesteads along the nebulous Coast Trail. Eventually, aided by State Senator James Rigdon, Roberts persuaded the California legislature to build his highway. Surveys were commenced in 1920; finally in 1937 the road was opened after years of arduous work by free and convict labor and an expenditure of $10 million. This spectacular

292 : : CHAPTER EIGHT

scenic highway, known as the "Carmel–San Simeon Road" or merely Route 1, has been compared by Aubrey Drury (in *California, an Intimate Guide*) with famed Grande Corniche of the French Riviera east of Nice. Widespread familiarity with Route 1 was delayed by World War II gas rationing, but traffic volume swelled after 1950 and especially after establishment of Hearst Memorial State Park in 1958 (Fig. 8-18). Traffic congestion has appeared despite new bridges and widening of the road, and choice vantage spots have been selected for private dwellings.[12] Winter rains often bring slides that block the road; two state-highway maintenance stations have crews continuously on call. Between the Sur River and San Simeon, all supplies had to be brought in by pack animals until 1937.

Scattered livestock ranching has occurred along this coast for a century; in spots marine terraces provide flat grazing land, but often the stock are pastured "on top" (i.e., on the ridge tops). Monterey (jack) cheese originated on the Molera Ranch in Big Sur Valley in 1892 in the days when only a "durable" product could stand the trip to market. This cheese, little known elsewhere until World War I, increased in popularity when European grating cheeses were unavailable and is now commonplace in California.

This enchanting, wild, often fogbound coast, which novelist John Hersey has compared with Shangri-La, consists of sheer slopes, surf and breakers, magnificent vistas, and rugged headlands. Many a vessel has gone ashore in bad weather; lighthouses at Point Sur and Piedras Blancas can be viewed many miles at sea on a clear night. In the spring lupine and ceanothus blooms appear at the most improbable places. Since the highway was completed a series of restaurants, inns, and lodges have been opened; some have achieved wide repute.

There are many delightful spots along this coast. At the south end of Carmel Bay is **Pt.**

[12] *Time,* December 28, 1959, intimated that enthusiasts consider architect Nathaniel Owings' residence "the most beautiful house on the most beautiful site in the U.S."

Lobos State Park, which has proved an inspiration to many an artist (Fig. 8-20). Here is enchanting little China Cove, sea lions on offshore rocks, walking paths (and wildflowers in spring), and the wind-contorted Monterey Cypress. A short distance away is Carmel Highlands, exclusive residential development overlooking Carmel Bay; its inn has attracted noted guests. Halfway between Carmel and Big Sur is Palo Colorado Canyon, a narrow valley lined with tall redwoods and containing secluded summer cottages. Nearby Notley's Landing was used to ship redwood and tanbark. Big Sur Valley is one of the most popular areas along the coast, visited by half a million annually—facilities are jammed in summer. Pfeiffer's Ranch, which has become **Pfeiffer-Big Sur State Park**, is an ideal family vacation spot, with camping, fresh-water swimming, horseback riding, and miles of hiking trails—if one can obtain a campsite. Along the valley are a number of rustic lodges. Overlooking San Simeon is **Hearst Memorial State Park**, whose $30-million castle was the fabled estate of the wealthy publisher (Fig. 8-18). Within two years after it was opened to the public in 1958, there had been 700,000 visitors. The park has much influenced tourism along the coast; around nearby Cambria ten new motels and thirty retail businesses were established by 1962.

THE MONTEREY PENINSULA

Few places in coastal California approach the Monterey Peninsula in scenic appeal, colorful history, and pleasant residential habitat (Fig. 8-20). The hilly peninsula, northwestern tip of the Santa Lucia Range, juts thumblike into the Pacific, separating Carmel Bay to the south from larger Monterey Bay (map, Fig. 8-19). Vizcaíno, who named the bay in 1602, was most enthusiastic about this portion of the coast; his endorsement inspired Portolá and Serra to establish a presidio and mission here in 1770.

Monterey (22,600) became the capital of

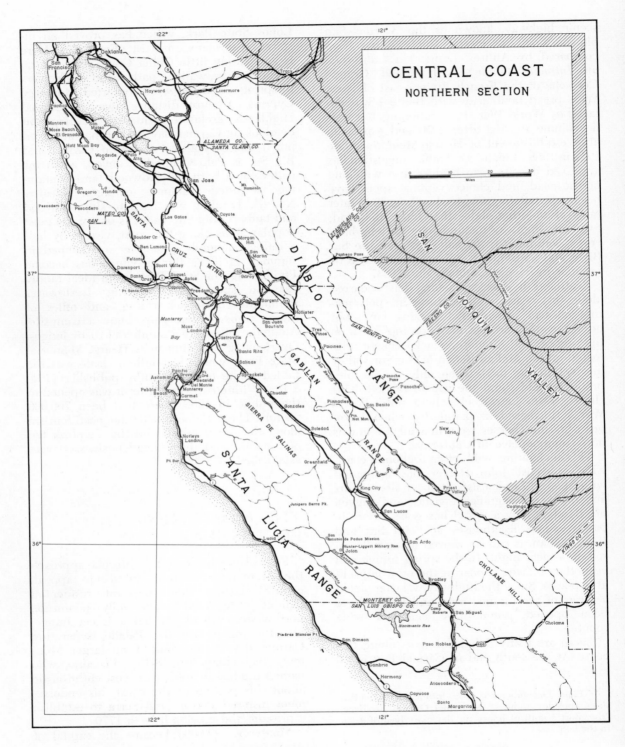

Fig. 8-19. MAP OF THE NORTHERN SECTION OF THE CENTRAL COAST.

Alta California in 1775; for nearly three quarters of a century it was the social and political center of the province, although Los Angeles at times surpassed it in population. By nineteenth-century United States standards Monterey was modest; even so Dana wrote more favorably of it than of other California villages.

Monterey lost its capitol and its importance after American statehood and with the Gold Rush—it languished for thirty years. There was local whaling in the 1860's and a little trade from surrounding ranches, yet the population stagnated around 1500 in number. This lack of growth helped preserve the colonial heritage for the present. Brewer, in 1861, felt that the town was still Mexican with pool halls and saloons much evident and drunken Indians conspicuous. With a favorable corridor eastward into the San Joaquin and the Mother Lode beyond, Monterey might have become one of California's largest cities. Instead, even agricultural development of Salinas Valley had limited effect on Monterey, bypassed by the main line of the Coast Route. In 1872 the county seat too was transferred to Salinas.

It was the Southern Pacific magnates who awakened Monterey—in 1878, after a branch rail line was built, the "Big Four" created the affiliate Pacific Improvement Company, which built Del Monte Hotel and hastened Monterey's development into a vacation spot of continental renown.

Commercial fishing came next with a salmon cannery in 1902. However, it was the rise of sardine fishing in 1916 that occasioned construction of nine canneries in four years and created "Cannery Row," setting for the Steinbeck novel. During World War I the Row had thirty canneries and employed several thousand workers seasonally. In the peak year of 1929 four-million cases of sardines were packed in this self-styled "sardine capital of the world." Suddenly after World War II the sardine mysteriously "disappeared"—the canneries have been converted into stores and warehouses.

Military activity, tourism, and retirement residence have kept Monterey alive. The local Army headquarters is the Presidio, a 360-acre preserve in its present site since 1902. Nearby is **Ft. Ord**, one of the nation's larger Army bases and an important indoctrination center. **Seaside** (19,000) has grown as a service center with motels, restaurants, and off-base residence for married military personnel. The Army maintains a language school at the Presidio, and the famed Del Monte Hotel has been a postgraduate school for Naval officers since World War II.

Monterey spreads back from the arc of its blue bay, sprawling over terraces and rising against the pine-sloped Santa Lucia Range. Its crudely rectangular street pattern reflects colonial origin. The community is a cultural hodgepodge with its "paisanos" (descendants of colonial settlers), Chinese, Italians, and many others. There is much tourist appeal, with the Presidio, historic adobes (better maintained than most colonial structures in California) and famed two-story Monterey-style dwellings that originated with the Larkin House in 1835. Monterey shares with its Peninsula significance as an art colony. Then there is Fisherman's Wharf, a good spot for a seafood dinner. The significant construction of motels in such an environment since 1950 is understandable.

Pacific Grove (12,000), which merges with Monterey on the southwest, is almost wholly residential; it began as a Methodist encampment in 1869. It was long a strict, righteous community with a strong chautauqua. The "made in the Middle West" atmosphere contrasts vividly with Monterey, and the waterfront is suggestive of New England. Here is Stanford University's Hopkins Marine Laboratory, a bathing beach, and even glass-bottom boats.

Carmel-by-the-Sea (4600) is south of the Peninsula in a cove on its own bay. This rustic Greenwich Village, in its pine-scented woodland, seems to have more aesthetic appeal than any other California coastal community, with its quaint cottages, its white-sanded beach, and its rocky headlands.

Mission San Carlos Borromeo, second in the chain, was originally located at Monterey. In 1771 it was moved to its present site on a terrace overlooking the lower Carmel Valley—a

Fig. 8-20. THE MONTEREY PENINSULA. The Peninsula forms the northwestern tip of the Santa Lucia Range. Monterey is in the foreground with the Naval Postgraduate School (lower left) and Presidio (lower right). Note Del Monte Properties (middle right), and Carmel and Carmel Valley in the distance. Pt. Lobos Peninsula (right rear) is the site of a picturesque state park. (Aero Photographers, Sausalito)

better agricultural site and removed from demoralizing influences of Monterey's military. San Carlos, built of local sandstone, is distinctive among the missions; it is now picturesque with its Saracenic-domed tower and floral setting. It served as unofficial ecclesiastical capital of the province—Father President Junipero Serra and his successor lived and died here. After secularization the mission fell into ruins, but has been much restored since 1884 and remains a Church property.

Carmel focuses upon a diminutive business district with a central parkway, known as The Village. With varied architectural styles and absence of neon signs and flamboyant advertisements it seems almost English with little "shoppes" featuring local paintings and handicrafts. Despite mission proximity, Carmel is not of colonial origin. The merit of its site was recognized by academician David Starr Jordan in 1870. Artists and writers began building cabins in the pines around 1904; their

numbers increased after the fire of 1906 destroyed part of San Francisco's "inspiration."

Carmel—without curbs, sidewalks, house numbers (there is no residential mail delivery), and street lamps in residential areas—contrasts strikingly with most California towns. Its beach has no beer halls or hot-dog stands although it suffers, for swimming, from fog and chilly water. Townsfolk have strived as hard to preserve the charming environment as most communities have fought to become "bigger and better." Carmel is indeed a dream for honeymooners and other tourists, writers and artists, and as a residence for increasing numbers of retired couples with means. Its inns and motels often display "no vacancy" signs, especially in summer and during the Bach festival in July.

Del Monte Preserve is one of coastal California's loveliest spots. Pacific Improvement Company commenced its developments on the Peninsula in 1879 and a few years later created the **Seventeen-Mile Drive** and **Pebble Beach**. Along the shore are such painted and photographed spots as Point Joe, Seal Rock, and, especially, Midway Point with its famed Lone Cypress. White sands, blue ocean, rocky promontories, and the hilly terrain clad with a dark-hued pine forest, famed too for its Monterey Cypress, form its appeal. In spring, fields of wildflowers burst into bloom. *Time* magazine has listed Cypress Point and Pebble Beach golf courses among the nation's ten finest. A myriad of private lands intersect the Seventeen-Mile Drive, flanked by many luxurious homes in varied architectural styles that are often screened by vegetation. Wealthy San Franciscans, top-rank military personnel, and other affluent senior citizens reside here. On the north shore of Carmel Bay is **Pebble Beach**, famed watering spot with Del Monte Lodge. Here hundreds of sports cars assemble each spring during the Laguna Seca races at Ft. Ord. South of Pacific Beach the Del Monte Properties Company has mined white dune sand since 1890. Its uses have increased through the years: plaster, stucco, and glass are important.

THE SANTA CRUZ COAST

Santa Cruz, about 50 miles north of Monterey Peninsula along the north shore of Monterey Bay, might be called "California's Atlantic City" (map, Fig. 8-19). Its setting is suggestive of California's other south-facing littoral, the Santa Barbara Coast (Chapter 7). Both areas had missions, both are noted aquatic playgrounds, both have agricultural moment, and both are preferred residential areas. However, the wooded south slopes of the Santa Cruz Range have redwoods as well as chaparral.

A number of land grants were awarded along this coast in 1833-1834; Mission Santa Cruz had been established in 1791. The Mexican period was characterized by the expected cattle ranching. Americans began moving into the area in the early 1850's; production of vegetables and lumbering in nearby redwood forests gained early significance. By 1900 general farming was being replaced by specialized agriculture. Today, strawberries and other berries, bulbs, cut flowers, and nursery stock are important east of Santa Cruz, and Brussels sprouts to the west. Mushrooms are grown underground in caves and in concrete cellars. Capitola is the center for production of begonia, dahlia, and tulip bulbs. Avocational gardening of barrister John H. Logan in 1890 accidentally produced the blackberry-raspberry cross known as loganberry. Dissected slopes east of Santa Cruz, long considered of little value, now command high prices as residential sites with views of Monterey Bay.

A remarkable agricultural change occurs immediately west of Santa Cruz, where lower terraces, long farmed, produce grains, beans, and especially Brussels sprouts; there is cattle grazing on lower slopes of the Santa Cruz Range. Santa Cruz County and the western littoral of San Mateo county to the north produce over 90 percent of the nation's Brussels sprouts.

Brussels sprouts—a biennial cabbage—produce small "heads" (sprouts) on stems. Although perishable, sprouts have been shipped throughout United States. Recently around 70 percent of the crop has been frozen. Much of California is either too warm in early fall or too cold in winter—hence its localization.

Santa Cruz was founded on the west bank of the San Lorenzo River in 1849, opposite the Mexican pueblo of **Branciforte**, about the plaza of ruined Mission Santa Cruz. Branciforte lost its identity in 1907 when it became part of Santa Cruz. By 1861 Brewer already found Santa Cruz an attractive American village. In the 1870's San Franciscans were attracted by its beach and its mild weather, sunnier than the Bayside city. Arrival of the Southern Pacific in 1880 enhanced its recreational use, which expanded after construction of a waterfront casino in 1906 and decline of Alameda as a resort town.

Santa Cruz (26,000) is the largest sea resort along the Central Coast (Fig. 8-21). It

Fig. 8-21. SANTA CRUZ AND MON-
TEREY BAY. *This famed resort and residence town is situated at the mouth of the
San Lorenzo River (running through middle
of picture). A new campus of the University
of California will occupy the marine terrace
north of the city (far right). California Route
17 extends laterally from the foreground to
connect with Route 1 at the interchange (near
center of picture). (Greater Santa Cruz Chamber of Commerce, photo by Air-Photo Co. of
Palo Alto)*

has a year-round use but is especially frequented in summer. Conversion of California
17 into a freeway, coupled with population
growth in the Santa Clara Valley, has much
increased its use. Santa Cruz has a good beach
of soft white sand that is cleaned daily. Its
breakers are "just right" for children and for
surfboard riders. Along the shore is the Casino, a boardwalk, and the Grove for Saturday
night dances. There is also a warmed salt-
water plunge for those who do not wish ocean
bathing. The municipal pier is the point of
departure for deep-sea fishing—albacore,
salmon, mackerel, ling, cod, and redsnapper
are taken.

Santa Cruz with its many Victorian frame
houses and its roses suggests an English town.
Small wonder this is one of the favored spots
in the state for retirement residence. DeLave-

age Park is forested with some redwoods.
There are suggestions of industrialization;
leather tanning, lumber processing, frozen
foods, and now chewing gum are among its
activities. A new branch of the University of
California, with a superlative hillside campus
site, will open in 1965.

Satellite Capitola and Soquel are small communities with rising residence by senior citizens. **Soquel**, in its early days a redwood logging camp, is now a center for bulbs, orchards,
and vineyards, mostly concentrated along
stream valleys. The new campus of Cabrillo
College, a county junior college, overlooks
the Pacific. To the south is **Capitola** (2000),
founded as a sea resort in 1876 and now the
center for large begonia gardens. It nestles in
Soquel Cove, has a fishing pier and bathing
beach. There are also eight state seashore

parks along the Santa Cruz Coast; those with overnight facilities become much congested.

THE HALFMOON LITTORAL

The Halfmoon Littoral, little known to most Californians away from the local area (in contrast to the eastside of San Francisco Peninsula with its constant traffic along U.S. 101), extends for 60 miles from San Francisco's southern outskirts toward Davenport (map, Fig. 8-19). The Littoral, like the Santa Cruz Coast, consists of marine terraces varying in width from yards to more than a mile. It is backed by the steep western slopes of the Santa Cruz Range, which is generally heavily wooded.

The Littoral long remained isolated, although it was visited first by Portolá in 1769 and was later the site of two Mexican ranchos. Until the 1920's most commerce was conducted by small coastal freighters, now replaced by Route 1. Whaling was once significant; later Portuguese and other farmers settled on the terraces.

Agriculture forms the dominant use of the Littoral still, although there are suggestions of urban encroachment. This windy, foggy coast has never had the appeal of the drier lowlands east of the Santa Cruz Range. Dairying, poultry, horticulture, and fog-belt vegetables constitute the principal agricultural pursuits. Winter grains also retain significance. Horticulture, which has gained importance in recent years, has become a multimillion dollar activity. Among the vegetables, artichokes and Brussels sprouts are most important, especially in San Pedro Valley and along Half Moon Bay. Other vegetables are grown: peas, beans, lettuce, cabbage, potatoes, and carrots.

The tourist potential of the Littoral has never been realized despite sandy beaches and headlands. San Franciscans sometimes fish in the surf. Lodging and restaurant facilities are rather modest. The weather-beaten farmhouses are suggestive of Maine. And the white buildings of Pescadero appear trim.

Urbanization may have been discouraged by the weather, but as vacant land disappears on the east side of the Peninsula, housing is appearing along Route 1. This is most evident in the north, especially around **Pacifica** (21,000).

THE RANGES

The southern Coast Ranges are more extensively used for ranching than any other major California uplands (map, Fig. 8-7). The traveler along Coast Highway scarcely appreciates the significance of these ranges, especially in midsummer when slopes are sun-browned and seemingly of slight consequence. Although such more southerly ranges as the Sierra Madre and San Rafael have limited use, collectively the southern Coast Ranges have much value for winter grains and spring grazing (Fig. 8-22), as watersheds, and in several instances as playgrounds. Locally there has been mining; in the past lumbering was important in the northwest.

THE SANTA LUCIA RANGE

The Santa Lucia, largest of the southern Coast Ranges, fronts on the Pacific from Monterey Bay to Estero Bay, a crow-flight distance of 125 miles. Through much of its length this complex fault-fold block presents a 3000-foot scarp wall to the sea. The Santa Lucia is a picturesque portion of California, with many landscapes to delight the visitor: the scenic Big Sur Country (previously discussed), Carmel Valley, San Antonio Valley, and Ventana Wild Area. Back-country portions of the range are suggestive of the Appalachians, including

Fig. 8-22. FALL PLOWING, SOUTHERN COAST RANGES. *No other California uplands seems to have so much acreage so suitable for livestock ranching and winter grains. This landscape is about 15 miles south of Maricopa.* (David W. Lantis)

a "Li'l Abner Dogpatch" atmosphere in some remote dwellings.

The colonial Spanish appreciated the valleys of the Santa Lucia Range, establishing two missions, San Carlos at Carmel and San Antonio de Padua northwest of Jolon. Following secularization the Mexicans awarded a series of grants along the coast northward past San Simeon and in the Carmel and San Antonio valleys. Sizable portions of the range, however, remained unused in colonial times.

Much of the range, except for the Carmel and San Antonio valleys and the coast, is still isolated. A series of roads winds from the Salinas Valley into the drier east side. Between Carmel and Cambria a single road, the **Nacimiento** south of Lucia, crosses the range; its western section winds down to Route 1 via a dramatic series of switchbacks. The western summits reach their apex in Junipero Serra Peak (5862 ft.); they receive some of the heaviest rainfall along the Central Coast and are densely wooded. Here western (lace) lichen, mistakenly called "Spanish moss," dangles from trees, and the damp forest floor has ferns.

On the fringe of this remote western portion of the range is **Hunter-Liggett Military Reservation**. The installation, purchased from the Hearst Corporation at the start of World War II, was used for maneuvers in connection with Camp Roberts in the Salinas Valley. More recently it has served the same function in connection with Fort Ord.

Ventana Wild Area (56,000 acres), inland from Big Sur Valley, was established in 1931. Proximity to urban centers and vacation spots makes this one of the more accessible forest wildernesses of California. Its best seasons are spring and early summer, when stream fishing is permitted and wildflowers bloom (in April). Because of late summer dryness and fire hazard, hikers must obtain a permit after July 1. Favorites with hikers are the two-day Pine Ridge Trail from Big Sur Park to Carmel Valley and Blue Rook Ridge Trail from Carmel Valley to Ventana Peak (4734 ft.).

There is varied livestock ranching within the Santa Lucia Range. The extensive dairying in the southwest was noted earlier in the chapter. In some parts of the back country hogs are allowed to run wild, feeding upon acorns. Beef cattle are grazed seasonally in the eastern (drier and more open) portion of the range.

The Carmel Valley is a charming, accessible,

and long-used portion of the range, extending inland for about 20 miles. Near its mouth are fields of artichokes. Inland the valley floor produces strawberries and begonias; few of its once famous pear orchards remain. Varied appeals include proximity to Carmel and Monterey, chaparral and oak-woodland slopes, spring wildflowers, the autumn gold of sycamores and cottonwoods, the purplish haze that softens slopes, and the shelter from chilling coastal fog.

The lower valley has achieved considerable recognition as a recreation area and residential site. Only two hours from San Francisco by automobile, it is popular with Bay Area residents, retired military personnel, and others. There are many little ranches along the valley, and a growing number of "picture-window" homes along the northern border. Near **Carmel Valley** (1100) with its varied retail services are lodges and guest ranches—usually complete with swimming pools. Down-valley 300-unit Hacienda Carmel, a retirement community, reflects growing popularity of the Valley for senior citizens.

San Antonio Valley displays the "interior" traits of the upper Salinas—a contrast from the lower Carmel Valley. The Spanish established Mission San Antonio in 1771; after secularization in 1835 it fell into ruins until its restoration since 1903. Ranchos were established late in the Mexican period. The attenuated San Antonio, followed by a major tributary of the Salinas River, is scenic—once it afforded a link along El Camino Real, but it has long been bypassed. The old rancho lands along the floodplain have water, but homesteaders on rolling uplands had less success. Plans for Salinas water storage were noted earlier in the chapter. Nacimiento Dam to the south has already become a vacation spot frequented especially by boating enthusiasts.

THE GABILAN RANGE

The anticlinal Gabilan Range, a continuation of the Santa Cruz Range southward from Pajaro water gap, forms an eastern wall for

Salinas Valley. It has rolling uplands clothed in chaparral or grass and oaks; the range is lower and less rugged than the Santa Lucia despite limited transverse highways. Southward it is called Cholame Hills.

The Gabilan has provided pasturage since colonial times; its northern segments were contained within Mexican ranchos. Today one is impressed by the extent of its utilization by flying along the range. Extensive areas are used for ranching and there is a maze of backroads; numerous check dams have been built along watercourses to provide water for livestock.

Recreational use tends to be centered at Fremont Peak State Park and Pinnacles National Monument. Fremont Peak (3169 ft.) affords a good observation point on clear days. **Pinnacles Monument**, with its eroded spires and crags, contrasts with the gentler slopes characteristic of the Gabilan. The relatively small (12,818 acres) monument was the site of Tertiary volcanism; the "pinnacles" are erosional remnants. Spring is the ideal season to visit the monument, which becomes dry and dusty later in the year. It is best appreciated afoot; a series of trails enables exploration of its jagged topography.

THE DIABLO RANGE

Innermost of the southern Coast Ranges is the attenuated and sinuous mass best named the Diablo Range despite local aliases (Mt. Hamilton, Call, and Temblor). It is structurally complex, with various prongs and intermont basins including the Oakland-Berkeley Hills.

Utilization is understandably varied since the range extends from The Knot in the southeast to Suisun Bay in the north. Its northern basins have become part of the Bay Area complex that will be discussed later. The Mt. Hamilton Range east of the Santa Clara Valley serves as a watershed for that lowland, as has been indicated. Throughout the Diablo Range, despite the fact that it is among the driest of the southern Coast Ranges, cattle ranching and production of winter grains form the typical use.

Mt. Diablo (3849 ft.), a landmark of the Bay Area and base point for land surveys over much of northern California, is the northeastern culmination of the region. Its original elevation has been reduced through erosion of the uparched mass, yet from its summit-lookout tower one can scan an area as large as the state of Ohio on a clear day. There is a highway to the summit, which has been a state park since 1931; tens of thousands annually drive up to enjoy the view. Picnic sites and campgrounds have been established.

Lick Observatory, atop Mt. Hamilton (4261 ft.), 13 miles east of San Jose, is situated on another prominent summit. The observatory, one of the smallest campuses of the University of California, was the gift of a San Francisco philanthropist. The 3113-acre site was selected because of atmospheric clarity; its 36-inch equatorial refractor telescope is among the largest of its type, and its new 120-inch reflector telescope is second to Mt. Palomar's in size. Alum Rock Park, a San Jose city park, lies at the western base of the range. It is suggestive of Los Angeles' Griffith Park with its chaparral setting; Alum Rock also has mineral springs and a bathhouse.

There are a number of small intermont lowlands within the folds and rifts of the Diablo Range. Those at the north end, part of the San Francisco Bay Area, will be considered later; they include San Ysidro, San Ramon, and Livermore. Farther south are Calaveras (northeast of San Jose), Halls, San Felipe, Isabel, Panoche (east of Pinnacles Monument), Little Panoche, Priest (southeast of King City), Peachtree, and Bitterwater. Many little sag ponds in these depressions have water intermittently. Because of the combination of isolation and aridity, livestock ranching and winter dry-farming of grains constitute the principal uses.

California has had two major centers of *quicksilver* (mercury) production, New Idria and New Almaden. Quicksilver has had strategic value in times of international tension; in more normal times California producers have been marginal because mining costs are lower in Spain and Italy. The **New Idria** group

extends for miles in San Benito County within the Diablo Range. The landscape is pocked with small workings—the district has been worked almost continuously for over a century. The New Idria mine itself has been one of the most productive, as well as one of the deepest, quicksilver mines in the world.

SOUTHERN RANGES

The southernmost ranges (Sierra Madre and San Rafael) are the wildest, most rugged, and most remote ridges in the Central Coast. Highest elevations in the entire region are found in the marginal Knot and in the San Rafael and Sierra Madre Mountains. Only a few winding dirt roads penetrate into this part of the Central Coast; much of it is barren and empty.

Northeast of the Santa Ynez Valley is **San Rafael Primitive Area**, established in 1932 and containing 75,000 acres within Los Padres National Forest. Core of the Area is 35,000-acre Game Refuge 3-C, established by the Secretary of the Interior in 1951 to protect the California condor. The condor, the world's largest flying "land bird," is a vulture. Unfortunately this wilderness contains little carrion for the condor, whose numbers have been reduced to perhaps 150. Thousands were killed during the Gold Rush after it was discovered that the primary condor quills made good gold dust containers. This wilderness is strictly for the husky backpacker—there are few trails and the terrain is rugged, with dense chaparral and steep cliffs. The northern portion is known as the "Hurricane Deck" because of interesting ventiform rocks.

The Los Padres (Sespe) wilderness, including The Knot adjacent to U.S. 99, was previously discussed in the chapter on Southern California. It is more accessible and much more frequented.

THE SANTA CRUZ RANGE

The Santa Cruz Range is the unique southern Coast Range—its distinctiveness results from proximity to residents of the Bay Area as well as to its physical features. It is the central California counterpart of the San Gabriel and San Bernardino mountains of Southern California—it affords city dwellers easy access to a forested uplands.

The appeal of the Santa Cruz has been magnified by its physical aspects. In contrast to the chaparral and grassland typical of more southerly and easterly ranges, the Santa Cruz contained extensive redwood and oak forests; some redwood remnants have been set aside as public reserves, whereas many others are privately owned—aesthetic values are now too high to permit cutting. This was, however, the first area to experience large-scale redwood logging, over a century ago. The range is a complex fault structure—two principal blocks are separated by the San Andreas Rift (which contains the sag ponds known as San Andreas and Crystal Springs lakes); there are also lesser faults. The northernmost block contains San Bruno Mountain and the city of San Francisco; one of the larger southern segments is Sierra Montara. Few if any California highlands are so laced with faults as the Santa Cruz. Although the Santa Cruz rises to summits of only 2,000 to 3,000 feet, it receives more rainfall than other parts of the southern Coast Ranges. Moisture, plus cool maritime air, and forests of redwood, fir, pine, and madrone, has given it an especial charm.

The cool Santa Cruz, still extensively wooded, makes an excellent playground for nearby urban residents. It also contains small farms and numerous homes of senior citizens and also commuters to peripheral cities. Heart of the range, suggestive both of the Appalachians and of English hill country, is San Lorenzo Valley north of Santa Cruz. Flanking California 9 are woods, wineries, delightful little restaurants and inns, and cool greenness that is unusual in the Central Coast in summer. The names too are charming and inviting: Brookdale, Quail Hollow, Ben Lomond, and Ice Cream Grade, to name a few. In the summer this area is one of California's most frequented uplands. Skyline Boulevard (California 5) continues northward to San Francisco. Scotts Valley, along Route 17 to the east, is more suggestive of Southern California

Fig. 8-23. *CEMENT PLANT IN THE SANTA CRUZ MOUNTAINS. Permanente Cement plant west of Campbell has an annual capacity of 8,500,000 barrels—the largest producer in California.* (Permanente Cement Company)

with its assorted amusements, but it is also an attractive residential area.

Several of the state parks in the Santa Cruz Range were established because of their redwood groves. **Big Basin Redwood Park**, one of the first redwood groves set aside (in 1902) for public enjoyment, has become one of the most frequented parks in the system in summer—in winter there is virtual solitude. Besides its big trees the park has several streams, miles of hiking trails, campsites, and picnic grounds. Farther south is the **Henry Cowell Redwoods State Park**, part of which was once a county park. Its Big Trees Grove (43 acres) has been popular since the 1880's.

The Santa Cruz is the only one of the southern Coast Ranges to have villages of consequence. Virtually all of its communities are residential in nature with resort facilities; Boulder Creek has a Lockheed missile installation. Most of the more significant towns are located in San Lorenzo Valley: **Ben Lomond** (1800), **Boulder Creek** (1300), and **Felton**

(1400). Marginal communities like Daly City, Woodside, and Hillsborough are better considered part of the Bay Area.

Mining has long contributed to the Santa Cruz economy. **New Almaden**, much less productive than New Idria (see Diablo Range), has been California's second source of *quicksilver*. These deposits south of San Jose have been known since 1845. New Almaden, whose 100 miles of tunnels extend below sea level, is now water-filled, but smaller mines in the vicinity have been worked intermittently since World War II. Manufacture of *cement* has had much more consequence. Market proximity is the primary factor in location of cement mills; the two in the Santa Cruz are near Bay Area markets.[13] Pacific Cement at Davenport, on the edge of the Santa Cruz Coast, is the older producer; the firm is also a major producer of sand and gravel. Permanente Cement west of Cupertino is a Kaiser affiliate established to produce cement for construction of Shasta Dam (Fig. 8-23). With more than three times the capacity of the Davenport mill, this plant is one of the largest in the world.

[13] California now leads the nation in cement manufacture. In 1961 the state's thirteen mills produced over 41 million barrels. There are four plants near the Bay Area, two east of the Great Central Valley, and seven near the Los Angeles Lowlands, chiefly in the Mojave Desert. Since limestone, which is widespread, is the principal ingredient, market determines plant location. One mill, at Redwood City, uses seashells and bay clay as its chief components.

THE SAN FRANCISCO BAY AREA

The San Francisco Bay Area [14] has been endowed with a superlative natural setting. Seldom has a conurbation evolved so completely around a hollow centrum, in this instance afforded by the waters of San Francisco Bay, which is approximately 45 miles long and 3 to 13 miles wide and verily suggests a crudely shaped California (Fig. 8-24). The aquatic lowland, framed by dozens of hillocks and a few conspicuous promontories, affords one of this earth's most felicitous blendings of land and water. It is Sybaritic and bejeweled, a charming landscape to titillate one's senses.

Four million people reside in this expanding metropolis, whose complexity is compounded by the presence of nine counties. The fringes of the Bay shore are rapidly filling and the conurbation is fast ingressing northward into the narrow lowlands of the Northwest (Chapter 10), southward into the Santa Clara Valley, and eastward into the intermont basins of the Diablo Range.

The Bay Area has the urban complexity associated with any great Occidental metropolis. Its functions become most involved in its three-dimensional heart, the city of San Francisco. On the periphery, the unifunctional suburban bedroom is far less complicated.

The Bay Area achieved its physical form with the end of the Great Ice Age. Melting of the continental ice sheets raised the level of the ocean, and sea water penetrated through the Golden Gate to flood the structural depression to the east, creating San Francisco Bay. This engulfment detached segments of the southern Coast Ranges to form such islands as Angel and Yerba Buena. The scalloped shoreline of the bay has headlands and peninsulas. The water of the Sacramento courses through Carquinez Strait, surging toward the river's ancient mouth outside the Golden Gate and mingling within the bay with the sea

[14] *The section on the Bay Area has been reviewed by James Parsons, University of California.*

Fig. 8-24. SAN FRANCISCO BAY AREA. Daly City, Colma, and South San Francisco (base of photo), San Francisco in center. Note how San Bruno Mountain delimits San Francisco on southeast. Marin Peninsula (upper left), the North Bay (middle rear), and the East Bay (upper right). (San Francisco Examiner)

water that daily rushes inland with the tide. The inflow and outflow of the tide effectively scours the bay to enhance its value for sea commerce.

The southern Coast Ranges are not as lofty here as elsewhere, but their complex old rocks have been faulted and folded and dissected into steep-sided hills. Elevations commonly do not exceed 2000 feet; noticeable landmarks include San Bruno Mountain and Twin Peaks, both less than a thousand feet high, Mt. Tamalpais (2604 ft.) and Mt. Diablo (3849 ft.). Like much of California, the Bay Area is riven by faults: the San Andreas, Hayward, and Sunol are the most conspicuous.

The Bay Area complex has evolved since the middle of the nineteenth century from a series of villages scattered along the bay strand. San Francisco, ideally situated for ocean traffic in the pre-railroad era, attained urban dominance so rapidly that potential rivals have never successfully challenged it. As in the Los Angeles Lowlands, coalescence of individual cities into a continuous metropolis along the east and west shores of the Bay has been a product of the automotive period. Vast housing tracts, suburban shopping centers, and physical linkage of separate political units have been especially marked since 1940. Despite construction of seven automobile bridges, the Bay still imposes a barrier to movement between various parts of the Bay Area.

The need for effective regional planning within the Bay Area has long been recognized. Plans proposed in the 1920's and 1930's foundered on the rock of local city and county partisanship. Pressures for regional planning have increased with population rise (lately at the rate of around 10,000 monthly). Such matters as atmospheric pollution, Bay pollution, the filling in of shallower margins of the Bay, rapid transit, water supply, urban renewal, parks, airports, and freeways concern residents of all nine counties.

Complexity of the Bay Area conurbation and organization of this book warrant successive discussion of these subdivisions: San Francisco, the East Bay, the Peninsula, the South Bay (northern Santa Clara Valley), Marin Peninsula, and the North Bay.

SAN FRANCISCO

San Francisco, sometimes known as Baghdad-by-the-Bay, has a beauteous setting that is approached by few cities elsewhere in the world. A perfect introduction to San Francisco is to sail into the Bay out of an offshore fogbank and through the Golden Gate on a sunny morning. Such an entry affords a leisurely enjoyment of the beauty of the bay, the whiteness of the "tilted city," the Presidio, the Marina, Alcatraz, Treasure Island and Yerba Buena, the Ferry Building, Coit Tower, the downtown skyscrapers, and the grass and oak-covered "far hills" of Marin and East Bay.

San Francisco has a favored location near the midpoint of the west coast of conterminous United States, with a lowland fringe around its nearly landlocked bay and with Carquinez Strait serving as a watergap into the Great Central Valley, richest and most productive agricultural hinterland of western America. Yet the immediate setting of the city itself poses transportation problems, for it lies at the northern tip of a hilly and narrow peninsula, surrounded on three sides by water.

"THE CITY"

San Francisco is the economic and cultural capital of central California, the financial core of western America and a considerable portion of the Pacific Area as well. San Francisco was almost born a city, for the Gold Rush forced that status upon it within months, denying it the normal evolution of most cities. From Eureka to Atascadero, and eastward into Nevada, when one says "I am going to The City," he *still* means San Francisco.

San Francisco is a city in the classical Occidental tradition (i.e., mature, complex, densely populated, a bit decrepit in places, with a pronounced "downtown" orientation). Population density is much higher per square mile than in Los Angeles—San Francisco is a vertical city, a city of apartment and flat dwellers.

Perhaps no other large American city so connotes Boston culturally. Yet the waterfront and the Bay bridges are suggestive of Manhattan. The "Top-of-the-Mark," and the Hotel Fairmont's "Crown Room" astride Nob Hill impart something of the spirit of the observation tower atop the Empire State Building. The traffic congestion of San Francisco resembles Manhattan, too, although it as yet lacks the subways and the tunnels that link Manhattan to its satellites. The Peninsular commuter trains of the Southern Pacific's Coast Line might be likened to the Long Island Railroad, but fortunately facilities are better maintained.

THE LANDSCAPE

San Francisco stands upon the northern tips of the hilly, wooded peninsula that separates the Bay from the Pacific Ocean, yet half of its terrain is flat rather than hilly. The maximum elevation is 929 feet at the summit of Mt. Davidson. The hills consist of the red cherts, sandstones, and shales of the Franciscan series (Jurassic), whereas low-lying sections consist of Quaternary deposits. The Pacific side of San Francisco is almost ruler-straight; the Bay strand, which was naturally indented, has been straightened by over a century of filling projects.

The maritime surroundings of San Francisco provide the city with one of the most equable climates in the nation (seasonal range 12°F., July average 58°F.). As the Hawaiian High shifts northward in summer, winds become more northerly but low interior pressure sucks moist ocean air inland. This air, flowing across the cool California Current and areas of upwelling of colder water from ocean depths, produces the characteristic fog for which San Francisco is famous. The warmest (and least foggy) month is September rather than July or August. Some find the coolness of the fog invigorating, but many prefer the milder weather of the Mission District (southeast San Francisco), the Peninsula, or the East Bay. San Francisco is one American city where a fur coat is not uncomfortable on an August evening.

The failure of any of the Spanish and English sea captains who visited coastal California in the sixteenth century to discover San Francisco Bay has long intrigued historians. It was not until 1769 that members of the Portolá expedition actually saw the Bay; Spanish explorations around the Bay in the following years did not reveal any stellar settlement sites. Nevertheless, at the insistence of Father Serra, a mission site was selected, and in 1776 the presidio was founded at Fort Point and Mission San Francisco de Asis ("Dolores") was established along a creek on the east side of the peninsula, a mile from the Bay shore. The Spanish colony on San Francisco Bay never became large; there were few Indians, the water supply was undependable, and the environment not ideal for crops. The garrison at the presidio was always modest; after 1835 regular troops were no longer stationed there.

San Francisco actually originated as the little port village of Yerba Buena, on a cove of that name, in 1835, the year after secularization of Mission Dolores. Its earliest buildings were at approximately the contemporary site of Portsmouth Square. Although a pueblo was never created, the U.S. Circuit Court still awarded the city the traditional four square leagues in 1865. As late as 1846 it was a village of not over forty inhabitants.

Yerba Buena was renamed San Francisco in 1847; later the same year the first dock was built at Clark's Point. For a few weeks after discovery of gold in 1848 San Francisco was almost abandoned. Within months, however, as word of gold discovery spread, the Mexican village became an American tent city with a "floating" population in the thousands. During mid-1850, the harbor was dotted with ships abandoned by crews off to the gold fields. For several years the city experienced much lawlessness—Portsmouth Square was the focus of gambling houses and saloons. Within three years six conflagrations swept the shanty town. The city expanded westward beyond Telegraph Hill, and Rincon Hill, somewhat less foggy, became the first exclusive residential district. As the city grew, it was extended into the shallow waters of the Bay with piles, redwood rafts, and fill.

In the late 1850's decline of mines occasioned much unemployment and bankruptcy; soon the wealth of the Comstock Lode's silver mines brought renewed prosperity. Gradually industry and commerce replaced precious metals in the city's economy. Industrial establishment appeared southward toward Hunter's Point; and the first refinery was built to process Hawaiian sugar. In 1869 the city was linked with eastern United States (via Oakland and trans-Bay ferries) by rail. In the interim immigrants from southern Italy had developed a fishing industry at Fisherman's Wharf.

No rival seriously challenged San Francisco as the colossus of the Pacific for more than a generation after the railroad. The Southern Pacific, called "The Octopus" by Frank Norris but more commonly "the railroad," monopolized overland trade within the state. The Pacific Mail Line, which had transported many gold seekers, anticipated arrival of the Central Pacific by opening its trans-Pacific trade.

As the city grew, railroad magnates and mining kings built mansions on Nob Hill, and cable cars began to operate in 1873, providing a partial solution to transportation problems posed by steep slopes. San Francisco acquired a reputation for fine food, partly because its society leaders imported French chefs. Meanwhile, the beginnings of Golden Gate Park commenced. The shipment of grain from the Great Central Valley to Liverpool and other world ports expanded outgoing commerce. With depletion of redwood forests near the Bay, lumber schooners began operating from the Northwest (Chapter 10).

San Francisco continued to develop in the 1880's; and shipping across the Pacific increased. The Spreckels expanded Hawaiian sugar production. Perhaps three fourths of all California's industrial output was fabricated in San Francisco. Population density was rising and blocks of multiple residences (flats) appeared. Robert Dollar, a shipper of Mendocino redwood, moved into the trans-Pacific trade and created a great steamship company. Then at the turn of the century, San Francisco

Fig. 8-25. THE DAY THE SKY BURNED. Market Street (left) and the financial district as seen from the Ferry Building. Florida has its hurricanes; California,
its earthquakes. No earthquake has been so destructive as the one associated with
movement along the San Andreas fault on April 18, 1906. Subsequently, much
damage was caused by earthquakes in Long Beach and Bakersfield. (The Southern Pacific Company)

commercial development was further promoted by Alaskan salmon and gold.

By 1900, San Francisco had a population of
342,000 and was the tenth city of the United
States. Montgomery Street, although no longer
on the waterfront, had become the financial
center of western America. Downtown streets
were cobblestoned, but many residential
streets remained unpaved. Market Street had
become a famed thoroughfare, and its Palace
Hotel, which cost over $3 million, was interna-
tionally known. Already the Barbary Coast
and Chinatown had become tourist attractions.

Movement along the San Andreas Fault at
dawn, April 18, 1906, caused the earthquake
that shattered homes, crumbled brick walls,
broke windows, and dishes. Gas hissed from
broken mains; water lines ruptured. In the
fiery two-day holocaust that followed, damage
approached $350 million in a four-square-mile
area with the loss of 452 lives and destruction
of 28,000 buildings (Fig. 8-25). The fire was
halted at Van Ness Avenue on the west after
the dynamiting of buildings. San Francisco,
a city of redwood, had fed the fire well.

The rebuilding of San Francisco took only
five years. Although little of the Burnham Plan

of 1904 was adopted, a more beautiful city replaced the rather ugly, if picturesque, Victorian metropolis.[15] Meanwhile, other forces were speeding the city's growth. The Panama Canal was opened in 1914 and a great fair, the Panama-Pacific International Exposition, was held in 1915. Opening of the canal created a market for San Joaquin Valley oil along the Atlantic seaboard. Expansion of irrigation agriculture in central California, especially in the Great Central Valley, made San Francisco and its satellites around the Bay the center of a vast food-processing industry.[16] War in Europe stimulated industrial growth, especially shipbuilding.

San Francisco achieved new significance as a port after World War I; coastwise trade expanded as refrigerated fruit was increasingly shipped to western Europe, coffee and bananas came from South America, trade and pleasure cruises developed with Australia and the South Seas.

San Francisco had grown into a city of 634,-000 by 1930, but it was no longer California's largest metropolis. A supplemental source of water was brought from Yosemite's Hetch Hetchy Valley; this controversial development was noted in Chapter 5. Labor strife on the waterfront in the 1930's coincided with expanding Oakland ocean commerce and at a time when Los Angeles commerce was swollen by petroleum shipments—San Francisco no longer had singular dominance as a west-coast port. Trans-Pacific air flights, meanwhile, were established in 1936. The Bay barrier was reduced with opening of the Oakland Bay and Golden Gate bridges. Although it showed only a slight population increase during the 1930's, San Francisco suffered less from the Great Depression than many American cities.

War in the Pacific (1941-1945) had a tremendous impact upon the city. Great numbers of service personnel moved in and out of San Francisco, and many military facilities were located in surrounding areas. A great volume of supplies moved westward from the Bay. Shipbuilding and ship repair became major industrial activities, and other types of industry were greatly expanded. Despite much new housing in the Sunset District and southward, residential facilities were seriously taxed.

San Francisco has prospered since World War II, yet much of the increased activity in the Bay Area has taken place on the periphery. There is little vacant land within San Francisco (whose city and county limits are identical) for residential or industrial expansion. **Stonestown**, in the southwestern corner of the county, one of the nation's outstanding suburban developments, was completed in the early 1950's. The 1960 census revealed that San Francisco had declined slightly in population, a reflection of younger couples deserting city apartments for suburban tract homes, of freeway construction, and of urban renewal in the Western Addition.

STREET PATTERN

San Francisco has a rectangular street pattern that is complicated by terrain, the city's early-day antecedents, and the shape of its peninsula (Figs. 8-24, 8-26, and 8-27). Market Street evolved from the trail down which *carretas* laden with hides and tallow rolled to Yerba Buena Cove. Jasper O'Farrell's 1847 revision of the original (1839) survey retained the northeast-southwest orientation for what has become the eastern portion of downtown San Francisco. Thus compass orientation of original portions of Los Angeles and San Francisco is almost identical.

Terrain was disregarded in the instances of Rincon, Telegraph, Russian, and Nob hills so that the automobile passenger is sometimes

---

[15] In 1904 a group of civic-minded San Franciscans employed Daniel H. Burnham, Chicago architect and city planner, to plan a new San Francisco. His proposal called for traffic circles, diagonal boulevards, one-way streets, a civic center, parks, subways, and a 30-mile Outer Boulevard. Political bickering, journalistic opposition, and public apathy prevented extensive use of the Burnham Plan.

[16] Much of the benefit of economic growth in northern and central California to San Francisco has been indirect: San Francisco has the corporate offices, the brokerage houses, the insurance companies, and the bank headquarters, rather than flour mills and food canneries.

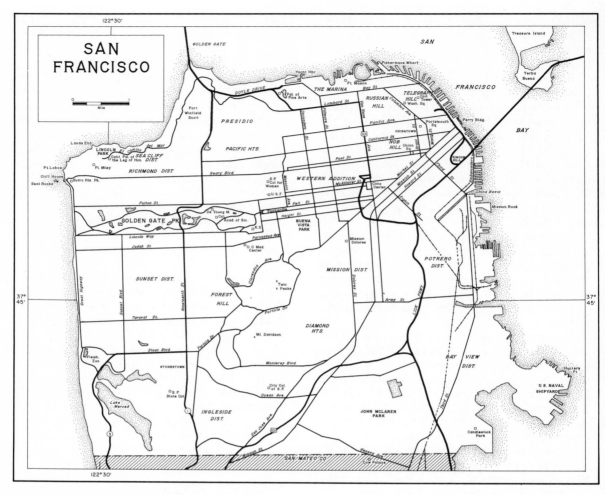

Fig. 8-26. MAP OF SAN FRANCISCO.

exposed to a roller-coaster effect.[17] The attenuated Golden Gate Park forms a break in the north-south street continuity of western San Francisco without serious results. Around the Presidio, Seacliff district, Buena Vista Park, and other elevations, streets conform more logically to the terrain.

Street pattern does not form the basic problem with respect to vehicular movement in

[17] By contrast the reshaping of Diamond Heights, whose steep slopes had long negated residential use, in the early 1960's was accompanied by much cut-and-fill, followed by creation of a street pattern appropriate to the topography.

San Francisco. Rather, it is cobblestones on steep slopes (fortunately, not too often wet during the year), narrow streets, one-way streets, absence of stop signs at numerous intersections, traffic congestion, and the problem of crossing Market Street. The new freeways, here as in other metropolitan areas, also confound drivers unfamiliar with the system. Because of its rather small size (forty-four square miles), San Francisco can be crossed in a comparatively brief driving time but the factors listed above plus blindness of intersections help account for accident incidence.

Fig. 8-27. SAN FRANCISCO. Panorama from China Basin (lower left) to the Presidio (upper left), with the central district beyond the Skyway. The Marina is on foreside of the Golden Gate Bridge, then Russian Hill, Telegraph Hill, and the Embarcadero toward the Bay Bridge. Alcatraz Island (middle, right margin) with Sausalito and Mt. Tamalpais behind. (San Francisco Chamber of Commerce, photo by R. L. Copeland)

San Francisco has relatively few principal thoroughfares. Market Street, of course, is internationally known; it is the principal downtown boulevard. The Embarcadero, 200-foot wide waterfront street, extends from Fisherman's Wharf to China Basin; upon it front the concrete piers of the Port of San Francisco. Third Street continues southward through the industrial district. Facing the Pacific is another wide avenue, the Great Highway. Much more traffic, however, moves along Nineteenth Street, south of Golden Gate Park, and Park Presidio Boulevard to the north, which serve as California 1. Portola Drive serves as the link between Route 1 and Market Street. Van Ness Avenue, marking the original western limit of the city, and Lombard Street serve as U.S. 101 between Lick Freeway and the Golden Gate Bridge, pending freeway construction. Geary, extending from the downtown area to the Pacific, is the principal east-west thoroughfare.

Freeways, which disregard a rectangular pattern, tend to bewilder the stranger, yet they have eased traffic flow through the city. Route 101 now utilizes James Lick (Bayshore) Freeway, which leads toward both the Golden Gate and Oakland Bay bridges. Construction was suspended on both the Embarcadero Freeway and Golden Gate Freeway in the early 1960's; principal arguments of San Franciscans against their completion appeared to be (1) they remove land from a city already short of space; (2) they desecrate the landscape.

THE CENTRAL DISTRICT

Downtown San Francisco, compact in size with many skyscrapers, long contrasted with the low Los Angeles skyline (Fig. 8-27). Since it was virtually rebuilt after the fire of 1906, nineteenth-century structures characteristic of downtown areas of many American cities are absent. The central district lies within a crude square (approximately two square miles) bounded by Van Ness (west), the Freeways (south and east), Broadway (north), the Bay (northeast). Principal functions include retail trade, government, finance, corporate headquarters, and tourism.

Union Square with its underground parking garage forms the core of the central district. Surrounding blocks contain first-class hotels, clubs, fine import shops, *the* department stores, specialty shops (art, music, furniture, books, perfumes, lingerie, jewelry) with tastefully displayed wares, tourist bureaus, restaurants, and night spots. A distinctive feature is the little sidewalk flower stalls, one of the city's trademarks. Foreign consulates, banks, and insurance companies are housed on Montgomery and California streets. Geary Street is the focus of the legitimate theater. The district also contains broadcasting studios and oil companies (less conspicuous than in Los Angeles).

Market Street, excellent for pageants and parades, bisects the central district. Lower Market Street has transportation offices, nautical supplies, and third-class hotels. Within a single skyscraper are offices of four of the five firms that dominate the Hawaiian economy. Southwestward beyond the Sheraton-Palace Hotel is the city's "Great White Way," grown a little shabby; it is flanked by theaters, restaurants and bars, and retail shops. Southeast of Market is "Skid Row" with inexpensive hotels and bus terminals. It acts as a buffer between the warehouse district and the downtown area; the rail station is toward the east side. Rincon Hill, the elite residential district a century ago, lies at the west end of the Bay Bridge; it is now a warehouse area whose summit is dominated by the Union Oil pylon.

The **Civic Center**, west of Market Street on the southwest edge of the central district, has a concentration of governmental activity around its central plaza. Buildings generally follow the French Renaissance style. Older granite and newer concrete structures house the city hall, public library, state offices (San Francisco and Los Angeles serve as sub-state capitals), civic auditorium, Opera House (where the United Nations was founded), and Veterans Building (which houses the Museum of Art).

Downtown San Francisco provides the nation with one of its favorite tourist centers. Multiple explanations for its appeal include its distinctive "character"—an aspect found in New York and New Orleans but uncommon in most American cities. In part this image is created by the resemblance to a many-tiered white wedding cake rising dramatically above the Bay. Too, there is the legacy of the exotic seaport, which San Francisco long shared with Shanghai and Marseilles. It has the facilities to house and feed the visitor well—few American cities enjoy such a reputation for varied cuisine. Its many hotels, including the second-generation Sheraton-Palace, the Drake and St. Francis on Union Square, the Mark Hopkins and the Fairmont atop Nob Hill, and the newer Jack Tar and Hilton, are much famed. Another aspect is the multiplicity of vistas, such as from Twin Peaks, Telegraph Hill, Buena Vista Park, or the upper stories of Nob Hill hotels. The Bay bridges have added another element, and the Bay itself with Alcatraz Island is a decided attraction. And where else is a Fisherman's Wharf so convenient to so many people? Few American cities can provide the foreign flavor of Chinatown, the Latin Quarter, and the Fillmore. Finally, there is of course the cosmopolitan population of the city.

RESIDENTIAL DISTRICTS

San Francisco has well-identified residential districts. Although there are extensive areas housing working people on modest incomes, basically it is a "moneyed" city occupied by middle-aged couples and wealthy widows. Yet there is an obvious number of elderly male derelicts. Property values in attractive sections tend to be prohibitive for younger couples with children. Young married couples often reside in a small apartment until arrival of the first child, and loss of an income and need for larger quarters prompt retreat to a suburban housing tract.

A TILTED CITY

San Francisco has been described as a "tilted city"—its terrain permits a considerable portion of the population to live on view lots overlooking city lights, the Bay, or the Pacific. In a frost-free environment the declivities provide charm; but the slopes frustrate the pedestrian and the motorist.

San Francisco is also a city of parks and squares and gardens. Some squares are small, perhaps occupying a single block, as Portsmouth Square, Union Square, and McCoppin Square. Because of population density and narrow (25-foot) lots, it is easy to overlook the extent of the parks. Gardens, so characteristic of backyards in many parts of the city, are generally hidden from street view.

The **Golden Gate** is San Francisco's largest park; with its "panhandle" it stretches across half the peninsula. It is more impressive than New York's Central Park, Paris' Bois de Boulogne, or Los Angeles' Griffith Park. It was set aside in 1868; however, its change from barren dunes and wasteland into a magnificent landscaping with more than 5000 types of plants is credited to John McLaren, who became superintendent in 1887.[18] There are miles of bridle paths and driveways, lakes, flower beds, wide expanses of grass. A flock of sheep browse on the green, and the reserve includes Deer Park as well as buffalo and elk. The park has two stadia, Golden Gate (for soccer and track) and Kezar (for football). Cultural activity is centered in DeYoung Museum and the California Academy of Sciences. At the western edge of the park two old windmills rise above Playland-at-the-Beach, an amusement center. Not far north along the coast is Cliff House, with Seal Rocks offshore and Sutro Heights Park above. Here also is Sutro Baths, built by the mayor who made a fortune from the Comstock Lode.

Farther north is 270-acre **Lincoln Park**, with excellent views of the Golden Gate from El Camino del Mar. It contains California Palace of the Legion of Honor, with the city's largest art museum. Nearby is small James D. Phelan Beach State Park, and to the west is another small park, Lookout Point.

OLDER DISTRICTS

The oldest portions of San Francisco were destroyed by the fire of 1906; however, around the fringes of the burned area there remain vestiges of late-nineteenth-century San Francisco. These include the Mission District and the Western Addition.

The **Western Addition** was a smart section of San Francisco in the 1870's when the "Old Set" settled there. Later it suffered badly from hasty post-fire growth. It has an assemblage of Victorian gingerbread with scrolls and exuberant trim. Row on row, block on block, are two-story duplexes with no space between houses and without greenery along sidewalks. Bay windows, Byzantine domes, and Gothic arches abound. The Western Addition has become something of an international district, housing Negroes, Jews with east-European antecedents, Japanese, Russians, Filipinos, and others. Adjacent to Post Street is "Little Osaka," a smaller Japanese concentration than "Little Tokyo" in Los Angeles. McAllister Street houses the city's principal concentration of second-hand shops. In the Western Addition too are the University of California's Extension Division and campuses of San Francisco College for Women and University of San Francisco, a few blocks apart on Lone Mountain.[19] On the southern edge of the district, Buena Vista Hill is gaining status as a residential section; Buena Vista Park on its summit, near the geographical center of the city, affords an excellent vista. Extensive renovation of the Western Addition has started, particularly in a strip along Geary Street, where an urban redevelopment program is underway.

The extensive area known as "South of Market" contains the adjacent Mission and Potrero districts; much of the city's working class has resided here since the great fire. The Potrero today is largely industrial and will be discussed later. The **Mission District**, with Mission Dolores, partially represents a filling of the lagoon that was once to northeast of the

[18] A new park, John McLaren, has been established in his honor in southeastern San Francisco. Candlestick Park, where major league baseball is played in a windy stadium, is also on the southeastern edge of the city.

[19] San Francisco is more important as an educational center than is sometimes appreciated. Besides these institutions, the University of California Medical College and Hastings Law School are in San Francisco, as well as San Francisco State College and San Francisco City College.

mission. Densely populated, the Mission contains a number of minority citizens and much "depressed housing" (i.e., slums).

"FOREIGN" DISTRICTS

Although the Western Addition houses peoples with ancestors recently from various parts of the world, several other districts help give the city its international seasoning. North of the central district and surrounding the three summits, Nob Hill, Telegraph Hill, and Russian Hill, now characterized by expensive apartments, are Chinatown and the Latin Quarter (sometimes "Little Italy").

Few "foreign districts" in American cities have achieved wider renown than **Chinatown**. This is not the original district that had acquired such a name for its opium dens and its mystic—that part of the city was destroyed by the fire of 1906. Contemporary Chinatown is a tightly packed district focused upon narrow Grant Avenue, its business thoroughfare, contiguous to downtown San Francisco on the northeastern slopes of Nob Hill. It is an interesting mixture of American and Chinese, neon signs and "Chinese" architecture. The grocery stores gives a better picture of the community than the souvenir shop. Originally the Chinese were miners and builders of the Central Pacific railroad; later they became domestic servants, produce sellers, gardeners. Today their activities represent the entire gamut of American life; this district represents the largest concentration of Canton Chinese in America.[20] It has gained importance as a garment-making center.

The Latin Quarter is bisected by diagonal Columbus Avenue between Telegraph Hill and Russian Hill. Originally this area, **North Beach**, was occupied by Irish. Later its confines, around the old Meiggs Wharf, were extended through reclamation from the bay by

fill. Eventually it took on more of an air of "Little Italy" or "Little Mexico"; today it has the international coloring of the Western Addition. Washington Square still has an Italian group although the Italians are now scattered throughout the city. Here the Church of Saint Peter and Paul is a landmark. Unlike Los Angeles, San Francisco has a relatively small Mexican population, but the Mexicans have long claimed an interest in the Latin Quarter. Telegraph Hill, the local "Greenwich Village" of the 1920's, is no longer the Bohemian haunt; long ago its shacks were replaced by apartment houses.

DISTINCTIVE DISTRICTS

San Francisco incomes average among the highest in America—the city has a concentration of banks, retail stores, insurance companies, and corporate offices. It is understandable that such a concentration of wealth should be reflected in attractive residential areas housing business and professional groups; these tend to occupy hillsites, and especially western San Francisco, the newer portion of the city.

The Marina, a newer (1920's) apartment district west of the Latin Quarter and north of the Western Addition, extends to the Presidio. The crumbling Palace of Fine Arts remains from the Panama-Pacific Exposition of 1915. On the northern edge is the Yacht Harbor—sailing in the Bay is popular.

Richmond, between the Presidio (northwest) and Golden Gate Park (south) is a populous area of modest dwellings. **Pacific Heights** on its eastern fringe has some fine dwellings—it is considered one of the city's best addresses. **Sea Cliff**, west of the Presidio, also has large, well-landscaped residences.

Sunset, south of Golden Gate Park and west of Twin Peaks and Forest Hill, is a newer residential district. As late as 1940 much of its southern portion was still empty sand hills. This district consists principally of single-family dwellings in an interesting combination of contemporary and "old San Francisco" architecture. To the southeast the expensive homes of **Forest Hill** and **St. Francis Woods**

---

[20] Burton H. Wolfe gave a scathing presentation of Chinatown in *The California Liberal*, February 1960, in which he censured the district as "The Unassimilated People," a ghetto of 80,000. The viewpoint of a native Chinese who came to America as a young adult is given by C. Y. Lee in his novel *The Flower Drum Song* (New York: Farrar, Straus & Cudahy, Inc., 1957).

ascend the slopes of Mt. Davidson and have views overlooking Lake Merced to the Pacific.

Newest districts in San Francisco, developed after World War II, are **Stonestown**, adjacent to Lake Merced on the San Mateo County line, and **Ingleside** to the east. The Stonestown shopping center is the single example within the city of the new suburban type with giant parking lots so characteristic of metropolitan Los Angeles. The skyscraper apartments of Park Merced were erected by the same company that developed Park La Brea in Los Angeles (Chapter 7). Here too is the new campus of San Francisco State College, whose extent contrasts with the former Western Addition site; to the east is City College of San Francisco.

ARMED FORCES

Military activities have always made a major contribution to the economy of San Francisco. In fact, the **Presidio**, established in 1776, is half a century older than the civilian community. Now it serves as command headquarters for the Sixth Army. This single installation, with one of the most inviting settings of any Army post in the nation, covers 1540 acres and has annual operating expenses in excess of $60 million, with approximately 17,000 military personnel and 3000 civilian employees. On its eastern edge is Letterman General Hospital and in the southwest, Marine Hospital. Not too distant is the large Veterans Administration hospital at Fort Miley, which overlooks Seal Rocks and the Pacific. East of the Presidio is 68-acre Fort Mason, at the western end of the Port of San Francisco, which provides an important military shipping point.

San Francisco is also the headquarters (in the Civic Center) of the Twelfth Naval District, which has a number of facilities scattered around the Bay Area. In southeastern San Francisco is the San Francisco Naval Shipyards at Hunters Point. Its dry docks, which date from 1868, were acquired by the Navy in 1939. These facilities, capable of handling the largest Naval vessels, had much importance during World War II. To the northwest the Marine Corps maintains a

Depot of Supplies. There is also the Naval Station on Treasure Island and Yerba Buena, with an adjacent Coast Guard Depot.

COMMERCE

MARITIME

Maritime commerce has been important to San Francisco since its founding; before establishment of Yerba Buena the Bay Area participated in the hide and tallow trade. Sheltered San Francisco Bay, naturally tide-scoured, also affords a water route into the Great Central Valley.

The **Port of San Francisco** extends from Fort Mason (northwest) to Hunters Point. Originally Yerba Buena Cove was a concave indentation, but the shoreline was smoothed through sea-wall construction and filling in of the enclosed lagoon. Dissatisfaction with waterfront speculators prompted the San Francisco electorate to yield port control to the state in 1863. Thus San Francisco has the nation's only important state-controlled waterfront. The Port Authority regulates forty-five piers, the intervening slips, concrete terminals and warehouses, and the Belt Line Railroad.

San Francisco's compact port, less spacious than that of Los Angeles, has suitable facilities for general cargo. Two areas are set aside for fishing vessels: (1) small boats that bring fresh fish to local markets from grounds off the Golden Gate tie up at Fisherman's Wharf (actually a small harbor between two wharves); (2) large purse seiners, which operate in Alaskan (summer) and South American (winter) waters, use China Basin in off-season. Foreign steamship lines and Sacramento river boats utilize odd-numbered piers north of the Ferry Building, whereas large American vessels (such as Matson liners) dock south of the Ferry Building. The state-owned refrigeration building near China Basin has facilities for transfer or storage of fresh fruits and vegetables. United Fruit lands bananas at China Basin, and nearby are lumber and cotton terminals. To the south San Francisco Naval Shipyard at Hunters Point has dry-dock facilities for large vessels. It had an important part in the Battle of the Pacific during World War II.

Facilities have been improved since the Grady-Carr report of 1934 (*The Port of San Francisco*) criticized the State Board's immobility and limited efforts to develop trade (in marked contrast to city-owned Port of Los Angeles). An outstanding addition was multimillion dollar Mission Rock Terminal, which opened in 1950.

San Francisco continues to rank among the leading West Coast ports, but its share of the commerce has sharply declined since World War I with expansion of Oakland, Stockton, Los Angeles–Long Beach, San Diego, Portland, and Seattle. In recent years San Francisco's foreign nonmilitary trade has approached $800 million annually. Leading exports include machinery and vehicles, cotton fiber, chemicals, animal products (especially powdered milk), metals, and grains. Major imports include vegetable products (bananas, coffee, copra), minerals (crude petroleum and metals), wood and paper, and foreign cars. Coastwise trade via Panama Canal and commerce with Hawaii is particularly important. Latin America and Oceania-East Asia are important import sources; east Asia (especially the Philippines, Korea, and Japan), northwestern Europe, and Australia are important export destinations.

Trans-Bay ferry service to the Ferry Building, whose volume once totaled 50 million passenger fares annually, was decimated after opening of the bay bridges, although service to Marin Peninsula was resumed in 1962. Rail freight by barge continues to be important between San Francisco and East Bay; Santa Fe, Southern Pacific, and Western Pacific railroads all maintain yards and wharves around China Basin.

RAILROAD

San Francisco's rail facilities are somewhat akin to those of Manhattan, with Oakland's position analogous to that of Jersey City. The original Central Pacific line from the east had its terminus in Oakland. Terminals of the Santa Fe and Western Pacific are also located

in East Bay. The Southern Pacific has maintained ferry service across the bay since 1861; its freight cars also cross the south bay via Dumbarton rail bridge. San Francisco acquired its single "main line" when the San Francisco and San Jose Railroad commenced service in 1864. This line was acquired by the Central (Southern) Pacific in 1868 and was eventually completed to Los Angeles as the Coast Line in 1901. Yard and terminal space is a problem in congested San Francisco; even the Southern Pacific has its facilities in Bayshore (northeastern San Mateo County), and the Santa Fe is in Richmond. The state-owned Belt Line Railroad provides service along the waterfront.

HIGHWAY

San Francisco highway travel benefits from the small size of the city, since only a single freeway (U.S. 101) enters the city from the south (in 1963); it merges with The Skyway, which carries the joint designation U.S. 40 and 50 as it leads to the Bay Bridge and Oakland. The Central Freeway, by which U.S. 101 was to link with California 1 at the Golden Gate Bridge, has never been completed. Opening of the bridges, the Oakland Bay in 1936 and the Golden Gate in 1937, much improved traffic through the city. Both bridges have received hundreds of millions of fares since their opening. The Bay Bridge has two levels; alterations effected in 1962 permit one-way traffic on each level.

San Francisco tends to be a terminal point for highway travel because of its size and location. Approximately 100 truck lines operate into San Francisco, but because of shortage of space there has been a tendency to locate terminals in East Bay.

MANUFACTURING

San Francisco was California's leading industrial center for three quarters of a century after the Gold Rush. As late as 1900 half of the state's industrial output was fabricated in San Francisco; it was not until the middle-1920's that Los Angeles became the state leader.

Whereas San Francisco tended to retain its national position (ninth or tenth) between 1919 and 1958, with a fivefold increase in value added by manufacturing, Los Angeles climbed from nineteenth position to third, with more than a thirtyfold increase in value added.

San Francisco manufacturing has diversity, but it cannot compare with Chicago or Los Angeles; it tends to be strongly oriented toward local markets (foods, clothing, metals). Foodstuffs are processed from imported raw materials (cacao, copra, coffee, and sugar) or California produce especially from the Great Central Valley (beef, fruits, vegetables, dairy products, beer, and soft drinks). San Francisco proper lacks the significance of Los Angeles in electronics, missiles, motion pictures, and automobile assembly—land was not available for plants within the city. There are scores of clothing firms, although output ranks well below Los Angeles. Men's clothing and ladies' coats and suits are significant; San Francisco has been gaining moment as a style center for winter attire (in contrast to the sports apparel of Los Angeles).

Manufacturing is almost wholly restricted to the two southeastern districts, Potrero and Bay View, with maritime and land transportation facilities. Industrial expansion is hampered by limited level terrain, congestion, high land values, and limited railroad frontage. Industrial expansion in the Bay Area since World War II has tended to occur almost wholly outside of the city limits. Even earlier, smelters, powdermakers, steel mills, and meat-packing plants had been forced to locate elsewhere. San Francisco firms have tended to establish new plants elsewhere but maintain offices and warehouse facilities in the city.

The harbor has encouraged "port manufacturing." Working of iron and steel has been conducted since the Gold Rush; the first machine shop was erected in 1849. Early locomotives and river boats were built in San Francisco. The old Union Iron Works, a pioneer firm, was absorbed by Bethlehem Steel in 1907, whereas Western Sugar had established its first San Francisco refinery in 1861.

PROSPECTS

One ponders the future of the dowager-mistress of the Pacific Coast. Sizable population expansion seems unlikely—already the density in San Francisco is among the nation's highest. Its population was exceeded nearly half a century ago by Los Angeles—presumably San Diego, Sacramento, San Jose, and even Fremont may become larger. Perhaps the San Franciscan can savor the prospects that his city cannot become the world's largest. Assuredly the residential appeal of the city cannot be denied. There remains the impelling urgency for more coordination between San Francisco and other Bay Area communities. With wise solution of its many urban problems, the location of San Francisco suggests that it should remain the cultural and financial center of central California.

THE EAST BAY

The East Bay or "Contra Costa," the coast "opposite" San Francisco, has had a subsidiary role to San Francisco since the founding of the Presidio. Since World War II, however, it has exceeded San Francisco in population. The East Bay is considerably larger with more flattish terrain; hence it was natural, especially after construction of the Oakland Bay Bridge, that much Bay Area population increase should take place here (map, Fig. 8-28).

Like San Francisco, the East Bay has coast-range topography. It extends from Antioch at the western edge of the Delta Lands (Chapter 9) westward and southward to Milpitas (Coyote Creek estuary). The East Bay is almost synonymous in extent with Alameda and Contra Costa counties. The most intensively utilized portions of the area are the edges of the tidal flats that flank the east shore of San Francisco Bay. The increasingly urbanized "back country" consists of the northern end of the Diablo Range with its intermont basins. The Diablo Range splits at its northern end

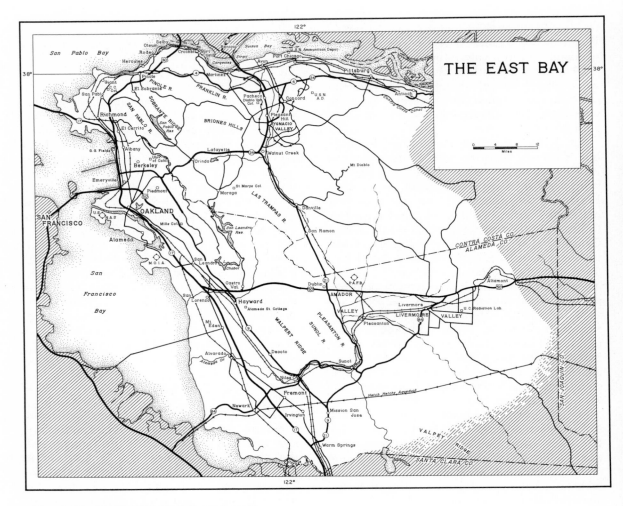

Fig. 8-28. MAP OF THE EAST BAY.

into the Berkeley-Oakland Hills (known to the south as Sunol Ridge) as the western prong and with Mt. Diablo as the high point of the eastern prong.

As the East Bay has developed into an urban complex of over a million people its individual communities have tended to coalesce, whereas its economic functions have become increasingly elaborate. They include residence, industry, commerce, retail and wholesale trade, higher education, mining, recreation, and agriculture. Agriculture, long a mainstay, has had declining significance with urban growth; in this respect the situa-

tion resembles outlying portions of metropolitan Los Angeles.

THE SETTING

In some respects the East Bay is physically more attractive than San Francisco. The climate has greater extremes with slightly warmer afternoons and cooler nights than San Francisco—it is frequently clear in East Bay when San Francisco is fog-shrouded.

Level topography is more extensive in the East Bay despite the Berkeley-Oakland Hills. The mudflats along the east side of the Bay, which made access difficult, were perhaps one reason for original establishment of San Francisco. Although the margins of the Bay were covered with tule marshes, much of the plain was grass-covered, with some groves of live oaks and floodplain forests of sycamore, willow, and oak along watercourses. The Oakland Hills had extensive redwood forests, of which vestiges remain.

SETTLEMENT

The Mission fathers found the East Bay attractive although the Spanish had ignored it for a generation after the founding of Mission San Francisco. Mission San Jose, established in 1797, became one of the more flourishing missions. Ecclesiastically, San Jose was successful; more baptisms were recorded here than at any other mission. An earthquake almost destroyed it in 1868, and the remains have never acquired the appeal of other missions.

Almost the entire East Bay was included in Mexican land grants—more than twenty ranchos were created prior to 1847. The single grant made during the Spanish era was the great Rancho San Antonio, awarded Luis Peralta in 1820; it included the land upon which the cities of Alameda, Oakland, and Berkeley have been built. By the close of the Mexican period Rancho San Antonio was one of the showplaces of Alta California. The East Bay contained some of the choicest grazing lands of the province. A single rancho, San Ramon, maintained as many as 14,000 cattle, 4000 sheep, and 400 horses.

Most East Bay lands passed rather quickly from Mexican to American ownership. Some choice properties, including Rancho San Antonio, were occupied by squatters. Although court litigation over this property continued into the 1880's, the Peralta family retained almost nothing from their holding. A few fared better by selling land, such as the owners of Valle de San Jose around the present community of Sunol. The Estudillos, owners of Rancho San Leandro, eventually took their case to the United States Supreme Court where Wiliam H. Davis, son-in-law of grantee José Estudillo, succeeded in ordering the squatters to pay for their land. Because of proximity to San Francisco markets, the East Bay agriculture went through cycles of cattle, grain, and sheep into specialized agriculture more quickly than most of Mexican California.

Towns appeared early in the East Bay. Antioch, Alameda, Hayward, Martinez, Niles, Oakland, Pacheco, and San Leandro were established in the first decade of statehood. Essentially these were farming communities, whose earlier settlers included many disgruntled gold seekers. Oakland was established in 1850 by squatters on Rancho San Antonio. Livermore and Pleasanton were platted later along the Central Pacific right-of-way.

GROWTH

Oakland served as the nucleus for population expansion in the East Bay. It did not grow rapidly, however, until the opening of the Central Pacific route in 1869; in fact, for many years thereafter it lacked deep-water harbor facilities. Throughout the nineteenth century the stranglehold that early settler Horace Carpentier, an ally of the "Big Four," held on the waterfront retarded growth. Hence the city remained principally residential. As late as 1900 Oakland was scarcely a seventh as large as San Francisco. The East Bay was not ravaged by fire after the earthquake of 1906, and thousands from San Francisco relocated across the Bay. There were other factors too that encouraged growth. Oakland had acquired a deeper dredged port in 1898, and the entry of the Santa Fe into the Bay Area in 1900 eliminated the rail monopoly of the Southern Pacific. Industrial development was a significant growth factor. A forerunner of the Pacific Gas and Electric began delivering electricity from hydroelectric plants in the Sierra Nevada, and the Standard Oil Company began construction of its refinery in the new town of Richmond in 1902. The population of Oakland trebled during the first decade of the twentieth century; Berkeley and Alameda also grew considerably.

The less foggy atmosphere of East Bay appeals to many people who consider San Francisco too windy and cold. The increasing congestion within San Francisco and high living costs have also encouraged many to settle along the eastern shore. An important development around 1900 that promoted such growth was the establishment by Francis M. ("Borax") Smith and his associates of the $200 million United Properties. This group developed street railways of East Bay into one system and created the Key System, suggestive of the Pacific Electric in the Los Angeles Lowlands (Chapter 7). It also succeeded in breaking the Southern Pacific's passenger ferry monopoly on the Bay, improved the Oakland waterfront, and developed a municipal water system. Smith's organization, although it overexpanded and became insolvent in 1913, attracted industry as well as people to the East Bay.

Industrial development in the East Bay was stimulated by such factors as the opening of Panama Canal, railroad facilities, land scarcity in San Francisco, agricultural expansion in the Great Central Valley, and the two World Wars. The Pacific theater in World War II was a tremendous factor in stimulating industrial development and population growth.

INDUSTRY

The East Bay manufacturing has developed more recently and is more diversified than that in San Francisco. It includes food processing (fruits, vegetables, flour, cereals, meats, dairy products) and allied industries (glass, paper, and tin-plate containers), auto assembly, shipbuilding and repair, steel fabrication, sugar and petroleum processing, chemicals, and machinery.

Industrial plants have tended to locate along railroad lines, deep-water facilities, and through highways. Increasingly, location is influenced by planning agencies. Availability of thousands of acres became a permissive factor as San Francisco became congested. The East Bay shipbuilding, originating in Alameda in 1902, was enhanced by military demands during both world wars. Population growth within California and availability of fuel and electricity as well as a large labor pool have been significant factors in recent years.

Oakland, Berkeley, Emeryville, Alameda, and Richmond have been the older centers of manufacturing. Since 1950 agricultural lands along rail lines and California 17 south of San Leandro have been converted to industrial usage; considerable expansion has also taken place in Richmond and elsewhere in Contra Costa County.

COMMERCE

Favorable transportation facilities, rail, highway, maritime, and air, have contributed to the economic growth of the East Bay (Fig. 8-29). The area tends to be physically isolated because of water on the west and north and the Coast Ranges to the east; these handicaps have been rather successfully modified.

Three trunk railroads serve the East Bay: Southern Pacific, Santa Fe, and Western Pacific (and its subsidiary the Sacramento Northern). Lines follow three principal corridors from the Great Central Valley. Tracks of the Santa Fe and the Southern Pacific follow the shores of Suisun and San Pablo Bays, whereas the Sacramento Northern utilizes a route through Walnut Creek and Moraga. Western Pacific and Southern Pacific follow a southern course through Altamont Pass, Livermore Valley, and Niles Canyon. An interlacing of trackage covers the lowland that forms the great urban complex of the East Bay; moles and piers project prominently into the bay at Richmond, Oakland, and Alameda to facilitate freight transfer between the East Bay and San Francisco. The Dumbarton and Benicia rail bridges cross the ends of the bay. The ease of auto travel across the Oakland Bay Bridge has forced abandonment of the Key System commuter trains, but function of the East Bay as an important residence for San Francisco workers continues.

The extensively developed Oakland waterfront and the Contra Costa shore from Richmond northward afford the principal centers for sea-borne commerce. Along much of the shallow shore, tidal flats have long been used for disposal of industrial wastes and sewage.

Oakland has over 20 miles of waterfront, two thirds of which is city owned. The harbor has three segments, Outer, Middle, and Inner. Outer Harbor, immediately south of the Oakland Bay Bridge, is flanked by facilities of the Oakland Army Depot. Middle Harbor, with bordering railroad moles (Southern Pacific to north, Western Pacific to south), is bordered by the piers and warehouses of the vast Naval Supply Depot, completed in 1942 at a cost of $15 million. The attenuated Inner Harbor contains most of the civilian facilities, with principal piers at Market Street, Grove Street, and Ninth Avenue. Alameda shares this waterway with Oakland. Oakland's maritime commerce is essentially cargo; San Francisco handles the bulk of the passenger trade.

Oakland's maritime development was long delayed by politics and litigation after Henry Carpentier acquired 37-year exclusive rights to harbor development in 1852. It finally required a Circuit Court decision in 1907 to give the city control and permit other railroads than the Southern Pacific to use the waterfront. A city Board of Harbor Commerce was finally established in 1927. Because of the longtime Southern Pacific waterfront domination, Oakland once suffered from poor railroad coordination. This problem has been corrected since the arrival of the Santa Fe.

Berkeley, despite its industrial moment, lacks maritime commerce largely because of an offshore shoal. A yacht harbor was developed in the 1930's and its municipal pier has been used for sports fishing. Despite much opposition, plans have been made to fill in the Bay shallows and sell the land for industrial use.

Richmond has a 7.5-mile waterfront, with both inner and outer harbors. Almost half of the waterfront is privately controlled, and the remainder is city or state owned. Private facilities include the Parr-Richmond Terminal and Standard Oil Company facilities. A protective seawall is secured to Brooks Island on the east. Numerous dockside facilities continue northward along the "Oil Coast" such as those of the Selby smelter and the California and Hawaiian sugar mill at Crockett.

The East Bay has only a single major commercial airfield, Oakland Municipal Airport located on Bay Farm Island south of Alameda. There is helicopter service between this field, the Ferry Building, and San Francisco Inter-national Airport. Oakland lacks the multitude of flight schedules of Los Angeles or even those of San Francisco.

Highway facilities have changed vastly since the days of the old Spanish trail that joined the East Bay ranchos with Mission San Jose southward to Mission Santa Clara. Construction of bridges, tunnels, tubes, and freeways has given the East Bay an excellent highway network. Five transbay bridges—Carquinez (1927), San Rafael, Oakland Bay, San Mateo (1929), and Dumbarton (1927)—connect East Bay communities with other parts of the Bay Area. The opening of San Rafael Bridge in 1956 eliminated a serious bottleneck and virtually marked the end of passenger ferries on the bay. Another ferry was eliminated with opening of the Martinez-Benicia Bridge in 1962. There has long been recognition of need of another bridge or a tunnel to reduce congestion on the heavily traveled Oakland Bay Bridge.

Tubes and tunnels have likewise eased and hastened traffic flow. Posey Tube between Alameda and Oakland was opened in 1928; during rush hours traffic jams have been commonplace. A second tube was added in 1963. The Broadway Tunnel (California 24), opened in 1937, facilitated suburban growth into intermontane basins of eastern Contra Costa County after World War II.

Much freeway development has taken place since 1947. By late 1958, Eastshore Freeway, extending the length of the East Bay from the Santa Clara Valley (and carrying designation of California 17 south of Oakland and U.S. 40 northward) and U.S. 50 eastward into the San Joaquin Valley had achieved completion. Downtown Oakland has been bypassed by means of a skyway (elevated) structure. Completion of U.S. 50 as an east-west freeway within Oakland limits did not materialize as rapidly.

CITIES

The communities between Richmond and Niles have grown and merged into a single conurbation sometimes called the "Metropolitan Oakland Area" (map, Fig. 8-28). Now urbanization is extending southward and northward—northward into the Oil Coast, south-ward into South Bay (northern Santa Clara Valley). Individual corporate communities vary somewhat in function from wholly industrial to purely residential. However, there is a tendency for railroads, docks, and industrial plants to be located near the Bay shore; then older housing areas and "downtown" retail centers; and finally, increasingly newer and more spacious housing upslope into the Berkeley-Oakland Hills and beyond into the intermont basins.

Richmond (72,000) is not one of the "original" East Bay communities; it was founded as **Santa Fe**, a village that developed around the western terminus of the Santa Fe Railroad established at Point Richmond in 1897. Richmond itself appeared slightly to the northeast in 1900. Its industrial future was assured almost from its founding; in 1902 the Standard Oil Company began construction of its great refinery and in 1912 dredging of the harbor commenced. As late as 1940 Richmond had a population of 22,000; besides Standard Oil and Ford Motor Company's assembly plant (now relocated at Milpitas), there were sixty industrial firms, as well as truck gardens and greenhouses. Perhaps no city in California was more affected by World War II; Richmond was called "California's War Baby"—the community expanded chaotically after Henry Kaiser opened great shipyards operating twenty-four hours per day. For a time public schools operated on triple sessions. The shipbuilding proved temporary, but many of the people remained in the temporary war housing; the 1950 population exceeded 99,000. After 17,000 temporary units were removed in the early 1950's, thousands left Richmond; subsequently the city has stabilized economically. In recent years, because of volume of oil shipments, Richmond has sometimes ranked third among California ports in cargo tonnage. It is also the site of Contra Costa College and has county administrative offices. Besides its industrial growth, Richmond has much importance in warehousing and wholesale trade.

El Cerrito (25,000), another younger East Bay city, was founded in 1909 as a suburban residential community. There is some manu-facturing but El Cerrito remains essentially a "bedroom." Industrial growth in Richmond and other nearby communities quickened the growth of El Cerrito after 1950; it now coalesces with Richmond.

Albany (15,000), like Richmond and El Cerrito, was founded in this century; like El Cerrito, it is basically residential. Along its western periphery is Golden Gate Fields (horse racing) and nearby the Western Regional Research Laboratory of the U.S. Department of Agriculture.

Berkeley (111,000) and the University of California are synonyms in the minds of many people. The city began with establishment of the university campus in 1866. It is California's eleventh largest community and gained many residents following the San Francisco fire and during World War II—vacant land is virtually nonexistent. Berkeley is a more complex community than many people realize. Its eastern section, around the campus and ascending the slopes of the Berkeley Hills, is academic, sophisticated, and residential. Here are many fine old homes, lovely gardens, and impressive views; around the campus apartment houses are now replacing some larger homes. The compact business district along Shattuck Avenue reflects the fact that Berkeley is a satellite of San Francisco and Oakland. The central portion of the community between Shattuck (east) and San Pablo avenues contains modest dwellings, often occupied by workers in factories of Berkeley or neighboring cities. Since 1940 there has been a significant increase in Negro population, which now exceeds 25 percent of the total population. Western Berkeley, along the railroad tracks and east of Eastshore Freeway, is an industrial area with food products, soap, and pharmaceuticals important.

The University of California is one of the world's great universities. The initial Berkeley campus (the university was originally in Oakland) occupies 720 acres that nestle against the Berkeley Hills. The university is world renowned for its faculty and for the caliber of its academic accomplishments. The beautifully landscaped grounds are covered with buildings of concrete or light granite, above which the Campanile (Sather Tower) rises

Fig. 8-29. *TRUCK TERMINAL AND THE EASTSHORE FREEWAY (U.S. 40). San Francisco congestion favors location of surface transportation facilities, such as truck depots, in the East Bay. This terminal has a 110-door dock to handle incoming and outgoing freight.* (Pacific Intermontane Express)

Fig. 8-30. *OAKLAND. Lake Merritt and Peralta Park (foreground) with the central district in the middle of photo and west Oakland beyond. Alameda (middle left), then Inner Harbor, Naval Supply Depot and Middle Harbor, and Outer Harbor (to left of Bay Bridge). Note path of the Nimitz Freeway (Route 17).* (Oakland Chamber of Commerce, photo by R. L. Copeland)

307 feet. Outstanding buildings include Doe Library, the Life Sciences building, Memorial Stadium, International House, and the Cyclatron. The Lawrence Radiation Laboratory on the slopes east of the campus has been one of the nation's principal centers of nuclear research. Recently skyscraper dormitories have been erected—a reflection of increasing shortage of space. Less-known Berkeley academic institutions include Armstrong College (business), several divinity schools, and state institutions for physically handicapped students.

Emeryville (2700), like Vernon in metropolitan Los Angeles (Chapter 7), is almost exclusively an industrial community, compressed along the Bayshore railroad tracks between Oakland and Berkeley. It was established around 1900 when San Francisco racetrack operators and meat-packers sought a new location. For a while railroad maps labeled it "Stockyards." The abolition of horse racing in 1911 resulted in industrial use of the racetrack site. In 1928 the local district attorney suggested that it was perhaps the most corrupt community in the United States. Draw poker, permitted by local option, is still conducted in six clubs. This heavily industrialized town contains more than a hundred factories, but has no churches or cemeteries and few

trees. Some senior citizens reside there because of its low tax rate. The population has been stagnant for decades. The East Bay's oldest steelmaker, Judson Steel, has operated in Emeryville since 1882.

The founders of **Oakland** (368,000), California's fourth largest city, selected their site well. It was established in 1850 beside San Antonio Slough (directly east of San Francisco—the slough has become Oakland harbor with a waterfront extending for more than 20 miles). Today Oakland encompasses a larger area than San Francisco and is one of the great industrial and commercial centers of the West (Fig. 8-30). It is the metropolis of the East Bay and ranks second to San Francisco as an industrial center in the Bay Area. Other important functions include commerce and retail and wholesale trade (and residence of course).

Downtown Oakland, focusing upon 12th and Broadway, is small for the municipal population—it lacks the professional and corporate offices that would be anticipated in a city of its size. An exception is Kaiser Center, the largest office building in western America. Unlike Los Angeles, Oakland does not have the numerous suburban shopping centers. This reflects the scope of specialty shopping that

THE CENTRAL COAST : : 323

takes place in downtown San Francisco. Also Oakland did not have the "empty" land for such extensive developments after World War II.[21]

Lake Merritt and surrounding Peralta (Lakeside) Park east of the downtown district suggests New York's Central Park, especially with its surrounding blocks of apartments. Oakland's Civic Center flanks the lake along its western periphery.

Older Oakland, the western districts toward the waterfront, has deteriorated into much substandard housing. Rows of dingy, poorly maintained homes, including many Victorian relics, occupy this part of the metropolis. Here is Oakland's "Harlem"; the city's large Negro population had its beginnings with porters and waiters on the railroads. Later their numbers were swollen by "Southern refugees" attracted by the high wages of World War II. Oakland has a highly heterogeneous population, like many port cities. However, individual districts have been less well defined than those of San Francisco. Mexicans, Chinese, Portuguese, and Italians are well-represented "ethnic" groups.

Oakland does have attractive residential districts, particularly in the eastern portion of the city, extending back into the Oakland Hills. Street patterns, conforming to the hilly terrain, are as perplexing as in any American municipality. Behind these more attractive residential quarters are the regional hillside parks, Roundtop, Redwood, and Joaquin Miller, suggestive of Griffith Park in Los Angeles. A new campus of Oakland City College was planned here. Northeastern Oakland includes the exclusive housing of the Claremont district. The rambling Claremont Hotel, a Victorian legacy, has long been a social landmark. Mills College, perhaps the best-known women's college in the West, is in southeastern Oakland.

21 Oakland, like San Francisco, Berkeley, and Alameda, has "reached its limits"; with destruction of houses (for freeways, etc.) since 1950 the population has declined. Oakland is now forced to use its third dimension, height (i.e., apartment houses).

Industrial Oakland flanks the waterfront and the railroad sidings. As in San Francisco, there has been considerable filling of the marshy Bayshore. Port-type manufacturing is important, including shipbuilding and repair. There is considerable food processing with many of the "raw materials" transported by truck from the Great Central Valley. The city has been a leading producer of calculating machines and also one of the important automobile assembly centers of the state. Other industries include furniture, paint, machinery, and chemicals. The important military installations, the Army and Navy depots, were noted in the section on the East Bay commerce.

Piedmont (11,000), an independent residential enclave surrounded by Oakland, is the East Bay's equivalent of San Marino or Beverly Hills (Chapter 7). This exclusive hillside community evolved at the turn of this century surrounding the resort spa, Piedmont Springs Hotel.

Alameda (61,000), a one-time orchard and garden town, is one of the oldest cities of the East Bay. Promoters sold many lots to ex-gold seekers in the early 1850's. In the 1870's significant numbers of San Francisco commuters settled in Alameda, and it was long a favorite Bay Area beach resort. Shipbuilding commenced around 1900; during World War I additional industry developed along the south side of Oakland Inner Harbor. During World War II Alameda was again a major shipbuilding center, with almost as much of a housing shortage as Richmond. The northern end of the island was converted into Alameda Naval Air Station. Although Alameda has many residents, it is now chiefly an industrial city.

San Leandro (66,000) like Alameda was founded in the 1850's and has likewise been a fertile garden spot. Through the 1930's the city remained a peaceful farm village with greenhouses, acres of flowers, fruit, truck crops, and dairy farms. Its residents included many Japanese and Portuguese. It was the leading center in the East Bay for cut flowers and nursery stock. Even before World War II Caterpillar and Chevrolet assembly plants had been erected. During the 1940's a tremendous

Fig. 8-31. FREMONT AND THE EAST BAY. Aerial view northward with Walpert Ridge, then Oakland and Berkeley Hills in the upper right. Fremont, an incorporation of Warm Springs (foreground), Irvington (center), Mission San Jose district (right middle), and Niles (at western entrance to the rail corridor eastward into the Central Valley). Hayward, San Leandro, Alameda, Oakland, and other East Bay cities are in the middle rear. (Fremont Chamber of Commerce, photo by Air-Photo Co. of Palo Alto)

housing construction took place, and the population doubled. Scores of factories (data processing, communications, paper, chemicals, etc.) have replaced farmsteads and rows of tract houses have been built. More expensive residences dot the San Leandro Hills, a continuation of the Berkeley-Oakland hills.

Hayward (73,000) began as a way point on the road (now U.S. 50) eastward across Altamont Pass to the gold fields in the 1850's. Later it became a farm village, and through the World War II years it was surrounded by fruit orchards, apricots and cherries, truck farms (spinach, peas, and tomatoes), dairies, and

poultry farms. Soon after the war urbanization of the East Bay overtook Hayward so that its 1940 population of 6547 has grown rapidly. Rows of tract houses and industrial plants have replaced the former farm lands. Hayward is the site of relatively new Alameda State College. Adjacent **Castro Valley** (37,000), **San Lorenzo** (24,000), and **Union City** (6600) are all experiencing suburban growth.

South of Hayward there is still much farmland—in 1961 Alameda County still had a farm production valued at over $31 million, principally from cut flowers, nursery stock, fresh milk, poultry, and truck crops. Urbanization

THE CENTRAL COAST : : 325

Fig. 8-32. SOUTH END OF THE OIL COAST. This view includes the Standard Oil refinery at Richmond (in the foreground), the San Rafael Bridge, and Mt. Tamalpais and the Marin Peninsula beyond the Bay. (Standard Oil Company of California)

is rapidly proceeding southward (Fig. 8-31). **Niles**, known as Vallejo Mills in the 1850's, remains relatively small despite its steel mill. However, urbanization has already commenced. **Fremont** (44,000), is a late amalgamation of a group of hamlets in southern Alameda County, encompassing more land within its political limits than any California city except Los Angeles. Urbanization has commenced; it seems inevitable that Fremont will become one of the larger cities in the West. The evaporation of salt from the waters of the Bay, a longtime activity at **Newark**, will quite likely prove ephemeral as land values rise. Industrialization is taking place. Ford Motor Company has an assembly plant at **Milpitas** (6700), and General Motors has more recently established assembly facilities in **Warm Springs**. These communities are situated in the border zone between the East Bay and South Bay.

THE OIL COAST

The northward extension of the East Bay along the shores of San Pablo and Suisun bays

has been called "the Oil Coast" (map, Fig. 8-28). The Bay lowland is replaced by spurs of the Diablo Range (such as Pinole and Franklin ridges), sometimes rising immediately from the edge of San Pablo and Suisun bays. Northeastward from Richmond to Antioch are a series of industrial communities, paralleling the shore and the rail lines, where "port-type" manufacturing is especially prominent. Construction of the Contra Costa Canal (see Central Valley Project, Chapter 9) added industrial water supply to other advantages for manufacturing plants. The rolling uplands are still used for grains and beef, although tract housing is moving into the area. Slopes have also been used for the "tank farms" of the great petroleum refineries. There are a number of other products, including steel, chemicals, containers, powder, and sugar.

The Oil Coast is one of California's two major petroleum-refining centers; Standard (at Richmond), Union (at Oleum), Shell (at Martinez), and Associated (at Avon) maintain refineries here (Fig. 8-32). This coast has been favored because of past isolation from urban concentration, deep-water facilities, ease of extending pipelines from the southern San Joaquin Valley and availability of sizable markets in the Bay Area and elsewhere in central California.

Smelting and explosives represented the earliest major industries established here. Two of California's major producers of powder and explosives maintained plants at once isolated spots along this coast for three quarters of a century; however, production at Giant has been suspended. Early operation in San Francisco had been related to the needs of the gold and silver camps and then railroad construction. Market areas now extend far beyond California. Atlas Powder, which had produced California's first dynamite in 1867, relocated at Giant in 1880 (the firm was then known as Giant Powder). A year later Hercules Powder Company established its plant at Hercules. Both firms had decentralized underground magazines, and facilities covered many hundreds of acres. Selby Smelter abandoned San Francisco in 1884 because of objections to air pollution caused by its operations. There was longtime collaboration between its cartridge factory and Benicia Arsenal. Its successor, American Smelting and Refining, processes such metals as gold, silver, antimony, and lead; company docks permit the unloading of ore boats.

One finds it hard to believe that now somnolent **Port Costa** in the late nineteenth century was one of the world's great wheat exporting centers. The "Port Costa Strip," favored by rail facilities, depth of water (averaging 30 feet at wharfside at low tide), and the Golden Gate outlet, extended for 4 miles; it served as the chief grain port of central California. In the middle 1880's, half of all the wheat ships sailing from the Bay loaded at the great warehouses, some built on pilings over water.

As elsewhere in the Bay area, canning of fish, fruits, and vegetables has significance along the Oil Coast; however, this area has never achieved the importance of either San Francisco or Oakland. A longtime landmark of this coast has been C. and H. (California and Hawaiian) sugar refinery at Crockett,

which has operated since 1897 in a former flour mill on Carquinez Strait. It is the world's largest cane-sugar refinery and one of two on the U.S. Pacific Coast; it was established by Hawaiian growers to provide easier access to continental markets. Raw sugar is transported from Hawaii in bulk (i.e., unbagged) form, thus reducing shipping costs.

The towns of the Oil Coast tend to be old communities; some were supply points en route to the gold fields and others were farm villages. Several were established as company towns. Since 1950 some have fused into a single agglomeration, a pattern characteristic of the East Bay farther south; however, interposition of large industrial firms makes conurbation difficult.

Martinez (9600), seat of Contra Costa County, was laid out in 1849. It has served as a bifurcation point for the Southern Pacific (junction of Valley and Shasta routes), has long been an industrial center, and serves as a service center for a considerable portion of northern Contra Costa County.

Port Chicago (1700) relies principally upon its Naval Magazine. **Pittsburg** (19,000), established hopefully as the "New York of the Pacific" in 1849, was intended to become California's leading seaport. For a time it was the outlet for Mt. Diablo coal mining. More recently its industrial growth has been much influenced by its Columbia Steel (affiliate of U.S. Steel) mill. Cold pig iron is shipped by rail from Geneva Steel in Utah and reheated at Pittsburg. Tin plate and structural steel are important products of the mill, largest in central California. Other industrial activity includes chemicals.

Antioch (17,000), a landing established during the Gold Rush, lies on the western border of the Delta Lands (Chapter 9). The city has been favored in recent years for industrial growth because of abundant flat land (in addition to such other advantages as tidewater location, water supply, fuel availability, etc.). Its diversified manufacturing includes paper, chemicals, machinery, and furniture, and it is a major center for generation of electric energy.

THE INTERMONT BASINS

A cluster of small intermontane basins between the Berkeley-Oakland Hills (west) and the Mt. Diablo prong of the Diablo Range (map, Fig. 8-28) forms the Bay Area counterpart of the San Fernando Valley in the Los Angeles Lowlands (Chapter 7). This "back country," despite warmer summers and colder winters, is not plagued by the summer fog of the Bay strand. Farming constituted the principal land-use from the days of Mexican ranchos. More recently, especially since opening of the Broadway Tunnel (on California 24), and with highway improvement, the urbanization that has characterized other fringes of the Bay Area has overtaken these little valleys.

AMADOR VALLEY

Large herds of Mexican cattle once roamed the floor of Amador Valley, along U.S. 50 east of the Oakland Hills beyond Hayward. Rancho land was sold to ex-gold miners and Irish immigrants in the 1850's. The valley was long a producer of dairy products and beef; vegetables became important after 1900—pump-well irrigation has been practiced since 1910. **Dublin**, a small "four corners" village, grew slightly until recent urbanization commenced. Eventual residential engulfment seems probable.

LIVERMORE VALLEY

An imperceptible divide separates the Livermore Valley from the Amador to the west. The final decision of the Secretary of the Interior regarding Mexican rancho boundaries made much acreage here available for preemption after 1871; grains (first wheat, later barley) long had moment. Vineyards became important in the 1880's as 4000 acres were planted in four years. Half a dozen larger wineries have long been known for their quality output, with white (including Sauvignon and Semillon) and red (including Carignane and Zinfandel) varieties. Sugar beets and dairying have also been important.

Pleasanton (4200), founded in 1867, has long been a local trading point with wineries. **Livermore** (16,000) likewise remained a slow-growing stable village for decades; it was only slightly larger in 1940 than it had been in 1900. It was a typical western "cow town" with a June rodeo. In the 1950's the eastward expansion of urbanization from East Bay caught the town in its surge. Agricultural lands have been replaced by housing tracts; numerous residents commute via freeway to employment in larger East Bay cities. Growth has also been promoted by local employment at Parks Air Force Base and the University of California Radiation Laboratory.

SAN RAMON VALLEY

The attenuated San Ramon Valley lies north of Amador Valley at the base of Mt. Diablo. Here orchards and walnut groves replaced beef and grain of earlier years. After 1950 the little village of **Danville** (3600) began growing; its orchards are being replaced by housing tracts.

MORAGA VALLEY

The Moraga Valley, between Oakland and the San Ramon Valley, was named for the ranchero who settled here in 1835. The Valley is a preferred residential setting and the site of St. Mary's College, which evolved from a tiny school held in the basement of St. Mary's Church in San Francisco in 1855; the college is under the auspices of the Brothers of Christian Schools. In the early 1960's, deciduous fruit orchards survived near the college. To the northwest, the eastern slopes of the Oakland Hills suggest Sherman Oaks, nestled in the northern slopes of the Santa Monica Mountains—although the oaks of this area afford a richer natural setting than the chaparral of Southern California. **Orinda** (4700), bisected by California 24, is especially attractive.

YGNACIO VALLEY

Ygnacio Valley is the largest of the intermont basins in the East Bay back country. Well served by railroads (Southern Pacific, Sacramento Northern, and Santa Fe), it has long been the most populous of these valleys. As early as the 1850's grains replaced beef cattle, and oaks were cut for timber, coal mine props, charcoal, and household fuel. During the wheat era **Pacheco** served as a shipping point. Fruits (pears, apricots, prunes, and peaches) had significance from the 1880's, and there were also extensive vineyards before Prohibition. Some vineyards were replaced by walnut groves with Walnut Creek as an important processing center—walnuts were brought from all over central California. The high water table was markedly lowered by intensive pump irrigation, which commenced in the 1920's. More recently Central Valley water has been brought by the Contra Costa Canal. Opening of the Broadway Tunnel and subsequent improvement of California 24 made the valley accessible to Oakland and other bayshore cities. There has been much suburban growth since 1946; California 24 has become a semifreeway.

Concord, Walnut Creek, and Pleasant Hill form the principal communities. All three were peaceful farm villages before the population spillover from the bayshore cities. Large shopping centers and blocks of tract housing have appeared. **Concord** (36,000), major city of eastern Contra Costa County, is chiefly a residential community despite its light manufacturing. Many of its inhabitants are employed in the large industrial plants along Suisun Bay. Adjacent **Pleasant Hill** (24,000) grew dramatically during the 1950's. It is the site of Mt. Diablo College. **Walnut Creek** (9900), like **Lafayette** (7000) farther west on California 24, houses many commuters to employment west of the Berkeley-Oakland Hills.

THE PENINSULA

One may well ask, "When is a peninsula not a peninsula?" Residents of the Bay Area do not consider the city of San Francisco part of the Peninsula, nor do they really include most of the Santa Cruz Mountains and the Pacific shore. In the sense that it is accepted here the Peninsula tends to have its western margin at Skyline Boulevard (map, Fig. 8-33). The Peninsula has long conjured various meanings. It has been associated with millionaires' estates and with San Francisco business executives commuting to gracious suburban homes. For

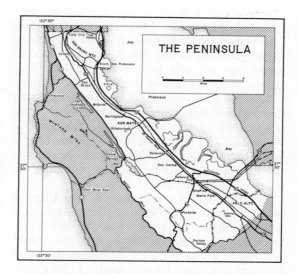

Fig. 8-33. MAP OF THE PENINSULA.

this has been the West Coast counterpart of New York's Westchester County, and it extends from South San Francisco to Palo Alto along the eastside of the entire Peninsula. To these almost hoary images one must now add miles of tract housing, diversified industry, and the whir of traffic along Bayshore Freeway, successor locally to El Camino Real, which became U.S. 101, as the major north-south artery.

Climate, in combination with the backdrop of the Santa Cruz Mountains and the blue waters of the Bay, has provided the appeal of the Peninsula. Although this area has the mildness of San Francisco, it has limited summer fog. But its most important physical attribute, in terms of recent population growth, has been location contiguous to San Francisco, affording space for urban expansion.

EVOLUTION

Occupance of the Peninsula has not followed the typical pattern of the Central Coast or even the Bay Area. There were no missions between Dolores and Santa Clara; however, bayshore grasslands afforded pasturage for mission cattle. As elsewhere along the Central Coast the land was apportioned into ranchos, beginning with Rancho de las Pulgas, awarded Jose Arguello in 1795. Most of the others were awarded during the Mexican era, including San Mateo in 1846. One, Rancho Buri Buri, site of the present-day San Bruno and Burlingame, was an early property of "cattle king" Henry Miller (Chapter 9).

The redwood forests of the eastern Santa Cruz Mountains were cut during San Francisco's early years. Mills were established at Woodside and Searsville (now covered by a lake) in 1850 and hauled by mule or oxen to the Embarcadero de las Pulgas, thereafter renamed Redwood City.

The practice of commuting to the City, so characteristic of the Peninsula for many years, was established in 1864 when the San Francisco and San Jose Railroad (now the Southern Pacific's Coast Line) inaugurated service through this area. Hence much of the Peninsula never experienced the sheep grazing and wheat farming that characterized evolution of many portions of California. Most Peninsular communities either were established with arrival of the railroad (as San Mateo and Menlo Park) or were founded previously (as Belmont and Redwood City). Belmont and San Bruno had their origins in early inns dating from stagecoach days.

Banker William C. Ralston was among the first of the San Francisco tycoons to establish estates on the Peninsula; in the early 1860's his Belmont estate was a central California showplace. Other prominent business leaders who settled here included Mills, Easton, Sharon, Parrott, Hayward, and Macondray. Leland Stanford established his country estate on the present site of the Stanford campus in 1876; most of the others located here soon after the railroad arrived. By the 1890's Burlingame had achieved a reputation as one of the early centers of country-club life in western America. Hillsborough, southwest of Burlingame, became the exclusive community of the Peninsula after 1912.

The earthquake of 1906 precipitated a mass migration of middle-income San Franciscans to the Peninsula. Few California counties have rivaled the growth rate of San Mateo County during the twentieth century. The 1950's was the fourth successive decade in which the population had virtually doubled.

After World War II tract developments replaced fields of flowers and vegetables that had been grown around Peninsular cities. Nevertheless, output in 1961 was worth over $16 million, with nursery stock and cut flowers the leading items. There are now more than 500 industrial establishments in the county, employing more than 25,000 persons. Yet the Peninsula remains an area characterized by incomes well above the state average, populated by people with superior academic training and strong cultural interests.

NORTHERN PERIPHERY

The northern periphery of the Peninsula is not a typical portion of the area. Geographically, the city and county of San Francisco could build a strong case for inclusion of the area that includes Daly City, Colma, and South Francisco (Fig. 8-24).

Daly City (45,000) was a product of the earthquake of 1906—its original inhabitants sought refuge there. For many years it was a "sporting town" known for its bars, prize fights, and greyhound races. Conversion of cabbage patches and hog farms into the Westlake housing development in 1949 started the city's transformation into a tranquil residential outlier of San Francisco. The population trebled during the 1950's. Adjacent **Colma** (500) might aptly be termed the "city of the dead," for it contains the cemeteries of space-short San Francisco; it also has farms for fresh market flowers. **Pacifica**, noted earlier in the chapter, reflects urban extension southward along the ocean.

South San Francisco (39,000) likewise lacks antecedents dating from nineteenth-century Peninsular drawing rooms. It was part of the original (home) ranch of Miller and Lux; after Miller established an abattoir, larger packers including Armour, Crocker, and Swift established similar concerns. The location was well chosen—it was near city markets, yet had San Bruno Mountain to shield San Franciscans from offensive odors. As the San Francisco waterfront became congested, shipyards were relocated along this portion of the Bay. Gradually other industries have been added. Although chiefly a manufacturing site, "South

City" has grown considerably as the home of industrial workers. It contains a widely known arena, the Cow Palace, used for sports and livestock shows, and also site of the 1956 Republican national convention. On its southern margin, east of San Bruno, is San Francisco International Airport. Originally this was the municipal airport, established in 1927—San Francisco was already too congested for a site within its limits. In the early 1950's new runways were added and an impressive passenger terminal constructed. Nevertheless, it cannot compare with Los Angeles International in volume and number of flights. A number of diversified light industrial plants, as well as motels and restaurants, have evolved near the airport.

THE MIDDLE COMPLEX

Even in the days before the Bayshore Freeway, through motorists between Los Angeles and San Francisco were so likely to be frustrated by a succession of stop lights that they would miss the beauty of the Peninsula towns. Today's motorist, speeding along multiple lanes, gains still less of an impression. Yet here are some of California's lovely garden suburbs, now mostly molded into a mosaic of urban continuity. More expensive residences are found on elevations into the Santa Cruz Range. Residents of these communities long looked askance at industry. However, population spiral and resulting governmental costs have recommended compromise. Zoning has permitted construction of dozens of light industrial plants, such as electronics firms and publishing houses—organizations that employ well-educated, skilled personnel.

San Bruno (29,000) evolved from a small Mexican village and an early highway inn. It serves as a residential community for many workers employed in plants of South San Francisco or at the International Airport. Its retail trade was much expanded as a result of industrial growth during and since World War II. Here too is Tanforan racetrack. Industrial firms produce lithography and electronic products. **Millbrae** (17,000) to the south is essentially residential although there is a large industrial tract on its margin.

The San Mateo conurbation (San Mateo, Burlingame, and Hillsborough) forms an especially attractive segment of the Peninsula despite rapid growth after 1945. **San Mateo** (70,000), although its homes tend to be more modest than those of its two neighbors, is an attractive community and the largest city on the Peninsula. Numerous shade trees epitomize all three communities. San Mateo, founded with arrival of the railroad, grew slightly in the nineteenth century. With demise of its early day millionaries, their estates were subdivided in the years after the San Francisco earthquake. The expanding central district contrasts with the smaller one of **Burlingame** (24,000), although both communities have quality specialty shops. San Mateo is well regarded for its junior college. Tract housing in Hillsdale and Sunnybrae, both within San Mateo limits, has accounted for much of its more recent growth. Eastern San Mateo has diversified industry including electronics, chemicals, and furniture. Distinctive **Hillsborough** (7500), suggestive of a less ostentatious Bel Air (Chapter 7) in a more lush natural setting, affords superlative views of San Francisco Bay. Its newer homes, less opulent than the mansions built before 1929, are sometimes obscured by walls and hedges; there are neither sidewalks nor a shopping center.

Once quiet **Belmont** (16,000) and **San Carlos** (21,000), literally "exploded" in the late 1940's—both had increased 300 percent in population by 1960. Tract housing and light industries have replaced the nurseries and flower patches that were conspicuous in the 1930's. William Ralston's Belmont estate has become College of Notre Dame. Accessible to scientists of Stanford Research Institute, these cities have become centers of the electronics industry, which has gained such importance on the Peninsula.

Redwood City (46,000), seat of San Mateo county, has benefited from the products of its environment. In its formative years it served as the shipping point for lumber from the redwood groves of the Santa Cruz Mountains. Later (in 1887) the Morgan Oyster Company planted "eastern" oysters in the bay, but the

Fig. 8-34. MENLO PARK AND SOUTH SAN FRANCISCO BAY. *This view includes Woodside (lower left), Atherton (middle left), and the north edge of Stanford Industrial Park (middle right). Note the wooded areas, tidal flats along the Bay, and Mt. Diablo beyond the East Bay.* (San Mateo County Development Association, photo by Air-Photo Service of Palo Alto)

activity was not too successful. Today Ideal Cement Company dredges oyster shells, which accumulated long before Captain John Morgan started his company, and converts them into cement—this is the only cement plant in California with a comparable raw material. Salt is evaporated from the bay, even as around Newark in the nearby East Bay. Redwood City has long been significant as the port of the southern bay. It has had industrial moment longer than most communities of the Peninsula, and it is also a shopping center and home of many San Francisco commuters. Industries produce tape recorders, packaging machines, paper, and foods.

THE SOUTH END

Menlo Park and Palo Alto are the twin cities of the southern Peninsula where it begins to merge rapidly into the full width of the Central Coast. Menlo Park originated with the

railroad, but Palo Alto, like Berkeley and in measure Westwood Village (in Los Angeles), evolved around a university campus. The Stanford campus is a partial separator of the two cities.

Menlo Park (27,000) has attractive residential areas and an impressive downtown district as well as new industrial establishments (Fig. 8-34). This portion of the Peninsula has become a center for electronics, publishing houses, pharmaceuticals, helicopters, and guided missiles. Stanford Research Institute makes a signal contribution to scientific progress and industrial growth. The city also has a well-regarded junior college.

Atherton (7700), practically a northern suburb of Menlo Park, is an affluent residential community, long known for its well-appointed estates and attractive homes. **Woodside** (3600) is sequestered into the eastern slopes of the Santa Cruz Mountains; it too has many expensive homes.

Fig. 8-35. STANFORD UNIVERSITY. Note the quadrangular groupings on this extensive campus, long known as "The Farm." Landmark in the center is the Hoover Library tower with the Inner Quadrangle to its left. Palm Drive leads from this quadrangle toward Palo Alto (beyond photo, upper right). (Stanford University, photo by Lloyd Provan)

Palo Alto (52,000) is located within Santa Clara County, on the dividing line between the Peninsula and the Santa Clara Valley. Partially because of the university the city has been a focal point for Peninsular art, music, and drama; it is another community of well-maintained homes and gardens. It serves as a retirement spot for many persons with cultural interests. Its downtown district is the ranking retail center of the southern Peninsula. Industrial plants produce electronics, processed film, foods, and plastics.

Stanford University, one of the nation's outstanding private educational institutions, was established by Leland Stanford on his "Farm" (livestock ranch) in 1887. Commonly regarded as the "Harvard of the West," Stanford has developed excellent undergraduate and graduate programs. It is also popular for its social life and as a residence school. The extensive campus focuses upon Palm Drive (which becomes Palo Alto's University Ave-

nue toward the east) and upon "outer" and "inner" quadrangles (Fig. 8-35). Prominent buildings include Jordan Hall, the memorial chapel, and Hoover Library. Earlier structures, with red tile roofs, were erected in the Romanesque style. The Medical School, long located in San Francisco, now has its quarters on the campus. Much of the original farm has been leased for residential and light industrial use (i.e., Stanford Industrial Park), thus augmenting the always critical finances of a private institution (Fig. 8-34). Accordingly, this portion of the Peninsula has become one of the nation's primary centers of scientific research.

THE SOUTH BAY
(Northern Santa Clara Valley)

The South Bay (northern Santa Clara Valley) until the late 1950's was not generally

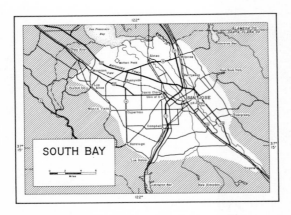

Fig. 8-36. MAP OF THE SOUTH BAY.

regarded as part of the Bay Area but rather as a distinct agricultural wonder. As farmlands available for urbanization vanished in the East Bay and on the Peninsula, occupance of Santa Clara fields and orchards north of Coyote Narrows was inevitable—the U.S. Department of Commerce forecast in 1959 that by 2020 South Bay (map, Fig. 8-36) will have become the most populous part of the Bay Area with a population approaching that of the entire Bay Area today. Many have deplored the haphazard manner in which subdividers have hedgehopped across the Santa Clara. With the spiraling of California population, especially in the Bay Area, it seems doubtful that any legal means could have successfully "stopped" this transition. During the 1950's only Orange County increased at a more rapid rate—between 1950 and 1960 the population of Santa Clara County increased from 290,547 to 639,615.

Before 1950 the northern Santa Clara Valley was characterized by the centrally located twin cities of San Jose and Santa Clara and by scattered farm villages and with peaceful residence towns along the base of the Santa Cruz Range. Subsequently, urbanization has spread outward from San Jose, and outlying towns have also been confronted by urban sprawl and new housing tracts.

Santa Clara (59,000) and **San Jose** (204,-000) are among California's oldest communities—they date from the founding of the mission and the first Spanish pueblo in 1777. They were originally linked by willow-lined *The Alameda* (whose old trees were cut down in 1887) but long ago coalesced. San Jose has been continuously larger since mission secularization. It is a county seat and one-time state capital (1849-1851). Like Los Angeles it experienced a brief land boom in the middle 1880's. But unlike Los Angeles it grew more slowly as a market town, processing center, and principal shipping point of the Valley. In 1950 its functions were somewhat suggestive of Fresno (Chapter 9). Its industrial growth was oriented toward the Valley's agricultural productivity—packing, canning, and drying of fruits. Santa Clara meanwhile remained a small satellite although it had many packing plants. Remains of the mission provided a foundation for the University of Santa Clara in 1851. As late as 1950 Santa Clara had only 11,000 inhabitants.

Downtown San Jose is relatively small and has been weakened economically by new suburban centers (Fig. 8-37). Despite its new civic center, many "housekeeping" functions have been transferred elsewhere. San Jose State College, oldest and long the largest in the California state college system, began as the state's first normal school, originally located in San Francisco. Like Chico State it has remained on its downtown campus too long to be moved elsewhere; Fresno State and San Francisco State, by contrast, were relocated on new fringe-area sites. The small campus, surrounded by apartment houses, is much congested. Despite the designation of "college," the institution is much more a university than many schools so designated by title. The downtown area is surrounded by an old residential district with much evidence of blight—the "typical" resident is a senior citizen of modest means. North of the core is a residue of old Chinatown, small in size and inhabited chiefly by minority groups and foreign born (Japanese).

The East Side, beyond Coyote Creek, has been altered since 1950. Files of modest tract houses, and three suburban shopping centers, have replaced truck farms and dairies. With elevation upslope toward the Mt. Hamilton

Fig. 8-37. DOWNTOWN SAN JOSE. Older industrial district and Southern Pacific tracks (lower left), central district (middle), The Alameda–East Santa Clara Street (right) extending diagonally across photo. View toward southeast with San Jose State College toward upper left. (San Jose Chamber of Commerce, photo by L. T. Jacobsen)

Range there are more expensive custom-built dwellings. The small San Jose Country Club district suggests the Western Foothills in residence value, lot size, and landscaping—its appeal is hampered by exposure to afternoon sun. On flat, unzoned county land south of Alum Rock Boulevard there are many shanties that house minority groups.

South of downtown San Jose, Willow-Glen was the urban fringe before 1950; along with the mansions of The Alameda strip, where office buildings are rising, and Rose Garden, surrounding the renowned municipal rose garden, it was a choice residential section. Here also is the campus of San Jose City College.

The West Side, east of the older Southern Pacific "commuters line" to San Francisco, includes **Cupertino** (3700) and **Campbell** (12,-000)—old farm towns coalescing into a conglomerate of middle-class tract housing. Campbell changed from farm satellite to suburb to neighborhood between 1955 and 1960. Located here are two large suburban shopping centers.

The Western Foothill Belt, situated in a "thermal belt," tends to have more luxuriant vegetation and has long appealed to newcomers from the East. For decades it retained a delightful rustic setting of charming villages amidst orchards. The Belt extends southward from **Mountain View** (31,000) and **Los Altos** (20,000) through **Saratoga** (15,000) to **Los Gatos** (9000). Upslope into the Santa Cruz Range, land values increase and lots become larger—there is a pronounced transition from Democratic to Republican voter registration westward. Saratoga has a minimum lot size of one acre. These are pleasant garden communities with many affluent residents—well-to-do senior citizens, San Francisco business and professional men, research scientists and engineers. This economic level is reflected in the caliber of the relatively young Foothill College in Los Altos.

Industrial activity in the Santa Clara Valley, dating from Dawson's backyard peach and pear canning in 1871, was almost wholly related to agricultural processing until 1950.

Fig. 8-38. MISSILE PLANT IN SUNNY-VALE. The 645-acre Lockheed missile plant (center) has provided one of central California's largest payrolls and has made a major contribution to the nation's space program. Moffett Field (left) and the south end of the Bay are also visible. (Lockheed Corporation)

Major firms prepared nationally known "brand" foods: canned goods by California Packing ("Del Monte") and Libby McNeill, dried fruits by California Prune and Apricot Growers ("Sunsweet"), wines from Paul Masson and Almaden, and eventually such frozen foods as Pictsweet. Food industries include around thirty-five canneries and a score each of frozen-food processors and dried-fruit packers. They justified evolution of FMC (Food Machinery and Chemical), manufacturer of mechanical processing equipment. Approximately a third of California's total fruit and vegetable output is accessible to South Bay plants by rail and truck. Besides crops grown locally, processing has included peaches, seafoods, artichokes, and potatoes. There is large-scale preparation of "mixes": fruit cocktail, mixed fruit, and salad fruits. The original industrial belt, paralleling the Coast Line of the Southern Pacific, has remained the principal manufacturing district.

Diversified industrialization appeared after 1950 as attractive industrial acreage vanished elsewhere in the Bay Area. The appeal of the Valley as a residential area has been an amenity for firms attracting "brains and skills." Electronics firms, which have tended to locate in **Sunnyvale** (53,000), represent a spillover from the Peninsula and the influence of Stanford Research Institute. Moffett Field and Ames Laboratory (NASA) are major foci of federal research. The Lockheed facility in Sunnyvale, whose approximately 20,000 workers has made it central California's single largest employer, has been one of the nation's leaders in missile production (see Fig. 8-38). Elsewhere new plants have tended to occupy scattered sites on the floor of the northern Santa Clara Valley—in Mountain View, Cupertino, and around San Jose.

MARIN PENINSULA

Marin Peninsula, north of San Francisco across the Golden Gate, affords a pleasing combination of bay and ocean, hills and vales, fog and sunshine (map, Fig. 8-39). The Golden Gate serves to isolate this northern outlier from the other southern Coast Ranges.

This northern extremity of the southern

Fig. 8-39. MAP OF MARIN PENINSULA.

Coast Ranges has experienced somewhat different utilization from much of the Bay Area. Until opening of the Golden Gate Bridge, the Marin Peninsula was largely isolated from the remainder of the Bay Area except by water transportation. Opening of the San Rafael Bridge in 1956 further lessened the transportation barrier. Once the Marin forest had economic value; more recently it has been a playground, suburban bedroom, and milkshed.

LANDSCAPE

Marin Peninsula's scenic appeal results from its combination of water, terrain, natural vegetation, and weather. The peninsula is a maze of hilly terrain, rising to Mount Tamalpais (west peak, 2604 ft.). Streams descend through steep canyons to form small fans or to enter some of the numerous embayments (Fig. 8-40). Though the bewildering array of slopes may appear to lack pattern, there is a definite northwest-southeast orientation: the parallel ridges, Inverness and Bolinas, on opposite sides of Tomales Bay are especially prominent. Along the relatively straight Pacific shore are impressive terraces with sea cliffs as high as 250 feet. The San Andreas rift almost separates triangular Point Reyes Peninsula from the remainder of the county. This isolated section has been the most sparsely

populated and least frequented portion of the area.

Before growth of San Francisco demanded lumber, Marin had more extensive forest cover, with redwoods in canyons. In a few years the forest had been cut; today the peninsula is mostly grassland, alternately seared or green and lush.

Width and height of the hills afford variation between foggy, wind-swept Pacific shores and the sunnier bayshore. This factor has furthered the appeal of eastern Marin as a suburban area—it is suggestive of the Peninsula south of San Francisco, although Marin is more scenic because of slope and indentation.

OCCUPANCE

More than 200 shell mounds suggest that prehistoric man found the Marin Peninsula a pleasant environment. Allegedly this is the locale visited by Sir Francis Drake with the Golden Hind in 1579, which he called *Nova Albion* and where he posted a brass plate proclaiming this land to be an English possession.

The Spanish made limited use of the peninsula; the twentieth mission, San Rafael Arcangel, was not established until 1817. Factors discouraging Spanish use may have been its position near the northerly end of the province and the difficulty of transbay navigation. The mission was established because it was felt that the climate of Mission Dolores was contributing to the high mortality rate of its neophytes. San Rafael was secularized within seventeen years; physical evidence of the original structure has been lost.

The Mexicans made greater use of the peninsula; a series of land grants was established. Sir George Simpson, a British visitor in 1841, was impressed with the ability of Marin's slopes to feed cattle throughout the winter. Grazing and dairying have persisted as the chief forms of rural land-use—terrain chiefly has made this area generally unsuitable for tillage.

Despite its physical charm, the peninsula acquired only a limited population before construction of the Golden Gate Bridge. In 1890 its total population was only 13,072. Between

Fig. 8-40. MARIN PENINSULA. The crumpled terrain of Marin County with Sausalito and Richardson Bay (middle foreground), Mill Valley at base of Mt. Tamalpais, Bolinas Bay (middle left), San Andreas rift, Inverness Ridge, Drake's Bay, and Point Reyes Peninsula (rear). (Aero Photographers, Sausalito)

1940 and 1960, however, the population increased from 52,907 to 145,545. During World War II the population was swollen temporarily by shipbuilding at Sausalito; more significant has been rising importance as a suburban home for San Francisco and East Bay commuters.

UTILIZATION

The economy of Marin County is varied despite emphasis upon suburban residence and recreation. Important functions also include commerce, government, and agriculture.

RECREATION

Scenic beauty afforded by hills and vales, trees and seasonally green grass, quiet bays and ocean breakers, coupled with proximity to urban masses, makes the Marin Peninsula one of California's popular vacation lands. Small **Muir Woods**, a 504-acre national monument dedicated to the famed naturalist is California's most accessible redwood grove; it nestles in Redwood Creek canyon at the base of Mt. Tamalpais. On pleasant weekends and holidays it becomes so congested that there is

concern for the well-being of its plants. Samuel Taylor State Park also has redwoods.

Mount Tamalpais, actually three summits all slightly over 2500 feet, affords excellent views of the Bay Area. It has been popular with hikers and picnickers since early days; a highway glides to the summit. Mt. Tamalpais State Park, 1900 acres, has camping and picnic grounds and a natural amphitheater for dramatic performances.

Beaches along Marin's western shore form the most popular center for salt-water bathing in the Bay Area. **Stinson Beach**, which has a state park with campsites, has long been popular. An additional six state beach parks are located along Tomales Bay. Waters of this shallow bay sometimes reach 78° in late summer; earlier, fog is a handicap.

Congressional action in 1962 will eventually convert much of **Point Reyes Peninsula** into a national seashore park. There was considerable opposition from dairymen, local residents, and subdividers. However, it has been widely recognized that such a playground is desirable as the Bay Area population increases.

Sports fishing and boating are popular along the eastern shore, in Richardson Bay and smaller coves, and in Bolinas Bay and Tomales Bay on the western shore. Salmon, perch, eel, and clams are popular seafoods.

Angel Island, scene of military installations and an immigrant station in the past, is to become another Bay Area playground (as a state park); as yet, its development has been limited.

Hilly terrain unsuitable for cultivation coupled with proximity to urban centers made the Marin Peninsula the leading San Francisco source of market milk from the 1920's. Previously, cheese and butter had been important products. Dairies have been concentrated in the west toward Tomales Bay and in the valleys tributary to San Pablo Bay. The 1954 census of agriculture revealed that 40 percent of the Marin farms were dairies, producing three fourths of the farm income; 85 percent of the milk was trucked into San Francisco. The dairies have been unusually large by California "averages"; the dairymen are generally Portuguese or Italian. Although dairying should continue in the northwest, it has been declining along U.S. 101 since 1941. Dairies have mechanized to the "ultimate" and have imported increasing quantities of alfalfa from the Great Central Valley and even from western Nevada. The Novato district, for example, reached its maximum milk production in 1950. Remaining eastside dairies, tending to become larger producers, are found in sites unattractive for subdivision, such as narrow valleys.

GOVERNMENT

Governmental functions on the peninsula are chiefly of a military or penal nature. The state prison at **San Quentin**, established in the 1850's, is one of the nation's largest and most widely known correctional institutions.

All of the armed forces have maintained installations on the peninsula. The Army bases facing the Golden Gate have lost some of their importance. The coastal guns once maintained at Ft. Cronkhite, for example, became inconsequential with the atomic-missile age. Ft. Barry and Ft. Baker are adjuncts of the Presidio: Ft. Baker for engineers and amphibious operations; Ft. Barry, as a rifle range. The Navy has maintained a net depot north of Tiburon, the Coast Guard has docks on Point Reyes, and the Corps of Engineers has maintained its Bay model at Sausalito. The Air Force maintains **Hamilton Air Force Base** south of Novato in connection with Bay Area defense and as an embarkation point for Pacific bases; radar facilities have been maintained on Mt. Tamalpais.

COMMERCE

Marin Peninsula provides a gateway to northwestern California, and conversely, into the Bay Area. This function has had added usefulness since opening of the Golden Gate (U.S. 101 and Route 1) and San Rafael bridges. Attendant services (motels, cafes, and service stations) have appeared. As a freeway, U.S. 101 provides speedy egress north from San Francisco. Traffic over the Sir Francis Drake Highway on the Point Reyes Peninsula is local and mostly of a recreational nature.

RESIDENCE TOWNS

The towns of Marin County are among California's most picturesque communities. Conversion of U.S. 101 into a freeway has affected some of them, in the same way that freeways have accelerated growth elsewhere on the margins of the Bay Area and fringes of the Los Angeles Lowlands. Despite the new housing tracts, slope and water contribute to a continuing appeal. The peninsula has long attracted business and professional people, and it has many expensive hillside homes.

Sausalito (5300), ascending the slopes west of Richardson Bay, does not have a site to become a large city. Perhaps for this reason it has long been popular with San Francisco commuters. Once it was a "wild" port town, but it quieted down around 1900. Every house has a view, and in the bay small craft have replaced the large sailing vessels of its earlier years. Artists and writers have found the town especially appealing—their influence is apparent in the central district. **Belvedere** (2100) across Richardson Bay is small but in many respects a similar type of town.

The three largest communities, San Rafael, San Anselmo, and Novato, are favorably located with respect to U.S. 101 and for commuting from East Bay and San Francisco; all three have more flat terrain suitable for residential construction than is typical along the eastside. **San Rafael** (20,500), seat of Marin County, serves as the primary retail trade center. **San Anselmo** (11,600), a pleasant residential town, is also the site of San Francisco Theological Seminary, largest western institution for training of Presbyterian clergymen. **Novato** (17,900), once a tranquil dairy village, experienced the most dramatic growth in the county during the 1950's; it is near Hamilton Air Force Base and has had much acreage suitable for modest tract housing (i.e., flat land, requiring less expense for streets, drains, gutters).

Mill Valley (10,400) and **Corte Madera** (6000) owe their names to early redwood lumbering, but their late growth has resulted from movement of commuters across the Golden Gate. Mill Valley commemorates the site of its redwood mill in Old Mill Park; Corte Madera still preserves some redwoods in Baltimore Park Grove. Mill Valley is experiencing a second boom; the first, belatedly, came with construction of an electric interurban railway from Sausalito.

Farther north, the terrain of Kentfield, Ross, and Fairfax has been conducive to more luxurious housing; lately all three have grown. **Kentfield** contains expensive homes dating from its early years half a century ago; it is also the home of College of Marin. **Ross** (2600) likewise has some large estates. **Fairfax** (5800) is larger than its two neighbors.

The villages of Point Reyes Peninsula are residential and resort towns. Climatically they tend to be less pleasant than those of eastern Marin County; their location has discouraged commuting. **Inverness** has been a weekend retreat for San Franciscans. **Point Reyes Station** is a dairying center with some facilities for the vacationist. Subdividers have been actively buying land along Route 1.

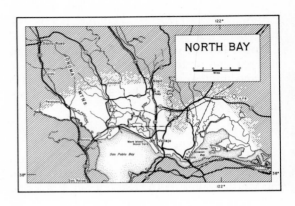

Fig. 8-41. MAP OF THE NORTH BAY.

THE NORTH BAY

The North Bay, the tidal flats north of San Pablo Bay between the Marin Peninsula (west) and the Delta Lands of the Great Central Valley (Chapter 9), reaches north into the south end of valleys of the Northwest (Chapter 10), Santa Rosa and Napa, and thus forms a transition zone between these regions (map, Fig. 8-41). A precise boundary can no longer be drawn, for like the South Bay, this is an area of transformation from rural to urban conditions—so far it has been altered less than other portions of the Bay Area.[22]

The North Bay has remained the northern march of the Bay Area, but it seems inevitable that in the future as the population pressure increases, land-use will become more intensive. Urbanization, mostly in the form of residential development along U.S. 101 and California 12 (via U.S. 40), is still relatively limited. Much of the North Bay remains sloughs and tule marshes along the lower courses of Petaluma Creek, Sonoma Creek, and Napa River, used principally as grazing lands for both beef and dairy cattle (Fig. 8-42). It is significant that parts of this area were not contained within colonial land grants although

[22] The reader will note that although Santa Rosa and Napa are included in this section as cities of the Bay Area frontier, their surrounding agricultural lands are still considered with the Northwest (Chapter 10).

Fig. 8-42. TYPICAL LANDSCAPE, THE NORTH BAY. *Beef cattle are grazing on Tubbs Island west of Vallejo.* (David W. Lantis)

Fig. 8-43. MARIN ISLAND AND THE NAPA RIVER. *The century-old Navy Shipyard is on the left with Vallejo Channel, which becomes the Napa River (rear right). North Bay pasturelands and Sonoma Mountains (rear), San Pablo Bay (left).* (Official U.S. Navy photograph)

the better-drained lands to the north and southwest were so utilized. Present-day returns from hay alone are sufficient to pay taxes and permit landowners to retain their properties in anticipation of eventual urban use. Away from the several cities, the most dramatic change of the 1950's was the construction of twelve crystallizing ponds, covering 12,000 acres, where Leslie Salt recovers sodium chloride from the Bay for industrial use.

The urban population of North Bay, around Benicia, Napa, and Vallejo especially, was expanded during World War II. Afterwards many temporary residents, war workers, moved elsewhere. Since 1950, however, a significant population increase has taken place.

THE CITIES

North Bay cities are scattered around the fringes of the area; most have port facilities of some sort. Peripheral to the Bay Area, their functions have long tended toward service for the surrounding countryside. California has had four state capitals; two of them, Benicia and Vallejo, have been in North Bay. Both aspired to rival San Francisco and both failed.

Vallejo (61,000) was established in 1850 by General Mario Vallejo as Eureka, the intended capital of California. The town was officially named Vallejo in his honor and was the capital from 1850-1852. Presumably the capital was moved to Sacramento because legislators were dissatisfied with Vallejo lodgings. Meanwhile, opening of a Naval yard in 1854 assured economic support. Then the California Pacific Railroad constructed a line from Sacramento to Vallejo, and it became a wheat port. In 1871 the railroad announced plans of extending its line to Salt Lake City; within weeks the Central Pacific (now Southern Pacific) gained control of the competing line, thus ending Vallejo's hopes of becoming a major rail terminus. Meanwhile, Vallejo had become a major flour-milling center.

Vallejo enjoyed steady growth until 1940; its many older business blocks reflect its age. During World War II the tremendous expansion of Mare Island Navy Yard created much temporary housing. After the war employment declined, and much of the temporary increase was lost. However during the 1950's the population doubled as commuters began establishing residence in the city. Vallejo has several industrial firms; the largest is a flour mill, one of the leaders in California.

Mare Island Navy Yard (Fig. 8-43) is situated on a hilly island at the mouth of the Napa River overlooking San Pablo Bay. The 3000-acre reserve was first selected as a Naval dock in 1851 and designated as the site of a Navy yard the next year. Besides much ship repair, the battleship *California* was built here. During World War II employment reached 40,000, with construction of submarines and other smaller craft. More recently atomic submarines have been built at Mare Island.

Benicia (6000) was also temporarily the capital of California. It was founded as Francisca in 1847; its planners expected it to become the major port of the Bay Area. When Yerba Buena became San Francisco, Francisca became Benicia. Literally, it never "got off the planning boards" before the Gold Rush "made" San Francisco. The state legislature convened there briefly in 1853 after it was driven out of Sacramento by flood water—the temporary capitol is now a state historical monument. The Pacific Mail Steamship Company maintained wharves and maintenance shops in Benicia from 1853 until inability to compete with the transcontinental railroad forced closure in 1881. Benicia Seminary, founded in 1852, is now Mills College in Oakland. The U.S. Army's Benicia Arsenal, established in 1851 is to be removed to Herlong (Chapter 1).

Benicia languished for decades, supported principally by the Arsenal and later by food-canning plants. During World War II, employment at the Arsenal reached 5700 and Benicia's population temporarily doubled. Since completion of the Benicia-Martinez highway bridge in 1962, residential growth is anticipated.

Napa (22,200) in no sense could have been regarded as part of the Bay Area before 1941. It was founded in 1848 and remains the service center of Napa Valley. It is the seat of Napa County and the site of Napa Junior College and a state hospital. Its economy has long been related to cattle ranching and grape growing. Considerable barge trade has been conducted with San Francisco via the Napa River. The city has a variety of industrial plants, including leather and leather goods, sports apparel, foods, steel products, and electronics; production of leather goods was an early activity. During World War II a number of war workers resided in Napa; more recently, the charm of the city has appealed to commuters employed in the Bay Area. The doubling of its population during the 1950's reflected its rising importance as a suburb.

Petaluma (14,000) has so far been affected relatively little by Bay Area population growth. Established in 1851 it remains the service center for ranchers of southern Sonoma County. Its prosperity has long been influenced by vicinal poultry farms; the city has called itself "Egg Basket of the World," with manufacture of incubators and other products. It is also a river port connected to the Bay. It is assumed that Petaluma will increasingly serve as a residence town for Bay Area commuters. **Cotati** (1900), long a somnolent poultry town, is abode of the new Sonoma State College.

Santa Rosa (31,000), seat of Sonoma County and site of Santa Rosa Junior College, is another old town, founded in 1852. It is still difficult to consider the city a part of the Bay Area. It has long prospered as the service center of the rich Santa Rosa Valley and has been well regarded as one of California's more appealing residential towns. It has been known, too, as the home of Luther Burbank, the plant "wizard." Its several score of industrial plants process local products and also manufacture shoes and apparel. It is anticipated that the city will gain importance as a suburban bedroom for the Bay Area; in addition to its setting and climate, it is now accessible by freeway (U.S. 101).

REGIONAL TRENDS

There is slight doubt that the Central Coast will remain one of the most important regions of California. Only Southern California has been affected more by military activities and the electronics era that dawned with World War II. New employment is identified with such activities as missile-launching at the Pacific Missile Range and missile-making at Sunnyvale. Military shipping, shipbuilding, and repair remain significant in the Bay Area. Military installations play a major role in the support of numerous communities. Immediate prospects of the Central Coast thus are related to unpredictable international affairs and federal policies.

Continued urbanization around the Bay Area seems a certainty—the population may double by the 1970's. The age of automation is evident in the host of electronics-type factories. Technological trends and the national economy seem to favor expansion in these industries. They should continue to be identified with the urban periphery of the Bay Area.

For the rest of California the Central Coast remains a service region—in terms of recreation, education, and travel. As long as Southern California and Great Central Valley populations burgeon, service functions of the Central Coast should grow commensurately. Such activities are particularly significant to smaller communities away from the metropolitan centers, such as Santa Cruz and Morro Bay.

San Francisco seems to be "losing out" commercially to Los Angeles and Great Central Valley cities. The trend from water shipment to trucks promises continuation of this development. Yet in the over-all picture of contemporary Bay Area economy, a declining dominance of its hinterland may not be readily apparent or significant.

What of the traditional dominance of agriculture in the rural Central Coast? The tendency to urbanize the best farmland first plagues the Central Coast, as it has Southern California—spectacularly in the instance of the Santa Clara Valley. Much farmland in the region seems out of reach of immediate urbanization. A pressing problem for many irrigated areas is depletion of groundwater reserves—the ultimate answer appears to be the California Water Plan (Chapter 9) and perhaps seawater conversion. Agricultural intensification is a likely response to the growing populations of San Diego, Los Angeles, and the Bay Area. Yet vast expanses of unirrigable grain and range land may see little more change in the future than in the past.

Fig. 9-1. THE HEART OF CALIFORNIA. Cotton harvest near Mendota. (Anderson, Clayton and Company)

CHAPTER NINE:: THE GREAT
CENTRAL VALLEY

THE GREAT CENTRAL VALLEY

It was an English writer on America who said that California's interior is divided into three valleys: the Sacramento, the San Joaquin, and the Great Central Valley. England has no monopoly on provincialism; there are people in San Francisco who think "The Valley" means that little vineyard-grown backwater called the Napa; San Joseans refer to the prune-filled Santa Clara as "The Valley"; while down Hollywood way a little corral full of stucco houses and station wagons known as the San Fernando rates local headlines as "The Valley." And well known is John Steinbeck's impudence in titling a book of his stories "The Long Valley," when everyone but eastern reviewers knew that it was the stubby Salinas he had in mind.[1]

Rice and cotton, pears and oranges, asparagus and sweet potatoes, all these and scores of other crops in impressive quantities—small

The introductory and Sacramento Valley sections of this chapter have been reviewed by Howard Gregor, University of California at Davis.

[1] Lawrence Clark Powell, "San Joaquin Vision." Reprinted from the October 1948 *Wilson Library Bulletin* by courtesy of The H. W. Wilson Company, New York City, and by permission of the author.

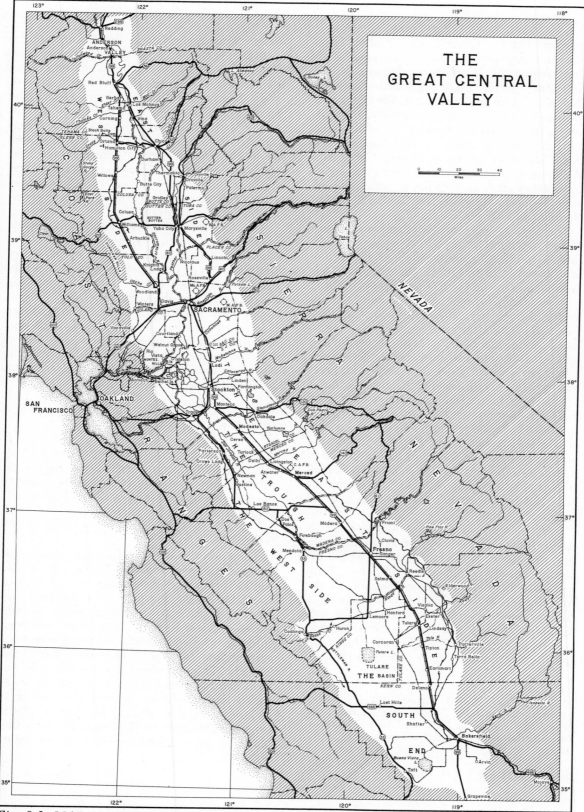

Fig. 9-2. MAP OF THE GREAT CENTRAL VALLEY.

wonder that the Great Central Valley fascinates the stranger interested in farming.[2] This long depression, California's banana-shaped heartland, yields more agricultural wealth than most of the nation's states. Yet despite its economic moment and its centrality, the Valley is scenically California's stepchild—one finds no romantic thrill in the widely known "local literature" of Frank Norris, Carey McWilliams, or John Steinbeck. Perhaps none of California's other regions has so little physical appeal—most visitors to the Golden State are charmed more by its deserts.

The Valley, an elongated structural trough of low elevation, is the "food basket of California," producing almost half of the state's farm income. In the twentieth century it has become one of the world's important irrigated regions—today three of its counties rank among the top ten nationally in total agricultural value. As a farming region it has superlative endowment—level terrain, productive soils, streams and groundwater for irrigation, a long season with a dry harvest period, good transportation facilities, and access to markets.

This long basin, only slightly smaller than the Sierra Nevada or the Mojave Desert, approximates 25,000 square miles in area yet houses only about 15 percent of California's people. It stretches for about 450 miles from Redding in the north to the foot of the Grapevine (the "Ridge Route" or U.S. 99) south of Bakersfield, thus extending more than half the length of the state.

The Central Valley, mountain-girt, is readily defined—the only break in its highland rim occurs at Carquinez Strait where the Sacramento River debouches into San Francisco Bay after receiving the discharge of the San Joaquin River. On the east there is a gradual transition from the valley trough into the Sierra Nevada and the Southern Cascade (see map, Fig. 9-2). The Klamath Mountains and the Southern Cascade merge to produce

its northern margin, and the linkage of the Tehachapi Range with the southern Coast Ranges provides a southern closure. The southern (i.e., Central Coast) and northern (i.e., Northwest) Coast Ranges define the western border.

The Valley has marked elongation with axis orientation in a northwest-southeast direction. Its width, though varying considerably, averages approximately 50 miles. On clear days the surrounding summits are readily visible—an impressive sight when the peaks are snow-capped after a winter storm.

The Central Valley is traditionally known as the Sacramento Valley northward from Sacramento and as the San Joaquin Valley southward from Lodi. Between these two subdivisions are the Delta Lands, the low-lying insular terrain at the confluence of the Sacramento and San Joaquin rivers. The northern Sacramento Valley, between Red Bluff and Redding, is sometimes called Anderson Valley, and the southern San Joaquin Valley, without natural drainage to the ocean, is also known as Tulare Basin.

THE LAND

The natural environment of the Central Valley, so important to its agricultural utilization, retains many evidences of its pristine aspects despite much human alteration of soils and vegetation.

GEOSYNCLINE

The Central Valley is a fault-fold basin with a long complex geologic history. It is the residue of a larger geosyncline east of ancient Cascadia whose margins were buckled upward to become the ancestral Sierra Nevada and the Coast Ranges. The Valley has been subjected to longtime alluvial deposition from surrounding highlands, especially the Sierra Nevada. The deposition has tended to be intermittent; at times, arms of the ocean penetrated into the basin. Beneath the surface is an unconsolidated alluvial fill that in places exceeds 2000 feet in thickness. Beneath this alluvium are sedimentary rocks several miles

[2] The terms "Central Valley," "Great Valley," "Great Central Valley," "Valley of California," and "The Valley" have all been used in the literature. They will be used somewhat interchangeably in this chapter.

in depth that have yielded much petroleum and natural gas.

The San Joaquin and the Sacramento valleys have had somewhat different histories despite their occupance of a single depression. Although the Sacramento Valley is more symmetrical, with the course of the Sacramento River flowing southward near its centerline (or even toward the eastern side north of Colusa), it has had a more complex evolution than the San Joaquin Valley. The San Joaquin is markedly asymmetrical with its north-south axis displaced westward. The Sacramento River enters its basin at the northern tip and flows southward with sufficient volume to transport its load. The San Joaquin and its principal tributaries enter their portion of the trough from the east, frequently with too little volume to transport their debris as the gradient decreases and stream flow lessens in summer.

RED LANDS AND FLOOD BASINS

The physiographic subdivision of the Sacramento Valley includes these units: alluvial uplands, low alluvial plains, flood basins, floodplains, and delta islands. The dissected *alluvial uplands* (terraces), which are discontinuous along both the eastern and western edges of the valley, represent an ancient valley floor, slightly uplifted and below whose level streams have cut the modern floodplain. They include the gravelly red lands and such low uplifted promontories as the Corning Ridge, the Dunnigan Hills, and the Montezuma Hills. The *low alluvial plains* lie between the contemporary floodplain and the dissected uplands; they include alluvial fans of tributary streams and have almost flat surfaces, well drained except during flood stage. The *flood basins* are flat, poorly drained surfaces from Butte County southward, between the alluvial plains and the floodplains. They form a system of sloughs, or tule marshes, surrounded by natural levees. There are seven such basins, five larger ones (Butte, Colusa, Sutter, American, and Yolo) and two lesser ones (Marysville and Sacramento). Although commonly dry, these areas have become shallow lakes following periodic floods; the silt from standing

water has repeatedly settled upon them. Since construction of bypass channels and erection of Shasta Dam, they have been less frequently inundated. The *floodplains* parallel the Sacramento and Feather rivers and extend from the river banks (natural levees) to the flood basins. The *delta islands* have developed south of the Sacramento Valley proper at the confluence of the streams whose waters flow toward San Francisco Bay; besides the Sacramento and the San Joaquin, delta rivers include the Cosumnes, Mokelumne, and Calaveras. Their mean surface lies at sea level, with natural levees forming the original fringes of individual islands. The interiors of these islands, sometimes 5 to 10 feet below sea level, were formerly tule marshes.

A distinctive landmark of the Sacramento Valley is the nearly circular **Sutter** (Marysville) **Buttes**, the erosional relict of an igneous mass that was later penetrated by molten rock to form a volcanic cone. An elevation of 2117 feet is attained in South Butte.

ALLUVIAL FANS AND TULARE BASIN

The physiographic subdivisions of the San Joaquin Valley, which occupies the southern two thirds of the Great Central Valley, are similar to those of the Sacramento Valley; they include dissected uplands, low plains, the valley trough, and the Tulare Basin. The *dissected uplands* represents a discontinuous zone of contact between the San Joaquin and the Sierra Nevada (east) and southern Coast Ranges (west). It varies in width from 2 to 15 miles and tends to be hilly in nature. On the west side of the valley it surrounds such anticlinal ridges as the Kettleman Hills, Lost Hills, and Wheeler Ridge, important sources of petroleum—these are outliers of the Coast Ranges. The *low plains*, much wider on the east side of the valley than on the west side, are the coalescing alluvial fans whose gentle gradient and size makes it difficult to perceive the scope of these alluvial aprons from ground level. They lie between the hilly uplands and the valley trough, and tend to have gentle local relief (not over 5 to 10 feet). The average width on the east side varies from 17 miles to the north to 45 miles on the Kings-

Kaweah "delta." These fans tend to be appreciably larger than those of the Sacramento Valley. The *valley trough* is somewhat comparable to the flood basins and floodplains of the Sacramento Valley. Natural levees are prominent along the lower San Joaquin River. Away from the river the overflow lands tend to be flat and poorly drained. The **Tulare Basin**, occupying the south end of the San Joaquin Valley, was long considered the result of "damming" by the alluvial fans of Kings River from the east and Los Gatos Creek from the west. It is now felt that the interior drainage has resulted from late subsidence. The Basin has contained intermittent lakes: the Buena Vista, southwest of Bakersfield, and the Tulare, west of Corcoran.

FERTILE SOILS

Soils of the Great Central Valley generally provide a productive medium for plant growth. There are, however, rather extensive alkaline areas on the east side of the valley trough in the San Joaquin Valley. Soils have formed from stream-transported detritus of volcanic (from the Cascade Range) or granitic (from the Sierra Nevada) bedrock. Texture varies from fine clays near the major streams along the trough to coarse sands and gravels on upper portions of the alluvial fans.

Many Sacramento Valley soils, members of the Chernozemic group (i.e., dark grassland soils), have much agricultural value. However, the "red-land" soils around the margins of the Sacramento Valley often contain hardpan, tend to be coarse, and are used chiefly for seasonal pasturage. In turn the flood basins are often underlain by poorly drained clays.

San Joaquin Valley soils likewise are usually productive. Lime-accumulating brown soils are widespread on fans east of the valley trough except for the little-reclaimed alkaline belt east of the San Joaquin River. Gray-desert alluvial and rendzina soils of the western San Joaquin are also productive when irrigated.

The deep peat and muck of the Delta Lands have formed highly productive soils upon drainage. The peat, mostly humus, is deep, but it is susceptible to fire destruction. Motor-

ists encounter signs along highways warning of peat inflammability.

HOT SUMMERS AND DECEMBER FOG

The climates of the Central Valley provide a distinctive feature. Introductory textbooks describe the Valley as representative of the interior Mediterranean (dry-summer subtropical) climate with summer heat and winter mildness—such a classification ignores the variation produced by latitudinal length and frequency of winter storms and rain-shadow position. Precipitation increases northward so that Redding averages over 37 inches annually, whereas Bakersfield receives less than six. It should be noted, however, that Redding is not typical of the northern Sacramento Valley—the average of 24 inches for Red Bluff is more representative.

Four climatic types are generally associated with the Great Central Valley (see Appendix A): subtropical desert, subtropical semiarid, and cool-summer and hot-summer phases of the dry-summer subtropical or "Mediterranean." Southwesterly portions of the San Joaquin Valley are assigned the designation of subtropical desert like the Colorado Desert (Chapter 4); winters tend to be milder in the San Joaquin than east of the Sierra Nevada in the Mojave. July in Bakersfield averages 84°F. Stepping out of an air-conditioned building in midafternoon is suggestive of a blast from an oven. Much of the remainder of the San Joaquin Valley, with heavier annual precipitation than the southwestern portion, is described as semiarid subtropics; Fresno, for example, receives nearly twice as much annual rainfall as Bakersfield.

The Delta Lands, modified in summer by cool air flowing inland from San Francisco Bay and the Pacific as a result of low interior pressure, is described as cool-summer subtropical ("Mediterranean"). Summer diurnal temperatures are tempered as much as 10°F. below those only a short distance north or south—Stockton has a July average of 73°F.

The Sacramento Valley is considered to be hot-summer Mediterranean. Summer afternoons tend to be about as warm as those in the

San Joaquin Valley but winter cyclonic storms, whose centers generally move eastward along a track well north of a line from San Francisco through Lake Tahoe, bring more precipitation than falls farther south—as was indicated above with reference to Redding and Red Bluff. The west side of the Sacramento Valley, in the shadow of the Coast Ranges, tends to receive appreciably less moisture than the east side—whereas Orland has a precipitation average of 17.5 inches, Chico averages 23.5 inches.

Winds are frequent in the Central Valley despite the apparent stillness of the air on a midsummer morning. Intense heating reduces pressure in summer, thus strengthening inflow of cooling Pacific air and bringing relief from temperatures that during hot spells may exceed 110°F.[3] Conversely, during periods of higher temperatures desiccating winds often blow. At times dust storms have been noxious in the southwestern parts of the San Joaquin Valley; stirring up of dry peat from the surface of the Delta Lands is also bothersome and represents economic loss of rich soil.

The Central Valley growing season is approximately nine to ten months long. While the observant traveler is cognizant of earlier "leafing out" around Bakersfield than around Redding, local altitude and air drainage tend to be almost more important than latitude. "Northers," polar air masses flowing southwestward from the Intermontane Region (Part One) across the Cascadian uplands into the Sacramento Valley, bring subfreezing winter weather, and are sometimes responsible for unseasonably late spring frosts or early autumnal frosts.

Another disagreeable feature, especially during December and January, is "tule fog." These low-lying radiation fogs, following periods of heavier rainfall and high humidity, may cover much of the Great Valley. For periods of three to ten days, until the reduced sunlight of this season is able to "burn off" the

Fig. 9-3. CHRISTMAS FLOOD, 1955. Rupture of the Feather River dike south of its confluence with the Yuba River "saved" Marysville (right) but flooded its twin, Yuba City. This single, statewide disaster, the worst in a century, affected 60 percent of California, caused "direct" flood losses of $200 million, and cost sixty-four lives. (California Division of Highways)

overcast, the weather remains clammy and skies may remain overcast both day and night. Traffic accidents increase on highways and communications slow down. Should the fog disappear in late afternoon, temperatures during the following night may drop sharply below freezing.

FLOODS AND DROUGHTS

The Great Central Valley experiences the wide annual precipitation deviation characteristic of Mediterranean lands. As was noted in Chapter 5, the Sierra Nevada above 3000 feet is the locale of some of the heaviest winter snowfall in North America. Total runoff from the drainage basin of the Central Valley has fluctuated between 63.3 million acre-feet in 1906-07 and 9.2 million acre-feet in 1923-24. Momentous floods have occurred periodically —especially in 1909, 1911, 1938, 1950, and 1955. The devastating flood at the 1955 Christmas season caused scores of millions of dollars'

[3] Residents of the Mendocino Coast predict summer temperature in the Sacramento Valley by the onshore "pull" of fogbanks. When the fog is "soupy" in Fort Bragg, a resident may greet a neighbor with "Guess the Sacramento Valley is sizzling again today."

damage, especially in Yuba City (see Fig. 9-3). Such floods are likely to follow winter storms, which bring warm rain from the central Pacific to melt the Sierran snowpack prematurely. Too rapid melting of the snow in spring likewise produces rapid runoff and has converted rivers into destructive ogres.

Drought too has wrecked havoc as in 1863-64, years that were so disastrous to California generally. In the twentieth century with expanded irrigated acreage, need for water conservation has become increasingly urgent. In the Central Valley, especially in the San Joaquin, increased pumping has seriously depleted underground supplies of water. The Central Valley Project and California Water Plan will be discussed later.

OAKS AND GRASSLANDS

The mosaic of natural vegetation in the Great Valley reflected drainage, water table, topography, soils, and precipitation. Grasslands, interspersed with xerophytic shrubs, floodplain forests (valley oaks, California sycamore, cottonwood, and willow), and tule marshes prevailed prior to plowing the land. Mixed perennial bunch grasses, dominated by needlegrass (*Stipa spp.*) were widespread and denoted adjustment to winter rain, summer drought, and probably fire.

Groves of trees fringed the watercourses (i.e., natural levees) and, especially in the Sacramento Valley, partially covered the well-drained red lands. In addition to the floodplain forests, broadleaf woodlands, dominated by the live oak (*Quercus agrifòlia*), interior live oak (*Q. wislizenii*), and deciduous California black oak (*Q. kelloggii*), have been prominent in the Sacramento Valley north of the Feather River and especially in Anderson Valley north of Red Bluff (Fig. 9-6). The trees have reflected the heavier precipitation and strongly suggest a Middlewestern environment that contrasts with the arid southwestern San Joaquin Valley.

Tens of thousands of acres of marshland prevailed in the Central Valley even in the early twentieth century. Such wetland vegetation was dominated by common tule (*Scirpus acutus*) and by California bulrush (*Carex*

spp.), reedlike plants growing 3 to 9 feet tall, and other coarse, grasslike perennial sedges and water grasses. Along the natural levees of the Delta Lands, in flood basins, and along stream banks upstream, willow thickets were common.

A THIRSTY LAND

Irrigation has been crucial relative to land-use over much of California. Its discussion in this chapter has particular validity since the Central Valley contains a sixth of all the irrigated land in the United States. Artificial watering of California fields commenced on a modest scale in the colonial period. In earlier years of American dominance livestock ranching and dry-grain farming remained the characteristic rural pursuits. A water company in Yolo County, however, furnished a means of irrigating wheat fields as early as 1856.

Establishment of early irrigation works was frustrated by the English doctrine of *riparian rights*, which entitled owners of riverain lands to unrestricted stream use. This humid-land concept was inappropriate for dry-summer California. Ranchers in proximity to Sierran gold fields sometimes utilized works developed in connection with mining activities. In 1887 the state legislature passed the Wright Irrigation District Act, which permitted groups of farmers to establish irrigation districts in order to divert water to lands away from streams. The irrigation districts have been a major force in providing water for Central Valley fields—a considerable number of canals, reservoirs, and other works had been undertaken even before 1930. Finally a new doctrine of "most beneficial use" was adopted in 1928—in the interim there had been much conflict over California water and many legal obstacles had been eliminated through legislative amendments to the Wright Act. In the late nineteenth and early twentieth centuries expanded water usage encouraged pumping of underground waters with inevitable water-table decline over extensive areas. Increasing consumption, especially in the Central Valley, hastened recognition of necessity for more specific planning. In 1919 the Marshall Plan was proposed by and named for the chief hydrographer of the U.S. Geological Survey. It became the framework of the Central Valley Project. California could not singularly undertake the program—in 1933 it was assigned to jurisdiction of the U.S. Bureau of Reclamation.[4]

THE CENTRAL VALLEY PROJECT

The Project (the CVP) recognizes that the San Joaquin Valley constitutes California's area of greatest water deficiency in consideration of present and future utilization, whereas the Sacramento River basin ranks second to the Northwest (Chapter 10) within California in water surplus. Hence, the CVP was commenced in 1935 with southward transport of water a prime purpose. The Project was begun in part because it provided depression-era employment as a public works program. It is a multiple-purpose program intended to: (1) contribute water for irrigating an additional 3 million acres, (2) lessen flood damages, (3) improve navigation on the lower Sacramento, (4) provide facilities for aquatic recreation, (5) yield hydroelectricity, and (6) check summer intrusion of salt water into the Delta Lands. Eventually the $2 billion CVP will include forty-eight dams, 20 major canals, and a number of powerhouses.

The initial phase of the CVP, completed in 1955, included these dams: Shasta and Keswick on the Sacramento, Folsom on the American, and Friant on the San Joaquin (see map, Fig. 9-4). It also encompassed five major canals: (1) the short Delta-Cross Channel, which delivers water into (2) the Contra Costa Canal, which in turn provides urban-industrial water for communities along the south shore of Carquinez Strait and Suisun Bay and also delivers water to the pumping station near Tracy, where water is lifted 200

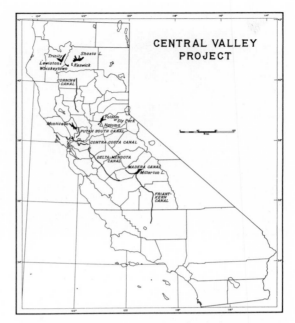

Fig. 9-4. MAP OF THE CENTRAL VALLEY PROJECT.

feet into (3) Delta-Mendota Canal and is transported southward 120 miles to Mendota Pool on the San Joaquin River (Fig. 9-5). Water (from the Sacramento basin) is provided for farms en route, which permits diversion of San Joaquin River water upstream, stored in Friant Dam, into (4) Friant-Kern and (5) Madera canals. The Friant-Kern Canal again transports water southward into the southern San Joaquin Valley. The Madera Canal conducts water northward on the east side of the San Joaquin Valley. Water stored in Pine Flat and Isabella reservoirs has also permitted much irrigation expansion in the southern San Joaquin Valley (i.e., Tulare Basin).

THE CALIFORNIA WATER PLAN

Continued population growth and agricultural expansion have emphasized the necessity for statewide water-resource planning. The state legislature authorized the California Water Plan in 1947, and a comprehensive program was submitted to the governor and the legislature a decade later. The Plan identifies the Northwest and the Sacramento River

[4] The California electorate barely approved of the Central Valley Project—in Los Angeles County there was a two to one vote against the program. A generation later, in 1960, the bond issue to start the California Water Plan passed only because of a tremendous "yes" vote in Southern California. These two election outcomes indeed reflect the cultural and economic chasm divided by the Tehachapi Range (i.e., south end of Sierra Nevada).

Fig. 9-5. THE DELTA-MENDOTA CANAL. This artificial, 4600 second-foot "river" transports Sacramento River water southward ("uphill") 120 miles along the west side of the San Joaquin Valley. (Bureau of Reclamation, photo by B. D. Glaha)

basin as areas of surplus water and proposes additional facilities to store 15 million acre-feet in the Sacramento Basin. In the San Joaquin Valley, identified as the chief area of persistent deficiency, eventual import of 8.55 million acre-feet annually is contemplated. Additional reservoirs and hydroelectric plants around San Joaquin Valley fringes are planned. Present inadequacy of flood-protection works throughout the Great Central Valley is recognized.

First units proposed in the state Plan are the $1.5 billion Feather River Project, including the Oroville Dam in the Sierran foothills and the California Aqueduct System. The 730-foot-high Oroville Dam (Fig. 5-35) on the Feather River, with a storage capacity of 3.5 million acre-feet, will be the principal storage unit; it is to be completed in 1968. Water will be delivered to the northern and southern ends of the San Francisco Bay Area, to the western San Joaquin Valley, and to Southern California by the Aqueduct System.

SETTLEMENT

The Great Central Valley has long afforded a home for man. Before the Europeans ar-

rived, it was perhaps the "heartland of ancient California." The Valley was a marginal area during the Spanish-Mexican period but has acquired new importance in the past century to become the "foodbasket of the West."

LAND OF THE PENUTIAN

Five Penutian linguistic families, residents of the central third of California in pre-Spanish days, utilized the Central Valley. The Valley tended to be less attractive for primitive folk than the Northwest (Chapter 10); it nevertheless afforded these people a relatively easy existence. Clothing was scanty and the unpretentious dwellings were commonly temporary abodes. In the Sacramento and eastern San Joaquin acorns were plentiful, and nut meal was a basic foodstuff. Preparation demanded the leaching out of the bitter poisonous tannic acid with water. Grasslands afforded varied game such as deer, elk, and rabbits. There were fish in the many streams. The mere variety of available foods, even including insects, minimized risk of starvation.

The *Wintun* found the Coast Ranges more attractive than the western Sacramento Valley, where their numbers were limited. The *Maidu* of the eastern Sacramento Valley seldom traveled far—they occupied a choice area with perennial streams. The *Miwok* of the lower San Joaquin were more ambulatory, migrating between the Sierra Nevada and the valley floor but spending much time in the foothills. The *Costanoans,* chiefly a coastal people, resided mostly around San Francisco Bay. The *Yokuts,* possessors of the upper San Joaquin Valley, differed from most California Indians in their tribal organization—most tribes were peaceful although the Chowchilla were known as fighters. Groups residing around Tulare and Buena Vista lakes were fishermen who employed tule rafts.

Records of these peoples are generally limited. Once the Americans entered the Great Valley the Indians tended to vanish. Refuge habitats were generally absent, and decimation from European diseases was doubtless critical.

THE SPANISH-MEXICAN PERIOD

The Spanish never achieved sufficient strength in Alta California to effect permanent Valley settlements. Exploration included the well-known trip of Gabriel Moraga into the Sacramento Valley in 1808. Contemporary names for some larger rivers form a legacy from the Spanish. **El Camino Viejo**, the back trail along the western side of the San Joaquin Valley, was utilized as a speedier way between San Francisco Bay and missions in Southern California than El Camino Real. Upon occasions parties were sent into the San Joaquin in search of escaped Indian neophytes from the missions.

Mountain men, both American and British, visited the Great Valley in the 1820's and 1830's. Jedediah Smith made the first of his several trips in 1827. The fur trappers left few records, except several diaries, of their travels. Seemingly the Valley provided significant numbers of pelts.

Despite some pasturage of mission livestock on San Joaquin Valley fringes, permanent Central Valley settlement was delayed until the Mexican era—more than fifty extensive properties were bestowed between 1836 and 1846. Cattle raising became significant; however, marauding Indians were a threat. During the Spanish period the populace was never sufficient to justify utilization of interior portions of the province. In addition to the hostile Indians, much acreage was periodically inundated by flooding rivers during wetter years. Hence retarded Valley settlement is understandable.

Most of the ranchos were awarded at the close of the Mexican period—some grants were assigned only months before the Mexican War began. In the Sacramento Valley repeated flood-basin submergence discouraged settlement; hence the slightly higher natural levees were selected. Most of the fertile alluvial tracts along the Sacramento River were bestowed as were most of the low plains along tributary streams on the east side of the valley.

On the west side of the Sacramento Valley the few ranchos were located along Cache Creek in the south. San Joaquin Valley grants were less widespread and fewer in number. Some holdings were intentionally selected where periodic stream overflow permitted livestock grazing.

THE AMERICAN PERIOD

The Gold Rush hastened Valley settlement and resulted in early founding of some of the presently larger cities. In fact many of the ranchos, particularly in the Sacramento Valley, had been assigned originally to Americans rather than persons of Spanish ancestry. Final decision pertaining to grant titles was delayed for over a generation and considerable squatting took place on deeded land. Many early Valley residents, who were originally lured to California by mining, turned to farming. Gold-field supply towns in central portions of the Great Valley that have retained their importance include Sacramento, Stockton, and Marysville.

Settlers had commonly migrated from humid climates, and many did not appreciate immediately the agricultural potential of the Great Valley with its dry summers. Since the mine camps afforded an outlet of beef, cattle ranching was dominant in the period between 1850 and 1867. Briefly, the smaller Mexican longhorns were the principal breed, but within a few years heavier American beef types were trailed westward. Among the large operators were some such as John C. Fremont and Edward F. Beale, who acquired rancho properties. During the cattle period much of the Valley remained federal land, unfenced and even unsurveyed. Cattlemen could occupy such land by control of waterholes (i.e., rivers). West of the San Joaquin River, Miller and Lux acquired vast holdings between Tracy and Mendota. Miller left his heirs a million acres and a million cattle, although some of his possessions were outside of the Central Valley. The wane of the livestock period resulted from decline in mining, drought, overgrazing, the "No Fence" Act, and arrival of the railroad.

The epoch of grain farming, 1867-1900, that followed did not eliminate livestock ranching. Sizable stretches, principally around fringes of the Central Valley, are still used for cattle ranching. Production of wheat and barley commenced somewhat earlier in the Sacramento Valley, where heavier rainfall encouraged autumnal planting and early summer harvest. A major consideration in pre-railroad days was the navigability of the Sacramento upstream to Red Bluff. Wheat, especially, was transported to such distant markets as China, Australia, and Europe. Barley was important, principally as feed for draft animals. By 1874, Dr. Hugo Glenn, owner of Rancho Jacinto in Glenn County, planted 41,000 acres of wheat.

Expansion of grain farming in the San Joaquin Valley followed construction of the Southern Pacific's Valley Line between San Francisco and Los Angeles.[5] The first wheat shipment by rail from the San Joaquin came from the Modesto district in 1870. Previously, wheat in the San Joaquin had been limited to the northern section where it was feasible

economically to haul grain by wagons to docks at Stockton.

California led the nation in wheat production for two years in the middle 1870's; the bulk of this output came from the Great Valley. In the Sacramento Valley alone, acreage increased from 200,000 in 1866 to 1 million in 1882. Great Valley production reached an apex in 1884; thereafter acreage declined. Diminution reflected (1) declining yields after years of successive production without crop rotation or fertilization, (2) low gluten content, (3) crop competition in California, and (4) cheaper wheat elsewhere.

A substantial portion of the Great Valley settlement since 1880 has been related to continued expansion of irrigation agriculture—a concern of several types of agricultural organizations. The Wright Act of 1887 was of prime importance, especially after several amendments, since it permitted a number of individual ranchers to establish an irrigation district. Other organizations included the individual and/or the partnership, the stock company, and the commercial group organized specifically to sell water to farmers. Most of the expansion has occurred in the water-deficit San Joaquin Valley, which has attracted settlers from all parts of the United States, from Europe, and from Asia. Increased acreage has tended to enrich the list of commodities produced rather than to continue simple replacement.

AGRICULTURE

It has been noted that the agricultural history of the Central Valley has brought additional crops rather than complete substitution. The first land-use stage, livestock ranching, still exists in peripheral areas or in conjunction with other stages. The second stage, grain farming, is sometimes practiced simultaneously with the third stage. Much grain farming is also peripheral, forming small wheat-barley belts around the edges of The Valley—today grain is grown for local flour, beer, or livestock feeding rather than for export. The third stage, irrigation agriculture, represents more

[5] Frank Norris wrote this description of the Central Valley in *The Octopus* (Garden City, N. Y.: Doubleday & Company, 1901): "The wheat, now close to its maturity, had turned from pale yellow to golden yellow and from that to brown. Like a gigantic carpet, it spread itself over all the land. There was nothing else to be seen but the limitless sea of wheat as far as the eye could reach, dry, rustling, crisp and harsh in the rare breaths of hot wind out of the southeast" (p. 202).

intensive land-use and has largely developed in the twentieth century. In some districts, complex crop mosaics have been created.

The Valley has become the major agricultural area of western United States, yielding scores of crops commercially and representing annual income in excess of a billion dollars (see table). Grains remain important—with barley grown more widely than wheat (Figs. 8-16, and 9-42). Livestock, including sheep, beef cattle, and dairy cows, graze upon natural pasture seasonally, and on irrigated pasture or grain stubble. Many varieties of deciduous fruits, including grapes, peaches, figs, prunes, pears, and cherries are raised. Numerous vegetables, such as tomatoes, squash, and asparagus are grown and generally canned or frozen for market. Field crops include cotton, sugar beets, potatoes, and alfalfa. In addition nuts (walnuts and almonds), olives, and citrus are produced.

LEADING GREAT CENTRAL VALLEY FARM PRODUCTS, 1961
(values in millions of dollars)

Livestock and Products	468
beef cattle and calves	216
milk	140
eggs	44
turkeys	34
Fruit and Nuts	403
grapes	174
peaches	65
oranges	43
almonds	29
walnuts	29
Cotton and Cottonseed	277
Grains	180
barley	79
rice	56
sorghum	20
Vegetables	166
tomatoes	62
white potatoes	36
cantaloupes	25
asparagus	17
Alfalfa Hay	105
Sugar Beets	30

Source: Agricultural Commissioners, Great Central Valley counties.

THE FARM

Agricultural units vary from the small family fruit farm to the corporate cotton ranches and extensive grain or beef operations. There tends to be correlation between type of product and farm size—greater acreage of grain than of cotton is required to support a family; in turn, the cotton farm must be larger than the grape farm. Irrigated properties are usually largest in the southern San Joaquin (Tulare Basin)—reflecting such factors as recency of land development and the cost of drilling deep pump wells. Large holdings have existed since the days of Mexican land grants and include individual and corporate holdings of thousands of acres.

Rural homesteads often obscure agricultural prosperity; many landowners maintain town residences. Many modest dwellings house field workers, renters, or foremen rather than owners. Collectively, rural dwellings do not evidence the general prosperity suggested in the Middlewestern corn-belt homesteads. Outbuildings tend to be limited in number, though machine sheds are conspicuous. Barns commonly are restricted to older districts. Larger properties often have barracks-like structures to house field workers.

LABOR

Labor shortage was not critical in the Great Valley during much of the nineteenth century —relatively few workers were required in cattle ranching and grain farming. Chinese, and later Japanese, came to California by the thousands. However, the Californian of European descent feared such competition; the Oriental worked long hours for modest pay. Such labor was discouraged in several ways —eventually the Immigration Act of 1924 excluded most east Asians.

Expansion of irrigation agriculture demanded additional seasonal labor; migratory workers were welcomed in order to provide a *cheap* supply when needed. Agricultural schedules that evolved between southern Arizona and the Canadian border provided a long work season. But many migrants have been destitute and often near starvation in midwinter. Moreover, they have lacked social status—their families, particularly the children, have been without the benefits accruing to sedentary people with accepted community position.

Much seasonal work was long accomplished by the compliant foreigner—the Filipino, Hindu, and Mexican, willing to accept lower wages and working conditions unacceptable to native-born Americans. The 1930's, a period of depression and Great Plains drought, brought thousands of displaced persons into the Valley and created the conditions dramatized by McWilliams' *Ill Fares the Land* and Steinbeck's *Grapes of Wrath*. During the decade considerable numbers of non-Americans, especially Mexicans, were repatriated.

World War II and critical labor shortages in West Coast defense plants gave many depression victims a chance to find a more adequate livelihood; and some have since become successful Valley landowners. They were replaced in the field by Mexican nationals and briefly by German prisoners of war.

More recently, extensive use has been made of the Mexican national, either as the illegal entrant ("wetback") or as the contract worker ("bracero"). In recent years organized labor has been demanding more favorable working conditions for native-born workers and elimination of competition from aliens. Eventually, it seems mechanization may eliminate migratory work entirely. The high degree of mechanization in California has resulted partially from labor shortage; the cost of machinery encourages cooperatives, hiring arrangements, and larger farm units.

MARKETING

The gold camps in the Sierran foothills provided a major impetus for agricultural beginnings in the Great Valley. This market was soon severely curtailed, and with expanded output it became necessary to rely upon more distant markets in eastern United States and in Europe. Even today western United States, with its large expanses of dry lands and mountainous terrain, affords rather limited markets. As various geographers have noted, the growing urban centers within California now consume increasing amounts of Great Valley

products. Still, Valley farmers watch prospective trade agreements between the United States and Europe's Common Market with apprehension.

Historically, the expansion of irrigation agriculture has been dependent upon worldwide markets (one finds Del Monte brand canned goods 'everywhere'). Attainment of such markets has required cheap labor, improved transportation media, quality control; cooperatives and corporations can afford extensive advertising.

COMMERCE

Transportation is very important in the economy of the Central Valley. In early years wagons and riverboats were significant, thus favoring the Sacramento Valley (with one-day trips to a navigable river) over the San Joaquin. Mining practices, especially hydraulicking, reduced the value of the Sacramento River for shipment by the 1870's, when serious railroad competition developed. More recently railroads, highways, and airlines have been the principal arteries of transportation.

RAILROADS

Three major railroads serve the Central Valley (see map, Fig. 9-2). The most extensive lines belong to the Southern Pacific, with its parallel routes covering much of the length of the Sacramento and San Joaquin valleys. In addition, the original "Central Pacific" line extends from the Bay Area through Sacramento into the Sierra Nevada. Farther north, the Western Pacific leaves the northern Sierra at Oroville with trackage into Sacramento and thence to the Bay Area. Santa Fe lines extend from Bakersfield northward across the San Joaquin Valley into the Bay Area. Principal rail points in the Central Valley include Bakersfield, Fresno, Stockton, and Sacramento.

HIGHWAYS

The Central Valley has a good highway network whose principal artery is U.S. 99, the "main street of California," extending the entire length of the Valley and approaching freeway status throughout this distance. Between Sacramento and Red Bluff this highway is actually two separate routes, 99W and 99E —99W tends to carry more through and commercial traffic (much emanating in the Bay Area) whereas 99E is used by local residents. Southward from Sacramento the single thoroughfare is the intensively used freeway into Los Angeles, carrying a tremendous volume of traffic, with many buses and trucks. Along the western side of the San Joaquin, California 33 approximates the projected path of Interstate 5.

A number of major highways cross the Great Central Valley with east-west trend. Most important are segments of two major transcontinental routes through Sacramento, U.S. 40 (Interstate 80) and U.S. 50. U.S. 40A, utilizing the Feather River canyon through the northern Sierra Nevada, has increasing use. Of consequence too are such highways as U.S. 299 and California 20 in the Sacramento Valley and California 152 and U.S. 466 in the San Joaquin.

AIRLINES

Air transportation in the Central Valley is largely feeder traffic, mostly north-south into San Francisco and Los Angeles. Pacific Air Lines serves larger communities throughout the Valley, and United Air Lines provides service southward from Sacramento. Sacramento is too near the Bay Area to provide frequent flights to eastern United States.

WATERWAYS

Relatively little commerce now moves along Central Valley rivers. Such bulky products as petroleum are carried as far north as Colusa on the Sacramento (Fig. 9-12). Since a dredged ship channel again converted it into a seaport in 1933, Stockton has been the major water outlet within the Central Valley. With completion of the Sacramento Ship Channel in 1963 freighter commerce again enhances the tug-barge traffic that now uses the lower Sacramento; the likely volume of sea-going cargo seems problematic.

The three principal subdivisions of the Great Central Valley—(1) Sacramento Valley, (2) Delta Lands, and (3) San Joaquin—have physical distinctions, differing histories, and contrasting utilization that seems to warrant more detailed discussion of the contemporary landscapes of these sections.

SACRAMENTO VALLEY

The Sacramento Valley suggests a transplanted Middlewest; a trip eastward from the Coast Ranges along California Highway 32 is reminiscent of the transition along U.S. 40 from western Kansas into Missouri. West of the Sacramento River (and west of U.S. 99W) one sees grain fields and grazing beef cattle; east of Orland such scenes are replaced by fruit orchards and an occasional cornfield. The towns, too, bear greater resemblance to those of the Middlewest than do most in California. Timeworn brick buildings in downtown districts and white clapboard dwellings in older residential sections are characteristic. Groves of deciduous trees along the Sacramento River and perennial waterways on the east side likewise suggest those of the lower Missouri basin.

The Sacramento Valley is only half as large as the San Joaquin Valley. An indistinct boundary between these two basins, between the Cosumnes and Calaveras rivers approximately at Lodi, has been noted. Despite its lesser size, the Sacramento drainage basin has twice the discharge of the San Joaquin basin.

There is still little difference in summer temperatures, but Sacramento Valley winters are appreciably wetter (especially in comparison to Tulare Basin) with greater likelihood of unseasonable frost.

The Sacramento Valley is readily divided into four land-use subdivisions: (1) Anderson Valley, (2) the West Side, (3) the flood basins (i.e., the Rice Bowl), and (4) the East Side. Their utilization will be discussed successively.

ANDERSON VALLEY

Anderson Valley,[6] northernmost portion of the Sacramento Valley, is semicircular in shape—about 30 miles north-south and thirty to forty miles east-west. It extends from Red Bluff to Redding, occupying the central portions of Shasta and Tehama counties.

The over-all physical appearance of the valley is much as it was when the geologist Brewer described it in 1862. The surface is underlain by the cemented formation known as the "Red Lands," which gave Red Bluff its name. Along its axis the Sacramento River has cut the "Iron Canyon." The undulating countryside, usually several hundred feet higher than the Sacramento Valley floor south of Red Bluff, is dotted with oak groves amidst grasslands seasonally green or seared a burned gold.

Most of the cultivated land lies along the narrow Sacramento floodplain north of Iron Canyon between Anderson and Redding; elsewhere extensive livestock ranching prevails. Rural incomes accrue principally from beef cattle, although there is some dairying and scattered deciduous fruit orchards. A significant increase in bedding strawberries since 1950 reflects shipment to major strawberry areas of the Central Coast (Chapter 8).

Wood processing constitutes an economic mainstay—logs are trucked from adjacent highlands to mills along the rail lines. Several

[6] The purist might restrict use of the term Anderson Valley to the alluvial valley of lower Cottonwood Creek.

LEADING SHASTA-TEHAMA COUNTY
FARM PRODUCTS, 1961
(values in millions of dollars)

beef cattle	10.4
irrigated pasture	3.3
market milk	1.5
strawberry plants	1.5
alfalfa hay	1.08
sheep and lambs	0.67
eggs	0.6

Source: Agricultural Commissioners, Shasta and Tehama counties. (Figures are mostly for Anderson Valley; statistics for portions of Tehama County south of Red Bluff are excluded as nearly as possible.)

of the operators are corporations whose holdings in the bordering Klamath or Southern Cascade mountains permit sustained yield operations. Prominent names include U.S. Plywood, Diamond National, Kimberly Clark, and Cascade Properties (Fig. 9-6).

Redding and Red Bluff, seats of Shasta and Tehama counties respectively, are the principal communities of the valley. **Redding** (12,-700), largest city of the northern Sacramento Valley, functions as service center for the extensive highlands country surrounding it except on the south. Located at the junction of federal highways 99 and 299, it is a gateway to major recreational areas and has importance as a tourist stop. It also has construction, mining, and wood products. Its newer subdivisions overlook the Sacramento River and have vistas of Mt. Shasta and Lassen Peak. Shasta College is one of relatively few junior colleges in extreme northern California.

Red Bluff (7200), erstwhile head of navigation on the Sacramento, is a livestock center. There are also several significant lumber operations in the vicinity; the largest is the $10 million Diamond National plant (Fig. 9-6). Red Bluff, like Redding, serves as a western gateway to Lassen Park. It is also at the junction of U.S. 99E and 99W.

THE WEST SIDE

The casual wayfarer, generally cognizant of Central Valley agricultural output but un-

Fig. 9-6. WOOD-PRODUCTS MILL, RED BLUFF. This $10-million Diamond National mill beside the Sacramento River utilizes logs brought from company tree farms in the Southern Cascade to the east. U.S. 99W and the Shasta route of the Southern Pacific Railroad are in the foreground. (David W. Lantis)

certain of location of more productive districts, probably finds the several score of miles between Arbuckle and Red Bluff a disillusioning experience as he speeds along U.S. 99W. Where are the legendary fields of alfalfa, rice, and cotton, the peach orchards and the vineyards? Unless this visitor is observant he may even overlook the narrow strips of irrigated floodplains along Sacramento tributaries that rise in the northern Coast Ranges. Because the West Side lies within the rain shadow of these highlands, the east-flowing creeks are commonly dry watercourses more than half of each year and provide limited quantities of water in contrast to such East Side rivers as the American and the Feather. This has tended to discourage development of irrigation districts—the land is generally watered from pump wells on individual properties.

Sizable portions of the West Side have never progressed beyond livestock ranching, the initial stage in American utilization of the Great Central Valley. The extensive tracts underlain by the Red Lands are not suitable for irrigation agriculture and generally are used only for seasonal pasturage. Over wide stretches the second historic stage (production of winter grains) persists—rainfall is sufficient

LEADING WEST SIDE FARM PRODUCTS, 1961
(values in millions of dollars)

Field Crops	
barley	9.5
irrigated pasture	4.0
seed crops	3.8
field corn	3.4
alfalfa hay	3.0
dry beans	2.0
wheat	1.1
Livestock and Products	
beef cattle	22.3
sheep and lambs	5.8
milk, market	2.7
milk, manufactured	0.9
hogs and pigs	2.5
wool	1.6
Fruits and Nuts	
almonds	7.8
prunes	4.0
olives	2.0
English walnuts	1.2
Truck Crops	
tomatoes	14.5
melons	2.8

Source: Agricultural Commissioners. (The West Side includes portions of Tehama, Glenn, Colusa, and Yolo counties.)

Fig. 9-7. OLIVE HARVEST, CORNING. The Corning District is a major producer of olives, picked ripe for local canning. (Bureau of Reclamation, photo by B. D. Glaha)

for dry farming. Such landscapes constitute the typical West Side scene. The almost tree-less plain is gently undulating. Ranch houses are scattered and properties are large. One can often drive some distance on back roads without meeting another vehicle. Specialized agriculture is largely restricted to the flood-plains of such east-flowing Sacramento tribu-taries as Elder, Thomes, Stony, and Cache creeks (see map, Fig. 9-2).[7]

Most West Side communities might be de-scribed by "courthouses, residences, freight cars, and filling stations." All except Davis and Woodland in Yolo County are "second-generation" California towns, founded in the 1870's along the Southern Pacific's Shasta line and evolving in the wheat-farming era. Their current populations are usually less than 5000 inhabitants. They have a settled look but tend to have fewer shade trees than East Side

[7] Completion of the Central Valley Project will en-hance the agricultural output of the West Side—additional canals are contemplated in this part of the Central Valley.

towns, which are much preferred as residen-tial communities. Service stations, restaurants, and motels reflect traffic flow along U.S. 99W; most of the larger towns are at the junctions of east-west highways with this major north-south thoroughfare.

THE GERBER DISTRICT

The Gerber District, dependent upon the relatively high water table along Elder Creek to permit pump irrigation, is without benefit of reservoir storage. Cropped land, largely located between U.S. 99W and the Sacra-mento River, is devoted to such products as sugar beets, alfalfa, and beans. **Gerber**, a small hamlet housing farm workers, has sig-nificance because it is the rail junction where Southern Pacific tracks serving the western and eastern sides of the Sacramento Valley converge—it is one of few Sacramento Val-ley towns that still has a railroad passenger station.

THE CORNING DISTRICT

The Corning District, along lower Thomes Creek, is also without benefit of reservoir stor-age. Water has been supplied by pump wells and water tables have declined. This situation is now changing; Sacramento River water be-came available in 1960 through the Corning Canal, a CVP unit that originates at a pump-ing station south of Red Bluff.

The district is California's third ranking area in the production of olives; approxi-mately 3500 acres are grown (Fig. 9-7). The Sevillano variety, the most popular here, is used for domestic consumption as eating olives—much of the processing is done locally.

Corning (3000) has grown since 1940—completion of the Corning Canal should foster additional growth. Besides the usual farm service functions, Corning has olive-packing and processing plants.

THE ORLAND DISTRICT

The Orland District lies along the flood-plain of Stony Creek and receives water from Stony Gorge and East Park reservoirs. The district is an early twentieth-century federal reclamation project developed as a model to demonstrate the effectiveness of this type of program. However, until completion of Black Butte dam the district will continue to suffer from insufficient water in drier years. The project is a memorial to pioneer Will Green, who struggled for half a century to bring irrigation to the Sacramento Valley. Properties generally remain small and individual incomes modest. An exception is corporate Mills Orchards at Hamilton City, producer of oranges, apricots, prunes, and other specialty crops. The district is the leading milk producer of the upper Sacramento Valley; prunes, almonds, and walnuts are also raised. Ladino clover seed is a distinctive specialty.

Orland (2500) is a stable crossroads community characterized by modest dwellings. Dairy products are processed here.

THE ARBUCKLE DISTRICT

The Arbuckle District does not lie along an east-flowing stream as do other West Side districts: water is pumped from the alluvial strata underlying the Sacramento floodplain. Fertile soils have promoted agricultural development for a locality that since 1892 has become an important California almond center.

YOLO COUNTY

Yolo County was an early locale of American occupancy in the Sacramento Valley; its settlement incentives included proximity to San Francisco Bay and extensive areas of Grade I soils. This was the only portion of the West Side where Mexican grants were made —several were awarded to Americans in the middle 1840's.

Yolo County, agricultural leader of the Sacramento Valley, ranks twenty-eighth nationally in farm output. This is understandable since its fertile alluvial surfaces are the most extensive in the Valley. Like the Santa Clara Valley (Chapter 8), Yolo County forms a "fruit bowl" with orchards of apricots, figs, freestone peaches, and prunes as well as vineyards. Its output has been somewhat less prodigious than that of its Central Coast counterpart. There are also groves of olives,

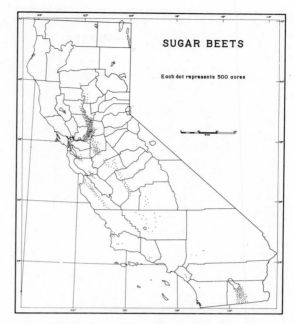

Fig. 9-8. MAP OF THE CALIFORNIA SUGAR-BEET ACREAGE.

almonds, and walnuts. Residents acclaim the county the "American sugar bowl"—a debatable contention, although it does rank second among California counties in beet sugar (Fig. 9-8). The nocturnal flow of cool ocean air moving inland through Carquinez Strait in late afternoon and evening is favorable for the beets. This phenomenon is also a consideration for tomatoes—the county is one of the nation's prime sources of canning tomatoes (Fig. 9-9 and 9-10). The landscape almost seems to exude bountiful harvests—rural prosperity is quite evident.

The Montezuma Hills to the south in Solano County separate Yolo County from the Delta Lands. The Hills form an interesting relict of the nineteenth century, with fields of wheat and barley, beef cattle, and sheep.

Woodland (13,500), seat of Yolo County, is an old farm town that is the largest West Side city and the service center for the prosperous farmlands that surround it. Its fecundity is apparent in its downtown district. Food processing (especially beet sugar), stockyards,

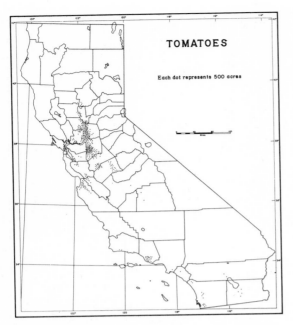

TOMATOES

Each dot represents 500 acres

Fig. 9-9. MAP OF THE CALIFORNIA TOMATO ACREAGE.

shipping sheds, and fruit- and vegetable-packing plants are conspicuous on the east side. There tends to be considerable bustle in the community, especially during the harvest season.

Davis (8900), also an early-day farm hamlet and Southern Pacific rail junction, has become one of the more attractive small cities of the Sacramento Valley. It is a college town —this is reflected in its handsome residences, numerous shade trees, attractive gardens, and the nature of its central district. Many residents commute to employment in Sacramento. The University of California at Davis was long known as one of the nation's outstanding agricultural colleges—its functions are now expanded to include other programs. Davis has encroached upon surrounding farmlands as the university has expanded.

THE FLOOD BASINS

The contemporary Flood Basins are located in the south-central portion of the Sacramento

Valley, occupying lands both to the west and the east of the Sacramento River (see map, Fig. 9-2). These areas have been reclaimed in the twentieth century and are now normally dry most of every year and throughout drier years. During periods of high water they have been repeatedly inundated to become temporary lakes as tributaries of the Sacramento have overflowed their banks. Repeated deposition from standing water has left dense clay soils. Hydraulic mining (Chapter 5) aggravated floods in the Sacramento Valley and raised the elevation of the flood basins. Joseph A. McGowan, in his *History of the Sacramento Valley* (New York: Lewis Historical Publishing Co., 1961) relates this anecdote in Vol. II, p. 175:

Tules, ten to fourteen feet high, covered the land so that farmers who lived all around the edge of the basin were called "rimlanders." It is said that a real estate man once sold 25,000 acres of this tule land to a southern California investor, assuring him that a levee four feet high would be sufficient to reclaim it. However, when the buyer first visited his newly acquired property in winter, he exclaimed, "They have sold me the Pacific Ocean!" According to the story, the investor held onto his land until he finally sold it for $25 an acre about 1910, thereby making a profit of $500,-000.

Repeated disastrous floods led to concerted flood-control action between 1905 and 1920; dikes were built and sizable portions were set aside as the Yolo and Sutter Bypasses after establishment of reclamation districts. Because the heavy runoff normally occurs during the cool season, it seldom interferes with cropping, especially since construction of Shasta and Folsom dams. By 1920, 400,000 acres of flood-basin land had been drained and were under cultivation.

Grains have thrived on portions of the flood basin since John Sutter raised a good wheat crop at his Hock Farm (near present-day Yuba City) in 1845. Wheat was the first major crop, but in this century it has been largely supplanted by sugar beets, alfalfa, and other grains (rice and barley). Repeated cropping of wheat without rotation depleted some soils so sufficiently that farmers were seeking new

Fig. 9-10. *TOMATO HARVEST NEAR WOODLAND. Mechanization has not
yet replaced all harvesting!* (David W. Lantis)

crops. Thus rice was welcomed and within a
few years became a leading product. The newest crop sensation is *safflower,* which has become a million-dollar commodity since 1950.

Safflower, an East Indian plant, is a composite
introduced into California in 1949 for use in the
paint industry; its seeds, which mature in a seed-
head, produce a colorless oil. It has become a
million-dollar crop as result of concern over low-
cholesterol diets. Barley drills and rice combines
can be used in its production—it makes an ideal
rotation crop for the Flood Basins. California is
the nation's No. 1 producer—the state acreage
in 1962 was 235,000.

LEADING FLOOD BASINS
FARM PRODUCTS, 1961
(values in millions of dollars)

rice	50.7
barley	11.1
sugar beets	10.6
sorghum	8.2
safflower	7.6
prunes	6.3
alfalfa hay	5.7

Source: Agricultural Commissioners of Glenn, Butte,
Colusa, Yolo, Sacramento, Sutter, and Yuba counties.

THE RICE BOWL

The Flood Basins in 1961 permitted California to lead the nation in *rice* output, producing a $60 million crop that represented a
fourth of the national yield (Fig. 9-11). The
Sacramento Valley lies near the poleward
limit of rice culture; in fact long-grain Chinese
and tropical Asiatic varieties cannot be grown.
Previous attempts at harvesting Chinese rice
on the cooler Delta Lands to the south failed.
Even in the Sacramento Valley nocturnal cooling shortens the growing season and makes
production precarious in years with early
autumnal rains. Market prospects for short-
grain varieties do not seem promising, and
attempts are underway to climatize long-
grain varieties.

The "rice bowl" is located principally in
Butte, Colusa, Glenn, Sutter, and Yolo counties; in the year of maximum output (1954)
350,000 acres were harvested. Despite the
nation's relatively small acreage it has been
one of the world's three leading rice exporters.
Periods of maximum production have been
achieved during times of crisis: World War I,
World War II, and the Korean emergency.
Federal-acreage controls, imposed in 1955,
have reflected expanding rice production in
countries that prefer long-grain rice.

THE GREAT CENTRAL VALLEY : : 365

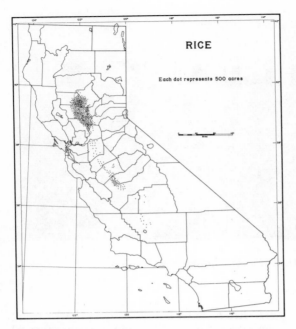

RICE

Each dot represents 500 acres

Fig. 9-11. MAP OF THE RICE ACREAGE IN CALIFORNIA.

The rice is grown paddy-style in shallow (6-8 in.) standing water as in the Orient. Because of its high-moisture demands the rice is raised upon heavy soils that are water retentive. Land slope is significant; there must be gradient enough to permit rapid drainage for harvest but even enough to minimize land preparation.

Sacramento Valley production has become a typically American operation, utilizing limited labor but requiring much machinery. Fields are prepared in April and then flooded. An innovation in the 1960's has been substitution of plastic dikes for earthen checks. Water-soaked seed is dropped from low-flying aircraft; fertilizer is also spread by plane.

Before DDT, mosquito control on the rice paddies was too expensive to attempt. California has thirty-seven subspecies of mosquitoes, including an Anopheles subspecies that can transmit malaria—between 1938-1947 there were 2298 cases of malaria in the state. An outbreak of the disease has been prevented more recently because of the absence of a suitable vector. Dozens of mosquito-abatement districts have been established.

Harvesting is effected as a single operation with specially built self-propelled combines that can move through wet ground. A three-man crew can now accomplish work that formerly required a hundred men. The rice is taken to dryers and thence to storage silos until marketing.

Allegedly before World War II California's machine-produced rice successfully competed in the Orient against the local hand-grown grain. Japan has approached self-sufficiency in rice since the middle 1950's. The small domestic United States market uses the short-grain varieties mostly in cereals.

The Flood Basins form part of the Pacific flyway for waterfowl. In fact the Sacramento National Wildlife Refuge has been established northwest of Colusa. Each autumn thousands of hunters frequent the flood basins for ducks and geese, as well as pheasants and grouse. A number of urban groups have established private hunting preserves.

ORCHARDS ON THE LEVEES

Natural levees flank the inner edges of the Flood Basins, paralleling the channels of the Sacramento and its chief tributaries. They possess friable soils with better natural drainage than the basins. Extensive strips south of California Route 32 (between Chico and Orland) have long been utilized for deciduous fruit orchards, particularly plums and peaches. Some of the more extensive areas, such as those around Yuba City, will be discussed in the next section. Since the middle 1950's a noticeable expansion of prune orchards has taken place.

RIVER PORTS

Most Flood Basins towns were founded along the Sacramento and Feather rivers—the natural levees tended to be drier and the rivers stimulated commerce. The Sacramento Valley relied largely upon river commerce before 1872. Most transportation between the San Francisco Bay Area and Sacramento moved by water, particularly during the Gold Rush, although Red Bluff was the head of navigation. During the zenith of wheat farming several river ports had much importance. Rail competition probably sounded the death knell for the riverboats; also, by 1860 channel silting

Fig. 9-12. TUG AND BARGE ON THE SACRAMENTO. River commerce has declined as a result of competitive transport media and because of channel silting. (Standard Oil Company of California)

resulting from mining operations (Chapter 5) was making river travel increasingly difficult. Many river towns long ago waned and most have even vanished from the maps. Knights Landing, Nicolaus, and Butte City remain as small villages, and Tehama, one-time seat of Tehama County, languishes. The extant towns house agricultural personnel, but there is no large "rice town." The grain is generally milled beside railroad sidings and moves to the port of Stockton by rail.

Colusa (3500) is now the largest town on the Sacramento between Sacramento and Red Bluff. It retains a little river traffic in bulk petroleum products (Fig. 9-12). Its economy, however, depends upon county government, farm trade, and the residence of farmers and retired ranchers.

THE EAST SIDE

The East Side (see map, Fig. 9-2), which first achieved importance with the Gold Rush, remains the dominant area in the Sacramento Valley economy—it possesses the largest cities in the Valley and a series of fertile agricultural districts on alluvial fans of west-flowing Sacramento tributaries. Although the West Side has more extensive acreage of good alluvium, the East Side is better watered. Away from the

LEADING EAST SIDE
FARM PRODUCTS, 1961
(values in millions of dollars)

Field Crops	
seed crops	3.4
alfalfa	3.0
beans, dry	2.6
hops	2.1
irrigated pasture	1.5
barley	1.4
Fruits, Vegetables, and Nuts	
peaches (canning)	16.5
almonds	9.5
prunes	8.2
tomatoes (canning)	4.7
English walnuts	3.0
olives	0.8
Livestock and Products	
cattle and calves	18.9
eggs	5.9
milk, market	6.7
milk, manufactured	4.0
sheep and lambs	1.9
chicks, hatching	1.9
turkeys	1.2
chickens	0.8

Source: Agricultural Commissioners of Tehama, Butte, Yuba, Sutter, and Sacramento counties.

stream valleys extensive East Side acreage rests on red lands and volcanic flows that merge almost imperceptibly into highland foothills on the east. On such unirrigated uplands seasonal grazing and dry-farmed grains constitute the characteristic use. Since long stretches of U.S. 99E lie upon these less productive surfaces, the highway traveler does not gain a true impression of East Side productivity.

East Side streams are perennial yet many of the smaller ones have not been dammed to conserve seasonal runoff from the Sierra Nevada and the Southern Cascade. The following irrigated districts will be considered: Los Molinos, Vina, Chico, Feather River Valley, and Sacramento.

LOS MOLINOS DISTRICT

The Los Molinos District is the most northerly area of irrigation agriculture on the East Side. Rancho Los Molinos in Mill Creek Valley was acquired by Joseph Cone, one of the more celebrated wheat barons, in the middle 1850's. Cone, who eventually acquired 100,000 acres, was chiefly concerned with wheat and sheep although he set out fruit trees including Bartlett pears. After Cone's death his heirs established a land company that built irrigation works, laid out the townsite of Los Molinos, and sold small tracts. Small properties still prevail; the district produces poultry, milk, and such deciduous fruits and nuts as almonds, walnuts, prunes, peaches, and apricots. **Los Molinos** (circa 750), service point for the district, is bolstered economically by trade of travelers along U.S. 99E.

THE VINA DISTRICT

The Vina District has been associated with some of California's prominent earlier American residents. Peter Lassen received 26,000-acre Rancho Bosquejo along Deer Creek in 1843. He established Benton City at the western terminus of Lassen's Trail, but the town disappeared after its populace left in quest of gold. A portion of the ranch was acquired by Henry Gerke, who introduced quality European grapevines into the Sacramento Valley and created one of California's finest vineyards in the 1870's. Senator Leland Stanford bought the Gerke lands in 1881 and added additional acreage so that his Vina Ranch reached 55,000 acres. Anticipating a market

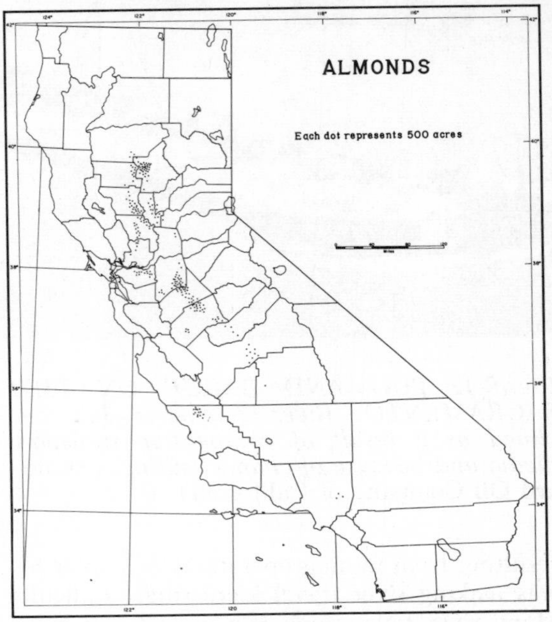

Fig. 9-13. MAP OF THE ALMOND ACRE-AGE IN CALIFORNIA.

for cheap California wine, Stanford planted nearly 3 million grapevines. He proved less successful in viticulture than he was as a railroad magnate; still, some of the vines remained until 1919. Stanford deeded the ranch to Stanford University, which sold it as small farms. Today the Vina District produces milk, deciduous fruits, and nuts. Trappist monks purchased a portion of Vina Ranch, including some of the Stanford buildings, in the 1950's.

THE CHICO DISTRICT

Conversion of the Chico District into one of the most productive farming localities in the Sacramento Valley was undertaken by John Bidwell, who came to California as co-leader of the first overland immigrant party. Bidwell purchased two contiguous Mexican ranchos, presumably with returns from gold mining on the Feather River. Thus he acquired the fertile alluvial fan of Chico Creek and smaller streams.

Wheat was the dominant nineteenth-century activity, but Bidwell was keenly inter-

Fig. 9-14. CENTRAL CHICO. Chico State College (left foreground), the warehouse district, the downtown sector, and residential blocks can be seen. (David W. Lantis)

ested in agricultural experimentation—he left 1800 acres of deciduous orchards when he died in 1900. Fruit raising, especially peaches, had already gained local importance; but years of low prices prompted orchardists to shift to plums, then to prunes. Almond groves were set out around Durham in the 1920's. The Chico District is now the state's leading producer of almonds (Fig. 9-13), and walnut acreage is expanding. Heavier soils toward the Sacramento River yield a variety of crops, including sugar beets (and hops in bygone years), alfalfa, beans, tomatoes, and field corn.

Chico (14,750), interior California's largest city north of Sacramento, was founded in 1860 as a dwelling place for Bidwell workers. Its nineteenth-century growth was based upon farm trade, freighting eastward across the mountains, lumbering, agricultural processing, and shipping. Chico alone among larger Sacramento Valley towns is not a county seat. Its functions were delineated with establishment of a normal school (now Chico State College) in 1887. Older residential streets have the white frame dwellings and large deciduous shade trees common in East Side towns (Fig. 9-14).

Chico, principally a residence town, has had limited industry. Diamond National long milled lumber here, but since completion of its Red Bluff wood-products plant in 1959,

matches remain its principal Chico product. Almonds and walnuts are also processed.

Chico's functions on a modest scale suggest those of Fresno in the San Joaquin Valley. Post-World War II growth has resulted from rising college enrollments and because of the mid-Valley location, which has prompted hundreds of jobbers and salesmen to reside here. Many of its senior citizens located in Chico because of the town's attractive physical appearance. Bidwell Park, with 2400 acres containing sycamore-oak woodland along Chico Creek, ranks second in size to Los Angeles' Griffith Park among city parks in the United States.

FEATHER RIVER VALLEY

The single most productive agricultural district of the Sacramento Valley lies along the plain of its chief tributary, the Feather River. This tri-county section extends for 50 miles between Sierran foothills on the east and the Sutter Buttes on the west. Prominent levees along the Feather, Yuba, and Bear rivers reflect the repeated threat of seasonal flooding. Miles of gravel heaped along the Feather and the Yuba attest the past importance of gold dredging.

The Valley, especially in eastern Sutter County, has long been the nation's leading source of canned peaches. The "Peach Belt,"

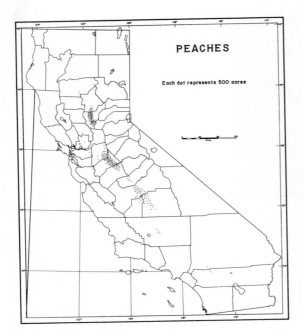

Fig. 9-15. MAP OF THE PEACH ACRE-AGE IN CALIFORNIA.

Fig. 9-16. THE PEACH BELT. The Feather River Valley, downstream from Oroville, is the world's chief source of canned peaches. (David W. Lantis)

extending southward from Gridley through Nicolaus, is situated on fertile brown alluvial soils (Fig. 9-16). Winters are sufficiently cool for peaches, and the long hot summers with low humidity are favorable. Clingstones, whose firmer flesh is better for canning than freestones, are the common type. The mature trees, dependent upon winter rains, will grow without irrigation.

The Peach Belt (or Tri-County district) reflects the momentum of an early start. John Sutter demonstrated the suitability of the Feather River Valley at the time of the Gold Rush. Expansion was slow before construction of the first cannery; in the 1890's orchards rapidly replaced wheat fields. In recent years the Belt has produced nearly half of the world's canned peaches. Most of the varieties used in canning originated locally after 1900. The canneries employ housewives and students from surrounding counties.

The peach has a relatively short commercial bearing span of about twenty years; hence some orchards have been replanted several times. Dif-

ferent varieties ripen from June through August. Orchard management is important—the fruit must be of fairly uniform size and relatively free of defects. Yields per acre have tripled since 1920 as a result of improved cultivation. Production of California clingstones has increased sixfold in the same period, reflecting increased yield per acre and much expanded acreage, especially in the San Joaquin Valley. There tends to be a sizable surplus, and 10 to 15 percent of the fruit is destroyed annually.

The Peach Belt ranks after coastal valleys in production of prunes. Some feel that with continued urbanization in the Santa Clara Valley the Feather River Valley may become the state's ranking source. A number of new orchards have been planted but so far remain scattered, without the concentration of the peach groves.

The upper Feather River Valley around Oroville is northern California's chief source of olives and oranges, as was indicated previously (Chapter 5). The trees are concentrated south of Oroville toward Palermo on residual soils at the contact between the Central Valley and the Sierra Nevada. Olives will produce well on soils generally unsuitable for many crops.

Navel oranges ripen several weeks earlier than in Southern California and thus benefit from advantageous market conditions. Agricultural colonies were established at **Thermalito** and **Palermo** in the late nineteenth century—water comes from facilities originally developed for mining operations. A "thermal belt" permits orange production, although the severe freeze of 1932, when temperatures dropped as low as 12°F., killed many trees, and sharply curtailed production. Previously, local enthusiasts had predicted that the Sacramento Valley would rival Southern California in production.

LEVEE TOWNS

The Feather River Valley has more towns of consequence than any other portion of the Sacramento Valley except the environs of metropolitan Sacramento. All three of the county seats are "levee towns" along the Feather River and were founded during the Gold Rush.

Oroville (6000), seat of Butte County, is located at the mouth of the Feather River Canyon (Chapter 5) with residential districts on slopes of Sierran foothills. The population within its limits is only slightly larger than it was during the Gold Rush. Oroville is a farm processing (olives) and shipping point, a Western Pacific division point, a tourist stop on U.S. 40A, and gateway to the Sierran "Feather River Country." It is anticipated that the town, enlarged since construction of the dam began, will grow after completion of Oroville Dam (Fig. 5-35).

The twin cities of Yuba City and Marysville are downriver from Oroville. **Marysville** (9500) began as a trading post in 1842 and served as gateway to the "northern diggins" during the gold period—briefly it was California's third largest city. Marysville is no longer a river port since mining operations

silted the Feather channel. It is the seat of Yuba County and service center for surrounding ranchers. It also benefits from proximity to Beale Air Force Base. Yuba College provides two years of higher education.

Yuba City (11,500), seat of Sutter County, tends to be less conservative than Marysville. Although it was founded in 1849, it was not affected by the Gold Rush—the village was located on the wrong (west) side of the river. Its growth has come largely since 1900 with rising agricultural productivity. Besides its fruit-packing houses it is a residential community for employees of Beale Air Force Base and even some Sacramento commuters. The city was ravaged by flood at Christmastide, 1955 (Fig. 9-3). Unlike Marysville, however, which is largely confined by dikes, Yuba City is expanding northwestward into orchards and is now larger than Marysville.

BEALE AIR FORCE BASE

The sprawling Beale Air Force Base east of Marysville was established as an Army training camp in 1942, with 86,000 acres. After World War II it was declared to be war surplus, but in 1948 it was transferred to the Air Force. This Strategic Air Command base is now tied to aerial defense of the Bay Area with three missile sites (Chico, Sutter Buttes, and Lincoln), and acts as the nerve center for electronic early warning along the Pacific Coast. The economic effect of this installation has been significant to the East Side.

THE SACRAMENTO DISTRICT

The Sacramento District, focusing upon the American River Valley and the city of Sacramento, is the most populous portion of the entire Central Valley. The American River Valley has served since the 1840's as the major transportation corridor from central California into the interior West via Donner Pass. John Sutter established the first white settlement in interior California here in 1839. In the Sierran foothills nearby John Marshall found gold in 1848. Today metropolitan Sacramento, with housing tracts encroaching upon farmlands, is one of California's faster growing urban centers.

Much of Sacramento County, exclusive of the Delta Lands in the southwest, is a rolling countryside underlain by iron hardpan soils, and thus has limited agricultural value. In rural areas land utilization has tended to remain basically the same for a century: seasonal pasturage is prevalent. Even the American River Valley, without the attenuated alluvial lowland of the Feather River, has limited agricultural value. A specialty crop east of Sacramento and also west of Wheatland (Sutter County) in the Bear River Valley is hops. The hop vines are trained to climb cords strung from horizontal wires attached to poles about 16 feet tall. During harvest in late summer the vines are cut down and the cones are removed by machine harvesters, dried, sacked, and shipped to breweries. The District also has dairies and poultry farms, reflecting the local market.

Sacramento (191,600), capital city of California, lies north of the state's geographical center athwart major routes between San Francisco Bay and eastern United States. Its site, somewhat unfavorable because of early floods, lies southeast of the confluence of the Sacramento and American rivers at an elevation of 20 feet. Its functions include government (including military bases), retail and wholesale trade, tourism, commerce, and manufacturing. Its growth is accelerating and some planners predict a larger population than that of San Francisco by 1980.

This was once the setting of **New Helvetia**, the eleven leagues obtained by John Sutter from the Mexicans in 1839. Sutter's headquarters, the trading post known as Sutter's Fort, was two miles east of the Sacramento River on higher ground. A trail led to the embarcadero (landing) on the river. South of the landing Sutter laid out Sutterville in 1844. The rival community of Sacramento grew up at the embarcadero when the Gold Rush began. Within seven months the upstart village had 10,000 residents and was the principal gateway into the Mother Lode Country (Chapter 5). It displayed boom-town aspects with many itinerants, saloons, and gambling houses. The town was plagued by early disasters— there were three serious floods between 1849

Fig. 9-17. *MAP OF SACRAMENTO.*

and 1853, and much of it burned in 1852. Meanwhile, Sacramento had become the capital of California, and the legislature convened there in 1852 although the capitol building was not completed until 1874.

Sacramento's early growth was promoted by upstream commerce destined for the mines; as early as 1856 a rail line was extended to Folsom. The Pony Express operated in 1860-61 with Sacramento as its western terminus. Eastward construction of the Central Pacific was commenced in 1863 from Sacramento, which housed its main office. Completion of the transcontinental link six years later added to the city's commercial importance. Additional revenue came forty years later with construction of a second trans-Sierran railroad, the Western Pacific.

Agricultural development of the Central Valley, especially in more northerly portions, also helped Sacramento to flourish. The city has again become a seaport; although much commerce moves downriver to the Bay Area,

Fig. 9-18. DOWNTOWN SACRAMENTO. View of the old section of the city (foreground) along the Sacramento River, with the central business district (middle left) and Capitol Park. (Sacramento City-County Chamber of Commerce, photo by Cartwright Aerial Surveys)

Sacramento is a major agricultural processing point.

The small downtown district has evolved north of Capitol Park and eastward from the original townsite (Fig. 9-18). It contains department stores and specialty shops, with hotels, restaurants, and apartment buildings also surrounding Capitol Park. As the rivers have restricted outward growth toward the west and north, the downtown area has become "off center" in northwestern Sacramento.

State government focuses upon **Capitol Park** with its attractive landscaping. The capitol and older structures are of classic Greek architecture, whereas newer office buildings toward the west are concrete structures in contemporary design. More than 20,000 state employees in Sacramento provide the city with a sizable payroll.

"**Old Town,**" blocks of antiquated brick buildings, extends eastward from the Sacramento water front and merges into the central district and Capitol Park (Fig. 9-18). This socially submarginal district is occupied by many single, male itinerants, low-income groups, and foreign born, especially Mexicans and Orientals. Crocker Art Gallery, one-time home of the rail magnate, and various "heritage" buildings are here. On its northern periphery are the passenger depot and adjoining Southern Pacific railroad shops.

Older residential districts, with streets shaded by large deciduous trees, suggest the Middle West but are atypical among California cities. Thousands of tree-sized camellias are conspicuous among shrubs and flowers. Newer residential blocks, toward the south and east, resemble other large California communities with subdivisions of tract houses. The city has no counterpart of Golden Gate (in San Francisco) or Bidwell (in Chico) parks; William Land Park, approximating the site of Sutterville, is the largest of several recreational areas.

Sacramento has evolved slowly as a cultural center, somewhat eclipsed by proximity to San Francisco. It has recently become a center of higher education; Sacramento State College was established in 1949, and south-side Sacramento City College provides two years of higher education.

Despite summer heat, Capitol Park, Crocker Art Museum, and Sutter's Fort help make it a tourist center; another major attraction is the State Fair in September. Plans have been suggested for renovation of many buildings in "old town" that have historic importance. The rivers provide opportunities for aquatic recreation such as boating and waterskiing.

Sacramento has gained importance as an industrial city. The significance of agricultural commodities was noted; older plants, including those manufacturing tin containers, are located in the northwest adjacent to the river and railroad facilities. They include the nation's largest processing establishments for almonds, rice, tinned fruits, and vegetables. Newer firms make soap and missile fuels— Aerojet, whose Sacramento plant was established in 1953, has employed over 15,000, and its payrolls have exceeded those of the other 300 industrial plants in the city.

Central location within California at junction of north-south and east-west routes on the state's largest river has always given Sacramento importance as a transportation center. Completion of the ship channel paralleling the course of the lower Sacramento with a turning basin west of the city has again made Sacramento a seaport. Water-borne commerce, particularly petroleum and agricultural products, has long moved by tug-drawn barges.

Land transportation has contributed much to the growth of Sacramento. The city is located on two transcontinental rail routes into the Bay Area from central United States. Service is provided by Western Pacific and Southern Pacific. The Southern Pacific's Valley line connects with its Shasta division, thus linking commerce between Southern California and the Pacific Northwest. Highway commerce is likewise significant, with two major east-west highways, U.S. 40 (Interstate 80) and U.S. 50 bisecting U.S. 99 (Interstate 5E). Sacramento has importance for truck and bus lines, and there are numerous motels on its periphery. The city lacks the importance of Los Angeles and San Francisco as an air center. It is served by United Air Lines and a north-south feeder line, Pacific Air Lines, but jet service is not maintained.

Nearby military installations have fostered Sacramento growth since 1940. In fact, Mather Field was originally activated as a World War I training field; after a period of inactivity in the early 1930's it has been a navigational training center since World War II. McClellan Field supplanted inadequate facilities at San Diego in 1936—initially three 5000-foot runways were constructed. In recent years, Air Force operations at these two bases have employed as many as 27,000 civilians alone—payrolls have exceeded $150 million.

Much metropolitan growth has been occurring outside the city limits—Sacramento has had significant "fringe-area" growth problems. Growth toward the north and east beyond the American River has been encouraged by good transportation (the Sacramento River creates a barrier to the west), higher land not subject to flooding, and employment (air bases and Aerojet). Satellites include **North Sacramento** (13,000), **West Sacramento** (circa 20,000), **Carmichael** (20,500), and **Arden-Arcade** (73,000). Slightly more distant are Roseville and Lincoln. **Roseville** (13,500) has some of the largest rail facilities in western United States, including retarder yards (reassembly of freight cars; capacity of ninety trains daily), shops (Southern Pacific freight car repair), and produce icing (Pacific Fruit Express allegedly has world's largest plant). Space shortage in Sacramento accounts for the size of these facilities at the base of "the hill" (ascent of Donner Pass). The economy of **Lincoln** (3200) has long depended upon local clay deposits and the large Gladding, McBean clay-products plant.

THE DELTA LANDS

The Delta Lands,[8] at the confluence of the Sacramento and San Joaquin rivers east of Suisun Bay, has been called "America's Holland" (see map, Fig. 9-2). Although this area like western Netherlands has been reclaimed, there are marked landscape differences. The Delta Lands does not have the lush greenness of the European country, nor the small properties, dense population, charming old cities, and quaint towns. Moreover, Delta Lands residents, despite threat of seasonal flooding, are not constantly plagued by fear of sea inundation.

Strictly, the Sacramento does not have a delta—its lower course is an estuary that debouches into the Pacific at the Golden Gate. Thus although the Delta Lands displays some deltaic features such as distributary channels (which merge into a single watercourse downstream at the east end of Suisun Bay), natural levees, islands, and marshes (and hence might be called an "interrupted delta"), it lacks the foreset layers of fresh deposition. To Professor John Thompson of Stanford University it has suggested the Fens of eastern England with its wetness and flatness. The Delta Lands is wider on its landward (interior) side, narrowing westward toward Antioch. Still it has the crudely triangular shape of a delta, with Stockton, Sacramento, and Antioch as its apices (see map, Fig. 9-2). On its eastern side it merges almost imperceptibly into the surrounding lowland.

Scarcely a century ago the Delta was a land of tule swamps and mosquitoes, extensively flooded seasonally and little known except to its Indian inhabitants and a few fur trappers (Fig. 9-2). Since 1850 it has been polderized to become an area of extreme productivity, both intensive and specialized. Professor

[8] *The Delta Lands has been reviewed by Thomas and Marcia (née McClain) Pagenhart, University of California at Davis.*

Thompson (see Bibliography) has noted that it was among the first deltaic areas to be reclaimed by advanced methods with employment of much machinery.

Earlier vegetation, characteristically reeds (*Phragmites spp.*) was largely replaced at a late preoccupance time by bulrushes or tules (*Scirpus acutus*). Their residue has created the soil-like mass of partially decayed humus known as peat, intermingled with river silts. The peat averages 18 feet in depth, reaching 40 feet in the west and thinning to 4 to 20 feet in the north. The area underlain by peat covers 307,000 acres; the Delta, however, is considered larger, encompassing 490,000 acres including marginal sections of "mineral" soil and 45,000 acres of water surface. The northern part of the Delta, with more mineral in the soil and less peat, has experienced less subsidence and is more fertile.

As late as 1850 nearly two thirds of the Delta was inundated during high tides. Even after reclamation serious flooding was experienced, more recently in 1928, 1936, 1938, 1940, 1950, and 1955.

Eight Mexican land grants were assigned on the Delta fringes in the 1840's. Settlement, which did not really commence before 1850, originated on the northern edge. Occupance was limited until passage of the Swamp Act in 1855. A section of land on Merritt Island had been diked in 1851; however, accord between state and federal governments on the extent of the swampland did not materialize until 1871. Meanwhile, additional land was occupied. By 1871 the state had sold virtually all of its swampland. Original parcels, first 320 acres and then 640 acres, had in some instances been accumulated into sizable holdings. One person, George D. Roberts, was the alleged transfer agent for some 250,000 acres. Reclamation costs and farming methods favored large holdings, which still prevail.

Fig. 9-19. CONTRA COSTA CANAL. View showing the southwestern edge of the Delta Lands with Mt. Diablo in the distance. This canal, 48 miles in length, delivers Sacramento River water to farmers and urban users in Contra Costa County. (Bureau of Reclamation, photo by A. G. D'Alessandro)

Fig. 9-20. TINSLEY ISLAND. This small island between Isleton and Stockton near Franks Tract still has a pristine landscape that contrasts with cultivated Empire Tract beyond (to north). The San Joaquin River Channel is in the foreground with White Slough in the distance. Note the pleasure craft and resort. (Aero Photographers, Sausalito)

Reclamation was a long, tedious, costly, and discouraging affair. However, it took place earlier than in some parts of the Great Central Valley, probably because of (1) proximity to markets, (2) good water transportation, (3) ease of irrigation, and (4) inherent fertility of the land. Repeatedly levees were swept away, land deluged, crops, livestock, and homes lost. Although half of the Delta had been recovered before 1900 and all of it by 1930, as late as 1885 only 8000 acres were completely reclaimed and relatively flood free. Although reclamation districts date from 1861 there was ineffective state regulation until 1911. Despite setbacks the land proved unusually productive and diking costs were amply repaid (although many pioneers were ruined financially). Building of levees has always been most tricky on the "light peat," which compresses and "sinks" under the weight of an alluvial levee.

The earliest levees, individual hand efforts, were a few feet high and not over 12 feet wide. After 1870 dikes tended to become corporate or reclamation-district projects, increasingly substantial. More recent dikes have been 100 feet wide at the base and 25 to 30 feet in height. Chinese labor was common on the

older embankments—since 1893-94 the "clamshell" dredger has been used widely. Earlier levees were raised from the peat sod of the "islands" and consequently failed; more recently dredges have utilized river muck ("blue clay"). Completion of Shasta Dam in 1944 reduced much of the threat of summer salinity and also lessened winter and spring flooding. The salinity has resulted from tidal inflow of ocean water at times of low runoff of Great Central Valley rivers—water released from Shasta Dam has regulated Sacramento flow.

Drainage early created a problem, particularly during periods of winter storms, and as subsidence continues, is a worsening problem. Since 1920 large electric pumps have been available; each district maintains one or more pumping stations on pilings above maximum flood levels. Much use is made of siphons for both drainage and irrigation; large-capacity siphons require only small pumps to start the siphoning.

Fire was widely employed to remove tules and weeds from the surface after reclamation. Burning depth was controlled by maintenance of a high water table. In former days "virgin" unburned peat proved difficult to plow, so firing was common despite early recognition of humus loss. By 1920 the caterpillar tractor, developed for Delta use, was often employed in plowing. Subsidence, resulting from burning, accelerated decomposition of peat exposed to the air after plowing, and loss through cropping has posed serious problems too. The average "elevation" of the center of the islands is now 10 feet below mean sea level. The center of the Delta has the lowest surfaces and the worst drainage and seepage problems.

The Delta climate is a modification of the interior dry-summer subtropical (Mediterranean) type associated with the Great Central Valley. This modification is especially effective in summer when there is a fairly steady flow of marine air through the Golden Gate and Carquinez Strait. As a result, although summer afternoons may become hot, evenings are generally cooler than the remainder of the Valley. The midday relative humidity tends to be somewhat higher than that in many parts of the Central Valley—Sacramento and Stockton are likely to seem even hotter than they are as a result. Ten months are frost-free, with a year-round season for hardier crops—the season tends to be somewhat longer than most parts of the Valley.

LAND UTILIZATION

The Delta raises approximately a tenth of the agricultural output of the Great Central Valley—it has yielded impressive harvests for a century and is California's leading source of asparagus, tomatoes, and pears. Besides physical advantages already enumerated (mild climate, level terrain, ease of irrigation, fertile soils), the moisture-holding properties of its peat are significant. Location permitted an early shift from the subsistence gardening of Gold Rush days. Potatoes, beans, and onions had become significant crops before 1880— even in the 1870's Chinese, Italian, and Portuguese tenants gathered bountiful harvests of truck crops. Unreclaimed swamps provided pasturage, and wheat, exported via waterways, was also a major crop. The Chinese were also instrumental in converting natural levees

into fruit orchards and truck patches. Contrariwise, important contemporary crops such as asparagus, celery, sugar beets, and tomatoes were not introduced until the twentieth century.

Significant land-use transitions have materialized through the years. For instance, much land which was not irrigated before 1900 yielded winter grains. With availability of refrigerated railroad cars, early-season shipment east was possible. Only in this century have "brand-name" canned goods and standardized produce become representative. By the early 1900's barley was the acreage leader, but potatoes were first in value; beans and asparagus were also major crops. By World War I mechanized agriculture had replaced the hand labor of the Orientals. New crops gained moment and fertilizers were applied in increasing quantities. Since 1930 winter grain has still occupied the largest acreage, followed by asparagus, field corn, and alfalfa; meanwhile, animal husbandry has declined.

TRUCK CROPS

The Delta has long been the nation's leading source of *asparagus*, the stalk of a perennial lily. Harvest, small scale for San Francisco markets in the 1880's, became nationally significant in the next decade when "rust" vir-

LEADING DELTA LANDS FARM PRODUCTS, 1961
(values in millions of dollars)

Vegetables	
tomatoes	22.4
asparagus	16.8
potatoes, white	3.2
onions	1.35
celery	0.35
Fruits	
pears	10.7
Field Crops	
sugar beets	9.6
field corn	8.4
alfalfa	8.3
barley	3.9
milo	3.3

Source: Agricultural Commissioners of Sacramento, San Joaquin, and Solano counties.

tually eliminated eastern output. Since the 1920's production has remained relatively stable, despite local changes of consequence—the Delta produces approximately half of the nation's asparagus.

Asparagus cultivation is marked by large fields and "cannery" ownership of the crop. Peat soils gave the Delta a longtime advantage in raising "white" asparagus (i.e., stalks growing below the surface in the peat were protected from the sun). Since the 1930's dieticians have encouraged Americans to eat green stalks. The Delta still furnishes almost all of the nation's canned white asparagus. It has retained an outlet for fresh green asparagus, particularly in the rising California markets.

A salient locational shift has taken place within the Delta, chiefly because of *Fusarium* wilt. Afflicted land cannot be successfully replanted in asparagus for many years without expensive fumigation. By the late 1930's expanded acreage in the northern Delta, center of production, became impractical because of the value of "clean" land for orchards. This situation coupled with disease, prompted a southward shift to "healthy" land.

The Delta peat also favors blanched *celery*. This late autumn crop, approximately 2000 acres, has been challenged by increasing Salinas Valley competition since 1950 (Chapter 8), whereas demand for blanched celery has declined. Yields in the Salinas also tend to be higher and transplanting is not practiced (in the Salinas), thus lowering production costs.

Tomatoes constitute a major canning crop of the Delta—production has been significant since World War I. With adjacent Yolo County to the northwest, the Delta has made California the leading national source. California has doubled its share of the United States canned output since 1940 and produces about half of the national total—high yields are a major factor (Fig. 9-9). Cool nights and deep soils favor late varieties (thus extending the cannery season), which are grown on mineral soils rather than peat. Since 1954 most of the crop has been field seeded, eliminating transplanting—this change has advanced the harvest period about two months. Tomatoes are not processed locally but are trucked to

Fig. 9-21. MAP OF THE FIELD CORN ACREAGE IN CALIFORNIA.

Tracy, Stockton, Sacramento, San Jose, and Oakland. In fact, most canneries have forsaken the Delta; they were relocated at sites with better labor supply.

FIELD CROPS

Field crops have always been important in the agricultural scheme of the Delta. *Wheat,* the first major crop, has been supplanted by barley, whereas sugar beets and field corn have become important in this century. Some growers always alternate "wet" and "dry" crops to kill off "wet" weeds or "dry" insects.

Barley, a late winter crop used for livestock feed, has largely replaced wheat since 1900 (Fig. 9-42). Barley is planted on peat lands in February, later than is common elsewhere in California. For approximately forty years acreage has remained constant with about 100,000 acres devoted to the grain annually. Yields are good but lodging has ofttimes been a problem.

Field corn has been grown since the first decade of this century; for forty years the

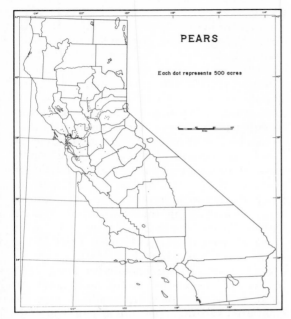

PEARS

Each dot represents 500 acres

Fig. 9-22. MAP OF THE PEAR ACREAGE IN CALIFORNIA.

FRUIT TREES

Deciduous fruit orchards became commonplace in the Delta by the late 1860's, particularly on the natural levees of the Sacramento River. Presumably, repeated floods and high water table discouraged production of such "pit fruits" as peaches, so that there has been gradual replacement by *Bartlett pears*, grown largely on the dikes and along the outer edges of the islands in the north, especially around Courtland.[9]

Pear growers received good returns in the 1920's, sometimes $500 to $1000 per acre, partially because the crop is the earliest in California. Combination of "blight" and depressed prices in the 1930's caused considerable replacement by asparagus; pear acreage declined from 16,500 in 1924 to 4900 in 1945. There has been little acreage fluctuation over the past twenty years although recently "pear decline" has threatened many trees (Fig. 9-22). Much of the fruit is shipped to canneries.

NATURAL GAS

A series of dry-gas fields in the northern Central Valley—discovered since 1936—has supplied as much as a third of the state's annual consumption. The oldest and largest field, Rio Vista in the Delta, has ranked among the nation's dozen largest reserves but has been rapidly depleted. Other fields have been developed as far north as Corning, and individual wells have been drilled as deep as 9500 feet. Beehive Bend, east of Willows, second largest field, has much expanded its output. As consumption has increased, a continuing search for additional gas has been made. P.G. and E. has used its Central Valley supply to balance seasonal market demands. Because no interstate commerce is involved, royalty owners have received more than is customary elsewhere. In 1960 northern Central Valley

Delta was California's only producer of consequence. In the 1950's considerable expansion took place elsewhere in the Great Valley, particularly in the San Joaquin Valley "Cotton Belt." Corn yields good returns on the peat—hybrid varieties produce as much as 120 bushels to the acre. Considerable north Delta land previously in asparagus now raises corn, suggesting central Illinois and leading California in production. Since World War II *milo* has tended somewhat to replace corn, especially on "altered peat" soils. This grain grows well on soils that remain moist later in the season and is rotated with alfalfa, tomatoes, and sugar beets.

The Delta forms the southern segment of California's leading *sugar-beet* belt, which extends northward into the Sacramento Valley flood basins (Fig. 9-8). Cool nights and a good water supply are physical assets, and beet yields are high. Acreage has tended to fluctuate less than in the San Joaquin Valley; the beets are grown under contract and are shipped to refineries to the north or south.

[9] The high water table in central portions of Delta islands poses a serious problem for many crops and negates production of trees and other deep-rooted plants (Fig. 9-20).

production of natural gas was valued at more than $20 million.

California has been among the nation's ranking producers of natural gas although its share of United States reserves is modest. Moreover, a tremendous expansion in California consumption has taken place—thus depleting reserves. In some years natural gas has ranked third (after petroleum and natural-gas liquids) among the state's mineral products. Until 1947, California could satisfy its own needs, but by 1957 two thirds of the natural gas was imported. Before 1962, imported gas came exclusively from the Southwest; natural gas destined for markets in central and northern California, distributed by Pacific Gas and Electric, entered the state south of Needles and thence was piped to Antioch for distribution. In 1962, Pacific Gas and Electric commenced delivery of Albertan natural gas into northern California through its own 1400-mile pipeline.

AQUATIC PLAYGROUND

The Delta has gained acceptance as a waterland paradise for the hunter, fisherman, and boatsman. This aspect of Delta economy should become more important as the population of surrounding central California increases. Most of the activity has occurred since World War II. Commercial salmon fishing was once important along this section of the Sacramento River, but it is no longer permitted; some canneries were long ago converted to processing of truck crops.

Sports fishing has become the chief lure of the Delta for many residents of marginal areas. Except for salmon, steelhead, and sturgeon, landed less frequently, the fish are varieties introduced from eastern United States: bass, catfish, bluegill, crappie, and sunfish. The most popular locality is probably around Frank's Tract (which was not economically reclaimable for agriculture after the flood of 1938!) and Bethel Island (see map, Fig. 9-2), near Antioch and more accessible to Bay Area sportsmen than most of the Delta. Fishing for striped bass, for which this portion of the Delta is particularly known, is especially popular in spring.

Posted properties restrict *hunting* within the Delta. Except for the pheasant-hunting spots, most of the desirable places for waterfowl are restricted to members of private gun clubs.

Water sports have gained popularity. Despite its maze of waterways, the Delta has limited appeal for swimmers; the waters tend to be either too murky or too saline. By contrast, water-skiing continues to gain momentum as it has elsewhere on California's inland waterways. With the exception of fishing, *boating* is probably the most common recreational activity. Boats can be rented at many landings; many visitors bring their own craft. Waters have sufficient depth for the largest yachts along charted channels. Frank's Tract is the focus of much boating (Fig. 9-20).

Exclusive resorts are nonexistent along Delta waterways. There are motels and hotels in Delta towns, but facilities available at some California vacation spots are absent. Camping sites have not been developed as they have in the Sierra Nevada or along the Pacific shores. For the motorist willing to take the time, California Route 24 from Antioch through Isleton to Sacramento affords a pleasant trip at almost any season. The peat subsoil discourages construction of wider (and heavier) roads. Generally as a scenic motoring area the Delta has only slightly more appeal than most other parts of the Great Central Valley. In this respect it differs appreciably from the charm of Netherlands countrysides.

LEVEE TOWNS

The Delta verily is not a land of cities—many of its service needs are provided in peripheral communities like Antioch, Stockton, and Sacramento. The typical town is drab, with a minimum of cultural amenities. In past years before mechanization replaced so much of the seasonal field labor, some towns were more colorful and more populous. The Chinese quarters of some villages, often in ruins, are still exotic. The leading communities are found in the northern and western sectors of the Delta along the levees that line the Sacramento River. The automobile has permitted agricultural personnel to reside in marginal cities. Humidity, dust, and cultural limitations have encouraged landowners to reside elsewhere. The "typical" village is a small agricultural residence town—**Walnut Grove**, the center of an older, wealthy settlement, and **Courtland** are slightly larger than most. Courtland for many years has been the focal point of pear orchards.

Rio Vista (2600), largest Delta town, was founded in 1857 but was relocated on its present site at the base of the Montezuma Hills after the flood of 1862. It is the principal community of the lower Delta and the site of the world's largest asparagus canning factory, but it is nearly as marginal as Antioch or Tracy. Rio Vista is supported by Delta agriculture as well as that of the Montezuma Hills to the northwest and also by recreation (particularly sports fishermen).

Isleton (1000), which began in the middle 1870's as a wharf at the junction of Brannan and Andrus islands, lost a third of its population during the 1950's. It has been more intimately related to Delta farming than Rio Vista—it boomed in the early twentieth century as an asparagus center and had three large canneries in the 1920's. Its economy depends upon retail purchases of cannery workers and field laborers. As the home of Caucasian farm owners and laborers, it is less picturesque than in the days when it housed many Chinese.

THE SAN JOAQUIN VALLEY

The productive San Joaquin Valley,[10] as large as Denmark, composes the southern Great Valley—it extends southward from Lodi and the Delta edges to the Grapevine at the foot of Tejon Pass (see map, Fig. 9-2). Despite hot summer afternoons, often too warm for human comfort, its long season, productive soils, and available irrigation water have permitted the Valley to become the nation's ranking agricultural area: Fresno, Kern, and Tulare rank among the top five farm counties of the nation. Scores of products are grown commercially, and only five states match the value of its enormous agricultural output.

The San Joaquin is scenically inferior for California, and recreation is less consequential in its economy than in either the Sacramento Valley or the Delta Lands. Yet position paralleling U.S. 99 makes tourism important—such facilities as motels are conspicuous.

Traditionally, the productive lands and hence the population foci were along the East Side on the great alluvial aprons built up by the San Joaquin and its principal affluents along the western base of the Sierra Nevada. Recently deeper pump wells and water stored behind Central Valley Project and other dams have given other portions of the Valley increased agricultural importance.

Four areas seem discernible upon the bases of agricultural history and contemporary landuse: (1) the East Side, (2) the Trough, (3) the West Side, and (4) the South End. They will be considered in succession.

THE EAST SIDE

The East Side, extending approximately from the north end of the Lodi District near Galt to the southern extremity of the Kaweah

[10] *The San Joaquin Valley has been reviewed by James Blick, University of the Pacific, and Chester Cole and John Crosby of Fresno State College.*

Fruits and Nuts
raisin grapes	82.7
table grapes	39.5
navel oranges	29.4
wine grapes	26.1
cling peaches	25.7
English walnuts	22.7
freestone peaches	20.0
plums	13.0
almonds	11.8
nectarines	10.3
Valencia oranges	8.5
cherries	7.5
olives	7.3
figs	4.7
strawberries	3.2
lemons	1.4

Vegetables
fresh tomatoes	10.3
processed tomatoes	7.5
white potatoes	4.5
sweet potatoes	3.8
onions	3.1
honeydew melons	2.3
watermelons	0.8

Field Crops
cotton lint	67.4
alfalfa hay	35.2
miscellaneous seeds	19.3
barley	15.2
irrigated pasture	12.8
dry beans	11.8
cotton seed	8.9
nursery stock	7.4
sorghum	5.8
sugar beets	4.3
native pasture	3.8
field corn	2.6

Livestock and Products
cattle and calves	78.8
market milk	39.7
chicken eggs	35.0
turkeys	31.8
chickens	12.2
milk, processing	6.8
hogs and pigs	3.6

Source: Agricultural Commissioners of San Joaquin, Stanislaus, Merced, Madera, Fresno, Tulare, and Kings counties.

Delta near Earlimart, has had a longer history of irrigation agriculture than other portions of the San Joaquin Valley (see map, Fig. 9-2). It has shared less than most of the other sub-

divisions in the Central Valley Project—many of its water facilities had been developed previously. Cropping patterns are complex and reflect repeated adjustments to physical and economic conditions—there is more diversity of cropping than in other portions of the San Joaquin. Many properties are small and usually intensively farmed. Population density is higher than elsewhere in the San Joaquin—almost all of the larger cities of the Valley are located here. In part both population and agriculture reflect the fact that the first San Joaquin railroad (the Southern Pacific's Valley Line) was constructed along the East Side.

The East Side consists essentially of the coalescing alluvial fans deposited by the San Joaquin and its major eastern tributaries west of the Sierran foothills. Hence the area has varying width, generally 20 to 25 miles. Soil textures become increasingly fine westward. The slope of the land diminishes, and there is a gradual merger with the Valley Trough. Older alluvial terraces at the base of the Sierra Nevada are extensive but less fertile than the recent alluvial surfaces—they approximate the Red Lands of the Sacramento Valley in terrain and use problems. Extensive areas are devoted to winter grains and livestock ranching.

To facilitate appreciation of the East Side, these six subdivisions will be considered (from north to south): Lodi District, Stockton District, Modesto District, Merced District, Fresno District, and Kaweah Delta (see map, Fig. 9-2).

THE LODI DISTRICT

The Lodi District constitutes the smallest agricultural subdivision on the East Side. Located in northeastern San Joaquin County it is also distinctive for its monoculture—few agricultural localities in California rely so completely upon a single crop as this District does upon the Tokay grape. The Lodi District forms the north end of the vineyard belt, which extends almost the length of the San Joaquin Valley with particular concentration around Lodi, Turlock, Madera, Fresno, western Tulare County, and Arvin (in the South End).

The semicontinuous zone of vineyards in the friable sandy soils on the middle portions of the alluvial fans of Sierran streams forms the most ubiquitous aspect of East Side agriculture, one of the world's principal concentrations of grape production. Its output of table wine and raisin varieties exceeds that of the balance of the North American continent. Production became significant in the late nineteenth century; for decades grapes have been California's leading fruit crop. The land is generally owner operated and properties tend to be small. Many farmers are first-generation Americans whose parents came from Mediterranean Europe or southwest Asia.

The Lodi District has extraordinary specialization in the red Hungarian grape, the Tokay, which is consumed both as a table fruit and as wine. In the final decade of the nineteenth century the farmers around Lodi shifted from grain farming to orchards and vineyards with watermelons a specialty crop. Gradually it was realized that the Tokay, a finicky variety with climatic particularity, was suited to the District because cooler air drifting inland through Carquinez Strait promotes high sugar content and deep red color. Soil is likewise significant; vineyards are largely restricted to Ramona sandy loam. Although farms are small (averaging 40 to 80 acres) and owner operated, vineyards cover 40,000 acres. The harvest season, commencing in late August, is celebrated in Lodi in September by a grape festival prior to the peak picking period. The Tokay ranks next to the Emperor nationally in sales among red table grapes. Since the fresh market is sometimes glutted by the Thompson seedless, some Tokays are stored and placed on the holiday markets in November and December.

Lodi (22,000), service center and Tokay growers' shipping point, is a "settled" community whose economy has been diversified by industrialization. Food processing, including breakfast cereals, is important; almost a score of wineries is located within the city or its environs. Other manufacturing includes tire-remolding equipment and concrete products. Monies spent by the thousands of Dakotans who make this city their "winter capital" adds stability to the economy.

Fig. 9-23. *GRAPE HARVEST, LODI.* (Lodi Chamber of Commerce)

THE STOCKTON DISTRICT

The Stockton District, south and southeast of the Delta, has varied agricultural output. Relief is negligible, the water table is generally high, and soils form intricate patterns. Slight environmental differences, grower preferences, land values, and market accessibility favor commercial production of several dozen commodities including fruits and nuts, truck crops, nursery stock, and market milk. A zone of poorly drained soils in the east (as around **Farmington**) is used for pasturage and affords a milkshed for Sacramento and Stockton. The area around **Linden** has long been an important producer of *sweet cherries* (Fig. 9-24). Soils and climate are favorable, and urbanization in the Santa Clara Valley (see Chapter 8) has prompted many growers to relocate in the Stockton District, which has become the state's leading producer. A disease, undiagnosed in 1962, threatens production—leaves on individual cherry trees wither and die within a few weeks. The District also now leads California in production of *English walnuts*—the principal San Joaquin Valley belt continues southward into the Modesto District (Fig. 9-25). This same portion of the Valley is witnessing a major expansion of almond acreage, and it is conceivable that it may replace the

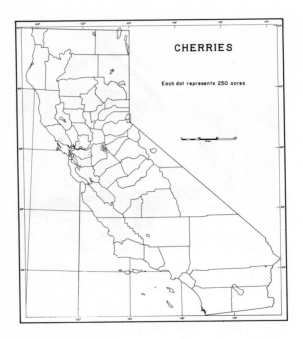

Fig. 9-24. MAP OF THE CALIFORNIA CHERRY ACREAGE.

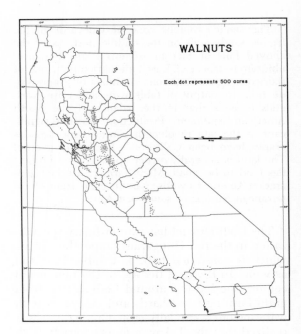

Fig. 9-25. MAP OF THE CALIFORNIA WALNUT ACREAGE

Chico District as the state's leading area (Fig. 9-13).

California is the world's leading producer of English (Persian) walnuts, with about 90 percent of national output. The nut now ranks after oranges and peaches among California tree crops. The walnut desires deep soils, long warm summers, and mild winters. Although it is deciduous and can tolerate considerable cold, late spring frosts can be critical. Until this century it was assumed that the walnut could not be grown commercially north of the Tehachapi. New varieties have been developed that yield better in central California than in Southern California. Urbanization has been an important factor in almost eliminating walnuts from Southern California since 1950.

The city of **Stockton** (86,000), seat of San Joaquin County, dominates this portion of California; it is the oldest city and still the second largest community (after Fresno) in the Valley. It was founded as Tuleburg in 1847, but became Stockton at the beginning of the Gold Rush and was the disembarkation

port for miners sojourning to the southern portions of the Mother Lode Country. In those days it formed a triumvirate (with San Francisco and Sacramento) as the largest cities of California. Like other central California towns it experienced a frenzied era characteristic of the boom days.

The growth of Stockton has mirrored the development of the San Joaquin Valley and the Delta Lands. Despite some core-area deterioration, much marginal expansion has occurred since World War II. Post-1940 growth has been stimulated by (1) opening of the ship channel in the 1930's, (2) industrial development, (3) agricultural shipment occasioned by situation at the "mouth" of the San Joaquin, and (4) military installations (such as the Army Storage Depot at Lathrop).

Stockton has long been sociologically segregated into "north" and "south" sides along its Main Street. Routes of major highways prevent the casual visitor from seeing the parks and attractive suburban residential sections. The city has for many years afforded off-season

Fig. 9-26. THE PORT OF STOCKTON. Although this municipally owned facility has been operated at a profit, one ponders the effect of the newly created Port of Sacramento. (Stockton Port District)

Fig. 9-27. THE MODESTO DISTRICT. Small farms, orchards, and fields of grain and vegetables are visible in this northwest view about 8 miles east of Modesto. The main canal of the Modesto Irrigation District is conspicuous. (Modesto Irrigation District)

residence for migratory workers; some social derelicts make the submarginal southern flank of the central district "unsafe" at night. It is anticipated that planned West End urban renewal will improve the environment. The many blocks of attractive residences, the campuses of Stockton College and Oxonian-type University of the Pacific, and suburban shopping centers are located on the northside. The southside contains modest older houses and industrial plants. Positions of the port (west) and industrial plants (south) promote city expansion into less productive farmlands toward the north. The urban site, at the edge of the Delta with the Port extending virtually to the Courthouse steps and the downtown district, has created problems of north-south traffic flow, storm-water drainage, and soils unsuitable for longtime septic-tank usage. Manufacturing includes agricultural machinery and implements, foods, paper, and containers. Tomatoes alone account for five canneries— Professor Blick reports that "the air smells of ketchup for weeks." Warehousing is important; relocation of English walnuts into northern California is reflected by the headquarters here of the cooperative Diamond Walnut Growers.

The Port of Stockton, opened in 1933, is a municipal corporation financed by a fifty-year bond issue. There is a 77-mile channel, 32 feet deep, to San Francisco Bay, and cargo, chiefly export of San Joaquin agricultural products and Nevada iron ore destined for Japan, is handled at a profit. Commodities generally come into the port by truck; in fact the pre-World War II "mosquito fleet" of small craft that hauled produce to San Francisco Bay has also largely been replaced by trucks. More than 600 ships call at the Port annually, and handle approximately 3.5 million tons of cargo. An industrial park adjacent to the port has agricultural-processing plants (Fig. 9-26).

Manteca (8300), on the southern fringe of the district, is a farm-supply center. It is a secondary highway junction and has diverse food processing (including sugar beets), canning, cheese, machinery, and farm implements.

THE MODESTO DISTRICT

The Modesto District, in central Stanislaus County, has long been one of the prosperous sections of the San Joaquin Valley. Like other subdivisions of the East Side it was once a vast wheat-growing area bounded on the west by the grazing lands of "cattle kings" Miller and Lux in the Valley Trough. For some decades the flow of the Tuolumne and Stanislaus rivers has provided the basis of "water, wealth, contentment, health" that appears on the large electric sign at 9th and I streets in downtown Modesto.

A Modesto legislator, C. C. Wright, initiated the Wright Act, which permitted establishment of mutual irrigation districts in California. Under this act, two contiguous irrigation districts, Turlock and Modesto, were created in 1887—together these irrigation districts form the Modesto District, a geographical entity. The two organizations jointly constructed La Grange Dam in 1891 on the Tuolumne in the Sierran foothills. Completion of the canal-distribution systems was delayed until the early 1900's because of legal còmplications in the Wright Act coupled with reluctance of some wheat farmers to become irrigators. By 1910 wheat had been largely replaced by orchards, vineyards, and alfalfa, with alfalfa the dominant crop. The districts again cooperated to construct Don Pedro Dam upstream from La Grange on the Tuolumne, second largest of the Sierran rivers in the San Joaquin basin. When it was completed in 1923, Don Pedro was the world's highest (284 ft.) concrete dam; when filled to capacity, it backed water 14 miles upcanyon. Evidence of ample Tuolumne water has been demonstrated more recently, and the two districts have cooperated with the city of San Francisco in watershed improvement. A much larger structure is under construction at the site of Don Pedro. Besides water, the two districts distribute their own hydroelectricity—income that "subsidizes" low-cost irrigation.

Early irrigation development at a time when construction costs were low (in comparison with present prices) has allowed the districts to operate at unusually low costs and has helped make Stanislaus County one of the ten agricultural leaders in the nation (Fig. 9-27). Differences in soil texture partially explains variations in land-use between the two districts. An apparent transition from loam to sand south of the Tuolumne River is reflected in a change from peach orchards to hayfields, vineyards, and dairies.

Early development and favorable physical environment has contributed to the District's rise to number-one position nationally in *peach* production (Fig. 9-15). Unlike the California peach situation in general, which has been characterized by declining acreage, output has been expanded around Modesto. Local canneries and longtime marketing arrangements are advantageous for the District. Stanislaus growers have not competed successfully in fresh freestone markets outside of California; the crop ripens too late and growing costs are higher (than in such humid, nonirrigated competitors as Georgia). Clingstones, formerly grown for dried fruit and now for canning, are all-important. Experience has demonstrated that peaches yield a higher return per acre than any other crop grown within the District. Farms are small—peach properties average around 40 acres, whereas those of viticulturalists are somewhat larger. Production of different clingstone varieties extends the harvest season over a period of many weeks, and specialization favors high-fruit standards with large yields.

The District is also a ranking center of United States *turkey* production. Turkey farms are located on poorer soils; local grains are available for "topping off" prior to marketing, chiefly within central California.

Grapes are not usually grown for fresh-fruit markets; table varieties ripen two to three weeks later than in San Joaquin districts farther south; hence they would require sale during a period of much competition (Fig. 9-29). Accordingly, varieties suitable for wines or raisins are grown. Scores of farmers north and east of Turlock raise such varieties as Carignane, Alicante, Zinfandel, and Thompson seedless.

Dairying has gained importance, particularly around Oakdale and west of Turlock (Fig. 9-36). In the Oakdale irrigation district, uncertainty of water supply has discouraged more intensive land-use on rolling terrain. Landowners have gradually shifted from sheep to beef cattle to dairying upon irrigated pastures. In the western Turlock district poor soils and a high water table have deterred alternative land-use, and dairying has been encour-

Fig. 9-28. BEARD INDUSTRIAL DISTRICT, MODESTO. Establishment of this industrial park, with rail spurs and California Route 132, has encouraged growth of manufacturing in the city. (Greater Modesto Chamber of Commerce, photo by Shoob Studios)

aged by the expanding California market for fresh milk and the migration of some dairymen from urbanized portions of Los Angeles County.

Productivity of the Modesto District has steadily expanded; numerous products have commercial significance. As was noted in discussion of the Stockton District, acreage devoted to almond (Fig. 9-13) and walnut (Fig. 9-25) orchards has increased, and Turlock remains an important source of cantaloupes and other melons that yield well on the sandy loams.

Modesto (36,600), fourth largest city in the San Joaquin Valley, is the metropolis of the District. Like most East Side towns it originated with arrival of the Southern Pacific in 1870; its growth was assured when it became the seat of Stanislaus County. Modesto is a crossroads town that also has agricultural trade and county government. Incorporation of a significant "fringe area" took place in the 1950's after passage of a needed civic-improvement bond program. By 1960 the city and its unincorporated residential outskirts approximated 80,000; a suburban center, McHenry Village, has been erected to the northeast. A noticeable improvement has materialized in the one-time Dust Bowl "tent town" west of the airport. Suburban growth and industrialization have contributed to economic deterioration of the southern end of the central district. Educational institutions include Modesto Junior College and Stanislaus State College in nearby Ceres (although a temporary campus is located in Turlock). Agriculture has been the basis for expanding manufacturing; canning, fresh freezing, and other types of processing are important. The industrial park in the southeast (Fig. 9-28) coupled with good transportation, concerted community effort, and location near the geographical center of California explain industrial diversification. Products include metals, cosmetics, wine bottles, paper boxes, and tin cans. Community income is further expanded by the sizable payroll at Modesto State Hospital.

Turlock (9100) is growing less rapidly than Modesto. Its older sections lie west of the railroad tracks, but the city is expanding eastward. Despite its overshadowing by Modesto, only 13 miles to the north, industrial growth has taken place—food products, toys, lumber, concrete products, and furniture are significant.

THE MERCED DISTRICT

Agricultural patterns of the Merced District have more intricacy than do those of the Modesto District; included are the northern limits of the San Joaquin cotton belt, discussed later. More modest agricultural production here has resulted from less fertile soils, a more limited water supply (from the Merced River), and delays in irrigation-district organization. Farming is characterized by dairying, with considerable acreage of alfalfa, grapes, fruits (especially figs and peaches), vegetables (particularly sweet potatoes and tomatoes), and irrigated pastures.

LANDHOLDINGS

Merced County mirrors the various types of rural properties that have been representative of the San Joaquin Valley. Four Mexican grants, awarded in the 1840's, were situated near the San Joaquin River where conditions favored grazing. Early American settlement, which began during the Gold Rush, took place along tributary stream courses, which provided water and grass. West of the San Joaquin River the vast Miller and Lux holdings, discussed later, were accumulated during the cattle era. As it extended its Valley line southward along the East Side, the Southern Pacific received large parcels of federal land. Other large East Side properties were accumulated early in the grain era when land was still cheap; the 42,000-acre Mitchell tract near Livingston is an example. However, the most successful attempts at irrigation development, the lands watered by the Merced Canal and absorbed into the Merced Irrigation District in 1922, consisted of smaller properties.

Several immigrant colonies also contributed to expansion of irrigation. In the early 1900's groups of Swedes and Japanese located on former wheat ranches along the Merced River. Even earlier an Azorean (Portuguese) colony had been established around Atwater.

Another form of landholding was promoted by the state of California with the Delhi State Land Settlement, a counterpart of the Durham colony in the Chico District of the Sacramento Valley. The program was formulated in 1917 because of much discontent with real estate operations in farmlands. The Delhi colony had obviously failed before its administration was assigned to the Turlock Irrigation District in 1930. As elsewhere in the Valley, real estate promoters also influenced settlement—most operations involved San Francisco or Los Angeles firms.

The large property, particularly common in the South End of the Valley and on the West Side, describes over half the agricultural lands of Merced County east of the San Joaquin River also. Such holdings are most prevalent along the Valley Trough. Despite 150 Merced County farms larger than 1000 acres, the average size of 3400 farms is 280 acres (in 1961). On the East Side, small farms and a relatively high rural population density exist. Large East Side holdings include a 4000-acre peach ranch of California Packing Company ("Del Monte") and Cello and Gallo vineyards near Livingston.

Merced County has become the seventeenth-ranking agricultural county of the nation. The Merced District (East Side) is the leading producer of sweet potatoes, fresh market tomatoes, and Kadota canning figs. Other important products are cantaloupes, almonds, raisin grapes, peaches (both freestone and clingstone varieties), and English walnuts. The well-known Merced sweet potato, grown on lighter soils around Livingston, was introduced by the Portuguese. Output, usually the Puerto Rican Velvet variety, cannot satisfy California demands, and Texas and Louisiana potatoes are imported. Italians developed the dairies and also truck crops, especially tomatoes.

The history of this irrigation development contrasts with that of the nearby Modesto and Turlock districts. The MID was not formed until 1919 although the Merced Canal was constructed previously by San Francisco interests, and the main canals and distribution system had been built before 1890. After need for additional water became apparent in this century, the firm sold its holdings to the irrigation district for $2.5 million. Finally in the 1920's the MID constructed Exchequer Dam on the upper Merced. Hastier development of District lands was retarded by the indebtedness of the MID. As in East Side districts previously discussed, this one has not been affected by the Central Valley Project. The dramatic expansion of irrigation agriculture that has occurred elsewhere in the San Joaquin Valley since 1950 is impossible here—greater productivity from these older East Side districts can come only from more intensive cultivation.

TOWNS

Merced (20,000) is the largest city in the District. It was founded beside the Southern Pacific right-of-way in 1870 and is the county seat. It is also an important highway junction with the central gateway into Yosemite Park via California 140 (the "All-Year Highway" through El Portal). Besides its farm trade Merced has expanding manufacturing that includes foods and wood products.

Other communities in the District were long quasi-stagnant. **Atwater** (7300), principally a farm-service town, has been affected markedly by nearby Castle Air Force Base and was the fastest growing city in the county during the 1950's. Nearby **Livingston** (2200) has food-processing industries.

CASTLE AIR FORCE BASE

This permanent bomber installation, which has had as many as 16,000 resident personnel, has augmented the population of surrounding cities.

THE FRESNO DISTRICT

The Fresno District, heartland of the San Joaquin Valley and world famous for its grapes (especially those dried as raisins), is the largest of the East Side subdivisions (see map, Fig. 9-2). Fresno County has become the nation's agricultural leader—its East Side segment is productive, but this status has been achieved principally through expansion on its West Side, considered later.

The Fresno District stretches from Madera to Kingsburg and occupies the compound alluvial fan formed by the San Joaquin and Kings rivers. Varied agricultural output, permitted by the environment, is typical of much of the East Side—the specialization of Lodi in Tokay grapes and Modesto in clingstone peaches is unique. Grapes, deciduous fruits, and nuts have long constituted the major products of the Fresno District. Transition from grains and grazing followed arrival of the Southern Pacific by less than a generation; by 1900 "colonies" of small farms had almost replaced the more extensive ranches of the previous era. Today approximately 80 percent of the District remains in small holdings, commonly owner operated—understandably cooperative marketing has been characteristic.

Water from the San Joaquin River was briefly diverted for irrigation around Fresno, but it was soon discovered that the Kings River could be used more advantageously. Early-day irrigation was inexpensive and much water was wasted. At one time there was a considerable artesian flow from hundreds of wells around Fresno. The artesian zone covered around 4300 square miles parallel to the Valley axis. With careless exploitation and rising water consumption, pressure was lost and pumping was commenced. Unlike more northerly portions of the East Side, portions of the Fresno District have been forced to utilize Central Valley Project water—the local water table has declined for the past several decades, even since construction of Friant Dam on the San Joaquin and Pine Flat on the Kings.

The District has wide renown for its *grape* production; it comprises one of the world's

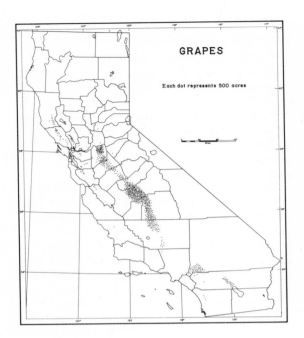

Fig. 9-29. *MAP OF THE CALIFORNIA GRAPE ACREAGE.*

Fig. 9-30. *DRYING RAISINS, FRESNO DISTRICT.* (California Raisin Advisory Board, photo by Jack Worsham)

principal sources and grows approximately 5 percent of the entire world output. This District produces more grapes than the remainder of California. As elsewhere in the state, the subtropical Mediterranean type, *Vitis vinifera,* is raised rather than the middle-latitude grapes native to eastern North America. The vinifera, ideally suited to hot, rainless summer lands, is grown under irrigation here. The plants will tolerate a variety of soils but prefer loose sandy textures; they are not too alkaline tolerant, a condition that has curtailed production westward into the Valley Trough.

Fresno viticulture commenced in 1873; the rise of raisin grapes coincided with emigration of Armenian grape growers. Profits were good and markets expanded rapidly, but economic fluctuations prompted formation of a cooperative, which has become the well-known Sun-Maid Raisin Growers of California. Through cooperation uniform quality has been achieved. At first only the light Fresno soil series were considered suitable; as irrigation practices contributed to rising water tables, the grape belt moved eastward.

The harvest, from August and into October, depends upon the variety—earlier grapes produce the bulk of the raisins. The grapes, placed upon paper between the rows of vines, dry into raisins and then are transported to the cooperative plant for processing (Fig. 9-30).

The San Joaquin Valley has proved ideal for raisins. Farther north there is greater likelihood of an early September or October rainstorm. The Muscat was the earliest raisin variety. Another vinifera, the Thompson seedless, has largely replaced the Muscat for raisins. This is an all-purpose grape; the surplus crop can be sold as fresh fruit or converted into wine. Considerable wine is processed around Fresno, but the District does not specialize in varietal grapes grown for this purpose to the extent that prevails in such areas as the Napa and Livermore valleys. The District produces mostly the less expensive "bulk" wines consumed in largest quantities in the United States.

Weather in the central San Joaquin favors table grapes because of more intense summer heat and earlier crop maturity than in localities even as close as Lodi. A number of vinifera varieties are grown in California; obviously there is much local specialization, as in the Coachella Valley

FIGS

Each dot represents 250 acres

Fig. 9-31. MAP OF THE CALIFORNIA FIG ACREAGE.

with its early table grapes (Chapter 4). Like the wheat harvest of the Great Plains, the grape harvest period northward in California occurs progressively later in the year from the Coachella Valley through Kern County into Fresno County and Lodi.

California generally vies for second position in *fig* production after Italy, the world leader; most of the crop comes from the San Joaquin Valley (Fig. 9-31). Half of California's figs are grown in the Fresno District, particularly upon the hardpan soils (older alluvium) north of Fresno, where each tree has to be "blasted in"; once the tree is planted, its roots reach downward to find water beneath the hardpan. The fig was introduced into California by the mission priests, yet has gained commercial importance only in the twentieth century. Rising production after 1900 followed realization of the necessity for caprification (pollinization) of the Smyrna fig by the fig wasp—the wasp had to be imported. This plant has proved ideal for the water-deficient San Joaquin, since it requires only three winter irrigations, thus does not "compete" against

grapes for "ditch water" in summer. The Calimyrna, a local "dried-fruit" variety, remains most popular. With increased canning, the Kadota became significant. More recently, consumption as fresh fruit has favored the Black Mission and Adriatic varieties. Fig growers have experienced periods of overproduction, but, more recently, growth of metropolitan Fresno has caused some northward relocation of orchards.

The third of California's outstanding *peach* producers (others are the Feather River Valley and the Modesto District) is located in the eastern Fresno District upon friable soils around Clovis, Sanger, and Reedley (Fig. 9-15). This is the leading source in western United States for the freestone varieties that are raised for drying, canning, and also as fresh market fruit. The more southerly latitude of Fresno favors earlier harvest and hence more successful fresh-fruit sale with less competition nationally from localities whose fruit ripens later. In the late nineteenth century California peaches were grown principally in the Vaca Valley and the Santa Clara Valley. Expansion of irrigation agriculture permitted the Fresno District to utilize its physical advantages and thus produce the freestone varieties in quantity.

Fresno (134,000) has for decades prospered because of the agricultural output of its surrounding District—wealth is reflected in many attractive residences. It is California's most centrally located larger city and provides services, shipping, processing, and distributing functions for a considerable portion of the central San Joaquin Valley. Petroleum and cotton elsewhere in the county (apart from the East Side) add to the trade conducted in Fresno. Like Chico in the Sacramento Valley, Fresno's central location in the San Joaquin recommends it as a residence town for the many hundreds of sales representatives and traveling salesmen whose occupation takes them into various parts of the San Joaquin Valley. It has also benefited from status as county seat and as site of Fresno State College (with relocation of this institution on a larger campus in northeastern Fresno, its

Fig. 9-32. *CENTRAL FRESNO. This view toward the northeast includes the wholesale district, retail district, and courthouse. As in many Valley cities, downtown streets are oriented in a grid paralleling the railroad right-of-way. Note the diagonal grid in the rear.* (Fresno Chamber of Commerce, photo by Chuck Dowell)

former campus became the site of Fresno Junior College).

Fresno, midpoint between California's two largest metropolitan areas on much-traveled U.S. 99, derives much income from services rendered to travelers: there is a conspicuous concentration of motels, popular as sites for conventions of statewide organizations. The city also serves as southern gateway into Yosemite and has highways leading to Kings Canyon and Sequoia national parks. Its expanded airport can handle jet planes.

It is appropriate that a metropolis of 200,-000 should have a central district with "skyscrapers," yet such structures seem incongruous in the vast openness of the San Joaquin Valley (Fig. 9-32). Fresno's outward growth is reflected in housing tracts and suburban shopping centers—it vaguely suggests metropolitan Los Angeles in its low-density "urban sprawl." As in most larger California commu-

nities, public transportation is inadequate. For more distant travel the city has railroad, airline, bus, and truck facilities. However, the barrier of the High Sierra to the east, noted in Chapter 5, does not allow Fresnoans a direct route into the North American interior.

Fresno has a larger industrial output than any other San Joaquin Valley city. Even here, however, agricultural processing tends to be dominant among more than 200 industries. Packaging of dried fruits and processing of wine and cottonseed oil are major activities. Other products include farm equipment, containers, and vending machines. Sun-Maid has relocated its raisin-packaging facilities in nearby Kingsburg.

Fresno dominates its District so completely that there is no other sizable city. **Madera** (14,500), seat of Madera County on the Fresno River, is the second largest community. It is an agricultural-service center with

Fig. 9-33. *FRIANT-KERN CANAL. This 160-mile canal extends southward from Friant Dam into Kern County; it has a capacity of 4000 second-feet. This view also shows orange groves near Lindsay.* (Bureau of Reclamation, photo by B. D. Glaha)

Fig. 9-34. *ORANGE GROVES, TULARE COUNTY.* (Perma Rain Irrigation)

significant agricultural processing, including meat packing, olives, and wine. Fresno satellites include **Clovis** (5500), **Dinuba** (6100), **Reedley** (5900), **Selma** (7000), and **Sanger** (8000); all were formerly farm-service towns that are becoming suburban bedrooms.

THE KAWEAH DELTA

The Kaweah Delta southeast of Fresno, might appropriately be entitled the Kaweah–Tule–lower Kings District (see map, Fig. 9-2). Water shortage delayed more extensive agricultural development earlier. This productive subdivision has no city comparable to Stockton, Bakersfield, or Fresno; yet nowhere else in the entire Valley is there such a concentration of smaller farm cities. In recent years Tulare County has challenged Fresno County for first place among the nation's leading agricultural counties. When eastern Kings County is added it is obvious that the Kaweah Delta is about the most productive subdivision of the San Joaquin Valley. In the twenty-year period 1941-1961 the farm output of Tulare County alone increased by $250 million annually. Leading products create the

intricacy of pattern characteristic of the East Side. Major crops that lend a measure of distinction to the district include oranges, olives, barley, grapes, cotton, and sorghum.

Westerly and southeastern portions of the Kaweah Delta, inherently fertile under irrigation, attained much expanded production after evolution of the Central Valley Project; these localities utilize much Friant-Kern Canal water (Fig. 9-33). Construction of Pine Flat Dam on the Kings provided additional water, which has allowed continued expansion. Earlier in the twentieth century, before the CVP, sizable acreages were dry-farmed. Cultivation of upper portions of this coalescing alluvial plain, irrigable from the Kaweah and lesser streams, or with pump-well irrigation, had undergone more intensive utilization earlier.

THE THERMAL BELT

South of the Kings River the eastern segment of the San Joaquin Valley forms an enclave within the Sierra Nevada: the upper (eastern) portion of the Kaweah Delta has crescentic shape. Here winter temperature in-

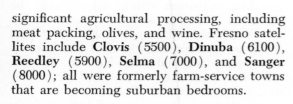

THE GREAT CENTRAL VALLEY : : 393

versions create the largest of several "thermal belts" of slightly milder climate less subject to killing frosts than areas toward the west. This particular Thermal Belt extends approximately 55 miles north-south from Elderwood almost to Terra Bella and attains a width of 10 miles. Almost by chance, as a result of planting oranges as shade trees around several homes, it was discovered that this locale is suitable for citrus—despite the severe freezes of 1879, 1880, 1897, 1913, 1922, 1937, and 1962.

George Frost, previously of Riverside, planted 100 acres of oranges near Porterville in 1890; the first carload was shipped east in 1893, and 4500 carloads were shipped annually by 1913. Severe frost in 1913, particularly disastrous on the fringes of the Thermal Belt, largely defined the limits of production for many years. Increasingly the dominant fruit has been the Washington navel orange, the winter fresh-fruit variety. Because of its consumption fresh this variety does not suffer the critical competition from Florida oranges that the Valencia variety has since the advent of frozen orange juice (see Chapter 7). The navel is more suited physically here too as the fruit is generally picked before likelihood of a killing frost.[11]

The Kaweah Delta now constitutes California's largest *orange* center—Tulare County had 48,000 acres in 1961 (Fig. 9-34). Two factors particularly have encouraged an extensive expansion of citrus production in the San Joaquin Valley since the middle 1950's—both are related to urbanization in the Los Angeles Lowlands. First, citrus growers of the Santa Ana Plain, San Gabriel Valley, and San Fernando Valley have literally been "pushed out" to provide space for subdivisions. Second, to avert heavy capital-gains taxes, the displaced growers have had to reinvest their money in

land (Fig. 7-37). Meanwhile, acreage northward into Fresno County and southward into Kern County has been planted in citrus. One can merely speculate about the prospects for some groves in view of disastrous freezes in past years. Lemons, climatically more sensitive than oranges, are largely restricted to upland sites east of Terra Bella—yet acreage doubled during the 1950's.

Tulare County is California's chief *olive* producer (Fig. 9-35). California is the only significant commercial source of olives outside of the Mediterranean Basin, where the long-lived tree is indigenous; domestic production in the United States does not satisfy the American market. Normally California cannot process olive oil inexpensively enough to compete with the Spanish and Italian product. Most California olives are dual-purpose varieties, increasingly significant as eating olives. The crop is grown in Tulare County both as a primary crop and also to provide windbreaks around citrus orchards. The tree is not demanding, although edible olives must be picked in November and early December before the likelihood of a killing frost. Olives will grow without irrigation, but irrigation assures larger trees and better harvests. The tree will tolerate a variety of soils as long as they are well drained and alkaline-free.

The Fresno District vineyard belt continues southward through Tulare County into Kern County—*grapes* are grown west of the citrus in the Kaweah Delta (Fig. 9-29). The deciduous grape is not plagued by the frost threat as is citrus, and since soils are suitable production has been important for some decades. The relatively low water requirement of the vine favored grapes in the years before CVP water became available; once established, grapevines can be grown with limited irrigation. However, with delivery of CVP water through the Friant-Kern Canal, grape acreage was expanded and water consumption per acre increased.

The Kaweah Delta has become the state's leading producer of *plums* since 1945; this is another of the rapid locational shifts characteristic of California (Fig. 8-11). As with other fruits, overplanting of plum orchards

[11] The orange tree can withstand much colder temperatures for a long period of time without critical damage than can the near-ripe fruit. San Joaquin Valley oranges ripen sooner because of hotter summers than in Southern California—the average July temperature in Porterville is 83.2°F. against 76.8°F. for Redlands. Previous discussion of grape maturation is not quite analogous.

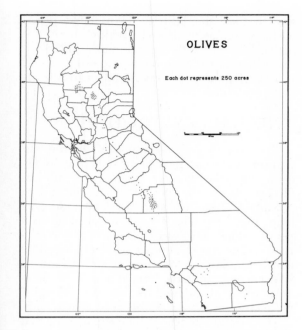

OLIVES

Each dot represents 250 acres

Fig. 9-35. MAP OF THE CALIFORNIA OLIVE ACREAGE.

occurred in the 1920's with a subsequent acreage decline during the 1930's. California grows over 90 percent of this perishable fruit. Orchards are now concentrated in the southern East Side (Tulare, Fresno, and Kern counties), in the Sacramento Valley near Yuba City, and in the Sierran foothills of Placer County. Expanded acreage in the Kaweah Delta reflects rising national consumption and the advantage of earlier ripening than that farther north; the fruit is largely consumed fresh.

The Fresno District *peach* belt likewise continues southward in the Delta; in fact Tulare County produces nearly as many peaches as the neighboring county. The Tagus Ranch has one of the largest orchards in the Valley southwest of Visalia, which is the major center for the peaches.

Alfalfa, sorghum, barley, and cotton are important crops on the western edge of the Kaweah Delta. Tulare County forms an important segment of the San Joaquin *cotton* belt, which is discussed later, although its

output has lagged behind Kern and Fresno counties. *Barley* has been dry-farmed for generations west of Terra Bella. The western portion of the Kaweah Delta has long been an important *dairying* area; Arden Farms has a processing plant at Tipton. In the 1950's many dairymen converted to Grade-A milk, reflecting the increased outlet in metropolitan Los Angeles.

Tulare County is further a significant producer of *vegetables,* especially white potatoes and tomatoes. Although total output cannot compare with Kern County, there is still a large acreage of potatoes for early markets around Visalia. Tomato acreage is minor in comparison to Yolo County and the Delta Lands, yet it constitutes an important fresh-market crop around Visalia—tomatoes are marketed in late June and in July.

MARKET TOWNS

There is a greater concentration of sizable farm towns in the Kaweah Delta than anywhere else in the San Joaquin Valley. This reflects the size and productivity of the district, crop distribution and diversity, spacing of parallel rail lines of the Southern Pacific and the Santa Fe, and inclusion of two counties within the subdivision. In contrast to the Fresno District, no one city became sufficiently dominant as to hamper growth of the others.

Visalia (15,800), long the largest Kaweah Delta city, is the seat of Tulare County, site of College of Sequoias, and widely regarded as one of the most attractive towns in the Valley. One of the oldest San Joaquin towns (established in 1852), Visalia was once a "cow town," but has functioned for some decades as an important agricultural point. When the town refused to "bribe" the "Big Four," the Southern Pacific extended its tracks southward toward the west and created a new community, Tulare, as the local station. If the railroad had passed through Visalia, one wonders if the momentum of its earlier beginnings would today make Visalia rather than Fresno the largest San Joaquin city. Visalia acts as a service center for Sequoia National Park (i.e., laundry, foods, etc.).

Tulare (13,800), twice fire-ravaged, was the "Bonneville" of the Norris novel *The Octopus*. Until 1891 Tulare was a Southern Pacific division point with repair shops—the shops were transferred to Bakersfield, and Fresno became the division point. More recently growth has depended upon the surrounding agricultural district. Tulare has gained population with more intensive agricultural use of the Kaweah Delta since CVP water became available.

Hanford (10,200), seat of Kings County, is on the western fringe of the Delta—its situation has permitted it to benefit from agricultural expansion on the bed of Lake Tulare and adjacent portions of the West Side as well. Location of a large rubber plant in the city in 1962 has widened its economic base. Like Tulare, Hanford was established with the arrival of the Southern Pacific; in fact, the famed Mussel Slough strife between settler and railroad, background for the Norris novel, centered here. Hanford was long concerned with the needs of cattlemen and dairy farmers. Today it remains a farm town, but the interest of the cotton rancher looms larger. Establishment of a **Naval Air Station** at **Lemoore** as a "spillover" of Moffett Field activities (Chapter 8) is a recent population influence. Increasingly, due to congestion in the Santa Clara Valley, operational functions are being moved to this new installation.

Porterville (8000), largest of the Thermal Belt citrus towns on the eastern fringe of the Delta, had early beginnings as a stagecoach station. Most of its growth has taken place since 1900 with expansion of its hinterland. The central district and more expensive hillside homes to the north and east reflect productivity of the Thermal Belt. Citrus-packing sheds flank the railroad tracks. There is also a community college, Porterville Junior College, and a state hospital. The city benefits somewhat from its status as a southern gateway to Sequoia National Park and adjacent parts of the Sierra Nevada. **East Porterville** (unincorp.) demonstrates the growth of the contiguous yet politically independent fringe, which is a problem of so many Valley cities.

Lindsay (5400) and Exeter (4300) are established Thermal Belt towns with less rapid growth than the District towns cited previously. Shipping sheds and packing houses are noticeable in both communities. Lindsay, somewhat larger, is an olive-processing center, whereas Exeter ships grapes and various fruits and vegetables.

THE VALLEY TROUGH

The Trough (north-south axis) of the San Joaquin Valley is located west of the Valley centerline—the greater amount of alluvial fill has been transported from the Sierra Nevada and has elevated the East Side (see map, Fig. 9-2). The Trough is flattish with a gentle slope northward toward the Delta Lands. The San Joaquin meanders sluggishly across the Trough; the master stream and its larger tributaries have formed a maze of channels, often abandoned to become "sloughs" with large expanses of tule-reed marshlands.

The Trough, underlain by compact soils that are frequently high in alkalinity, has no single sizable community. It is the most sparsely populated portion of the Valley, an area that contains many large properties more often used for grazing purposes than for farming. In the past, extensive areas have been inundated, generally in late spring with melting of Sierran snow fields and when streams have overflowed their channels. The problem of flooding becomes less common with construction of additional multipurpose dams in the Sierra Nevada.

One finds it strange today that the Trough might once have been considered more desirable than other portions of the San Joaquin Valley. During Mexican days it was attractive for grazing because it had water when much of the Valley was dry and barren. Hence cattle ranchos were established along the Trough. Then the cattle barons, Miller and Lux, acquired vast acreages here after the middle of the nineteenth century. They purchased thousands of acres as "swamp lands" from the state of California at $1.25 per acre. Later during the heyday of the wheat farmer, there was a conspicuous absence of settlement in the Trough (i.e., the East Side was the preferred area for grain).

The Trough is gaining more importance in the second half of the twentieth century as the population of California and the nation grows.[12] Locally there are considerable acreages of rice and sugar beets, crops more tolerant of alkaline conditions and suitable for heavy soils. Much land continues to be used for pastoral purposes, to provide forage for beef cattle and dairy cows.

LEADING TROUGH
FARM PRODUCTS, 1961
(values in millions of dollars)

market milk	40.7
beef	39.6
milk, manufactured	16.9
alfalfa hay	15.8
irrigated pasture	10.8
rice	5.6
sorghum	4.0
sugar beets	3.7
sudan grass	1.1

Source: Agricultural Commissioners of Stanislaus, Merced, Madera, Fresno, and Kings counties.

DAIRYING

Expansion of dairying along the Trough has been one of the dramatic agricultural changes in the Central Valley since 1950. Pertinent factors include (1) population growth in California, (2) urbanization in the Los Angeles Lowlands and the San Francisco Bay Area, and (3) shift of more productive San Joaquin Valley lands into fruits and vegetables.

Stanislaus County has long ranked second to Los Angeles County among all dairy counties of the United States (Fig. 7-24). Dairy farming, which began on the West Side in the 1890's, has been relocated along the Trough since 1950. Many erstwhile East Side dairies, located in the Modesto District, have been

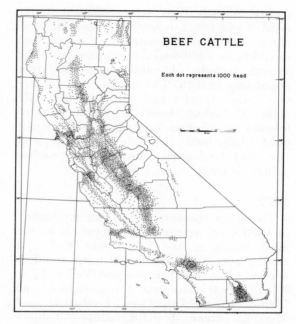

Fig. 9-36. *MAP OF BEEF CATTLE IN CALIFORNIA.*

converted into fruit and nut orchards. Others now grow vegetables or raise replacement heifers (for the Los Angeles dairy belt especially). On the East Side, dairying tends to be concentrated in the western portion of the Turlock District, where soils are unsuitable for orchards. Many of the large Los Angeles dairymen have purchased their own heifer farms in the San Joaquin Valley. Between 1946 and 1956, Stanislaus dairymen increased the number of their milk cows between 80,000 and 97,000. Copley, in his thesis, indicates that this was probably the largest single increase in the nation.

Virtually all of the Grade-A dairies in Stanislaus County had been relocated east of the San Joaquin River in two belts by 1960: (1) in the Trough and (2) on the hillsides of the Oakdale Irrigation District. It is now assumed that the Trough will become the leading dairy belt of California, supplying market milk to the Los Angeles Lowlands and the San Francisco Bay Area and that Stanislaus will replace Los Angeles as the nation's leading dairy

[12] Professor Chester Cole of Fresno State College in 1958 estimated that reclamation of alkaline lands, including leveling, application of gypsum, installation of irrigation works, and fertilization, would probably average between $225 and $300 an acre. Alkalinity has resulted from salts concentrated in the upper layers of the soil as a result of (a) lateral migration of groundwater; (b) evaporation after overirrigation; (c) "ponding" of flood waters in natural depressions.

county. Already there is a significant movement of milk into Los Angeles from both Stanislaus and Merced counties. Factors that should favor additional dairy expansion in the Trough include (1) anticipated California population growth, (2) central location between Los Angeles and San Francisco, (3) ability of Ladino clover and Sudan grass to tolerate the alkaline "hardpan" (which is not good alfalfa land), (4) adequate water, and (5) much land away from expanding metropolitan districts.

RICE

The major concentration of rice production in California, as previously noted, is in the flood basins of the Sacramento Valley; a smaller output has developed from Mendota northward in the San Joaquin Valley (Fig. 9-11). Rice is concentrated in western Fresno County around Dos Palos, Firebaugh, and Mendota where it helps reduce alkalinity (through cultivation techniques). The environment is similar to the flood basins of the Sacramento, but rice farming in the San Joaquin evolved more recently. In both areas farming is conducted on an extensive scale with a high degree of mechanization. The longer growing season of the San Joaquin may afford it prospects if a suitable long-grain variety of rice can be developed for California.

SUGAR BEETS

Land reclamation and increased water availability under the CVP has permitted expanded sugar-beet cultivation in the Trough, especially in Fresno County (Fig. 9-8). Output remains relatively small in contrast to such leading California counties as Imperial, Yolo, and San Joaquin. As elsewhere, the beet pulp provides cattle feed.

SHIPPING POINTS

The Trough towns are small, with fewer trees, less settled appearance and less affluence than the East Side cities. They provide shipping facilities for surrounding agricultural areas as well as residence for farm workers. Some trade is engendered locally, but many farmers con-

duct their retail shopping in the larger East Side county seats. **Mendota** (2100), located along a spur rail line from Fresno in 1895, has shown recent growth with vicinal agricultural expansion. **Firebaugh** (2100) has agricultural-processing plants (including rice and alfalfa dehydrating) and shipping sheds. **Dos Palos** (2000) was founded as a rail station in 1889 and gained residents after location of a nearby agricultural colony three years later; like the others it remains a farmers' town.

THE WEST SIDE

The West Side of the San Joaquin Valley, between the Trough and the southern Coast Ranges, extends southward from the Delta to the South End (Kern County) and includes the floor of old Lake Tulare (see map, Fig. 9-2). Irrigation agriculture was established here relatively late—for decades after the East Side was dotted with orchards and vineyards, and much of the West Side remained seasonally parched grazing land.

A climatic map (see Appendix A) suggests why irrigation agriculture was delayed in this portion of the Valley. The West Side is mostly either a desert (south) or semiarid; it lies in the lee of the southern Coast Ranges. The intermittent streams which flow eastward from the Diablo Range have formed alluvial fans but have relatively small volume in contrast with their Sierran counterparts on the East Side. Their beds are dry washes during the months when water is critically needed for irrigation.

The Spanish became acquainted with the West Side relatively early in the colonial period. In fact they established the "shortcut" mission bypass **El Camino Viejo** between the Los Angeles Lowlands and the San Francisco Bay Area, which was noted earlier. One might consider it strange that several ranchos were established on the West Side during the Mexican period. However, this portion of the Valley was closer to occupied sections of the Central Coast than the remainder of the San Joaquin. Also the ranchos were located upon the alluvial fans of larger streams; the remainder of the West Side remained in its pristine state.

THE CATTLE KINGS

The San Joaquin was not an important producer of beef cattle during the Mexican period. Yet after the Gold Rush commenced, the raising of beef cattle expanded and the West Side became an important livestock area. The "greatest cattlemen of them all" was the firm of Miller and Lux, dominated by one-time German butcher boy Heinrich Kreiser (Henry Miller). During the era of cattle dominance on the West Side, Miller and Lux acquired thousands of acres between Tracy on the North and the San Joaquin "bend" west of Fresno. Their holdings began in 1857 when they obtained an option on part of Rancho Santa Rita; eventually they gained 247,000 acres in Merced County alone. Land was accumulated in various ways: (1) One was direct purchase of rancho property from Mexican owners. In some instances this was effected as it was in the Central Coast and Southern California, through loans at ruinous interest followed by foreclosure. (2) Much land was gained by purchase of land script, at perhaps 50 percent of value, that had been given to Civil War and Indian wars veterans. (3) Again, Miller and Lux encouraged their employees to take out homesteads, which were then purchased at low prices. (4) A tremendous acreage in the Trough was acquired under the California Swamp Act by which marshlands could be purchased at $1.25 an acre. Upon his death in 1916 Miller reportedly still held 161,000 acres in Merced County alone. Chester Cole in his dissertation on Fresno County (see Bibliography) reported that "A common saying in the San Joaquin Valley is that Miller made three fortunes ... one for himself, one for his partner, and one for his attorneys" (p. 144).

Indirectly Miller and Lux were responsible for the major portion of earlier irrigation development on the West Side. After a San Francisco firm had constructed the San Joaquin and Kings River Canal, Miller and Lux demanded their riparian rights and forced the canal builders to sell them the ditch for a third of its cost. It watered more than 150,000 acres and was one of the nation's largest schemes at the time. The canal provided the cattlemen with surplus water, partially used to reclaim alkali lands along the Trough.

SETTLEMENT

West Side occupance proceeded more slowly than along the East Side. Additional deterrents besides the vast holdings of Miller and Lux were dryness and the absence of adequate transportation before the Southern Pacific built its westside line in 1890.

In addition to livestock, dry-farmed wheat constituted the chief source of late nineteenth-century livelihood. Graham, in his thesis (see Bibliography) dealing with Merced County, estimates that during the grain-farming period the "typical," nonirrigated West Side acreage experienced three successive occupances, reflecting inability to obtain an adequate livelihood in a land of so little precipitation. Los Banos, focus of Miller and Lux operations, was the single West Side town before the railroad era. The federal government granted the Southern Pacific rights to alternate sections around Los Banos, but the railroad never obtained title. Consequently, this land became available for homesteading around 1885.

Several groups of European immigrants settled on the West Side. Several score of Basque families, who came to California at the time of the Gold Rush, located at the base of the Diablo Range as sheepmen. Miller and Lux imported a group of south Italians in the middle 1870's as laborers on their ranches. Some gradually purchased small holdings from homesteaders and bought water from Miller and Lux—they sold vegetables to Miller and Lux employees and other West Side residents.

Smaller West Side farms appeared in the 1890's following construction of the railroad. Another factor was the death of Lux in 1887 —Miller was forced to sell some of their lands to satisfy the demands of his partner's heirs. Accepting the changing times, Miller constructed an "upper canal" and sold additional water of his own volition. Extensive sale of Miller lands was delayed for a decade after his death; in 1926 the corporation formed by

LEADING WEST SIDE
FARM PRODUCTS, 1961
(values in millions of dollars)

Field Crops
lint cotton	77.3
barley	22.2
alfalfa hay	15.0
cotton seed	9.8
wheat	5.9
dry beans	5.4
permanent pasture	3.3
field corn	1.9

Livestock and Products
cattle and calves	19.1
market milk	15.7

Fruits and Nuts
apricots	3.2
English walnuts	1.7

Vegetables
cantaloupes	19.7
fresh tomatoes	4.5
canning tomatoes	2.5
bell peppers	2.2
onions	2.1
green lima beans	1.9
watermelons	1.5
potatoes	1.1
green peas	0.9
cucumbers	0.9
carrots	0.7
cauliflower	0.7
lettuce	0.7
spinach	0.4

Source: Agricultural Commissioners of San Joaquin, Stanislaus, Merced, and Fresno counties.

his heirs began sale of remaining Miller holdings, which had included 530,000 acres in 1916.

In the 1890's Dos Palos, Los Banos, and Gustine became the foci of more intensive land-use as much acreage was obtained from Miller for colonization. Thus, after 1900, Portuguese dairymen bought tracts, usually of 20 to 40 acres. Many Portuguese, who were impecunious upon arrival, rented for a while. Yet much of the West Side remained untilled until the 1930's. Cotton farming, discussed later, was a corporation operation that demanded pump wells often more than 2000 feet deep and individual pumps able to provide sufficient water for an entire section (640 acres) of land.

As on the East Side, distinctive subdivisions have evolved on the West Side. In part because the period of irrigation agriculture has been shorter, land-use patterns have not become particularly intricate on the West Side; hence a simple subdivision into Northern and Southern sections seems sufficient.

THE NORTHERN WEST SIDE

The Northern West Side extends northward from Los Banos to the Delta Lands (see map, Fig. 9-2). Basic distinctions between this section and the Southern West Side are (1) greater annual rainfall totals, (2) absence of cotton—the season becomes too short and the threat of early autumnal rains too risky, and (3) a longer history of irrigation agriculture.

Precipitation is between 10 and 15 inches annually; rainfall tapers off southwards—in some years the Southern West Side does not receive more than five inches. Partially because of precipitation and also because of better access to market in the pre-railroad era (before 1890) the Northern West Side had considerable dry-farmed grains. Over sizable portions of the entire San Joaquin Valley, shipping costs tended to be a determining grain factor before the railroad, except for districts that could ship down the San Joaquin River.

Miller and Lux indirectly fostered the rise of irrigation agriculture despite their own concern with beef cattle. Besides sale of water from their San Joaquin and Kings River Canal, they constructed roads. The number of livestock they marketed provided a major incentive to the Southern Pacific to build its West Side line. Most irrigation agriculture took place after the railroad was constructed although alfalfa had been introduced into the area previously. In the present century, dairying and general farming prevailed until 1950; more recently specialized agriculture has appeared.

DAIRYING

Dairy farming has been one of the major rural activities of the Northern West Side. Full-time dairying followed the arrival of a Swiss dairy farmer who built a creamery in

Gustine in 1892. A number of early dairymen were former employees of Henry Miller; others moved from the Central Coast or came directly from Europe. Eventually there were hundreds of Italian-Swiss, who established a Swiss Club of Stanislaus County. Meanwhile, Azorean Portuguese, who generally started out as hired milking hands, gradually established dairies. Distance from market favored processing; most of the milk was converted into cheese, butter, condensed milk, and ice-cream mix. By the late 1920's Bay Area retail distributors began trucking fresh milk to city markets.[13] As early as 1890, Stanislaus County ranked fourth in California in butter production and between 1905 and 1920 it vied with Humboldt County for leading status. R. C. Cole, in *Soil Survey of the Newman District* (1938) estimated that the area between Crows Landing and Newman had more milk cows per acre than any other dairy belt in the United States. As population increased in the Bay Area there was a marked shift from manufacturing milk to market milk during the 1930's; quality of cows improved and milk output increased. After World War II insistence of the metropolitan areas upon Grade-A milk demanded that dairymen improve their facilities. Milk buyers seldom deal with dairies with less than sixty milking cows. Accordingly dairies have largely disappeared from the Northern West Side except in San Joaquin County as land has been converted into truck farms and orchards. Dairymen who elected to remain in this type of farming commonly relocated along the Trough, as was indicated previously. During the 1950's between 1400 and 1500 dairies in western Stanislaus County alone were converted into fruit or vegetable farms. The deserted and decaying dairy barn is still a common feature on the landscape.

FRUITS AND VEGETABLES

The changing rural landscape of the Northern West Side since 1950 represents a transition quite characteristic of the dynamic economic geography of California. Fruit orchards on a limited scale had been planted south of Tracy as early as the 1920's. Even in the 1920's, some dairymen began to shift to production of beans, enticed by a comparable return for less effort—when the bean market "softened" they returned to dairying. After World War II the costs of converting smaller dairies to Grade-A milk output was almost prohibitive.

The physical advantages of the Northern West Side have long been recognized as suitable for fruits and vegetables—various factors prompted shifting land-use after 1950 (Fig. 9-37). (1) Previously this area had been unable to compete against the Santa Clara Valley in such fruits as apricots—the Santa Clara had the advantages of early start, location, and packing facilities. (2) Urbanization of the Santa Clara Valley prompted some of its orchardists to follow the example of Southern California citriculturalists who moved to the Kaweah Delta; to avoid excessive capital-gains taxes, they have invested in West Side orchards. Land, which had been relatively cheap, has increased rapidly in price. (3) West Side dairymen were willing to sell their farms and buy cheaper land in the Trough, which would enable them to develop larger farms necessary to operate Grade-A dairies. (4) The Central Valley Project has made additional water available through the Delta-Mendota Canal, and new irrigation districts have been established. By 1959 the Tracy-Patterson district alone had 5000 acres of tree crops, with apricots, almonds, and walnuts the acreage leaders. Some cherries have been planted, but soil conditions are not always suitable.

The Northern West Side, originally treeless, now displays groves of cottonwood, Lombardy poplars, and eucalyptus as windrows (Fig. 9-38). Fences tend to be limited, and fields are frequently leveled to grade. Decaying milksheds, braceros in the fields, mechanized harvesters, open-sided implement sheds, orchards, and fields of truck crops have become typical. Despite the shift from dairying, alfalfa is still a common rotation crop. Truck crops include spinach and garden peas, which are trucked

[13] Lantis unenthusiastically recalls an all-night World War II trip by milk train from Fresno through Los Banos and Tracy to Oakland. Who would have thought there were so many "whistle stops" in this part of California!

to market centers like Tracy, Manteca, and Modesto.

EX-DAIRY TOWNS

The typical Northern West Side town is the little farm village beside the Southern Pacific's West Side line and California Highway 33. Communities tend to be at least a generation younger than those of the East Side, with fewer shade trees and a less stabilized air— this is analogous to the contrasting East Side and West Side towns of the Sacramento Valley noted earlier in the chapter.

Tracy (11,300) is the largest and least typical West Side city; it is a service center for the Delta Lands as well as the Northern West Side. It also has much importance as a Southern Pacific rail junction, with hundreds of railroad employees. Older than most West Side towns, Tracy was founded with a rail station in 1878. Its industries, despite some diversification, emphasize food products: dairy goods, sugar refining, wine, vegetables (especially tomatoes). Presumably the H. J. Heinz plant formerly in Berkeley was relocated here because of lower taxes, available land, good transportation, and availability of tomatoes locally. Shipping of agricultural products is likewise important. Nearby is the pumping station of the Central Valley Project, which lifts Sacramento River water (brought by the Delta Cross Channel) 200 feet into the Delta-Mendota Canal.

Los Banos (5300), second largest of Northern West Side towns, lies at the southern end of this area. Because it began as headquarters for Miller and Lux operations, it too is older than most West Side communities. It has long been the second largest city in Merced County and has persisted as a ranching and milk-handling center.

Smaller towns include **Gustine** (2300), a longtime dairying point now surrounded by truck farms; **Newman** (2200), another dairying-farming town; and **Patterson** (2300). Patterson, with a unique circular street pattern in its central district, is a growing community with ranch-style residences. Reflective of surrounding land-use changes is a frozen-foods processing plant opposite a creamery.

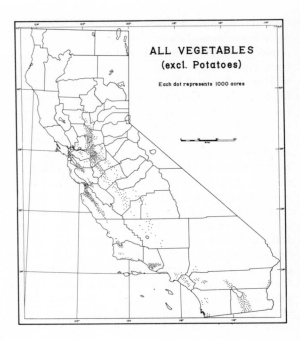

Fig. 9-37. MAP OF THE CALIFORNIA VEGETABLE ACREAGE.

THE SOUTHERN WEST SIDE

The Southern West Side (essentially western Fresno County), extending from Los Banos to the northern edge of Lake Tulare, has had a differing land-use from the area just discussed. In this latitude most of the Miller and Lux holdings were to the east in the Trough. South of the northward bend of the San Joaquin River at Mendota surface water for irrigation development has been inconsequential; pastoral uses commonly prevailed until the 1930's. Indeed this section and portions of the South End still contain the largest tracts of noncultivated land in the entire San Joaquin Valley today. Locally, particularly around Coalinga, oil-field development promoted population growth in the early twentieth century; the petroleum will be considered with discussion of the South End.

Agricultural development in the Southern West Side has not been typified by colonies and small farms. Nineteenth-century attempts at homesteading on alluvial fans often failed;

Fig. 9-38. LAND PREPARATION NEAR PATTERSON. (Caterpillar Tractor Company)

by 1870 much of the land was being acquired by large companies that established livestock operations. The few firms that tried extensive grain farming between 1880 and 1900 usually had limited success. Except in the wettest winters fallowing was usually necessary to assure a good barley crop. The account of farming on the Southern West Side since 1900 has been largely the late evolution of the giant cotton farm. Such operations have not been suitable for the "faint-hearted" or for the individual unable to obtain financing.

The South West Side ranch strikingly contrasts with the typical East Side property and even from many on the Northern West Side. It is not aesthetic; farming here has been a business, not a way of life—the landscape is nearly treeless and virtually fence-free. Properties are large, usually entailing many hundreds of acres and sometimes many thousands of acres. Cole (see Bibliography) in 1950 noted that sixty ranches in southwestern Fresno County averaged 4175 acres. The capital investment for an individual property often exceeds a million dollars—understandably this has been an area of corporate farming. In the early 1950's "raw land" was relatively inexpensive for California (i.e., $50 to $100 an acre) but the cost of development has been sizable—particularly land leveling, installation of an irrigation system, and purchase of equipment.

Water has been the critical factor in land development on the Southern West Side. Without either stream flow or imported water (pending such California Water Plan supply as the Feather River Project), it has been necessary to pump. Approximately 600,000 acre-feet has been "mined" annually for a generation; the water table has been dropping 15 to 20 feet per year since 1940. By 1961 the average pumping depth was 600 feet! Much of the pumped water is "fossil" (or connate) water, sealed within the earth by overlying strata of clay and hence not a renewable resource. Furthermore, the clays form a deep dike along the Trough which prohibits westward movement of water percolating underground from Sierran streams. Pumping has resulted in local subsidence, especially between Los Banos and the Kettleman Hills and principally on alluvial fans. Soil compaction and subsidence damages pump wells and makes construction of irrigation canals more difficult.

The pump wells, often capable of providing sufficient water for an entire section (640 acres) with a single unit, vary in depth from 400 to 4000 feet; some of the largest wells employ 300-horsepower motors or diesel engines and may lift water 800 feet. As early as 1953, 800 of the 1000 wells on the West Side were more than 500 feet deep. Such wells cost from $25,000 to $80,000 each to drill and because of corrosion (due to minerals in the water) have an average life expectancy of only seven years.

Dominant Southern West Side crops are cotton (discussed later), barley, and alfalfa; since 1930 there has been a tremendous expansion in acreage of each of these crops. This combination makes steadier use of the land, rebuilds soils, and provides "filler crop" substitutes when cotton acreage quotas have been reduced. There has also been a significant increase in acreage of vegetables and melons—this area has become the nation's chief source of cantaloupes.

Coalinga (6000) allegedly is a corruption of Coaling (Station) applied when the Southern Pacific built a spur line to nearby mine camps. Oil became its dominant activity in 1896; Coalinga received another economic boost in the late 1920's with the spectacular oil exploration in the Kettleman Hills south of the town. By 1910 Coalinga had a temporary population of 10,000 and became California's largest petroleum city. Increasingly, its economy has been influenced by agricultural development to the east. Coalinga College serves western Fresno County. The domestic water supply problem of Coalinga dramatizes the water problem of the Southern West Side; there is a dual-delivery system: separate taps for drinking water and for washing water. **Huron** (1300) is an agricultural hamlet to the east; **Avenal** (3100) is a petroleum town and way point on Highway 33.

LAND OF COTTON

Expansion of irrigation agriculture in the San Joaquin Valley has witnessed additions to rather than replacement of older crops. Cotton has usually appeared in localities that had not been watered previously: (1) less alkaline portions of the southern Trough, (2) the Southern West Side, (3) western segments of the Kaweah Delta, and (4) the South End. Two sources of water have become available for the rapidly expanded cotton acreage since 1930: pump wells and Central Valley Project water delivered by the Friant-Kern Canal.

The legend of California cotton has had several chapters; the earliest crops presumably were grown by the mission fathers. Attempts in the late nineteenth century were hampered by insufficient markets, labor shortage, unfamiliarity with irrigation culture, high production costs, and competition from other crops. Output in California increased after 1900, especially in the Imperial Valley during World War I years (Chapter 4). A major handicap in the early 1920's was the problem of suitable

variety; attempts to grow long-staple cotton had not been very successful.

The state College of Agriculture experimented with various varieties. By the middle 1920's it was realized that "upland" rather than "long staple" would prove the most successful. Varieties from Africa and Asia as well as native American cotton were tried. By 1924 it seemed apparent that native American upland types (Acala, Pima, and Durango) offered considerable promise. Acala supporters obtained legislative action in 1925 that restricted production in the Colorado Desert and the San Joaquin Valley to that variety. Through continuing experimentation, an improved strain, Acala 4-42, has been developed and yield per acre has continued to rise. Acala 4-42 produces medium bolls with 1- to 1-3/16-inch fibers of much strength; it can be harvested early and is suitable for mechanical picking. Yield has more than doubled in the past forty years and record output now exceeds 1100 pounds per acre. The San Joaquin Valley has become the nation's largest single-variety cotton grower.

Cotton has been California's most valuable single crop (but third commodity after beef and milk) since 1949 after a rapid acreage expansion in the 1940's (Fig. 9-39). In good years the net return has approached half a billion dollars. Boll-weevil damage and crop diversification in the South, federal price supports (since the 1930's), and World War II cotton demands contributed to the expanded output in the San Joaquin Valley. Cotton has become the leading crop of the five counties of the southern Valley (excluding Merced County) and been a major factor in making Fresno, Tulare, and Kern the three top-ranking counties nationally in total value of farm products. During the Korean emergency in the early 1950's a maximum of 1.4 million acres was planted; besides culture on newly plowed land, cotton partially replaced alfalfa, melons, and grains. California has achieved second place (after Texas) in total output while ranking only fifth among the states nationally in acreage. Yields far superior to those in the South account for the production greater than that of most traditional Cotton Belt states.

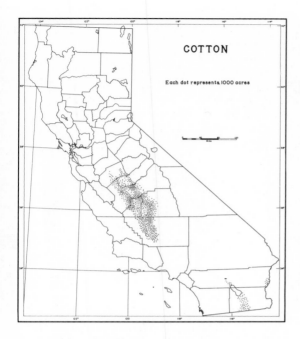

Fig. 9-39. *MAP OF THE CALIFORNIA COTTON ACREAGE.*

Fig. 9-40. *COTTON HARVEST. The mechanical harvester has largely replaced the hand picker since 1950.* (Greater Bakersfield Chamber of Commerce)

Cotton farming in the San Joaquin Valley is typified by the large size of fields and farms, extensive use of machinery (including harvest —Fig. 9-40), considerable application of fertilizer (soils tend to be low in nitrogen), and irrigation. Sprinkler irrigation has become widespread since 1950. There is no established rotation scheme; crops commonly grown in rotation with cotton include barley, alfalfa, and potatoes (Figs. 9-42, 9-43, and 9-45).[14]

[14] Although the Middle West is the nation's principal source of barley, California ranks first among individual states (Fig. 9-42). Barley long ago replaced wheat as the state's leading cereal grain. It is consumed largely as local livestock feed although a significant amount of grain from the western Sacramento Valley, Tulelake (Chapter 1), and the northwestern San Joaquin Valley is used for brewery malt making. Approximately half of California's barley is grown in the San Joaquin Valley, with western Fresno County the leading producer. Cotton farmers help amortize high "capital" (investment) costs by raising barley as a winter crop.

Differences in soil texture do not materially affect cotton yield although production declines if soils are too saline. In contrast to many crops grown in the Central Valley, there is no correlation between California population growth and cotton production, since the state does not have a cotton-fabrication industry. After the cotton has been ginned locally it is shipped to mills in New England or the South; then some of the cloth is returned to California for use in making clothing.

Large, in 1957 (see Bibliography), cited the importance of the federal government in California cotton production. Since the middle 1930's cotton prices have been maintained artificially through price supports. After the Korean emergency United States produced a cotton surplus, and the Secretary of Agriculture applied marketing controls nationally. Since allotments were based upon long-term records, western states such as California and Arizona were cut back more severely than

Fig. 9-41. BARLEY HARVEST, KINGS COUNTY. California leads the nation in barley production. (United Aerial Survey)

southern states. Hence nearly 400,000 acres less cotton were grown in California in 1954 than in 1953. When acreage is curtailed, farmers tend to grow cotton on their best land, apply much fertilizer to increase yields (thus profiting from high federally supported prices), and place other acreage in alternative crops. Long-range prospects anticipate expanded cotton acreage in the San Joaquin Valley. Without acreage control, California conceivably might become the nation's leading producer.

THE SOUTH END

The South End of the San Joaquin Valley, contained mostly within western Kern County (third largest in California), extends north into the bed of Lake Tulare (see map, Fig. 9-2). Physiographically, the South End encompasses the bulk of Tulare Basin, an area of internal drainage. This arid land, hottest and driest portion of the entire Central Valley,

receives the natural drainage from the Sierra south of the Kings River and partly from the Kings as well. However, since construction of Lake Isabella on the Kern and Pine Flat on the Kings River, Buena Vista Lake southwest of Bakersfield and Lake Tulare in Kings County, both sometimes sizable water bodies before white setttlement, have almost disappeared.

The South End has differed economically from various other sections of the Valley, particularly the East Side. The rural landscape was long typified by extensive grazing lands and dry-farming with large uncultivated tracts and also oil fields. The Kern River was used for irrigation, but without large storage reservoirs only limited acreage could be watered. Such an environment promoted the large property; the corporate farm has been a representative feature of South End land-use.

Water has wrought a great transformation in the South End. Between 1939 and 1949 cultivated acreage in Kern County alone almost doubled. The gross value of the county's agri-

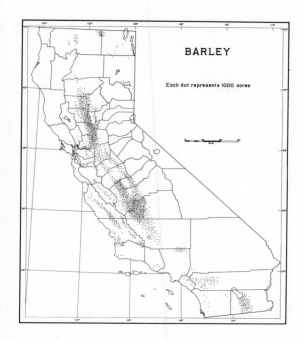

Fig. 9-42. MAP OF THE CALIFORNIA BARLEY ACREAGE.

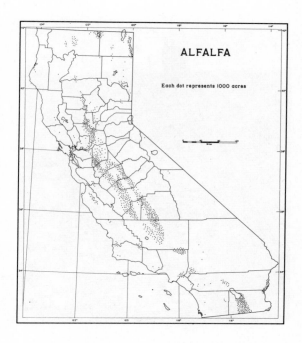

Fig. 9-43. MAP OF THE CALIFORNIA ALFALFA ACREAGE.

cultural output in 1939 was $26.4 million; by 1960 it had reached $246 million, and Kern was one of the nation's top three agricultural counties. Expansion was permitted by drilling of deep pump wells, as on the Southern West Side, and evolution of sprinkler irrigation. Construction of Lake Isabella on the upper Kern and Friant-Kern Canal, a major unit in the Central Valley Project, have also been consequential.

South End commodities in large measure reflect the general agricultural picture of the Valley, but there are still distinctions. Cotton is the most extensively grown crop. Alfalfa is important as are grains (especially barley and sorghum, also wheat and field corn), sugar beets, grapes, deciduous fruits, and several truck crops. The production of Irish potatoes is impressive; indeed this area ranks second in the West (after the Snake River Valley of Idaho), and world-record yields per acre have been established (Fig. 9-45).

THE POTATO PATCH

Potato farming in the South End first achieved moment in the early 1930's. The single important variety is the White Rose, or "California Long White," an all-purpose potato marketed nationally in late spring. The White Rose, planted shortly after New Year's Day, is harvested between late April and July —this variety has singular tolerance for early-season heat (Fig. 9-44).

The "potato belt," underlain by sandy soils, extends from Shafter through Bakersfield southeastward into the Arvin District (Fig. 9-45). Major expansion, which began in 1931 occurred around Shafter and resulted from low prices for competitive crops. Through high yields and effective marketing, Kern growers successfully captured the national "off-season" market that had been dominated previously by growers along the Gulf Coast. Expansion in the Arvin District, on fields famed for wild-

Fig. 9-44. POTATO HARVEST, SHAFTER. The South End is the nation's primary source of "out-of-season" Irish potatoes. (Kern County Land Company)

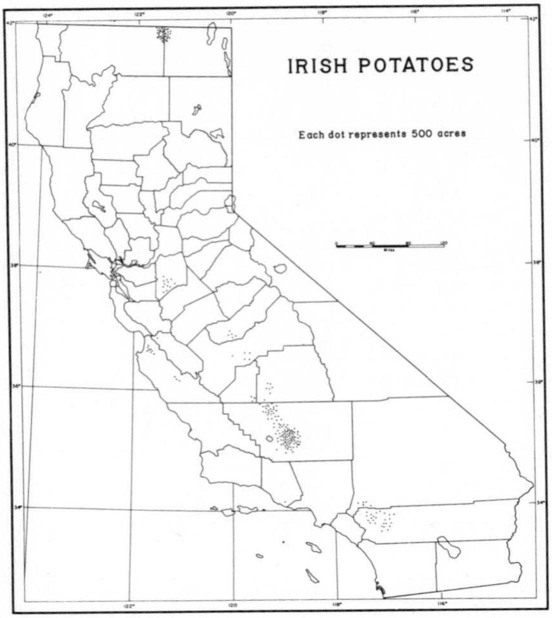

Fig. 9-45. MAP OF THE POTATO ACRE-AGE IN CALIFORNIA.

flowers as late as 1950, followed construction of Lake Isabella and extension of the Arvin-Edison canal southward from the Kern River.

THE CORPORATION RANCH

The South End, like the Trough and the Southern West Side, has long been a land of large rural properties. From the beginnings of extensive grain farming in the 1880's until the development of the Central Valley Project, the small operator was handicapped. Aridity and low yield per acre (for dry-farmed grains) negated much success for the average home-steader. In this century costs of well drilling and land reclamation have continued to dis-courage the small farmers.

The South End has been advantageous for large-scale farming for several reasons: (1) land was inexpensive, (2) availability of cheap labor and development of large machines tended to perpetuate "the system," and (3)

state and federal land policies favored the large property here. The federal government encouraged settlement through homesteading, but the low return from such arid land made homesteaders soon conducive to selling for "al-most nothing." The state government, through the Swamp Act, virtually "gave away" large tracts subject to seasonal overflow (i.e., Buena Vista and Tulare lakes). Large ranches have had their origins in (1) expansion by more successful homesteaders, (2) the "Swamp" lands, (3) several Mexican ranchos, (4) rail-road grants, (5) combination of tracts ob-tained with Veterans (Civil War) script, and (6) school lands.

Wills (in his thesis written in 1953) identi-fied five types of large holdings in the south-ern San Joaquin Valley: (1) the land-and-cattle company, (2) the bonanza wheat farm, (3) the "factory" farm, (4) the "indirect" landholder, and (5) the miscellaneous opera-tor. Representatives of the land-and-cattle

LEADING SOUTH END FARM PRODUCTS, 1961
(values in millions of dollars)

Field Crops
lint cotton	101.3
alfalfa hay	17.5
barley	15.9
cottonseed	12.0
misc. seed crops	2.8
nursery stock	2.8
sugar beets	2.2
sorghum	2.1
safflower	1.9
irrigated pasture	1.9
dry beans	1.9
wheat	1.3

Livestock and Products
cattle and calves	26.8
market milk	4.7
sheep and lambs	2.5
market eggs	2.3
turkeys	0.75

Vegetables
potatoes (white)	27.0
cantaloupes	5.0
watermelons	1.8
onions	1.7
sweet corn	1.4
carrots	0.9

Fruits
grapes, all types	25.2
peaches	2.4
plums	1.4
navel oranges	0.6

Source: Agricultural Commissioners of Kings and Kern counties.

company have included such firms as Tejon Ranch (discussed previously in Chapter 5), Miller and Lux, and Kern County Land Company. The bonanza wheat farm, significant in the nineteenth century, tended to persist longer on the rough lands of the foothill perimeter and on the bed of Lake Tulare, subject to recurrent flooding. The "factory farm," described by a few firms in all parts of the Valley, is a twentieth-century phenomenon; the largest one in the South End has been DiGiorgio Fruit Company in the Arvin District.

DI GIORGIO FRUIT COMPANY

This corporation, reputedly the nation's largest combined producer of fresh deciduous and citrus fruits with a significant wine output as well, was founded by a Sicilian immigrant. Besides the 10,000-acre "home ranch" north of Arvin, DiGiorgio owns more than a score of other ranches, packing houses, a lumber mill in Klamath Falls, Oregon, and other interests. Its operations outside the San Joaquin Valley include Florida citrus and vegetables, Idaho prunes and cherries, Washington deciduous fruits, Sacramento Valley pears and peaches. Permanent housing is maintained at Arvin.

KERN COUNTY LAND COMPANY

This expanding corporation was founded in 1890; however, its origin goes back to 1874 when James Haggin invested some of his Comstock Lode fortune in Kern County land upstream from the holdings of Miller and Lux. Haggin challenged Miller in the courts over water until 1888, when the two reached agreement on Kern River flow. Long essentially a cattle company with hundreds of thousands of acres in California and elsewhere in the West, Kern County Land Company is also concerned with oil and irrigation agriculture (Fig. 9-46). Its cattle are imported from all over the West and fattened in the San Joaquin Valley for the California market.

The corporation has rights to a considerable portion of the natural flow of the Kern River. It has developed extensive agricultural acreages in Kern County upon which it grows potatoes, sugar beets, cotton, and alfalfa. Between 1941 and 1952 it added 47,000 acres of cropland in Kern County, largely watered by pump wells.

THE 160-ACRE LIMITATION

The maximum size of individual landholdings allowed to receive water under large-scale programs in the Great Central Valley has been an issue since the beginnings of the Central Valley Project. From its formation in 1902, the U.S. Bureau of Reclamation has followed a policy of water distribution to provide "the greatest good for the greatest number," or a maximum of 160 acres per person (or 320 acres for husband and wife). The two farming corporations cited above represent major op-

Fig. 9-46. OIL WELLS AND VEGE-TABLES, KERN COUNTY. (Greater Bakersfield Chamber of Commerce, Rorex photo)

ponents of the 160-acre limitation. Landholders in older districts (such as Modesto) or in areas that have been developed through such means as deep pump wells (West Side and South End) have not been restricted. Water users dependent upon the flow of the Kings and Kern rivers successfully circumvented the 160-acre limitation when Pine Flat and Isabella dams were constructed partially as flood-control units by the Army Corps of Engineers.

More recently with plans to provide additional water to the western and southern San Joaquin Valley through the California Water Plan, the 160-acre limitation has become an issue again, since the state of California and the Bureau of Reclamation are jointly constructing the 2-million acre-feet **San Luis Reservoir** west of Los Banos as a CWP-CVP storage unit. A number of California political leaders sided with the larger landholders in opposition to the federal limitation. A state-federal compromise has been arranged; accordingly landholders who receive water from future California Water Plan developments

will presumably pay considerably more for their additional water than the landholders who will receive water through the Central Valley Project.

PETROLEUM

Long before the sensational expansion of irrigated acreage "black gold" had converted the South End away from an economy wholly dependent upon cattle and grains. The San Joaquin Valley, last of the six oil-producing "Tertiary Basins" to be discussed in California, has ranked second in total output to the Los Angeles Lowlands. Together these two areas were largely responsible for making California the nation's leading petroleum producer between 1900 and 1936 and second-ranking producer until 1958.

LEADING OIL FIELDS OF CALIFORNIA
(production in thousands of barrels)

FIELD	1960 PRODUCTION	1960 RANK	CUMULATIVE PRODUCTION	CUMULATIVE RANK
Los Angeles Lowlands				
Brea Olinda	5927		277,409	
Coyote, West	2684		195,484	
Dominquez	3546		225,851	
Huntington B.	16,550	(2)	667,787	(4)
Inglewood	4557		221,463	
Long Beach	5093		814,321	(3)
Montebello	1229		171,071	
Richfield	1966		138,967	
Santa Fe Spr.	2861		579,037	(6)
Torrance	2235		155,568	
Wilmington	27,550	(1)	884,534	(1)
Ventura				
South Mountain	6718		89,548	
Ventura	16,462	(3)	632,480	(5)
Central Coast				
Cat Canyon	4712		134,203	
Cuyama, S.	12,160	(6)	139,237	
Orcutt	928		122,512	
San Ardo	11,517	(7)	102,199	
Santa Maria V.	1823		131,260	
South San Joaquin Valley				
Belridge, S.	4569		85,615	
Buena Vista	9756	(8)	522,546	(7)
Coles Levee, N.	4893		108,846	
Edison	2960		87,081	
Elk Hills	4368		256,311	
Greeley	2455		85,156	
Kern Front	2027		97,487	
Los Lobos	7008	(10)	354,300	
Lost Hills	1503		84,661	
McKittrick	1245		106,847	
Midway-Sunset	13,936	(4)	848,879	(2)
Mount Poso	2847		141,452	
Rio Bravo	2876		96,320	
West San Joaquin Valley				
Coalinga	7502	(9)	521,662	(8)
Coalinga, East Ex.	13,096	(5)	361,019	(10)
Kettleman, North Dome	3434		429,769	(9)

Source: California Division of Oil and Gas.

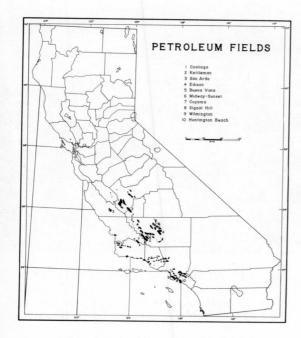

Fig. 9-47. MAP OF THE OIL FIELDS OF CALIFORNIA.

The presence of petroleum has been known under the surface of the San Joaquin Valley for about a century, but production did not become significant until the opening of the Mc-Kittrick field in 1887 and the Kern River field east of Bakersfield in 1899. Billions of barrels have been recovered from more than a score of fields. Some of California's deepest wells have been drilled as oil men have gone farther into the earth. Peak output at some fields, such as Kern River, was achieved in the first decade of this century. For others the peak came in the 1920's and 1930's. Most productive field has been Midway-Sunset; especially spectacular was the Lakeview gusher in this field, which came into production in March 1910 and in a brief "lifetime" of eighteen months had yielded 9 million barrels of crude oil. Perhaps no portion of the nation has been more intensively explored; despite a continuing search there has been no spectacular new field in many years. Production is slowly declining despite rising California consumption.

Petroleum from the southern San Joaquin Valley is marketed locally on a modest scale with Bakersfield as the refining center. Considerably more crude oil is delivered by pipeline elsewhere in California: (1) the Oil Coast of the San Francisco Bay Area, (2) Avila on San Luis Obispo Bay, (3) Estero Bay near Cayucos, and (4) across the Tehachapi and Transverse ranges into the Los Angeles Lowlands.

Although conservation appeared belatedly, the San Joaquin Valley generally did not experience the wasteful "town-lot" drilling of the Los Angeles Lowlands (Chapter 7). The Kettleman Hills, where production has been dominated by Standard Oil Company of California on leases of federal land, has been a good example of well-spaced wells. A valuable Naval reserve in the Elk Hills is being saved in case of future national military emergency.

OIL-AND-COTTON TOWNS

The urban landscape of the South End is somewhat contrary to that in other parts of the San Joaquin Valley because of the prevalence of the petroleum towns strung along California Highway 33: Maricopa, Taft, and McKittrick. Water is a precious commodity in this desert portion of the Valley—trees and lawns are limited. Also, there is usually a temporary air to mining towns, even longtime petroleum producers. Elsewhere the "typical" town is the local farm center. The South End now has a single metropolis, Bakersfield.

Bakersfield (57,000), cattle town of yesteryear, began to change its physiognomy with the arrival of the Southern Pacific Railroad. Its economy was transformed still more with the rise of the petroleum industry and more recently by agricultural expansion in Kern County. Bakersfield has the unincorporated "fringe-area" population previously noted in other Central Valley cities—its metropolitan population exceeds 150,000. It is a pass city, guarding the northern approach to the "Ridge Route" and the western end of the Tehachapi Pass crossing. It is situated south of the Kern River; its central district, which focuses upon 19th and Chester, had to be largely rebuilt

Fig. 9-48. DOWNTOWN BAKERSFIELD. The central district was extensively rebuilt after the earthquake of 1952. (Greater Bakersfield Chamber of Commerce, Rorex photo)

after the earthquake of 1952 (Fig. 9-48). The city has limited industrial importance; retail and wholesale trade, county government, tourism (wayfarers on U.S. 99 support many motels, restaurants, and service stations), and shipment of petroleum and agricultural products are all important. The railroads continue to have significance in the economy. Of the more than half of the metropolitan population that resides in the "unincorporated fringes," the Negro district east of U.S. 99 is conspicuous. A new residential area has evolved on the river terrace south of the Kern surrounding the campus of Bakersfield College. Hart Memorial Park, with recreational facilities, lies along the Kern River to the northeast.

Delano (12,000), Kern County's second city, is on U.S. 99 and like many communities along this highway originated with the arrival of the Southern Pacific in the 1870's. It serves principally as a farm-service center and shipping point; there is also agricultural processing. South of Delano is **Wasco** (6800), oil-field town and shipping point; it serves the Shafter potato district to the south.

Arvin (5300), southeast of Bakersfield, had its origins as an agricultural colony early in this century. Its growth as a farm-supply point has been promoted since Kern River water has been brought to its environs.

Corcoran (5000), at the northern fringe of the South End in Kings County, is a growing community that has benefited from agricultural expansion on the floor of old Lake Tulare. Machine shops, a large cotton gin, cattle-feed lots, and grain elevators all denote its reliance upon surrounding farmers.

Taft (3800), largest of the oil towns in western Kern County, was established early in the twentieth century with development of the petroleum industry locally. Paucity of large shade trees reflects the desert-like environment. A large fringe-area population gives a total 1960 population of around 8500, but like most of the "oil towns," Taft is declining in population. Its sectional importance is suggested by the presence of Taft Junior College.

412 : : CHAPTER NINE

REGIONAL PROSPECTS

The Great Central Valley continues to gain momentum as an agricultural empire. Several million acres yet to be placed under irrigation by future Central Valley Project and California Water Plan programs indicate that the Valley should participate in anticipated population growth of the nation's most populous state. A significant expansion is expected on the west sides of the San Joaquin and Sacramento valleys and in the South End of the San Joaquin. One can assume that future farming will become largely mechanized, with a likely introduction of new crops and more intensive cultivation.

Technological advances make summer heat more tolerable indoors but the Central Valley is still plagued by several months when afternoons "don't have too much edge on Hell!" Significant numbers of senior citizens, especially local residents, are spending their retirement years within the Valley but the region does not have notable appeal for out-of-staters.

Many Central Valley cities are attempting to lure industries in order to achieve economic diversity. In promoting such ambitions, the Sacramento, Stockton, Modesto, Fresno, and Bakersfield districts seem more favored, located more or less as they are between California's two major population conurbations, than communities of the central and northern Sacramento Valley. Yet many sports enthusiasts in the Bay Area and the Los Angeles Lowlands visit friends and relatives in the northern Sacramento Valley and yearn for an economy there that would enable them to escape from their own urban congestion.

Fig. 10-1. FORT BRAGG AND UNION LUMBER COMPANY. Fort Bragg, principal community of the Mendocino Coast, is situated on a marine terrace whose seaward edge is dominated by the mill of Union Lumber Company, a major redwood producer. (Union Lumber Company, photo by Clyde Sunderland)

CHAPTER TEN:: THE NORTHWEST

THE NORTHWEST

The Northwest envelops one tenth of California, yet it contains fewer people than San Diego—less than 5 percent of the state total. One is almost everywhere conscious of its slopes; from many promontories the forest seems to spread across the land like a green coverlet nestled over the furled blankets of an unmade bed. Save for its lumbering the Northwest does not make a dramatic contribution to the California economy. This is not a land of cities—or of industrial plants other than lumber mills. Livelihood is close to the earth —lumbering, agriculture, and tourism are the principal pursuits. Precipitation, often heavier than elsewhere in California, exceeds 100 inches annually in wetter spots. Soon the Northwest will become a major exporter of water and hydroelectricity to more populous portions of the state. The Trinity River Project is a harbinger of future developments.

The Northwest has remained isolated, even until the present time. Much of this area is

This chapter has been reviewed by Alfred R. Butz, Santa Rosa Junior College.

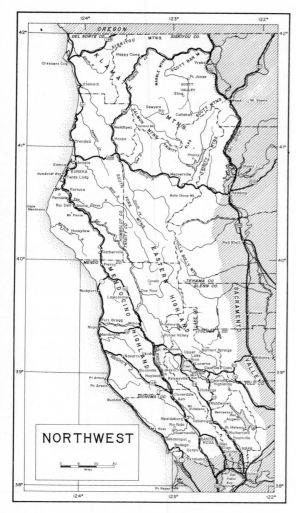

Fig. 10-2. MAP OF THE NORTHWEST.

little visited and unknown to most Californians, and many local habitués are suspicious of everything in California south of San Francisco. It has much scenic appeal, but must compete with the Sierra Nevada, and is often the loser. Outside contacts have improved considerably since the 1920's, yet the Northwest still has only one important north-south highway, U.S. 101. The region has never had a north-south railroad into Oregon—in fact, no rail line has been built in Lake County, less than a hundred miles from San Francisco! Coastal

contacts by ocean have been minimized by the scarcity of good harbors.

The Northwest forms a transition, physically and culturally, between more southerly portions of California and Oregon and Washington. Although its climate still has most aspects of the dry-summer subtropical, it begins to suggest the temperate middle-latitude (marine west coast) lands to the north. On its southern periphery, agricultural activity is distinctly Californian; still, over much of the area lumbering is more characteristic—an economic aspect more representative of western Washington and Oregon than most of California.

The Northwest is that portion of California north of the San Francisco Bay Area (Central Coast) and west of the Southern Cascades and the Sacramento (Great Central) Valley (map, Fig. 10-2). Specific definition of the southern border becomes more difficult as the Bay Area urbanization encroaches upon the Santa Rosa and Napa valleys.

THE LAND

TERRAIN

The Northwest is a rough land, generally of moderate elevations, with relatively narrow valleys; there is often a constricted coastal ledge (Fig. 10-6). Drainage is almost wholly westward into the Pacific. Rivers are large (for California) and their canyons afford east-west land routes although the streams themselves are not navigable.

THE KLAMATH MOUNTAINS

This highlands is an ancient mass worn down to what some call a "peneplain"—then uplifted with gentle bowing (warping); it is again in the process of erosion. Although moderately even ridgelines are widespread around 6000-feet elevation, the Klamath contains some of the most rugged terrain in California; higher summits exceed 8000 feet. Separating the uplands are deep, steep-sloped canyons of such large rivers as the Klamath, the Trinity, and their principal tributaries. The Klamath, presumably an antecedent stream, has cut its gorge across the width of the Mountains; in fact, the drainage divide is near the eastern periphery so that most rivers empty directly into the Pacific rather than discharging first into the Sacramento. Higher portions of the Mountains, especially the Trinity Mountains, were glaciated during the Great Ice Age and display serrated summit ridges, U-shaped valleys, and little lakes (Fig. 10-12). Rocks, usually metamorphic, tend to be older than those in many parts of California.

The Klamath serves as the group name for several distinct units that, lacking any recognizable relationship, are known by such individual names as Trinity Alps or Scott Bar Mountains. The **Siskiyou** in the northwest, extending into Oregon, like much of the Klamath is slightly arcuate. To the south the **Marble Mountains** is impressively rugged. Farther south, and drained by the Salmon, New, and Trinity rivers, is the highly dissected Salmon Mountains. Paralleling the upper Trinity with a north-south orientation is the **Trinity Range,** which includes the dramatically glaciated Trinity Alps, whose apex is Thompson Peak (9002 ft.), highest point in the entire Northwest. On the eastern edge of the Klamath, Bully Choop Mountain and Castle Crags, an intrusive mass, form significant landmarks. In the extreme south the summits of the **Yolla Bolly Mountains** are as high as those to the north.

The bewildering complexity of drainage patterns results from several periods of mountain building as well as the influences of lithology and faulting. Structural basins are generally small; the most significant is Scott Valley in the northeast (Fig. 10-14).

THE NORTHERN COAST RANGES [1]

These ranges have several features representative of the California Coast Ranges in

[1] Too frequently the terms *Coast Ranges* and *Pacific coastal mountains* are confused. The Peninsular and Transverse ranges are coastal mountains, as are Olympic in Washington and the Coast Mountains in British Columbia. The Coast Ranges include the southern and northern, in California, and the Oregon Coast Range. The northern Coast Ranges of California extend from Marin County to the Oregon border.

their entirety: parallelism of landforms, predominance of folded and faulted sedimentary rocks, and marine terraces. Yet the striking linear arrangement of the southern Coast Ranges is absent. This is especially true in the north despite the 150-mile ridge extending from Oregon to the Yolla Bolly Mountains. This ridge, especially conspicuous from the air, has such local names as **Rattlesnake** and **South Fork**—it forms a definite boundary between the Coast Ranges and the Klamath. Unlike the southern Ranges, the San Andreas fault does not extend the length of those in the Northwest; it disappears beneath the Pacific north of Point Arena. The faults have the same northwest-southeast orientation as south of San Francisco Bay despite less regularity of trend. Streams tend to flow northwestward along fault depressions; a trellis drainage pattern is characteristic.

The Franciscan sedimentary series are even more widespread in the northern Coast Ranges than farther south. Graywacke (a sandstone), shales, conglomerates, and altered layers are widespread. There are local lava flows and much serpentine. Landslides, sometimes due to high clay content, are relatively commonplace during the rainy season; surface routes are often blocked.

Marine terraces are often spectacular, as elsewhere along the California coast. Some, a thousand feet above sea level, suggest recent mountain building, whereas lower ones reflect sea-level changes during the Great Ice Age. Likewise, as farther south, submarine canyons extend outward beneath the ocean floor. Particularly significant is the Mendocino Fracture Zone, where a submarine escarpment extends westward more than 1500 miles.

There are two basic highland units in the northern Coast Ranges: (1) paralleling the Pacific is the **Mendocino Highlands** (or Plateau); (2) east of the structural depression occupied by the Russian and Eel rivers is the larger **Eastern Highlands.** The Mendocino Highlands, a westward-sloping, maturely dissected plateau, reaches a width of 20 miles. It is lower and less rugged than the Santa Lucia Range, its coastal counterpart in the southern Coast Ranges. It is nearly breached by the valley of the Navarro River, and farther south the water gap of the Russian River traverses its width. The Eastern Highlands seem more complex and elevations are higher; Black Butte and Snow Mountain exceed 7000 feet. There are three somewhat parallel ranges separated by structural depressions. Clear Lake lies in the rift between the two more westerly uplands, Mayacmas Range (which continues to the south as Napa Range) and Bartlett Ridge. To the east is the Gravelly Ridge–Rocky Ridge–Vaca Mountains mass. Generally there is a maze of hills and small structural basins, less well defined than the features of the southern Coast Ranges. The extreme south end, with parallel ranges and intervening basins known as Santa Rosa, Sonoma (Valley of the Moon), and Napa valleys, is more suggestive of the Coast Ranges south of San Francisco Bay. In addition there is a relatively youthful volcanic area, which includes Mt. Konocti and Mt. St. Helena, extending from Clear Lake to the San Francisco Bay. The many hot springs are related to vulcanism, as is the new geothermal power plant at The Geysers.

A TRANSITIONAL CLIMATE

A portion of the Northwest has dry-summer subtropical ("Mediterranean") climate, yet the intricacy of relief affords significant local variations.[2] California's northern boundary reaches 42° latitude—the Northwest tends to form a transition between the hot dry-summer lands to the south and the cooler, moist climes of Oregon and Washington (see Appendix A). The Hawaiian (Pacific) High exerts much less influence here than it does farther south; hence the Northwest experiences the effects of more storms out of the North Pacific basin. Rainfall tends to be heavier, the wet season longer, and storms more frequent

than farther south. As elsewhere in California, however, there is a wide variation in precipitation from one year to the next.

Precipitation decreases southward and toward the east. Crescent City receives an average of 74 inches, Eureka 39, San Francisco 22. Rain falls on twice as many days annually in Eureka as in San Francisco. Although precipitation records for highlands stations are limited, exposed uplands in Del Norte County apparently receive in excess of 100 inches annually.[3] Winters are wetter than elsewhere in the state; the forest floor is often saturated. Higher summits in the Klamath and in the Eastern Highlands remain snow-covered much of the winter; over much of the region moisture falls as rain.

The North Coast littoral is damp even in summer, windswept, and often overcast. Throughout the year, coastal residents of Del Norte and Humboldt counties can expect dense fog at least once a week.[4] The fogbanks, reaching a thickness of 1500 feet, form when warmer maritime air drifts eastward across that great ocean-river of the eastern Pacific, the cool California Current. Fog becomes more commonplace in summer when winds blow continuously from the northwest as the Hawaiian High shifts north with the sun. Besides cooling of air flowing across the California Current, upwelling of colder water from depths close to shore further cools the air. Upwelling causes lower surface temperatures than along the coasts of Oregon and Washington. Even when summer skies are clear, the cloud banks rise over the nearby ocean, hanging ominously and ever threatening to move inland. Rising midday temperatures usually cause the fog to "burn off" the land; the banks remain offshore and flow inland in the evening. The fog influences areas within

---

[2] Students in introductory courses learn that the dry-summer subtropical climate (Koeppen's Cs) is found on west coasts between 30° and 40° latitude. Small-scale world maps show the temperate middle latitudes (marine west coast, or Cfb) extending southward virtually to San Francisco along the coast.

[3] Honeydew in the Mattole Valley (Humboldt County) received 174 inches of precipitation during the winter of 1957-58. The average annual precipitation at Monumental in Del Norte County is 109 inches (although the period of record was limited).

[4] During World War II the incidence of fog prompted the Federal government to conduct its FIDO (fog dispersal) experiments at Arcata airport.

10 to 20 miles of the coast. Interior valleys, unaffected by fog, sometimes become quite warm in summer.

AN EVERGREEN LAND

The "green" portion of the conservation slogan "Keep California Green and Golden" has particular applicability to the Northwest. Despite other vegetation types, this is principally a land of conifer forests (chiefly redwood, Douglas fir, yellow pine) and chaparral. Interior valleys are characterized by a mixed coniferous and broadleafed woodland, interspersed with considerable grassland; grasses are also found on upper slopes of many interior Coast Range ridges.

The coast redwood (*Sequoia sempervirens*) is restricted to a belt within approximately 20 miles of the ocean where drip from summer sea fogs helps reduce temperature and provide sufficient moisture for the trees to endure the long drought season. Tallest of North American plants, these magnificent trees in virgin stands vary in height from 100 to 340 feet; diameters commonly exceed 10 feet. Although there are scattered groves as far south as the Santa Lucia Mountains, the coast redwood is largely restricted to the Northwest. It is commonly found in heaviest stands along streams flats, where it produces a tremendous board footage per acre. The trees, often growing in pure stands, create cathedral-like areas in which the sunlight filters down softly; the forest floor is often covered with ferns and mosses (Fig. 10-7). On slopes, Douglas fir (*Pseudotsuga taxifòlia*), white fir (*Àbies concolor*), western red cedar (*Chamaecyparis Lawsoniana*), hemlock (*Tsùga héterophýllia*), California bay (*Umbellulària califórnica*), and wax myrtle (*Myrìca califórnica*) often grow with the redwood.

Inland from the redwood belt is the Douglas fir forest. In the northern half of the Northwest this association reaches eastward across the Klamath. Its stands are often dense, yet this tends to be more open forest than the redwood; there is much undergrowth. Such plants as bay, bigleaf maple (*Acer macro-*

phyllum), madrone, and tanbark oak (*Lithocarpus densiflora*) grow in the association.

The yellow-pine forest penetrates westward into the Klamath. This forest type, the most extensive in California, is more characteristic in the Southern Cascade and the Sierra Nevada. An open forest with less undergrowth than the Douglas fir, it reflects hotter and drier summers, and colder winters.

Chaparral forms an extensive cover particularly in the Eastern Highlands of the northern Coast Ranges. Two widely distributed phases are chamise and chamise-broadleaf. Chamise (*Adenostoma fasciculatum*) forms dense thickets toward the Sacramento Valley, especially on south-facing slopes. The chamise-broadleaf includes scrub oak, California laurel, manzanita, various ceanothus, and such conifers as Douglas fir, yellow and sugar pine. The red berries of the toyon make a colorful addition to autumnal landscapes; in spring, the redbud is covered with magenta-hued blossoms.

SETTLEMENT

The Northwest has had a longer history of occupance than its modest population would suggest. It has had significant numbers of Indians, despite limited totals today. The region was never of consequence to the Spanish; yet it was one of the first areas in California to be settled by Americans.

THE INDIANS

The Northwest, particularly in the west and north, constituted a more favored habitat for American Indians than did most parts of California. There were salmon and other fish in the perennial streams. Acorns, as in many parts of California, were abundant in more southerly valleys. There was a variety of berries, nuts, and seeds and assuredly as much small game as in most parts of the state. There was not the continuous effort to avert starvation that prevailed in more niggardly regions. Such tribes as the Yurok placed more emphasis upon materialism than was typical of California Indians.

The Northwest, transitional between California and the Pacific Northwest, had greater ethnic complexity than other California regions. Athapaskan, Algonquin, Hokan, Yukian, and Penutian linguistic groups were represented.

The four *Athapaskan* tribes (Tolowa, Hupa, Chilula, and Mattole) apparently had been longtime Californians. They were North Coast hillfolk who resided seasonally along streams during the salmon runs. The Hupa, residents of Hoopa Valley along the lower Trinity, have perhaps survived more successfully than most California Indians because of their inaccessible habitat. In fact there is still a Hoopa Valley reservation.

The *Algonquin* (Yurok and Wiyot) were coastal peoples. These skilled wood craftsmen built plank houses and dugout-redwood canoes in which they successfully navigated rocky streams. They achieved the highest cultural levels of the California Indians and were quite materialistic. They measured their wealth in fine obsidian blades and decorative dentalium shells. Like many California Indians, they valued acorns in their diet and they even grew a little tobacco for their own use.

The *Pomo* (Hokans), residents of the Mendocino Highlands, the Russian River, and the Clear Lake Country, occupied an environment truly favored for hunter-gatherers. The Russian River Valley, the heartland, was a land of abundant oaks and small game, bulbs and seeds. Pacific shores provided mussels, fish, and sea lions. Clear Lake, perhaps focus of the largest population, supplied waterfowl and fish; even young tule shoots had dietary significance.

The *Yuki* (Yukians), long-headed mountainfolk of the upper Eel Basin, were culturally inferior to their neighbors. They did not build boats, and they were less skilled as fishermen than some Northwestern tribes. Their conical earth-covered dwellings were more primitive than the planked houses of the Athapaskans and Algonquins.

The *Wintun* (Penutians) occupied the eastern margins of the Northwest although they are commonly regarded as Sacramento Valley people rather than hillfolk. The portion of the Eastern Highlands held by these hunters was one of the most niggardly portions of the entire Northwest.

EUROPEAN COLONIALS

Like northern California in general, most of the Northwest was virtually unknown to Europeans before 1825. Culturally, this was an "empty" no-man's land between Spanish America to the south and England's western outposts and Russian America to the north.

The Russians did establish an outpost along the Sonoma coast in 1809, following the visit of Count Rezanof to the San Francisco Presidio three years earlier. Russian settlements in southeastern Alaska—a wet, inhospitable land distant from Czarist Russia—needed foodstuffs. The Russians grew a little wheat in California, some of which was shipped to Alaska. They also were successful in obtaining pelts of the numerous sea otter. Ft. Ross was established in 1812; the Russians claimed this portion of the California coast. Following the Monroe Doctrine and the decline of their Alaskan activity, Russia's California settlement languished, especially with the decline of sea-otter operations. In 1841 the Russians left Alaska; the California property was sold to John Sutter.

Seemingly the Spanish ignored even the southerly fringes of the Northwest prior to establishment of Ft. Ross. Concern over Russian encroachment prompted Spanish exploration. The founding of Mission San Francisco Solano (Mission Sonoma) occurred in 1823, after Spain had granted Mexico its independence but before the actual political transfer in California.

More activity materialized in the Northwest during the Mexican period than had transpired in the Spanish period. Ultimately more than a score of land grants was awarded; as in the Great Central Valley most were not made until the 1840's. Early settlement attempts in the Santa Rosa Valley were discouraged by Indian opposition. The Mexicans then directed their efforts toward the Sonoma Valley; the pueblo of Sonoma was established at the mission site in 1835.

Alta California was ruled at the time by a capable governor, Jose Figueroa. With support from the central government, Mariano Vallejo supervised efforts to stabilize the northern frontier against Russian assault. Several hundred settlers located in the Sonoma Valley. Soon a series of grants had been awarded in the Sonoma, Napa, and Santa Rosa valleys. As in the Sacramento Valley, some ranchos were given to early American pioneers or to non-Spanish Europeans. These included the most northerly coastal rancho, *Albion*, north of Ft. Ross along the Mendocino coast. The most northerly of all Mexican ranchos was given in the Russian Valley north of Ukiah in 1845.

Much of the Northwest remained in Indian possession when the Gold Rush began. It was far from Mexico City, and both Spain and Mexico appeared too weak to expand their activities. San Francisco Bay formed a decided transportation barrier. The numerous Indians discouraged much penetration. The rugged, forest-covered terrain held little appeal to Hispanic peoples.

THE AMERICANS

American settlement in the southern valleys of the Northwest began in the early 1840's. Early arrivals included a sprinkling of mountain men, fur trappers who elected to establish residence in California, and members of early immigrant overland parties. These lowlands, along with the Sacramento Valley, afforded the best opportunity to obtain good unclaimed land as Mexican grants. The early Americans here were active in the Bear Flag Republic and subsequently in the achievement of a state government.

"Gold fever" had tremendous importance in quickening exploration and occupance of less accessible reaches of the Northwest. After discovery of gold at Reading's Bar on the Trinity River in 1848, thousands were searching the sand bars of canyons to the west within a year. Major centers included Scott Valley, Hamburg, and Orleans in the Klamath canyon and the Trinity canyon around Weaverville. The La Grange mine northwest of Weaverville for many years remained one of the world's largest hydraulic operations.

Gold mining prompted development of seaports along the North Coast. The first harbor, Trinidad, was in use in 1850.[5] Shortly thereafter Arcata, Crescent City, and Eureka were established. Need for overland transportation to the gold fields prompted opening of several traces. Besides the chief interior north-south passage, the California-Oregon Trail (Chapter 6), routes were extended into the Klamath canyon from Trinidad and eastward from Humboldt Bay to Weaverville.

With ill luck at mining or with decline of such operations, many miners became farmers. The Southern Valleys (Napa, Sonoma, and Santa Rosa) had a particular appeal, yet some of the choice lands there had already been selected as ranchos in the 1840's. Rise of agriculture developed rapidly around the flanks of Humboldt Bay, logged early. Mild climate and meadowlands favored dairying; ocean transportation to San Francisco provided a market for cheese and butter. Even in more remote areas like Lake County, the good arable land was occupied by 1860.

Redwood lumbering also got an early start. The forests approached the strand of Humboldt Bay, and by 1854 there were seven mills operating in Eureka. Partially because timber was available much closer to San Francisco and the Sierran gold camps, the Northwest did not lead the state in production in the 1850's. Yet in 1869 alone 75-million board-feet of redwood was processed around Humboldt Bay.

CONTEMPORARY ACTIVITIES

The economy of the Northwest basically has the foundations that were created a century ago. Relations with the land are direct; this is a region of lumbering, agriculture, and fishing. In the later twentieth century tourism has increasing moment. By contrast mining no longer has much significance. Manu-

[5] Although Humboldt Bay had been visited by the Yankee captain, Jonathan Winship and the *O'Cain* in 1806, Trinidad was *the* known harbor when the Gold Rush commenced. Humboldt Bay had got "lost" after 1806!

facturing has slight consequence, except for processing of lumber and agricultural products.

LUMBERING

Forestry is the primary source of livelihood in the Northwest—the whine of the saw, the smell of newly cut wood, and the ashy blue cloud of smoke from the trash burner are commonplace. There is the ever present threat of a logging truck around the next bend in the road. This region is California's prime source of wood products and forms a major explanation of why California ranks second nationally (after Oregon) in lumber production. Far more of the Northwest is forest-covered than is generally true elsewhere in California; the extent of the three forest types is shown in the chart below.

	PRESENT VOLUME	ACREAGE
Douglas Fir Coast Range	75-billion bd. ft.	2.0 million acres
Pine	61-billion bd. ft.	2.4 million acres
Redwood	36-billion bd. ft.	1.9 million acres

Source: California Forest and Range Experiment Station, Forest Statistics for California, 1954, pp. 22 and 31.

Fantastic reserves of timber remain despite a century of heavy and often wasteful cutting. Although 23-billion board-feet of redwood were cut between 1903 and 1951, there were still 36-billion board-feet standing a decade ago. Northwest lumber output has as its primary outlet the California market; "export" markets are secondary. Although approximately half of the redwood and half of the pine leaves California, over three fourths of the Douglas fir is consumed within the state.

REDWOOD

The coast redwood forests of the Mendocino Highlands, the Eel Valley, and coastal sections of Humboldt and Del Norte counties have been logged longer and more thoroughly than the other forests; operations commenced more than a century ago. Lumber could be readily shipped from Eureka and smaller ports and landings to San Francisco, where it was valued for siding and for

Fig. 10-3. LOGGING OPERATIONS NEAR CLOVERDALE. The "cat" skids a large log to the landing where it is then trucked to the mill. (Caterpillar Tractor Company)

shingles. The forests are high in quality with long branch-free boles and trees of great size, which yield 25,000 to 300,000 board-feet per acre.

Lumbering has always been arduous, even dangerous, in the redwood belt. Much of the terrain is steep-sloped. Since snow is infrequent, in the past year-round logging was conducted despite brief stoppages during winter storms. More recently winter logging has been drastically reduced because of the difficulty of mechanical operations during the wet season; today, mills generally stockpile in summer. Originally, logs were moved to the mill with animal power (or floated down rivers). Then machinery was introduced with steam-powered donkey-engines, "highlines," and logging railroads. Eventually the crawler tractor and then diesel equipment became available (Fig. 10-3).

Contemporary operations vary from the relatively small "peckerwood" or "gypo" mill, whose principal concern is immediate profit, to the large corporation, which practices scientific forestry with tree farms and operates on a vast scale. Logging begins with the estimate of the timber cruiser and the logging engineer, who determines means of getting the timber to the mill; firms commonly construct their own truck trails today. Next come the fallers, who fell the trees with portable power saws. The tree is stripped of its branches and cut into sawmill "lengths" (twenty to forty feet). Logs are next trucked to the mill and either dumped into the mill-pond or stockpiled for winter use. The log is cut into various sizes and forms by automatic saws, graded and sorted, artificially dried in a kiln (or air-dried in the main yard if the mill is running ahead of demand), and finally it is planed.

The redwood forests are commonly on private property.[6] Humboldt County ranks first in California in reserves of standing saw timber; for many years the county has led the state in lumber production. The great mills of Samoa, Arcata, Eureka, and Scotia constitute some of the largest redwood plants. Douglas fir is also trucked in from forests toward the east. The Mendocino Coast was the leading producer before World War II, but its virgin stands have largely been depleted; its output is a poor second to Humboldt County. Timber reserves, slightly less than those of Siskiyou County, rank third in the state; of late, considerable second-growth redwood has been cut.[7]

DOUGLAS FIR AND YELLOW PINE

Dispersal of the lumber industry into the rough interior of the Northwest from accessible tidewater came late. The logging railroad has never been a factor; timber is trucked to local mills, even to tidewater. Besides costs of railroad construction, the extent of national forests and terrain problems has discouraged private railroads.

The Douglas fir forest, immediately inland from the redwoods, was not logged too extensively before 1940. Lumbering was delayed

[6] *The Los Angeles Times* (October 23, 1956), in reporting the sale of Hammond Lumber Co. to Georgia-Pacific Corp. for $75,000,000, noted that the purchase included 4-billion board-feet of standing timberlands, a tenth of all California's commercial redwood.

[7] It does not take a millennium to produce marketable redwood. Saw-timber can be grown within forty to seventy years. An impressive little redwood grove on the Chico State College campus was planted in this century. This growth rate does not justify wasteful practices, of course.

until consumption increased and more accessible supplies of fir were depleted; meanwhile, suitable trucks and roadbuilding equipment became available. About half of the Douglas fir lands are privately owned; holdings tend to be large. Douglas fir is now the leading species of wood cut in California and the Northwest; it is much used for rough construction. Perhaps half of the private lands are in possession of stockmen who consider logging an adjunct of ranching.

Farther east the pine forests still contain much virgin timber. These forests tend to be less accessible than pine holdings farther east in the Cascade and Sierra Nevada. The tremendous population growth of California after 1940, with its expanded lumber consumption, has justified logging. Much of the timber comes from national forests; lumbermen bid for cutting rights. No major center has evolved in either the fir or pine belts; in fact, many logs are trucked to Yreka, Redding, Weed, or Eureka. Considerable timber, especially fir and pine, is hauled to mills in Oregon —the observant traveler is impressed with the volume of logs moving north on U.S. 99 and 199.

FISHING

The North Coast (map, Fig. 10-2) ranks below the southern and central coasts of California in significance of both commercial and sports fishing. The continental shelf is narrower here than off the Southern California coast, and the fishermen lack such vicinal markets as San Diego, Los Angeles, and San Francisco. Much fish is now transported by truck to the San Francisco Bay Area. Too, the commercial fishermen of this area generally have not gone great distances from port; it will be recalled that the fishing fleets of San Pedro and San Diego operate into Mexican and even Peruvian offshore waters. It is understandable that only a tenth of the state catch comes from the Northwest. Yet with larger boats, permitting more icing, longer trips are being made.

North Coast fishing differs in several respects from areas farther south. One difference is in the varieties taken. This area is

California's chief source of flounder (sole); rockfish, tuna, and salmon are also caught. The North Coast is the state's leading producer of shellfish with over a third of the state catch; crab and abalone are important. Another difference is that fishermen tend to be of different national backgrounds: Scandinavians and Italians. Principal centers include Eureka, with approximately 500 commercial vessels, Crescent City, and Fort Bragg–Noyo.

AGRICULTURE

The Northwest is the least attractive portion of California's Pacific Borderlands for agriculture. The cool, foggy coast, rough land, forest cover, and wetness make much of the region unsuitable. It is not surprising that significant farming is largely restricted to the Southern Valleys, which have better soils, more sunshine, less rainfall—and better accessibility to market.

Despite limited importance of agriculture, some Northwestern products have considerable moment. The Southern Valleys are a major producer of grapes; the wines of Napa Valley, especially, have an international reputation. The Southern Valleys also constitute a significant source of such deciduous fruits as plums, prunes, and apples; Lake County produces pears. The flanks of Humboldt Bay and the areas immediately north of San Francisco Bay have considerable dairy cattle. The Santa Rosa Valley has long been one of the leading poultry centers of California. Agriculture will be discussed under specific subregions later in the chapter.

LIVESTOCK RANCHING

Pastoral activities, widespread in the Northwest, constitute an extensive rather than intensive land-use. Sheep and cattle have both been important, although at different periods and in dissimilar parts of the region. Livestock is logical here—climate, slope, and isolation tend to favor animals over crops. There is much grassland or brushland suitable for grazing.

The northern Coast Ranges, especially in Sonoma, Mendocino, and Humboldt counties, have been a major California producer of sheep since the 1880's. Ranches tend to range from 1000 to 20,000 acres; 2 to 5 acres per sheep per year are needed—distance from the ocean is significant (influence of moisture). The cool climate coupled with wet winters has favored production of long-staple wool. The physical environment is advantageous; it permits winter grazing on hillsides so that lambs can be produced on the range and shipped to market in late winter when there is limited competition from other parts of the nation. Sheep decline reflects weak mutton markets, substitution of synthetic fibers for wool, and overgrazing. Sheep have also long browsed within Sonoma County orchards.

Beef cattle were initially significant in the Mendocino Highlands before the advent of sheep ranching. By the 1880's the environmental advantages for sheep had become evident. Locally, beef cattle have declined in the past century in the Southern Valleys as well. The rise of irrigation agriculture reduced pasturage for the cattle.

The Northwest has not been a leading California beef center in this century although beef is one of the leading products of the region. For many decades the principal foci have been the Eastern Highlands and the Klamath Mountains. Over much of this area terrain is rugged and valley lands for ranch headquarters (with fields for supplemental feeds) are relatively small and scattered. Rainfall tends to diminish eastward. Much land is now national forest preserve. As elsewhere in the West, the Forest Service has steadily reduced the number of livestock that can be taken to mountain meadows in summer. Round Valley and Scott Valley have local significance as beef centers.

MINING

Mining was historically significant in some sections of the Northwest although this region does not today make a major contribution to California mineral production. An estimated $150 million in gold was removed, primarily from the Klamath Country. A gold revival occurred in the 1930's, but was halted with

World War II; rusting dredges along the Scott and the Klamath bear testimony to this activity (Fig. 10-13). Gold stimulated subsequent activities: settlements, transport routes, seaports, as well as historic sites for the tourist.

As in many portions of California, sand and gravel now constitute the leading minerals of the Northwest. Since this area does not have the volume of construction characteristic of more populous localities, even the output of these widely distributed and common minerals is usually modest.

Lake and Sonoma counties have ranked after New Almaden and New Idria (both in Central Coast) as a source of California quicksilver. Production tends to be erratic since California cannot compete too successfully against Spanish production in "normal" times. Between 1850 and 1950 less than a fifth of California output came from these counties, particularly from the Mayacmas Range. Few mines have been active since 1953.

COMMERCE

Most transportation forms are less well developed in the Northwest than in most portions of California. Terrain, heavy winter rains and landslides, and limited population form major impediments. Location is perhaps the greatest handicap—the Northwest is an isolated corner away from major routes. There has been no justification for subsidization of through transport.

Deep-sea commerce has had local significance for over a century. Eureka (Fig. 10-4) and Crescent City at present constitute the significant ports. Before World War II considerable lumber was shipped from Noyo. Passenger traffic, once important, is negligible. The bulk of the commerce has consisted of export of wood products.

No through east-west or north-south rail lines cross the Northwest. Del Norte, Lake, and Trinity counties lack rail lines entirely. A single major route, Northwestern Pacific (a Southern Pacific affiliate), extends from Marin County to Eureka. This road was created in 1907 with merger of seven shorter lines and was operated jointly by the Southern Pacific and Santa Fe until 1929.[8] Subsequently, the Southern Pacific has had complete control. Through service was not available to Eureka until 1915 because of difficulty of constructing the Willits-Lively section through the Eel Valley. With continued highway improvement since the 1920's, passenger service has declined; operations ceased south of Willits in 1958. The *Skunks*, diesel-gasoline combination passenger-freight units, are popular with summer tourists, especially since they have received national publicity (Fig. 10-5). The Skunks are operated by California Western Railroad, a Union Lumber Company subsidiary, over the 40-mile route constructed in 1911 to ship lumber from Fort Bragg to Willits.

Highways have been difficult to construct in the Northwest and remain generally inferior to those in more populous portions of the state. The typical back road, without hardtop all-weather surface, is seasonally muddy or dusty. Many major routes remain narrow and winding. U.S. 101, westernmost of the state's three principal north-south arteries, is an exception. Even on this highway, as long as freeway sections remained unbuilt, summer traffic dragged behind lumber trucks on tortuous sections through the Redwood Heartland. Scenic Route 1 has been gradually improved; it is still narrow, curvaceous, and comparatively slow, especially during periods of fog. In winter, landslides are apt to block sections of this and other roads. U.S. 299, principal east-west thoroughfare of northernmost California, has been improved; it links Redding and U.S. 99 with Humboldt Bay. Farther south, much work remains to extend California 32 to the coast. California 20, now rebuilt, is also an important east-west artery. As over much of the nation, buses afford a major means of public conveyance.

Commercial air service is limited in the Northwest. Pacific Air Lines offers daily

[8] Before the depression of the 1930's and decline in passenger traffic, the Santa Fe intermittently considered an extension of service into the Willamette Valley of Oregon via this route.

feeder service between San Francisco and Portland, with stops at Santa Rosa, Ukiah, Arcata, and Crescent City. Private planes have reduced isolation; in recent years, helicopter service has been available into some remote sections.

RECREATION

The Northwest appears to have good prospects as a recreational center as the California population rises. It possesses a variety of splendid scenic locales: the seashore, redwood forests, highlands, and perennial streams. Development as yet has been relatively modest. Accessibility is still limited and facilities inadequate or virtually nonexistent. The severe competition of the Sierra Nevada, Southern Cascade, Central Coast, and Southern California was noted earlier. One can imagine the popularity of the Northwest if located in Illinois or Kansas, for example. Accessible portions of the Northwest have long been popular with residents of the San Francisco Bay Area. These include the lower Russian River Valley (west of Santa Rosa) and the environs of Clear Lake.

The North Coast has been little exploited. However, it should be remembered that the Central Coast littoral south of Monterey has only been extensively frequented since the 1950's. The cool, foggy weather of the North Coast understandably has slight appeal for residents of San Francisco. However, a series of state beach parks has been created (Fig. 10-6).

In summer, the most congested portion of the Northwest is the Redwood Heartland, bisected by U.S. 101. Here has been developed the densest concentration of state parks in California. The area is seasonally popular with California residents as well as visitors from other parts of the nation; hence facilities become overtaxed.

Perhaps the least seasonal of Northwestern centers is Lake County, where a number of city dwellers maintain cottages. Even here there is an emphasis upon the summer season and aquatic recreation. However, retirement residence is consequential—over 20 percent of Lake County residents are over sixty-five.

Destined to become one of the West's major alpine centers is the Klamath Country, now rather isolated and slightly developed. With growing congestion in the Sierra Nevada, this area is bound to achieve greater popularity. After the Pacific coast, it is already the chief focus of sports fishing in the region.

The remainder of this chapter will be concerned with a more specific consideration of principal subdivisions of the Northwest. In turn (1) the North Coast, (2) Redwood Heartland, (3) Southern Valleys, (4) Lake County, and (5) the Klamath Country will be discussed.

THE NORTH COAST

For a century the North Coast has been one of the two principal foci of human activities in the Northwest; the other is the Southern Valleys. The Coast was available early because of ocean transportation; more recently the Russian-Eel corridor, followed by U.S. 101 and the Northwestern Pacific Railroad, has added to its accessibility.

The North Coast resembles northeastern Anglo-America (i.e., New England and the Maritimes) more than the remainder of California does. Some visitors see in Mendocino the epitome of the small New England village —this is not strange since the town's founders came from that area. Others find the shoreline with elevated terraces, stacks, coves, and rocky edges a near replica of Canada's Gaspé Peninsula. Surely with its frequent fogs this Coast resembles northeastern Anglo-America. Some find that the setting around Cape Mendocino, with its ferns, its sheep, and its windswept bleakness, is suggestive of the Scottish Highlands.

Much of the Coast is abrupt with sheer headlands; in places steep escarpments rise precipitously from the water's edge. Hence arable land tends to be somewhat restricted. In the past, loading of lumber has taxed the most skillful block-and-tackle men. Human habitation is concentrated in three sectors:

Fig. 10-4. HUMBOLDT BAY AND EU-
REKA. Samoa (left margin) and Arcata (rear).
(The Greater Eureka Chamber of Commerce)

(1) Del Norte Coast, (2) Humboldt Bay
Littoral, (3) Mendocino Coast (map, Fig.
10-2).

THE DEL NORTE COAST

The Del Norte Coast is craggy except for
the low lagoon zone between the mouth of
Smith River and Crescent City (map, Fig. 10-
2). Virtually all of the agriculture in Del
Norte County is restricted to this small area.
Elsewhere the Coast Ranges rise immediately
from the edge of the Pacific. There are less
than 50,000 acres of farmland; the entire
county has less cultivated acreage than many
larger Central Valley ranches. In this foggy
environment dairying constitutes the principal
farm activity; limited local markets and distance from large urban centers necessitates
processed products.

An agricultural specialty of this locale is the
hybrid Easter lily developed along the lower
Smith River in the late 1930's by Sidney Croft.

The bulbs gained popularity in the United
States during World War II when Japanese
bulbs were unavailable. Del Norte growers
have maintained a national market for Easter
lilies despite Japanese competition.

Crescent City (3000), on a crescentic, south-
facing harbor, is seat of Del Norte County.
Founded in 1853, it remains the only significant community in the county. Its harbor, protected by a rock breakwater with tetrapods
(25-ton concrete blocks), includes separate
facilities for lumber shipment and for commercial fishing. Plywood veneer is produced.
The town affords a trading center for the surrounding countryside and is a gateway to the
Rogue River Country (southwest Oregon)
via U.S. 199.

THE HUMBOLDT BAY LITTORAL

The Humboldt Bay Littoral has been a
principal center of activity in the "upper"
Northwest for a century. Its leading commu-

nity, Eureka, is the ranking trade center of the entire region and is without rivals in population. Redwood lumbering, the leading economic pursuit of the Littoral, has already been discussed; here is California's leading lumber center.

Humboldt Bay is one of the outstanding natural embayments on the Pacific Coast between San Francisco Bay and Puget Sound. Fourteen miles long with a maximum width of four miles, it is sheltered well by two sandbars. A sparsely populated hinterland has restricted the ocean commerce largely to export of lumber, fish, and dairy products; imports include petroleum and manufactured goods.

The lower Eel Valley and the north and south flanks of Humboldt Bay are the only agricultural areas in Humboldt County. This situation was recognized from earliest American settlement; the better lands were occupied in the 1850's. A cool, foggy climate and abundant grasses for pasturage proved ideal for dairy cattle, which has dominated rural land-use for a century. Some dairymen are descendants of early Italian-Swiss settlers. Besides the dairying some nursery stock is grown.

Eureka (28,000), seat of Humboldt County, is chief metropolis and principal seaport of the Northwest (Fig. 10-4). It sprawls along the tidal flats and lower terraces beside the eastern edge of the Bay. It serves as the area's chief retail and wholesale center and is an important tourist stop, particularly in the summer. Its northwestern quarter is dominated by sundry waterfront activity including fish docks; older Victorian structures house taverns and third-rate hotels. The downtown retail core lies to the east. Along the Bay to the south are lumber mills and veneer plants. Eureka also has a woolen mill and a new P.G. and E. atomic power plant. The ornate Carson House in north Eureka, once home of a lumber magnate, is a landmark. The city's Sequoia Park contains a sizable grove of coast redwood. **Samoa** (600) is a suburban lumber town across the Bay.

Arcata (5200), near the northeast edge of the Bay, has lumber and plywood mills and is the site of Humboldt State College. **For-**

Fig. 10-5. THE SKUNK—ONE OF AMERICA'S UNIQUE TRAINS. *Daily Service is maintained between Fort Bragg and Willits by the Noyo Chief, alias the Skunk (name given because of fumes from its diesel engine), over the tracks of the California Western Railroad, a subsidiary of Union Lumber Company. Considerable redwood lumber is transported during nocturnal hours. (Union Lumber Company, photo by Ed Freitas)*

tuna (3500) and **Ferndale** (1100) are dairy villages in the lower Eel River Valley.

THE MENDOCINO COAST

The Mendocino Coast (synonymous with the Mendocino Highlands) extends from the mouth of Tomales Bay northward beyond Cape Mendocino. This dissected upland has such west-flowing streams as the Mattole, Noyo, and Navarro. In the south the Russian River has cut a watergap across this western Coast Range block to reach the sea at Jenner. There are no extensive coastal plains nor any sizable anchorages comparable to those of Humboldt Bay. Human habitation is generally restricted to broader coastal terraces

Fig. 10-6. THE PICTURESQUE MENDO-CINO COAST. The scalloped, wave-cut coast, though often foggy, charms the visitor. Russian Gulch State Park on the left is crossed by Route 1 with its graceful, arched bridge. (David W. Lantis)

around Fort Bragg (Fig. 10-1) and Point Arena. The longtime significance of lumbering has been noted.

There is limited arable land along the Mendocino Coast. Only in the vicinity of Point Arena do the coastal terraces widen to permit much farming; land-use is largely devoted to dairying. This area is a marginal supplier for the San Francisco market. Poultry, especially eggs, has some importance around Fort Bragg. Sheep are grazed on the more uneven coastlands. Elsewhere agriculture is largely limited to a few interior valleys within the Highlands. Anderson Valley, focusing on Boonville, is the county's only significant apple producer.

Apart from the valleys, the Mendocino Highlands has long constituted one of California's major sheep ranges. Climate favors year-round grazing; past overgrazing, coupled with foreign competition and the rise of synthetic fibers has contributed to a recent decline in sheep.

The Mendocino Coast has increasing popularity as a summer vacation land despite chilly ocean waters. The lower Russian River Valley, around **Rio Nido** and **Guerneville**, serves as a Bay Area center for weekend outings, summer cottages, boating, and swimming. Its warm river water and cool forested setting has much appeal, although its weekend con-

gestion creates an amusement-park atmosphere at times. In winter the Russian River at its mouth near Jenner is popular with sports fishermen who come first for silver salmon, then for steelhead. Armstrong Redwoods State Park, among the more southerly of the Northwest's sequoia grove preserves, is much frequented. **Fort Ross**, a state historical monument, has particular interest because it represents California's only contemporary evidence of the Russian period.

Highway 1 does not traverse the entire Northwest; it turns inland near Rockport to connect with U.S. 101. The Mendocino Coast has been less frequented than more southerly sections of the California shore despite scenic appeal. A group of state parks has been established; some have camping facilities (Fig. 10-6). Sports fishing is popular, but more visitors enjoy the marine landscapes and spring displays of rhododendrons. The area around Mendocino is attracting artists, and there is suggestion that it may acquire the popularity with Sacramento Valley residents that the Central Coast locales such as Monterey Bay, Morro Bay, and Pismo Beach have for residents of the San Joaquin Valley (Chapter 8).

Mendocino Coast towns are small and generally stagnant. Some have rustic charm; catering to the tourist is important. **Fort Bragg** (4400), second city of Mendocino County, has varied functions (Fig. 10-1). It provides a local service center for farmers, fisherfolk, and lumbermen, many of Scandinavian or Italian descent. Union Lumber Company is a ranking producer of redwood. Fort Bragg is also the important tourist stop along this coast. **Mendocino** (700) is gaining popularity as an artist colony; some envisage it as the future "Carmel of the North Coast."

REDWOOD HEARTLAND

The Redwood Heartland (or Eel River Country) might be considered the core of the coast sequoia country, which once had a north-south stretch of 450 miles (from the Santa Lucia Mountains into southern Oregon) and an average width of 20 miles. The coast redwood belt was still virtually "virgin forest" in 1847. And in the days before the donkey engine (late nineteenth century) cutting remained sufficiently modest as to foster regrowth—the donkey engine and accompanying wire cable drag-out entailed complete "logging off," thus negating natural reforestation. By 1920 half of the *Sequoia sempervirens* were gone. Fortunately some of the finest remaining groves were in the less accessible upper Eel Valley, now paralleled by the Redwood Highway (U.S. 101).

SAVE-THE-REDWOOD

Early in the twentieth century a few conservation-minded individuals and groups became concerned over redwood destruction. Leaders included John Muir and the National Geographic Society. Before the Save-the-Redwood League was incorporated in 1920, such groves as Armstrong, Big Basin, Bohemian, and Muir Woods had already been set aside. At first the League favored a national redwoods park but decided instead to seek sanctuary for groves along U.S. 101 as state parks. By 1960 such preserves encompassed 70,000

Fig. 10-7. THE REDWOODS OF DYER-VILLE FLATS. *View of the forest floor in Humboldt State Redwood Park.* (U.S. Forest Service)

acres of redwoods—one eighth the acreage of the entire California state park system.

VACATION LAND

The majesty of the giant trees has appealed to sufficient Americans to assure protection of some magnificent groves. The Redwood Heartland thus is one of the tourist centers of northern California. Yet a flight over this area, or travel along a sideroad lateral from U.S. 101, makes one appreciate how much of the forest has fallen prey to the lumberman.

The Heartland is a land of recreation—and of lumbering. The Pacific Lumber Company plant at Scotia is the world's largest redwood mill—and there are many smaller operators. A Garberville service-station attendant, queried on a quiet December morning about local employment, replied: "In summer we live off the tourists, the rest of the year off each other." A myriad of restaurants, gift shops, and sun-

Fig. 10-8. FREEWAY THROUGH THE REDWOOD HEARTLAND. The four-lane bypass on Highway 101 permits the nature lover to drive more leisurely over the old road while the through traveler and the logging truck can hasten along the freeway. (California Division of Highways)

dry attractions (such as fish ponds: "You catch 'em, we fry 'em) line U.S. 101. One marvels that there is sufficient business in this sparsely populated land to warrant such activity, until one drives along this route on a summer week-end. State-park campgrounds display "no available campsites" signs in early morning; by midafternoon many motels have "no vacancy" signs. Basically, tourism consists of driving along the highway, perhaps saunter-ing along shady trails within the groves. In 1956 the Save-the-Redwood League won a partial victory when it was agreed that the new 101 freeway route should be a partial bypass of the groves and the old highway would become a one-way drive through the redwoods (Fig. 10-8).

Essentially, the core of the Heartland is 22,-500-acre **Humboldt State Redwood Park** with a series of groves (Fig. 10-7).[9] It includes the

[9] There are many redwood state parks outside of the Heartland. The Central Coast contains Pfeiffer–

13-mile strip known as "Avenue of the Giants" and Bull Creek flats, hailed as the "world's finest forest." Since 1952 Bull Creek has offi-cially been known as the John D. Rockefeller, Jr., Redwoods Forest (13,000 acres). Farther south and extremely well known is Richard-son Grove State Park.

The Redwood Heartland has no dominant town. A series of hamlets are scattered along U.S. 101. The largest is **Willits** (3400), which is actually well south of the Heartland. How-ever, this lumber and ranching center might be called the "southern gateway" to the Heart-land. **Garberville** (1000), long a sheepmen's center, owes much seasonal economy to tour-ism. **Scotia** (1100) is a company lumber town; many lumbermen live in nearby **Rio Dell** (3200).

THE SOUTHERN VALLEYS

The Southern Valleys area (Santa Rosa, Sonoma, Russian River, Napa and lesser ones), long the most densely populated portion of the Northwest, is the only significant agricul-tural subregion. This area is peripheral to the San Francisco Bay Area and increasingly rep-resents a marginal appendage of the Central Coast.[10]

The Southern Valleys edge northward be-tween ridges of the northern Coast Ranges like fingers extended from the wristlike Bay Area (maps, Figs. 8-2 and 10-2). The Santa

Big Sur, Henry Cowell, Big Basin, and Portola. Others in the Northwest include Samuel P. Taylor, Armstrong, Paul M. Dimmick, Mailliard, Montgomery Woods, Van Damme Beach, Russian Gulch, Admiral William H. Standley, Standish-Hickey, Grizzly Creek, Prairie Creek, and Jedidiah Smith. Then there are the *Sequoia gigantea* reserves in the Sierra Nevada, including Se-quoia National Park.

[10] Sonoma and Napa are called "Bay Area coun-ties." Because of urban encroachment here, the larger urban centers were discussed with the North Bay sub-section of the Bay Area. Here is a good example of the difficulty of delimiting regional boundaries. Pro-fessor Butz notes that Santa Rosa, discussed with the Bay Area in Chapter 8, is one of the leading service centers for the Northwest, with a conspicuous con-centration of regional medical facilities, for example.

Rosa–Russian River and the Napa are long and narrow; the Sonoma, shorter and more stubby.

This area is an aesthetically satisfying part of pastoral California. Despite the long summer drought with seared countrysides, there is a suggestion of rural England during winter storms and spring drizzles when the rich greens of the grasses and the parklike groves of oaks are memorable.

THE SANTA ROSA VALLEY

The Santa Rosa Valley, heartland of Sonoma County, focuses upon Petaluma and Santa Rosa. Many consider it one of California's more pleasant Coast Range lowlands. With its northern extension (Upper Russian Valley) it has been somewhat a counterpart to the Santa Clara Valley south of San Francisco Bay. In summer it is appreciably cooler than the Great Central Valley; in winter it is cool, damp, and lush green.

The Santa Rosa is known for its fruits, especially apples, grapes, and plums, and for its poultry. South of Petaluma on the meadows extending northward from San Pablo Bay is the dairy landscape previously noted in the North Bay subsection of the Bay Area (Chapter 8). Proximity to urban markets has long provided an assured fresh-milk market. Besides the dairies, rows of eucalyptus, planted as windbreaks, are a distinctive feature of the countryside.

Within a ten-mile radius of Petaluma is the once self-styled "Eggbasket of the World." The Valley of the South (Chapter 7) has so expanded its egg output that the Petaluma area is not properly even the "eggbasket of California" now, although it remains the major source for the Bay Area. Petaluma became an early user of incubators in the late nineteenth century; such seaports as San Francisco, Los Angeles, and even New York were willing to pay a premium price for white-shelled eggs with light-colored yolks. Eventually more than a score of hatcheries were operating, and the landscape was dotted with poultry farms, more than 2000 in number. Most of the White Leghorns were kept within weather-beaten houses. In spite of improvement of Petaluma quality, the national poultry situation in the late 1950's caused marketing changes. Despite favorable climate with winter mildness, California poultrymen must pay a higher price for feed than operators in some parts of eastern United States. A nationally glutted market for fryers and stewing hens resulted in importation into California of lower-cost poultry.

The **Gold Ridge**, hilly western fringe of Santa Rosa Valley along California Route 12 north of Petaluma, focuses upon Sebastopol. Its summers are cooler than much of the state and winters cold enough to provide dormancy. It contributes much to California's ranking after Washington among Western apple-growing states. As one of California's two chief apple-producing districts (Fig. 8-10), the Gold Ridge has long specialized in the Gravenstein, a golden summer apple much used for applesauce; other varieties include the Rome. Some fruit is shipped fresh to urban markets and **Sebastopol** (2700) has processing plants as well as shipping sheds. Poultry houses are scattered among the orchards, and there is also dairy farming.

Land-use patterns become more complex around Santa Rosa than on the margins of the Santa Rosa Valley. Next to the Santa Clara Valley, this locale has been a major producer of prunes, especially the French variety (Fig. 8-11). Santa Rosa plums are less significant. In part the importance of these fruits resulted from the research of Luther Burbank, a Santa Rosa resident. Although less famed than the Napa Valley, the Santa Rosa has been a long-time source of such better-quality dry table wines as Burgundy, Sauterne, and Zinfandel. Grapes are grown on lower slopes as well as the valley floor, usually on small family-owned properties north of Santa Rosa. Sonoma County champagne and sparkling Burgundy are regarded among the nation's best. There is also an appreciable acreage of walnuts in the Santa Rosa Valley.

THE UPPER RUSSIAN VALLEY

Northward from Santa Rosa there is a gradual transition into the Upper Russian Valley (which is known locally by a series of other names). The Upper Russian shows no evidence yet of the Bay Area expansion evident around Petaluma and Santa Rosa. Evergreen forests become more conspicuous along the flanks of this narrow, attenuated depression. The economy becomes less dependent on farming, and lumbering has more moment; however, wood processing is generally of the "in-transit" nature—logs are trucked from the north and finished lumber is then marketed to the south.

Agricultural products of the Upper Russian Valley suggest those of the Santa Rosa: hops, grapes, deciduous fruits, and livestock. Around Healdsburg and Asti there are vineyards. The Sanel Valley (around Hopland) has been one of California's chief hop producers for a century. The Ukiah area is the focal point of Mendocino County's agricultural activity; besides truck crops for local use, pears, prunes, grapes, and hops are significant. Irrigation water is stored in Lake Pillsbury and the newer Lake Mendocino.

Healdsburg (4800) is an agricultural town with wineries; lumber is also produced. **Ukiah** (9900), the largest city, is the seat of Mendocino County. It is also a midvalley trade center and tourist stop. Its several lumber mills and wood-products (plywood and masonite) plants accounted for much population growth in the 1950's. More recently there has been much unemployment during periods of curtailed markets in the construction industry.

THE SONOMA VALLEY

The open-ended Sonoma Valley, sometimes known as the "Valley of the Moon" (and inspiration for a popular song of that name in the 1930's), dangles like an appendix from the southeastern side of Santa Rosa Valley. Many regard it as one of the choice residential areas of California; many affluent senior citizens have established homes here. Because of proximity to the Bay Area, increasing urbanization seems inevitable.

In contrast to many productive California lowlands, the Sonoma is undulating with many "small landscapes" suggestive of New England or the Appalachian Highlands. The valley floor as well as hillsides is dotted with small residential "ranches." Plum and prune orchards, vineyards, and grazing lands with herds of beef cattle or flocks of sheep are intermingled into a complex land-use mosaic. A crude rectangle of narrow winding roads and long lanes leading to sheltered homes crisscrosses the Valley. Somnolent villages like **Glen Ellen** and seasonally flowing creeks add to the charm, as do many large trees and beds of flowers around homes.

THE NAPA VALLEY

The Napa Valley is the best known of the Southern Valleys; its fine dry wines have world renown, ranking with the best from Europe and elsewhere. *Time* (December 28, 1959) noted that claret from the Beaulieu vineyard is stocked by the famed George V Hotel in Paris. The valley, nearly twoscore miles long, extends from the margins of San Pablo Bay to the foot of Mount St. Helena, 4344-foot landmark of the Southern Valleys. The landscape has a settled patina that sometimes seems more European than Californian.

The Napa was one of the earliest centers of American agriculture in California; some early emigrants located here even before the Mexican War. Gradually distinct land-use patterns have evolved. South of Napa the lower valley merges into the North Bay portion of the Bay Area: on treeless meadows grazing of beef cattle is characteristic. Between Napa and Yountville the traveler sees orchards of deciduous fruits (peaches, cherries, plums, and prunes) and walnut groves. Increasingly, where there is more summer heat and sandy soils, the land produces grapes. The upper valley, particularly around St. Helena, is devoted almost exclusively to vineyards.

THE WINE INDUSTRY

The Southern Valleys, especially the Napa Valley around St. Helena, has long been noted for *quality* rather than quantity of wine produced. The bulk of the nation's less expensive wines comes from the San Joaquin Valley.

Napa Valley wines, like those prepared elsewhere in the Southern Valleys, are the result of family operations that generally date back several generations. Through long experimentation, varieties have been developed that respond best to slight differences in cli-

Fig. 10-9. GRAPE HARVEST IN THE NAPA VALLEY. *Newly harvested grapes at Mont La Salle Vineyards are trucked to the nearby winery.* (The Wine Institute, photo by Joe Munroe)

Fig. 10-10. MONTICELLO DAM AND LAKE BERRYESSA. (Bureau of Reclamation, photo by A. G. D'Alessandro)

mate and soils.[11] Rainfall for instance increases from 31 inches annually at Napa to 38 inches at Calistoga. Grape varieties, although all members of the Old World family *vinifera*, have been modified to become "California varieties." The European ancestry of Zinfandel, for example, has been lost, and it is considered a "native" California variety.

Within the small area of the Napa Valley are grown the 10,000 acres of grapes that make the equivalent of a number of European white, red, and rosé types approaching those coming from Italy, France, and Germany. *Holiday* (September 1958) rated Cabernet Sauvignon the world's best red Bordeaux, Pinot Chardonnay the world's best white Burgundy, and listed Pinot Noir, Grenache, and Johannisberger Riesling as excellent. With so many wines produced in such a small area, "vintage year" becomes less significant than in Europe. A good year for one variety may be a less successful year for another variety. There also seems to be less variation from one

[11] Important climatic factors include length of season, total seasonal heat, dates of fall and spring frosts, growing-season humidity, winter temperature, and air temperature. Microclimates around St. Helena are "optimum" in the Napa Valley.

year to the next than is true of European wines.

THE VILLAGE GREEN

Unlike Napa (which was discussed in Chapter 8), valley towns tend to be small agricultural centers. Climate, proximity to the Bay Area, and an air of quietude may explain why they have much popularity as homes for senior citizens, many from metropolitan backgrounds. **Rutherford** is a farm town whose environs include several famed wineries. **St. Helena** (2700) is the nation's leading shipper of quality dry wines. It is also a retirement spot with a large sanitarium. **Angwin**, in the hills to the east, is site of sectarian Pacific Union College. **Calistoga** (1500), at the head of the valley, is a crossroads town, local farm center, and longtime health resort. Like the Lake County spas to the north, Calistoga's hot springs are a result of volcanic activity.

LESSER VALLEYS

North and east of the Napa Valley are several smaller lowlands. Some are isolated; all display climatic transition between the Southern Valleys and the Sacramento Valley—colder in winter, hotter in summer. The **Vaca**

Fig. 10-11. THE HIGHLANDS OF LAKE COUNTY. Mount Konocti (4100 ft. elevation) and the eastern end of Clear Lake are visible here. (David W. Lantis)

Valley is a contact zone between the Bay Area, Delta Lands, and Sacramento Valley. There is a large military installation, Travis Air Force Base, on its southern edge and urbanization around **Vacaville** (11,000) and **Fairfield** (15,000) has reduced fields (sugar beets, tomatoes, grains) and orchards (apricots and prunes). Both communities increased in population by more than 300 percent in the 1950's.

Berryessa Valley, where there were 35,000 acres of grains and cattle pasturage in 1950, is covered with waters of Lake Berryessa, backed up behind Monticello Dam on Putah Creek (Fig. 10-10). This Bureau of Reclamation project was constructed to provide water for Solano County. The lake has popularity for water sports and boating.

Pope Valley to the north is used for livestock ranching. An old resort, Aetna Springs, nestles against the western hills.

LAKE COUNTY

Lake County has many aspects representative of the entire Northwest: quasi-isolation, sparse population, limited agricultural land, inadequate public transportation. Although settled early by Gold Rush Anglo-Saxons, it

remains unknown to many Californians. Heart of the county is Clear Lake, largest natural body of fresh water *entirely* within California. It has an area of 85 square miles but averages less than 20 feet depth. Some writers have likened its setting to the English Lake District or Loch Lomond, analogies more apparent in April than in August.

During the late nineteenth century Lake County remained a land of semi-self-sufficiency with grains and livestock. Southern quicksilver mines made an intermittent contribution. Recreation significance for San Franciscans developed early; it was cooler than the Central Valley, less than 100 miles from "The City," and, most important, it had mineral springs.

Recreation has been an important facet of the economy for decades. There were three early centers: (1) Cobb Mountain and its surrounding volcanic areas, (2) upland springs east of Clear Lake, and (3) springs west of Upper Lake. Clear Lake itself lacked immediate popularity. The important mineral springs had resorts by the 1880's; they held a particular appeal for health seekers. Best known was Bartlett Springs, whose palatable waters made it one of the nation's best-known mineral spas. Rise of automotive travel with improved roads to more distant vacation spots coupled with growing disinterest in mineral waters doomed the springs.

Paved roads brought changing recreational use. In the 1920's **Clear Lake** finally began to enjoy popularity: sports fishing, bathing, boating, and, more recently, water-skiing. Eastshore resorts have been favored because evening breezes help dispel the gnats (by the 1950's chemical sprays were reducing this nuisance but upsetting the ecological balance). The lake is pleasantly warm in summer but becomes quite murky later in the season. Hence some visitors prefer the smaller Blue Lakes to the northwest.

Lake County has become a weekend center catering particularly to the growing Bay Area population. Many city dwellers have constructed cabins, particularly along the southeastern lake margin. Choicest lake frontages have acquired considerable value. Cobb Mountain resorts, once mineral spas set in pine forests, now provide appeals for younger visitors: dancing, dining, swimming, horseback riding, golf. Best known is Hoberg's, used also for group conferences.

PEARS AND BEEF

Agriculture constitutes an important source of Lake County livelihood. Arable land is scattered; "small landscapes" fittingly describes the tilled patches—there are more than a dozen small basins. Big Valley and Scott Valley have the most consequence. Combinations of fertile soils, level terrain, and sufficient water are uncommon; access to market was once a serious handicap. Grains, important in the late nineteenth century, were consumed locally for food or feed; by 1890 hay acreage exceeded grains. Deciduous fruits and walnuts gained importance in the early twentieth century. Walnuts had largely replaced prunes by the 1920's. Extensive hillside plantings of walnuts have been made more recently on volcanic slopes south of Mt. Konocti (4100 ft.).

In season, signs in Los Angeles supermarkets announce "Lake County pears." Since 1940 the County has produced a tenth of the California crop, particularly the Bartlett variety. Reputation for quality fruit yields a return that justifies higher shipping costs. Although trees reached a maximum acreage in the late 1920's, yields per tree have increased appreciably with improved disease controls.

Big Valley, south of Clear Lake, is the leading agricultural center. Pears are grown on the better soils; there are also irrigated pastures. Some grains are still raised, as are walnuts. The swampy southwest shore of the lake has discouraged its use for recreation although Clear Lake State Park occupies a rocky promontory. A small Pomo Indian rancheria is a memento of pre-American occupancy.

Aesthetically **Scott Valley** affords a more pleasing rural landscape than Big Valley, but it has less agricultural output.[12] Its floor, underlain by alluvium, and the adjacent lower slopes are devoted chiefly to pears.

LAKESHORE TOWNS

Most Lake County communities are situated along the shores of Clear Lake; their names sometimes conjure more appeal than the towns present: Upper Lake, Nice, Lucerne, Clearlake Oaks, Clearlake Highlands. The majority are resorts, occupied largely by senior citizens except during the summer-holiday season.

Lakeport (2300), the county seat, is scarcely more than a hamlet. Besides services for vacationists it acts as the subregional trade center. Its site affords attractive vistas across the lake. **Kelseyville** serves as a produce packing and shipping center and affords residence for farm workers.

THE KLAMATH COUNTRY

The Klamath Mountains, occupying the northeastern third of the Northwest, perhaps ranks after the Sierra Nevada among California highlands in scenic beauty. Yet this

[12] Gudde, *California Place Names,* notes that there are forty spots in California named "Scot" or "Scott:" *This* Scott Valley should not be confused with Scott Valley in Siskiyou County.

*Fig. 10-12. THE TRINITY ALPS. The ice-scoured peaks of Trinity County
contain the highest points in the Northwest.* (David W. Lantis)

wrinkled land (Fig. 10-12), isolated and
scantily peopled, remains alien to numerous
Californians. Besides its habitants, mostly
lumbermen or cattlemen, visitors are outdoorsmen: campers and sports fishermen. Its population of perhaps 30,000 is slightly larger than
that of the Northeast or the Trans-Sierra.
Most towns that appear on highway maps are
crossroads hamlets that have less than 100
inhabitants. Weaverville, the largest community, has fewer than 2000 residents.

The typical road is still unpaved, dusty in
summer and perhaps impassable in winter,
but isolation is being reduced. U.S. 299 has
been markedly improved. Yet the old wagon
trail (Route 96) along the Klamath River
remained largely unpaved until the late 1950's.
Private airplanes have made the Klamath
more accessible for affluent sportsmen.

Despite enduring seclusion, the Klamath
Country was settled early by Americans. Gold,
recovered in smaller quantities than in the
Sierra Nevada, brought thousands of miners
in the 1850's. A surprising number of towns,
such as Orleans, Etna, Happy Camp, and

Sawyer's Bar, originated over a century ago
as boom-period camps.

INDIAN TERRITORY

It was noted earlier that the Northwest was
a favored portion of California for the American Indian. As elsewhere in the state, Indian
peoples were decimated in the first decades
of statehood over much of the Northwest.
Loss of traditional homes and ways of life,
disease, and open strife took heavy toll. Even
in the Klamath, entry of miners and stockmen
soon eliminated Indians from much of the
region. Such peripheral military posts as Ft.
Humboldt (Eureka) and Ft. Jones, also Ft.
Gaston in Hoopa Valley, were established to
maintain peace and protect white settlers.
Though plagued by ignorance of tribal ways
and stringent funds, the Bureau of Indian
Affairs gradually became more effective. Nome
Lackee reservation, in the Coast Range foothills west of the Sacramento Valley, was rendered unsatisfactory because of white settlement within three years of its establishment

in 1854. The Round Valley and Hoopa Valley reservations have been more successful.

Despite some peaceful penetration by whites, the Indians were never eliminated from these two areas. The **Hoopa Valley** reserve was established in 1864 and the government reimbursed white settlers for improvements they had effected there. Like the Apaches of central Arizona, the Hupas and other Indians in Hoopa Valley have held lands rich in timber. Today, when logs are removed by private lumbermen, the tribe is compensated. There are approximately 850 Indians on this reservation and around 2000 total in the vicinity.[13] Individuals hold parcels; when relinquished, such holdings are purchased by the tribe and resold to another Indian. Increasingly the Hupas are managing their own affairs. Their children attend local public schools with whites. In his thesis on the reservation, G. E. Anderson in 1956 quoted the Area Director of the Indian Service in Sacramento: "Hoopa Valley is much like any other thriving American community except there are more Indians—American citizens who are part and parcel of the larger community around them." The Indians fish, till small parcels of valley land, and work for lumbermen or stockmen of the area.

ECONOMY

The economic activities of the Klamath Country are modest. They have included mining, lumbering, livestock ranching, water development, and recreation. Mining no longer has consequence. Lumber production was inconsequential before World War II. Many logs are now trucked out but increased processing takes place at such points as Happy Camp, Hoopa Valley, and Fort Jones.

[13] Humboldt County ranks third, behind Los Angeles and San Diego, in total contemporary Indian population. The Hoopa Reservation is the largest (87,000 acres), most populous (in California), and has the largest accumulation of tribal funds. Los Angeles numbers demand explanation—many Indians, such as Navaho and Hopi, have migrated from elsewhere. Indians in and around the Hoopa include the Hupa, the Yurok, and Karok.

Livestock ranching is the basic land-use in the Klamath. However, limited terrain favorable for irrigated pastures and haymaking is a handicap. Much land is within national forest confines, and since 1900 the Forest Service has sharply reduced the permitted carrying capacity of mountain meadows to prevent overgrazing. The foci of ranch operations are those relatively few basins with larger amounts of arable land.

The Klamath Country, like much of the Northwest, constitutes an area of surplus water well beyond the limited present local needs. In the past, availability of sufficient water elsewhere in the state negated development here. The first project to divert water from the Klamath Basin southward began in 1955 with construction of the **Trinity Project**. It makes an additional 1.4 million acre-feet of water available to the Central Valley Project (Chapter 9) for use in the Sacramento Valley, Delta Lands, Bay Area, and San Joaquin Valley. Chief unit is Trinity Dam, whose reservoir can store 2.5 million acre-feet behind a mile-long earth-fill dam 465 feet high. From the reservoir, located on the Trinity River northeast of Weaverville, water is tunneled into Whiskeytown Reservoir on Clear Creek (a Sacramento tributary). A second tunnel conducts water to Keswick Dam north of Redding. In addition to water for irrigation, the dams will reduce flood threats and also permit power development; much recreational use is envisaged.

Recreation forms an increasingly important use of the Klamath Country. Location and lack of accessibility have discouraged such activity in the past. Even now, time and distance (or cost if more rapid travel is employed) discourage most Californians from visits to the area for a weekend. Facilities are more primitive than in more frequented areas. Yet perennial streams and alpine lakes afford some of California's finest sports fishing.

Several subdivisions of the Klamath Country are distinctive because of physical charm or economic use. These include (1) Scott Valley, (2) Round Valley, (3) Trinity County, (4) the Klamath Canyon, and (5) the Wilderness Areas.

Fig. 10-13. *RUSTING DREDGE ON THE SCOTT RIVER.* (David W. Lantis)

Fig. 10-14. *SCOTT VALLEY AND THE MARBLE MOUNTAINS. Boulder Peak, behind the hamlet of Greenville, rises to 8317 feet.* (David W. Lantis)

SCOTT VALLEY

This valley is one of the more pleasant intermont basins in the state (Fig. 10-14). During many months annually the higher summits of the encircling mountains are snow-capped. The Scott River meanders across its flattish surface through lush meadows that support herds of beef cattle. The contemporary utilization is based upon livestock ranching, lumbering, and recreation. Ranchers have adequate summer ranges; during the summer hay-making is a characteristic activity. Once this basin was a major gold-mining center; at least one rusting dredge on the upper Scott testifies to activity in the 1930's (Fig. 10-13). **Fort Jones** (500) originated as an Army post on the California-Oregon Trail in 1852; it lies at the north end of the valley. It provides local services and also has a lumber mill. Rival **Etna** (600) has been associated with mining; its economy has languished for several decades. **Callahan**, erstwhile gold camp, is a gateway into mountain recreation sites.

ROUND VALLEY

This circular basin in the Coast Ranges of northeastern Mendocino County shares in the isolation and rural qualities of the Klamath Country. As late as 1963 there were no paved roads through the valley, and the nearest railhead is **Dos Rios**; **Laytonville** on U.S. 101 is 12 miles farther west. The Valley had no white residents when the federal government en-

visaged an Indian reservation in the early 1850's. Before the reservation was established in 1856 cattlemen had entered the Valley. The reservation survives, but its lands lie mostly in mountainous terrain to the north.

Round Valley is cattle country. Its alluvium produces good grass; with white oak groves there is a vernal suggestion of an English estate. Local residents insist that Henley Oak is the largest in the world. **Covelo**, a quiet cow town and the single community, has experienced little twentieth-century change except for addition of several motels and service stations. The Eastern Highlands of the northern Coast Ranges have been ignored economically except for Lake County and Round Valley. Elsewhere chaparral-covered slopes are characteristic; autumnal deer hunting is one of few uses over wide stretches.

TRINITY COUNTY [14]

This highlands county, ranking fifty-second in population among the state's fifty-eight counties in 1960, forms a southern "heart" for the Klamath Country. Author James Hilton (*This Week*, January 22, 1952) allegedly regards its county seat, Weaverville, as his

[14] The population of Trinity County virtually doubled during the 1950's, reflecting a temporary influx of construction crews for Trinity Dam. More recently the population has declined. This fact reflects the sometimes passing validity of statistics (Fig. E-5).

440 :: CHAPTER TEN

idea of a mundane Shangri-La. The county has a maze of steep slopes with little flat terrain. Although it is traversed by U.S. 299, most of its confines are accessible only afoot or on animals. Like Lake and Alpine counties, it has no rail lines. Gold mining prompted its organization as one of the state's original counties.

The contemporary economy depends upon forestry, tourism, and livestock. Three fourths of its land lies within Trinity National Forest. Cutting of Douglas fir has much expanded since the mid-1950's; the county ranks among the ten leading timber producers of California. Weaverville and Hayfork have mills.

Livestock ranching is hampered by terrain. Principal centers include the small valleys of Hayfork and Hyampom along tributaries of the Trinity River southwest of Weaverville. Some hay is made, and a little grain is raised for livestock feed.

The picturesque mining camp of **Weaverville** (1700) with its old buildings and history, is county seat and the only town of consequence in the area. Besides government activities, including the headquarters for the Trinity National Forest, it has lumber processing, is a tourist stop on U.S. 299, and is a gateway to mountain recreation spots. Much of northern Trinity County, within a wilderness area, is discussed later.

KLAMATH CANYON

"When Los Angeles discovers the Klamath Canyon, there will be no more wilderness in California," one longtime observer of the California scene recently warned. The Klamath River canyon affords the only low-elevation crossing of the Klamath Country. Despite low elevation, it is readily understood why this (Highway 96) is not the principal east-west route through northwestern California. From U.S. 99, where it is only a dozen miles south of the Oregon border, the river follows a tortuous course toward the southwest so that it is about a hundred miles south of the border at Weitchpec, where it is joined by the Trinity River. Although the Klamath is perennial,

it is a wild mountain stream that has never been suitable for navigation.

Despite an early wagon trail between Weitchpec and U.S. 99, it is only within recent years that this route (California 96) has been paved. Highway improvement continues but rugged terrain along the lower Klamath coupled with limited utilization has discouraged a good road northwestward from Weitchpec to U.S. 101. Recently lumbering has much expanded along the Klamath; it has encouraged highway improvement. Mill towns include Happy Camp and Orleans, the latter a one-time gold camp that was once county seat.

Year by year the Klamath Canyon achieves recognition as a recreational area. It has appeal for sports fishermen. The Klamath is perhaps the most reliable river in California for autumnal runs of salmon and steelhead, extending 200 miles upstream from its mouth. Lodges are limited in number and somewhat rustic. The principal community is **Happy Camp**, a tourist haven and lumber town.

THE WILDERNESS AREAS

Three of California's more spectacular alpine sections in the Klamath Country have been set aside within national forests as wilderness areas. These are (1) the Salmon-Trinity Wilderness Area north of Weaverville, (2) the Marble Mountain Wilderness Area west of Scott Valley, and (3) Middle Eel-Yolla Bolly Wilderness Area west of Toomes Camp (and Red Bluff). The former two both exceed 200,000 acres and among the primitive national forest preserves of California rank after the High Sierra Wilderness Area (Chapter 5) in size.

The largest, **Salmon-Trinity Wilderness Area**, contains more spectacular scenery than the other two. In the west is Thompson Peak, at 9002 feet the highest summit in the Northwest. Farther east is the magnificent glaciated expanse of the Trinity Alps (Fig. 10-12). Although summits are less than 9000 feet, local relief exceeds 6000 feet and the serrated summit ridges and descending spurs are steep. The small U-shaped canyons contain beautiful little lakes.

These wilderness areas promise to play an expanding role as California outdoor recreation sites. In accord with the philosophy of the wilderness area, paved roads are absent. Gravel access roads penetrate the margins of all three areas. But to gain familiarity with them, one must travel afoot or by animal. Some of the state's finest trout fishing is afforded along little streams and in hidden lakes. The lakes along the South Fork of the Salmon, especially Big Caribou, and near the headwaters of Stuart Fork of the Trinity have particular appeal.

THE FUTURE

Prospects for the Northwest depend upon California growth and prosperity—state markets are the primary outlet for forestry and agricultural products. Continuing California growth will briefly expand Northwest lumbering, especially in the Douglas fir and pine forests.

Commuters, senior citizens seeking retirement homes, and perhaps industrial growth should link the Southern Valleys more closely to the Bay Area complex—with particular significance as "residential bedrooms." Remaining agriculture is likely, increasingly, to emphasize fresh milk, eggs, and truck crops for immediate markets. Momentarily, the threat of pear decline and a continuing drop in milk consumption per capita trouble some farmers.

Most Northwestern vacationists are Californians. Expansion of tourism along Highway 101, the Mendocino Coast, and Lake County

seems inevitable. It is conceivable that a genuine tourist boom may never materialize in the Klamath Country. Increasing mobility may permit the average vacationist to seek out more exotic and more distant lands such as Hawaii and other Pacific isles and Alaska.

Further development of water resources is likely. Trinity Dam portends future trends. Such developments should stimulate recreation, perhaps *even* attract some industry. Flood control, hydroelectricity, and improved roads are assured results. The Klamath and several forks of the Eel are good sites. Distillation of sea water for Southern California and the Central Coast might delay rapid utilization of Northwestern water.

The expanded California construction industry has demanded much Northwestern lumber since 1945. Yet the present trend in forestry cannot be continued indefinitely. Cutting rates still greatly exceed regrowth. Decreasing supplies of timber may cause many mills to curtail operations before 1970. The Northwest must increasingly rely upon a harvest of planned regrowth, not upon "mining" of the forest. Wood by-product industries are relatively new. More pulpwood, paper, plywood, and more elaborate industries may appear in the Northwest. Competition from other areas, technological changes, water availability, and regulation of stream pollution are considerations.

Mining prospects are always speculative. New discoveries affect small areas, usually briefly. Substantial increase in the market price of gold might prompt renewed mining in the Klamath Country.

There is nothing to suggest that, apart from the Southern Valleys, the Northwest is likely to become highly urbanized. It appears certain to remain marginal in the California economy.

APPENDICES

APPENDIX A:: CLIMATE

Climatic amenity is California's prime physical asset, immeasurably more precious than all the gold ever taken from the Sierra Nevada. Much of the diverse agricultural productivity, the incentive for immigration, and the pleasure of residence have depended upon the sunny subtropical weather for which the Golden State has become an American synonym.

Radiant sunshine and dank fog, lip-parching desert heat and cooling sea breezes, cold north winds and the enervating Santa Anas, long droughts and driving rains—the newcomer soon learns that there is more than one version of "California climate." Even within the city limits of San Francisco and Los Angeles he finds departures from the legendary type. Save for its nearly universal summer dryness, over two thirds of California is sufficiently wet, dry, cold or hot to suggest climatic characteristics more commonly associated with the other forty-nine states. Climatic diversity is advantageous, too, for its contribution to landscape variety and a broad array of economic resources.

Temperature and precipitation constitute the basic components of climate. To appreciate California's several climates, prior consideration is given to the principal controls of these elements. They are outlined next and followed by description of climatic types.

CONTROLS

TEMPERATURE

Marked differences in temperature occur within California. The all-time high was 134°F., recorded below sea level in Death Valley. The record low was —45°F. at Boca (north of Lake Tahoe) at 5532 feet elevation. These contrasting sites are indicative of the major controls of California temperature: (1) latitude (2) elevation and (3) continentality.

LATITUDE

The location of California nearly midway between the equator and the North Pole produces temperatures that are neither tropical nor polar but rather subtropical and middle

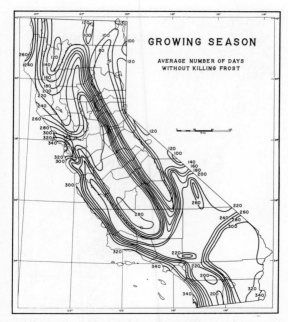

Fig. A-1. *AVERAGE GROWING SEASON.*

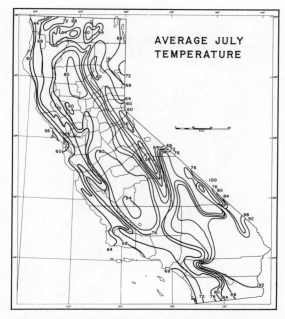

Fig. A-2. *AVERAGE JULY TEMPERA-TURE.*

latitude—hot to cool summers and mild to cold winters prevail. Somewhat lower latitude promotes subtropical conditions in southern California. Barring effects of controls other than latitude, temperatures decrease as one moves northward in California and the *growing season* (the number of continuous frost-free days) shortens (Fig. A-1). For example, average January temperature is 55°F. at San Diego, 50°F. at San Francisco, and 47°F. at Eureka. The corresponding growing seasons are 365, 356, and 331 days respectively.

ELEVATION

The basic effect of latitude is strikingly modified wherever high elevations occur in California. Temperatures commonly decrease with elevation above sea level since the thinner atmosphere of higher altitudes cannot so effectively retain upward rising earth heat. Thus the mountains and loftier plateaus of California normally are colder than adjacent lowlands (Figs. A-1, A-2, and A-3). Summits of the Peninsular Ranges near the Mexican border, for example, are colder in winter and have more snow than the coastline on the

Oregon border. At low elevations subtropical conditions extend far into northern California. Winter mildness in low-lying areas of the state is due partly to the fact that invading cold air from the higher elevations of interior western North America must heat due to compression while descending to lower elevations.

CONTINENTALITY

Prevailing westerly winds off the Pacific Ocean help shield much of the Golden State from polar continental air masses so familiar in eastern United States. Temperatures of interior districts tend to be more extreme than those of coastal sites since land surfaces heat and cool more rapidly than oceans. For any given California latitude and elevation summers are usually warmer and winters colder as one moves inland eastward. Understandably, such interior locations as Death Valley and Boca, where there is reduced penetration of oceanic air, tend toward temperature extremes.

The Golden State is noted for its moderate coastal temperatures and for its rapid transition to extreme interior temperatures, exag-

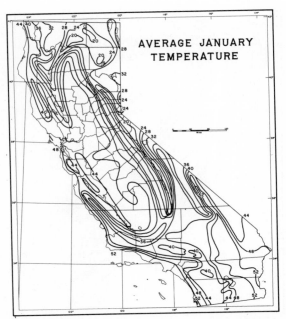

Fig. A-3. *AVERAGE JANUARY TEMPER-ATURE.*

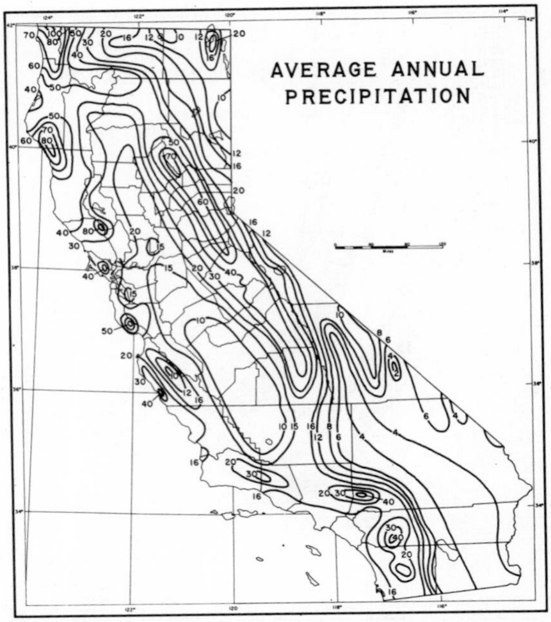

Fig. A-4. *AVERAGE ANNUAL PRECIPI-TATION (INCHES).*

gerated by the summer coldness of the ocean and by mountain ranges. Mountains that parallel the coast retard air movement. Thus, in summer cooler maritime air does not readily penetrate into the heated interior (Fig. A-2), nor in winter does polar continental air from the interior easily cross the Sierra Nevada and other ranges (Fig. A-3).

In summer an unseasonably cool ocean prevails along the shore from Oregon to Mexico; it is created by winds that drive surface water away from the shore with resultant *upwelling* of colder water from the depths. Air moving landward is chilled sufficiently to produce coastal fog or low stratus clouds. Cool sea breezes and stratus cover produce uniquely chilly summers along much of the California coast.

PRECIPITATION

There is appreciable precipitation variation within California; the state is wettest in the northwest and driest in the southeast (Fig. A-4). Honeydew in the northern Coast Ranges has recorded an all-time annual maxi-

mum precipitation of nearly 191 inches. By contrast Bagdad, a lower Mojave Desert station, has gone without precipitation for more than two years. Like temperature, California precipitation varies with latitude, elevation, and continentality. Principal controls include (1) atmospheric circulation and (2) landforms.

ATMOSPHERIC CIRCULATION

California's precipitation originates almost wholly from middle-latitude *cyclonic storms* ("lows") that develop over the north Pacific Ocean and move eastward across North America. Moisture within each storm is produced when air is lifted and cooled. California lies on the southern edge of the usual storm tracks across the continent; hence precipitation generally decreases southward in the state.

In opposition to the cyclonic storms is the *Hawaiian (North Pacific) High*, a "ridge" of high-pressure air centered over the subtropical Pacific Ocean. Near the coast, air descending from this vast "ocean-whirl" source region is not conducive to precipitation as it subsides. In summer the Hawaiian High, which shifts northward with the sun, is at full strength while storms are weakest; storms pass farther north so that California is virtually rainless during the summer months.

Nearly the entire state is significantly drier in summer than during the winter "half-year." Midsummer precipitation is confined largely to southeast deserts and the adjacent Sierra Nevada, Transverse, and Peninsular ranges, which become subject to unusual invasion of moist air masses from the Gulf of Mexico or even the tropical eastern Pacific Ocean. Resultant winds and flash floods in the desert, although infrequent, are locally destructive. Forest fires, caused by lightning, may be unaccompanied by rain even in northern California mountains.

LANDFORMS

High mountains complicate the simple scheme of northward-increasing precipitation in California. Mountains accelerate the lift of air within cyclonic storms, resulting in heavier (*orographic*) precipitation. Even near the Mexican border annual precipitation approaches 40 inches where the Peninsular Ranges have sufficient orographic effect. Precipitation is heavier on windward (Pacific-facing) slopes, where air is rising and oceanic moisture is readily available. As a storm moves inland, its moisture supply is depleted. Air that descends interior-facing mountain slopes becomes warmer and drier to create *rain shadows,* dry belts which extend well to the leeward of the mountains. Accordingly, desert or semiarid climates extend nearly the length of eastern California; such conditions prevail even in the southern San Joaquin Valley (Fig. A-4).

THE SEVERAL CLIMATES

The latitudinal position of California creates two principal temperature divisions, *Subtropical* and *Middle Latitude*. Ordinarily Subtropical climates with mild winters prevail between approximately 25° and 40° latitude in both hemispheres; poleward of 40 degrees, Middle-Latitude climates with colder winters are the rule. California's adjacent ocean and its landforms somewhat modify this generalized latitudinal arrangement of worldwide temperatures. Thus the north coast and Sacramento Valley are considered subtropical even though they reach poleward of the 40th parallel. Conversely, broad expanses of California highlands, extending appreciably equatorward of 40 degrees, have harsher winter conditions than those normally associated with subtropical lands. In Figs. A-5 and A-6, Subtropical climates are indicated for areas where mean minimum temperature in January is above freezing; where minimum temperature is below 32°F., the middle-latitude designation is used, even though middle-latitude seasonality may be absent.

Precipitation is a second major variable in identifying climatic subdivisions. All major gradations in moisture, arid, semiarid, subhumid and humid, occur within the Golden State. In general the higher mountains and north coast are relatively humid (though summer drought is characteristic); the eastern interior is arid or semiarid; and the Sacramento Valley, southern Coast Ranges, and southwest fringes of California are essentially subhumid. Actual moisture supply is a function of evaporation as well as precipitation, making precise delimitation of moisture categories doubly difficult. A simplified notation, which differentiates *Desert* and *Semiarid* areas from moister climates, is used in succeeding paragraphs. Portions of California where average annual precipitation is less than 8 inches are designated as Desert, while areas which receive 8 to 12 inches annually (longtime averages) are considered to be Semiarid.

SUBTROPICAL CLIMATES

DESERT

The subtropical deserts of the world basically express the effects of the subtropical high pressure cells (i.e., the North Pacific, or

Hawaiian High, in the case of California). The state's north-south trending mountain ranges afford an additional control. The subtropical desert is restricted to the southwest San Joaquin Valley, Death Valley, the southeastern Mojave Desert and the Colorado Desert. Irrigation is necessary for all crops and there is generally a sparse natural vegetation that commonly affords limited forage for animals. The subtropical desert, low in elevation, is characterized by intensive summer heat and mild winters. The growing season is virtually year-round for hardier crops; in protected sites even more sensitive subtropical crops can be grown in winter.

INTERIOR SEMIARID

The interior semiarid subtropics represent transitional zones between the deserts and adjacent more humid areas. They are largely restricted to portions of the San Joaquin Valley surrounding its more arid southwestern segment and to the western periphery of the Colorado Desert. East of the San Joaquin desert, semiarid conditions reflect lessening rain-shadow influence as one moves eastward toward the Sierra Nevada with its evident orographic aspects. In the western Colorado Desert a narrow semiarid zone extends along the lower slopes of the Peninsular Ranges. This climatic subdivision has temperatures and a growing season comparable to the subtropical deserts.

COASTAL SEMIARID

The small zone of coastal semiarid subtropics in the San Diego Country indicates the greater dominance of the Hawaiian High than in areas farther north. Many consider it to be one of the nation's choicest residential climates although it is transitional toward the fog desert of Baja California to the south. Morning fog and sea breezes help prevent unusually hot weather. Well-drained slopes are sufficiently frost-free to permit such tropical trees as lemons and avocados. The growing season is practically year-round with quite mild winters.

DRY-SUMMER SUBTROPICAL (MEDITERRANEAN)

These categories have given California its vaunted reputation as a residence land. They prevail in coastal and near-coastal areas from Oregon to Mexico and inland through portions of the Coast Ranges and the Central Valley—in total about a third of the state. Termed "Mediterranean" because of climatic analogy with portions of the Old World they are exclusively Californian within the United States. Most of the state's commercial fruits, flowers, and vegetables, and most of its urban population, are concentrated in these areas. Winters are mild and in most areas have considerable sunshine, interrupted only by the occasional cyclonic storms that bring most of the yearly precipitation. Annual precipitation exceeds 12 inches; hence there is sufficient moisture for woodland, brush, grass, or forest vegetation and also for some grains and fruit farming without irrigation. Summers are nearly rainless. Summer sunshine and temperatures increase sharply with isolation from the maritime air of the seashore. Three phases of Mediterranean climate in inland succession are therefore identified: *Fog Belt, Mild Summer,* and *Hot Summer* (Figs. A-5 and A-6).

MIDDLE-LATITUDE CLIMATES

DESERT

Eastern California, north of its subtropical deserts, still reflects rain-shadow position and seasonal dominance of the Hawaiian High. Yet it is less insulated against outbursts of polar continental air from the northern interior of North America so that the virtual year-long growing season of the Colorado Desert is markedly reduced. Moreover, this is "High Desert" whose altitude is commonly at least half a mile higher than that of the "Low Desert" to the south (and also to the west in the San Joaquin Valley). Most of the Mojave Desert and adjoining depressions within the southern Basin Ranges carry a Middle-Latitude designation. Altitude seems valid justification for also assigning the Carrizo Plain and Cuyama Valley to this type.

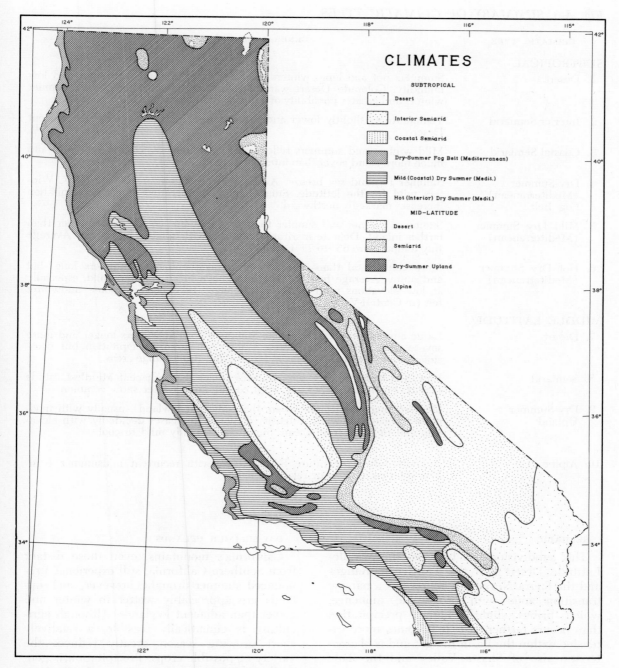

CLIMATES

SUBTROPICAL

- Desert
- Interior Semiarid
- Coastal Semiarid
- Dry-Summer Fog Belt (Mediterranean)
- Mild (Coastal) Dry Summer (Medit.)
- Hot (Interior) Dry Summer (Medit.)

MID-LATITUDE

- Desert
- Semiarid
- Dry-Summer Upland
- Alpine

Fig. A-5. THE CLIMATES OF CALIFORNIA.

Fig. A-6. SUMMARY OF CLIMATIC TYPES.

CLIMATIC TYPE	GENERAL CHARACTERISTICS

SUBTROPICAL

1. Desert — Summers hot and long, winters mild and brief. Perennial drought and low humidity. Colorado Desert warmer than San Joaquin Valley with sunnier winters and greater possibility of summer thunderstorms.

2. Interior Semiarid — Temperatures slightly lower and precipitation a little heavier than adjacent Desert.

3. Coastal Semiarid — Mild winters and summers reflect oceanic influences. Higher humidity and much more cloud cover than interior Semiarid.

4. Dry-Summer (Mediterranean) Fog Belt — Summer fog and sea breeze. Average July temperature 50° to 64°F. Winters mild for the latitude. Small annual temperature range. Precipitation increases markedly northward.

5. Mild Dry Summer (Mediterranean) — Summers warmer and sunnier than Fog Belt but cooler and cloudier than farther inland. Definite maritime influence with some summer fog. Average July temperature 65° to 71°F.

6. Hot Dry Summer (Mediterranean) — More continental than other Mediterranean climates. Summers long, hot and sunny. Average July temperatures above 71° F. Winters mild, especially at low elevations with good air drainage. Likelihood of some midwinter fog (in Central Valley).

MIDDLE LATITUDE

7. Desert — Large annual temperature range. Summers hot but winters longer and more severe than Subtropical Desert. Winter maximum precipitation but occasional summer thunderstorms in Mojave and Basin Range areas.

8. Semiarid — Elevation higher; hence temperatures cooler than adjacent Middle-Latitude Desert. Precipitation heavier, with considerable winter snow common.

9. Dry-Summer Upland — Winters longer and more severe than adjacent lowlands, usually with moderate to heavy snowfall. Intensity of winter increases decidedly with elevation and isolation from ocean. Summers generally mild to cool.

10. Alpine — Average July temperature below 50°F. with recurrent midsummer frost. Precipitation tends to be relatively light.

SEMIARID

This subdivision lies between the Middle-Latitude Desert and the Transverse Ranges and the Sierra Nevada. It represents a narrow transition zone with orographic influence, which brings slightly higher precipitation than occurs farther east. It becomes more extensive within the Basin Ranges and is characteristic also of Shasta Valley and the Tule Lake Basin because of rain-shadow location. The more northerly basins have a better four-season definition than is generally found in California; yet they do have summer dryness.

DRY-SUMMER UPLANDS

California's mountains, even those distant from Southern California, still experience pronounced summer drought; however, such uplands are appreciably wetter in winter and cooler than adjacent lowlands. Although agriculture is climatically feasible, a relatively short growing season greatly reduces the variety of possible crops. Precipitation is generally adequate to support growth of forest or heavy woodland. Even on the colder eastern margins annual precipitation exceeds 12 inches, whereas much of the Middle-Latitude Uplands receives more than 30 inches of pre-

Fig. A-6. (Cont'd.).

REPRESENTATIVE STATIONS (WITH ELEVATION)	JULY TEMP.	JAN. TEMP.	GROWING SEASON	ANNUAL PRECIP.	ANNUAL SNOWFALL
Brawley (Imperial Cty.), −119 ft.	91°	53°	10.6 mo.	2 in.	−1 in.
Maricopa (Kern Cty.), 660 ft.	86°	47°	10.3 mo.	6 in.	−1 in.
Fresno (Fresno Cty.), 331 ft.	82°	45°	10.1 mo.	9 in.	−1 in.
San Diego (San Diego Cty.), sea level	69°	55°	12.0 mo.	11 in.	−1 in.
Del Monte (Monterey Cty.), sea level	61°	48°	9.9 mo.	15 in.	−1 in.
Eureka (Humboldt Cty.), sea level	56°	47°	11.1 mo.	38 in.	−1 in.
Santa Barbara (S. B. Cty.), sea level	66°	53°	10.0 mo.	18 in.	−1 in.
San Jose (Santa Clara Cty.), 95 ft.	67°	48°	10.0 mo.	14 in.	−1 in.
Redlands (San Bern. Cty.), 1352 ft.	77°	50°	9.7 mo.	15 in.	−1 in.
Colusa (Colusa Cty.), 60 ft.	78°	45°	9.0 mo.	15 in.	−1 in.
Trona (San Bern. Cty.), 1700 ft.	89°	43°	8.1 mo.	4 in.	−1 in.
Tehachapi (Kern Cty.), 3970 ft.	76°	39°	5.8 mo.	11 in.	38 in.
Doyle (Lassen Cty.), 4280 ft.	71°	31°	3.2 mo.	10 in.	24 in.
Seven Oaks (San Bern. Cty.), 5075 ft.	63°	38°	2.9 mo.	27 in.	57 in.
Placerville (El Dorado Cty.), 1890 ft.	72°	41°	5.9 mo.	41 in.	7 in.
Tahoe (Placer Cty.), 6228 ft.	61°	26°	2.4 mo.	30 in.	219 in.
Weaverville (Trinity Cty.), 2050 ft.	71°	37°	3.9 mo.	36 in.	27 in.
White Mountain (Mono Cty.), 12,470 ft. (short-term record)	45°	6°	0.5 mo.	13 in.	131 in.

cipitation, part of which falls as snow. Elevations range from near sea level (in the north) to almost 12,000 feet. Fig. A-5 reveals that this climatic type encompasses about a third of California. It is the primary climate of the northern Coast Ranges, Klamath Mountains, Southern Cascade Range, Modoc Plateau, and Sierra Nevada. A wide range of temperatures and precipitation characterizes this area, which includes a few lowlands (and highlands in Southern California) that technically might be classed subtropical. The area's small population and relatively simple economies make additional subdivision inappropriate here.

ALPINE (ARCTIC)

Conditions suggestive of polar lands prevail above 12,000-feet elevation in California. The largest extent lies within the Sierra Nevada with smaller areas on Mount Shasta and in the White Mountains. Temperatures, as along Arctic coastlines, are too low for agriculture or even for true forest growth. Although there are diminutive perennial snowfields (especially on north slopes), the seasonal conditions of continuous darkness or continuous light of polar lands are absent. Windswept expanses of barren rock are common although stunted vegetation is found in favored localities.

APPENDIX B:: LANDFORMS

Diversified landforms provide a principal ingredient in the geographical intricacy of California. The common topographic types— plains, hills, plateaus, and mountains—are all widespread within the state. California has greater complexity of geologic history than most states; its exposed formations range from ancient (pre-Cambrian) to contemporary (Cenozoic). Its shoreline and its contiguous submarine landforms add variety. Thus the Golden State affords a remarkable natural laboratory for students of geography, geology, and other earth sciences.

LANDFORM DIVISIONS

Individual plains, hills, plateaus, and mountains are grouped into physiographic divisions for purposes of statewide comparison. The State Division of Mines delineates eleven major units,[1] listed below (see also Fig. B-1).

[1] Norman E. A. Hinds, *Evolution of the California Landscape*, Bull. 158, California Division of Mines, 1952.

When California landforms are described in relation to the remainder of the continent, larger groupings are recognized; thus this list includes the broad North American physiographic provinces of which the California divisions form segments:

North American Cordillera
Intermontane Plateau System
  1. Basin Ranges
  2. Mojave Desert
  3. Colorado Desert
  4. Modoc Plateau
Pacific Mountain System
  5. Cascade Range
  6. Sierra Nevada
  7. Klamath Mountains
  8. Coast Ranges
  9. Transverse Ranges
  10. Peninsular Ranges
  11. Great Valley

The importance and dramaturgy of California terrain prompted arrangement of this book primarily in terms of physiography;

LANDFORMS OF CALIFORNIA

Valley Fill

0   40   80   120
Miles

KLAMATH
MOUNTAINS

MODOC
PLATEAU

CASCADE
RANGE

GREAT
VALLEY

SIERRA
NEVADA

COAST
RANGES

BASIN-
RANGES

MOJAVE
DESERT

TRANSVERSE RANGES

PENINSULAR
RANGES

COLORADO
DESERT

Fig. B-1. LANDFORM DIVISIONS.

Fig. B-2. CHARACTERISTIC ROCKS AND STRUCTURES OF THE LANDFORM DIVISIONS.

LANDFORM DIVISION	MAJOR LITHIC TYPE	GENERAL STRUCTURE
1. Basin Ranges	Complex [a]	Fault blocks
2. Mojave Desert	Complex [a]	Fault blocks
3. Colorado Desert [b]	Sedimentary	Faulted downwarp
4. Modoc Plateau	Volcanic	Lava flows as fault blocks
5. Cascade Range	Volcanic	Igneous tableland capped by volcanoes
6. Sierra Nevada	Granitic-metamorphic	Tilted fault block
7. Klamath Mountains	Granitic-metamorphic-sedimentary	Folds-faults
8. Coast Ranges	Sedimentary	Folds-faults
9. Transverse Ranges [c]	Sedimentary (western), Granitic-metamorphic (eastern)	Folds-faults (western) Fault blocks (eastern)
10. Peninsular Ranges [d]	Sedimentary (western), Granitic-metamorphic (eastern)	Folds-faults (western) Fault blocks (eastern)
11. Great Valley	Sedimentary	Downwarp

[a] *i.e.*, sedimentary, volcanic and granitic-metamorphic rocks occur widely.
[b] Also called "Salton Trough."
[c] Also called "Los Angeles Ranges."
[d] Also called "San Diego Ranges."

details of the eleven landform divisions are included within individual chapters.[2] To facilitate comparison, however, rocks and structures characteristic of the divisions are summarized in Fig. B-2 and partially located on Fig. B-3. The remainder of this appendix is concerned with selected earth-molding processes most pertinent to the general nature of the landform divisions.

GEOMORPHIC PROCESSES

Most Californians reside on relatively flat land within sight of mountains; predominantly, the Golden State consists of smooth lowlands and rough uplands. Such topographic extremes are common where earth sculpture by *gradation* is outpaced by pro-

[2] Further reading is listed in the bibliography.

found *tectonic* activity on a large scale. Fundamental earth disturbances are commonplace to most of the Pacific Rim, including western North America. Here deep-seated crustal forces impart an impressive north-south grain to the terrain, basic to consideration of human habitation of the Golden State. These processes are chiefly responsible for the over-all arrangement of California's highlands and plains. They contribute heavily to the design of individual surfaces and to the state's patterns of soils and mineral resources.

INTRUSION

During Mesozoic times nearly a fifth of California experienced cooling of subterranean magma which created *batholiths*, great masses of granitoidal rock. Older strata overlying these intrusions were subjected to pressure and heat from the magma and were *metamorphosed*, greatly altering their identity. Subsequent disturbances, discussed later un-

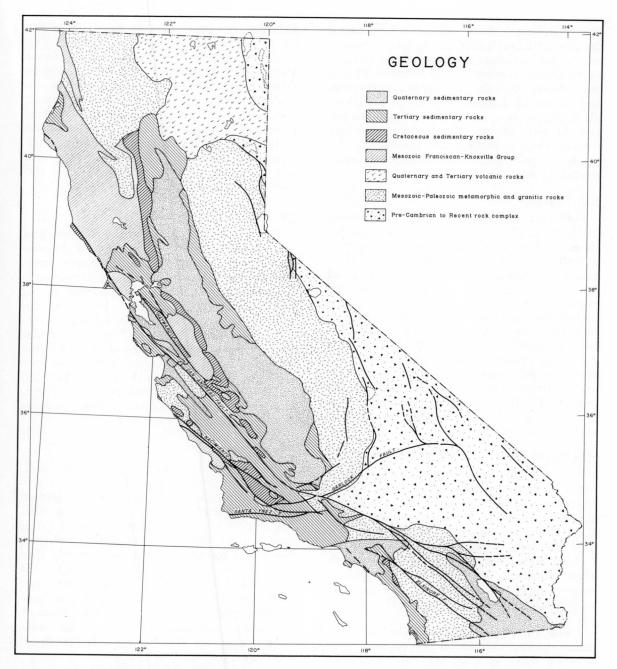

GEOLOGY

- Quaternary sedimentary rocks
- Tertiary sedimentary rocks
- Cretaceous sedimentary rocks
- Mesozoic Franciscan-Knoxville Group
- Quaternary and Tertiary volcanic rocks
- Mesozoic-Paleozoic metamorphic and granitic rocks
- Pre-Cambrian to Recent rock complex

Fig. B-3. MAJOR LITHIC TYPES.

der "faulting," have elevated numerous granitic-metamorphic bodies to form a nearly continuous mountain backbone from Oregon to Mexico. It consists of the Klamath Mountains, Sierra Nevada, and eastern Transverse and Peninsular Ranges (Fig. B-3). Comparable highlands have arisen in the Basin Ranges and Mojave Desert. Besides their rugged scenery these mountains are notable for deposits of gold and other metallic minerals related to intrusion.

ERUPTION

Following the major intrusions, primarily in Miocene, Pliocene, and Eocene-Pleistocene times, molten magma spread across more than a tenth of California to produce distinctive volcanic landscapes. Eruption has occurred upon the granitic-metamorphic zones and elsewhere as well. The largest volcanic areas include the Cascade Range, with its string of individual conic peaks, and the Modoc Plateau, with its assemblage of thick lava sheets (Fig. B-3). Extensive volcanic landforms also occur in the Basin Ranges, Mojave Desert, and northern Sierra Nevada. In most eruptive areas of California deposits of valuable minerals are notably absent unless nonvolcanic rocks are also present.

EROSION AND SEDIMENTATION

Streams, valley glaciers, waves, and winds erode landforms of tectonic origin to produce sediments, which are deposited on low-lying surfaces. Alluvium is the most important of the California sediments; river deposits compose the typical mantle on lowlands of the Golden State (Fig. D-1). The usual smoothness, thickness, and accumulated groundwater supply of the alluvial lowlands are major assets for agriculture as well as urbanization.

Older alluvium and other sediments eventually become indurated to produce *sedimentary rocks*, such as shale and sandstone. These are particularly widespread in the western half of California; their materials were derived from highlands to the east and apparently also from a western land mass (Cascadia) long-vanished beneath the Pacific.

Sedimentary rocks compose the bulk of the Coast and western Transverse Ranges (Fig. B-3) and underlie the alluvium of the Great Valley, Los Angeles Basin, and Colorado Desert. Elsewhere there are appreciable deposits in the Basin Ranges and Mojave Desert. Sedimentary formations, particularly of Tertiary age, are the source of petroleum and natural gas. Thus California's output of such minerals is confined to the Great Valley and the southern Coast, western Transverse, and western Peninsular Ranges.

DOWNWARPING

The Great Valley, Colorado Desert, and such lesser depressions as the Los Angeles Basin have resulted from long-term subsidence which may be continuing. Downwarping and sedimentation are concurrent; in the aforementioned lowlands, sedimentary deposits attain a thickness of several miles, overlying harder, little-known "basement" rocks. The larger downwarped units of California can be grouped with the series of coastal lowlands in western North America, which includes Alaska's Susitna–Matanuska Valleys, the Puget Sound–Willamette Trough, and the Gulf of California.

FOLDING

In coastal California particularly, sedimentary rocks have been folded into corrugated uplands, subsequently roughened through erosion. Folding, augmented by other diastrophism, tends to form elongated ridges and valleys that trend northwest-southeast. Since the terrain trends more westerly than does the shore, many valleys front upon the ocean. Folded structures describe the Coast and western Transverse Ranges, and such metamorphic complexes as the Klamath Mountains and Sierra Nevada foothill zone, where resultant topography exhibits strong northwest-southeast orientation.

FAULTING

More extensive than folding within California is crustal breakage and movement along faults—cleavages that may be miles in both length and depth. Earthquakes result from faulting, and the record of their damage is dramatic evidence of far-reaching and continuing crustal rupture. Major faults occur in all the landform divisions and major rock types; they often mark the contact of contrasting forms (Fig. B-3). Crustal breakage in California most commonly trends northwest-southeast, as illustrated by the San Andreas Fault, the longest in the state, which extends at least 500 miles from Point Arena to the Salton Sea and doubtless beyond.

Large crustal blocks may move vertically along a rupture zone to form imposing mountains and depressions which are especially commonplace in the Basin Ranges. Where blocks rise or drop along fault zones, there are commonly *scarps*, abrupt slopes which often are scenic spectacles yet major obstacles to traverse. The venerated east face of the Sierra Nevada ranks among the world's larger scarps. Contorted fault-block mountains, depressions, and clear-cut scarps also describe

the topography of much of the Mojave Desert and eastern Transverse and Peninsular Ranges. Whether vertical or horizontal, rupture often produces a swath of lowland across scabrous terrain, influencing river runoff and coastline configuration and presenting locational advantages for transport routes. Along the San Andreas system, examples include Pajaro Gap (east of Watsonville) and Tejon, Cajon, and San Gorgonio Passes.

In sedimentary localities of California, folding and faulting commonly coincide, subtly combining with erosion to create surfaces of multiple origin. In many depressions, including the Great Valley and Colorado Desert, faults are obscured by fresh alluvium; earthquakes, or trapping of groundwater or petroleum, may be more significant by-products than surficial expression. California lowlands customarily originate with some phase of crustal movement. Where such causality is known or suspected, a given lowland may be described simply as *structural* in origin.

APPENDIX C:: NATURAL VEGETATION

Foremost though it is in population and agricultural output among the fifty states, in area California is still clad more or less in natural vegetation. Only 14 percent of the Golden State is urbanized or cultivated. Hence the pre-European vegetation distribution remains largely unaltered despite plant composition modified within the formations by fire, logging, and grazing. Natural vegetation contributes significantly to the state's economy: California ranks second to Oregon in lumbering; the value of range-cattle output approaches $40 million annually; and forestry forms the chief economic pursuit for nearly 20 percent of the state's area, and grazing for another 30 percent.

There is marked correlation between plant distribution and climatic expression. At opposite extremes in the Golden State are the verdant forests of the northwest and the desert shrubs of the southeast (Fig. C-1). More than half of California, however, is climatically and botanically intermediate and exhibits considerable mixing of grasses, shrubs, and trees.

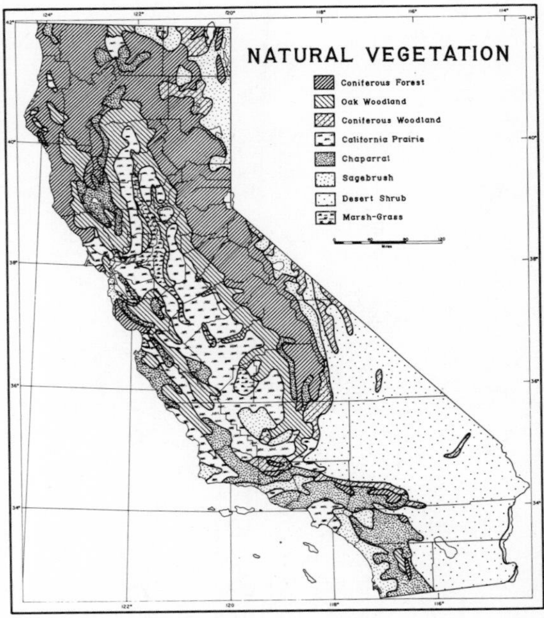

Fig. C-1. NATURAL VEGETATION.

Fig. C-2. SUMMARY OF MAJOR VEGETATION CATEGORIES.

CATEGORY	ORIGINAL COVERAGE	ASPECT AND COMPOSITION	UTILIZATION
Coniferous Forest	21%	Needleleaf evergreen trees. Density, growth rate, and understory thickness tend to increase northwestward. One or two species often clearly dominant, especially redwood along North Coast, Douglas fir inland from redwood belt, Ponderosa-Jeffrey pines in lower Sierra Nevada and Modoc Plateau, red fir at 8000-9000 feet in Sierra Nevada, and lodgepole-whitebark pines above 9000 feet in Sierra Nevada. Over half the forest area is more mixed, with common associates of Ponderosa-Jeffrey pines including Douglas fir, white fir, sugar pine, and incense cedar.	Most species commercially useful. One fourth of original timber has been cut. Annual cut is about twice the annual net growth. Half the area is administered by federal government, partly for recreational use. Grazing common except in redwood and Douglas-fir belts. Most cutover areas are in brush and woodland or have returned to forest.
Oak Woodland	11%	Grassland as described for California Prairie, with trees scattered or in groves. Several species of deciduous and evergreen oaks are dominant; subordinate trees are mostly broadleaf deciduous.	Primarily grazing. Heavy forage growth especially in winter and spring. Trees mainly unused.
Coniferous Woodland	3%	Sagebrush as described below, with piñon pine and/or juniper bushes scattered or in groves.	Primarily grazing. Fair forage growth. Piñon and juniper mainly unused.
Grassland ("California Prairie")	22%	Treeless grassland, originally dominated by perennial bunchgrasses and other herbaceous plants. Majority of associations now consist of introduced annuals of inferior quality.	More than one-half displaced by farming and urban. Remainder grazing. Heavy forage growth, especially winter and spring.
Chaparral	9%	Broadleaf evergreen shrubs, dominated by chamise, scrub oak, manzanita, and ceanothus. Forms impenetrable thickets when well developed. Replaces forest and oak woodland following fire in some localities.	Minimum use other than for watershed covering.
Sagebrush	8%	Shrubs and semishrubs dominant but considerable understory of grasses, especially in interior areas. Shorter and less dense than fully developed chaparral.	Primarily grazing. Fair forage in the interior, especially in winter. Poor forage in coastal areas.
Desert Shrub	25%	Shrubs, usually small and scattered, are dominant, particularly creosote bush, burroweed, and shadscale. Much bare ground despite presence of grasses, cacti, wildflowers, etc.	Largely unused. Relatively small portions displaced by farming and urbanization.
Marsh Grass	−1%	Mostly perennial herbs to 9 feet high. Dominated by bulrushes (including common tule) cattails, spike rushes, sedges.	Largely displaced by farming. Remainder used for grazing and recreation.
Barren	1%		

The map of natural vegetation broadly reveals elevation differences, which form an important control of climate (Appendix A). Thus in the south consequential forests are not found below 5000 feet nor in the north is grassland common above 4000 feet. In sequence eastward across the Cascade and Sierra Nevada, grassland becomes woodland, which in turn is replaced by forest with increasing altitude. Such *vertical zonation* is typical of the larger mountain masses; however, details vary with the locality.

Edaphic (i.e., ground) conditions are significant in the delineation of statewide vegetation mosaics. Extensive chaparral stands are confined mainly to areas with thin soils, whereas forests of appreciable density typically require moderate to deep soils for their prosperity. Tules and other plants of the marsh-grass group once dominated the water-logged bottomlands of the Great Valley.

Where water tables, though underground, are still accessible, *riparian* vegetation, commonly arboreal, is supported. Thus strips of flood-plain forest follow Great Valley streams as well as those elsewhere in the state, even in desert areas.

Major categories of California's natural vegetation, located on Fig. C-1, are described in Fig. C-2.

APPENDIX D:: SOILS

California's soils, by-product of the state's oft-stated climatic, geologic, and botanic diversity, are exceedingly variable. Most of the world's great soil groups are represented in the Golden State and more than 500 distinct soil series are recognized. The broad statewide transition southeastward from humid forest lands to arid shrub country is an important influence upon soils: alkalinity tends to increase, color lightens, and organic matter decreases southeastward in California. Soil texture (particle size), contrariwise, often is more directly influenced by parent rock than by climate or vegetation. Thus sandy loams commonly occur on granitic surfaces, clay-textured soils are prevalent on the volcanics of the northeast, and clay loams are typical on Coast Range shale and sandstone.

Slope, through its effects upon erosion and deposition, is another critical determinant of soil conditions. Because of California's strongly contrasting terrain, its over-all soil qualities are more dependent upon landforms than upon other controls. The primary distinction therefore is between *lowland* (or *transported*) soils as one category and *upland* (or *residual*) soils as another. The former normally are generally favored for cultivation, whereas most of the latter are used less intensively, often not at all.

TRANSPORTED (LOWLAND) SOILS

Major California soil categories rated *excellent*, as well as most of those rated *good* or *fair*, are transported; they are derived from alluvium or other unconsolidated deposits. Such soils typically are deep, reasonably even surfaced and situated in the lowest, and hence usually the warmest, localities. Gentle relief alone may impart to them primary consideration where farming is oriented toward mechanization and irrigation. More often than not, problems, such as drainage, encountered in some transported soils are outweighed by their aforementioned advantages.

Most larger California lowlands possess three distinct groupings of transported soils:

terrace, valley basin, and *valley.* Along coastlines and valley margins where water levels
once stood relatively higher, benchlike ter-
raced topography is common (Fig. D-1). Now
elevated above subsequent large-scale deposition, *terrace* soils commonly are older, have
denser subsoils, and are more subject to erosion than other lowland categories (Fig. D-2).

Present depositional surfaces, by contrast,
tend to be smoother and fresher. Their lowest
portions, the *valley basin* soils, often are
poorly drained and excessively acid or alkaline. Often such soils have shown remarkable
improvements through drainage, tillage, and
other corrective measures. *Valley* soils,
located on gently sloping alluvial plains, have
few of the handicaps of basins or terraces;
they are usually superior for agriculture.

RESIDUAL (UPLAND) SOILS

Residual soils are derived directly from the
underlying bedrock. Erosion in varying degrees is almost universal and many residual
soils are shallow. Colder climate resulting
from characteristic upland location is another
common handicap. Residual soils are more
widespread and perhaps more diverse than
transported types; however, their general lack
of intensive use makes it inappropriate to recognize their many subdivisions here.

A fifth of the Golden State is classed as
lithosol (literally "stony soil") which is of

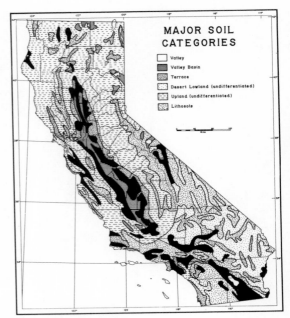

Fig. D-1. SOILS.

shallow depth and commonly on slopes pro-
hibitively steep. Fault scarps and mountain
summits are representative locations. Such
sites are considered virtually nonproductive
even for forest or pasture. Other *upland* soils
are more productive but vary greatly in depth,
slope, and fertility. Only a small portion of
these soils is cultivated.

Soil categories described above are located
in Fig. D-1, and their outstanding qualities are
summarized in Fig. D-2.

Fig. D-2. SUMMARY OF MAJOR SOIL CATEGORIES.

CATEGORY	EXTENT OF STATE	SOURCE AND DEPTH	SITE	QUALITY RATING	COMMENTS
Valley	11%	Slightly weathered alluvium. Deep.	Elevation inter-mediate between valley basins and terraces. Surface mostly smooth to gently sloping. Drainage good.	89% excellent to good	The state's best all-pur-pose agricultural soils. Nearly all farmed or urbanized.
				11% good to fair	Undulating and droughty due to sandy, wind-modified nature. Found especially along coast, in desert, and in Merced and Fresno districts, San Joaquin Valley.
Valley Basin	5%	Mostly slightly weathered, heavy-textured alluvial or lake deposits. Deep.	Lowest portions of valleys. Surface nearly flat. Drain-age poor.	50% mostly good	Requires artificial drain-age. Peat and muck in Sacramento–San Joaquin Delta rates excellent when drained.
				50% very poor	Excessive salinity or alkalinity common in San Joaquin Valley and Mojave Desert.
Terrace	6%	Extensively weath-ered alluvium; lake, or marine deposit. Deep.	Higher portions of valleys and coastal benchlands. Surface gently sloping to undulat-ing with occasional steep dropoffs.	59% good to fair	Moderately dense subsoils.
				41% fair to poor	Permeability limited by extreme claypan or hard-pan, especially East Side of Great Central Valley and portions of deserts.
Desert Lowland (undifferentiated)	16%	Weathered alluvial and lake deposits. Deep.	Valley, valley basin, and terrace soils for which surveys incomplete.	Excellent to very poor	Uncultivated, commonly because of water defi-ciency.
Upland (undifferentiated)	41%	Moderately weath-ered underlying bedrock. Deep to fairly shallow.	Surface rolling, hilly to steep. Usu-ally higher than the above-listed soils in a given locality.	88% fair to poor	Generally too steep for cultivation. Productive for forest or forage.
				12% good to fair	Surface rolling, depth moderate; developed under grass cover. Mainly Coast Ranges and Sierra Nevada foothills.
Lithosol	21%	Slightly weathered underlying bed-rock. Very shallow and stony.	Surface rough; slopes steep.	Nonagri-cultural	Generally associated with chaparral, desert shrub, or noncommercial forest.

APPENDIX E:: POPULATION

Although California has become the nation's most populous state, many residents remain undecided whether that historic day was properly one for pink champagne or black crepe. Certainly large and rapid growth has been an outstanding characteristic of the Golden State. Population increment has been greater in most successive decades since statehood; the 1860's, 1890's, and 1930's were exceptions (Fig. E-1). California has gained more than 5 million new inhabitants in the last decade alone. To their own incredulity, the more uninhibited boosters have often lived to see their rash forecasts of population gain become fact.

Optimism, which continues to run rampant so far as population is concerned, may itself be an important stimulant to growth. But the state has changed markedly since the days when population gain was widely considered a desirable goal. Californians have become increasingly aware of the burdens implicit in growth—the responsibilities to provide employment, transportation facilities, schools, hospitals, and recreation opportunities for the new masses. State and local government expenditures absorb a rising share of total personal income; one wonders if the growing national influence of California will be used to obtain additional outside assistance to meet these needs.

IMMIGRATION

California's remarkable growth is best understood with reference to immigration, particularly since natural increment approximates the nationwide average and the booming number of babies in the Golden State would not have occurred without the tremendous immigration of recent decades. Movement into the state accounted for over 60 percent of the population increase during the 1950's; more than half of contemporary residents were born elsewhere.

Migration to California has been partially a response to economic opportunities, positive or imagined. Most incomers are not and never have been retired or otherwise supported directly by continuing personal income accrued elsewhere. Employment may not necessarily

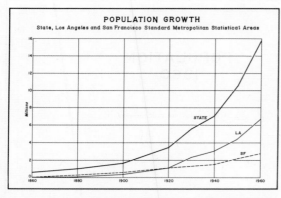

Fig. E-1. POPULATION OF CALIFORNIA, LOS ANGELES AREA, AND SAN FRANCISCO BAY AREA, 1860-1960.

be the chief attraction, yet it is essential for the livelihood of most new arrivals. Thus the population graph (Fig. E-1) reflects the state's economic history; it suggests the modest growth of early agriculture. After 1900 growth was notably augmented by oil, motion pictures, tourism, military activities, and eventually the burgeoning defense-oriented economy which materialized in World War II. In addition immigration itself has been an economic catalyst. New citizens provide a labor force and are also consumers of such California industries as foods, construction, and home furnishing. Significant income is transferred to California with the establishment of newcomers in the State. Ultimately, however, new basic industries become necessary.

The propiuity of "California living" has been another migrational magnet. One recent nationwide survey concluded that "climate" has taken precedence over "job opportunities" as motivation for settlement in the state. To many migrants California's living conditions may be the immediate incentive—existence of livelihood is assumed. The Golden State's famed amenities have tended to compensate for such obstacles to migration as distance, unfamiliarity, and disruption of social ties. One ponders, too, what intrinsic worth the migrant attaches to the prestige of California residence.

California settlement of course has been impellent as well as alluring—national conditions have favored relocation whenever local opportunities have diminished elsewhere. Improved transportation, more leisure time, and increased wealth to cushion the transition between successive employments have permitted increased mobility. Military service in California has provided unsolicited advertising of much value—so also have the enthusiastic communications directed by countless new arrivals to kinfolk elsewhere. Immigration thus becomes partially self-sustaining; it may also be self-defeating to the degree that it devours California's supply of jobs and resources, particularly scenery, space, and climate.

POPULATION DISTRIBUTION

There is marked disparity of population density in the several Californias, as has been suggested repeatedly in this book. Large areas remain almost empty; sizable concentrations are restricted to relatively small portions of the state (Fig. E-2).

URBAN-RURAL

California is among the least rural states—86 percent of its inhabitants have "urban" residence. Dispersed farmsteads are remarkably limited in consideration of the state's agricultural significance—only 2 percent of the population actually has such habitation. Most of the "rural" population resides in small towns. Domicile of farm people in villages is facilitated by absence of livestock on many specialty farms, ease of travel throughout the year, and employment of temporary farm labor (often housed and seasonally employed in towns rather than upon farms).

URBAN AREAS

Los Angeles and San Francisco, the largest cities, are the nuclei of California population—their metropolitan areas house nearly 60 percent of Californians. Each metropolis actually forms a vast *urbanized area* in which

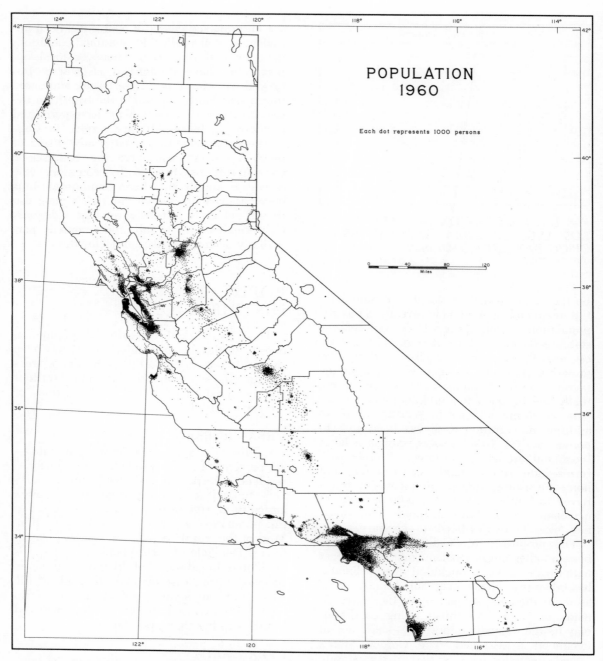

Fig. E-2. POPULATION OF CALIFORNIA, 1960.

the central city is flanked by its satellites, some of which like Oakland and Long Beach are large cities within their own rights. The built-up zone contiguous to the central city, within the common commutation zone, is considered part of the urban complex. A multitude of individual political units is involved: metropolitan Los Angeles in 1962 contained eighty-five incorporated cities, the San Francisco Bay Area, fifty-eight. Collectively these communities tend to form inseparable economic and social composites; yet proposals advanced to merge them administratively have seldom availed. Strong hometown sentiment and vested interests preserve political separation. Citizens usually lose attachment for neighboring towns that provide employment, once the work day is ended.

The census delimits nine other urbanized areas besides metropolitan Los Angeles and San Francisco. These nine house nearly 20 percent of all Californians. Only two, Fresno and Bakersfield, are actually completely detached from the San Francisco Bay Area or coastal Southern California where three quarters of the state's population is located.

Like the larger urbanized areas, many lesser cities of California also are encompassed by suburbs, many of them politically unattached. To provide a more complete impression of urban California, populations of both *geographic city* (*urbanized area*) and *political city* are listed for leading cities in Fig. E-6.

URBAN LOCATION

California population distribution, apart from the larger cities, occurs in scattered alignment oriented toward productive lowlands and their connective surface routes (Fig. E-2). Initial occupance stemmed primarily from farming; even away from agricultural centers, services for through travelers as well as the immediate needs of the individual remote area have invited settlement along commercial arteries.

Other conditions have determined the location of many California towns. The coastal strand has attracted much settlement—utilization has depended upon shipping, fishing, and recreation as well as terrace farming. Occu-

pance where mining, recreation, or military activities prevail tends to have a "where you find it" setting; yet presence of lowlands and facility of transportation are often locational qualifiers. Lumber towns, although ultimately fastened to a specific resource, are generally on the forest periphery where cutting first occurred and shipping facilities are favorable.

The importance of early sites is visibly reflected in contemporary locational patterns. For example, Los Angeles, San Francisco, and San Diego were firmly established by 1800; at least a dozen Spanish mission sites have become substantial cities. To a remarkable degree the early conditions of productivity and travel, important locational factors, persist to the present.

Some established subregional centers have tended to expand and discourage the rise of significant competitors in areas of new development, particularly because California travel conditions are relatively easy. Recent examples include the status of Taft after discovery of oil in rural Cuyama Valley and Klamath Falls, Oregon, relative to irrigation expansion in Tule Lake Basin. Such services as finance, government, education, entertainment, and specialized trade, are usually concentrated in relatively few communities while a much larger number of communities have more mundane functions. Much recent military and manufacturing enterprise has also gravitated to larger cities; in fact, such activity locates elsewhere only if space requirements necessitate. Thus cities whose original site was rational may "outgrow their environment" and encounter contemporary handicaps. The new mobile California "way of life" unfortunately often creates problems of urban water shortage, traffic congestion, air and water pollution, and obliteration of valuable cropland.

MULTIPLE RESIDENCE

A number of Californians have two or more domiciles although the census reports only one. Vacation places are particularly obvious —habitation is typically seasonal in more isolated areas such as the Sierra Nevada and other highlands, the southeastern deserts, or the Northwest. For several months each year such environments accommodate far larger numbers than are formally recorded in population statistics. It is commonplace for wealthier families to maintain substantial homes in contrasting seasonal settings, as in San Francisco and Lake Tahoe or in Beverly Hills and Palm Springs. Near the large metropolitan centers there is commonly a zone of more perennial albeit temporary residence with sea resorts, mountain cabins, and desert "homesteads." Transient agricultural workers often have numerous residences even though there is often a home base—this group and senior citizens help account for the impressive number of house trailers and trailer courts. Population of such areas as the Great Central Valley and the Colorado Desert thus fluctuates widely during the course of the year.

CHANGE

Population growth has not only been disparate in the several Californias; some counties and towns have actually shown recent decline. The southern third of the state is growing especially rapidly—this has been a continuous trend since 1900. More than half of California's population now resides south of the Transverse Ranges—the San Fernando Valley is the geographical center of population (Fig. E-3).

Growth is particularly evident on the periphery of the larger metropolises, particularly Los Angeles, San Francisco, San Diego, and Sacramento (Fig. E-4). The majority of the state's recently incorporated cities are situated in these fringe areas. Elsewhere important contributors to population increase include expanded irrigation in the Central Valley, coastal military installations between San Francisco and Los Angeles, additional lumbering and construction in the Northwest, and increased tourism and retirement in outlying districts.

Four counties and over two dozen communities lost population between 1950 and 1960 (Fig. E-5). Most of the towns are small—decline reflects deterioration of a single activity such as lumbering, mining, or railroading. Most of these declining communities are located in sparsely populated parts of California where other activities do not provide sufficient substitutional employment. Recently, population decline has been notably absent from northwestern and southern parts of the state.

The inordinate number of political cities in the Bay Area which lost population during the 1950's included San Francisco, Oakland, Berkeley, Richmond, and Alameda. Small nonexpandable limits of these cities prevented their outward expansion to compensate for residential demolition and desire (especially by younger couples with growing families) for the more spacious housing offered by suburban tracts. Although the total population of the Bay Area is rapidly increasing, gain is largely peripheral. Comparable population loss around the core of central Los Angeles has been obscured by continued availability of "open" land in the San Fernando Valley and other districts within the extensive political limits of the city.

Fig. E-3. SHARE OF STATE POPULATION IN SELECTED COUNTY GROUPS, 1860-1960.

COUNTY GROUP	PERCENT OF CALIFORNIA POPULATION					
	1860	1880	1900	1920	1940	1960
Los Angeles–Orange	3	4	13	29	42	43
San Diego	1	1	2	3	4	7
Other Southern California counties [a]	3	3	6	7	7	8
Great Central Valley	24	20	18	18	16	14
San Francisco Bay Area [b]	33	51	46	35	26	24
Remainder of California	36	21	15	8	5	4

[a] Santa Barbara, Ventura, San Bernardino, Riverside, and Imperial counties.

[b] Sonoma, Napa, Solano, Marin, Contra Costa, Alameda, San Francisco, San Mateo, Santa Clara, and Santa Cruz Counties.

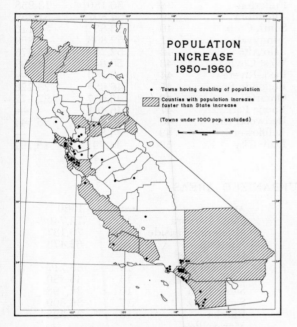

Fig. E-4. POPULATION GROWTH, 1950-1960.

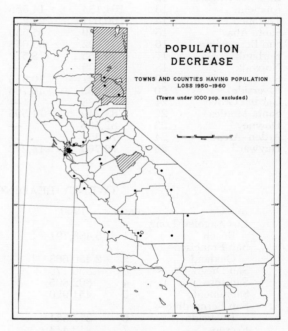

Fig. E-5. POPULATION LOSS, 1950-1960.

Fig. E-6. URBAN POPULATION.

FIFTY LARGEST CITIES

CITY	RANK	1960	1950	CITY	RANK	1960	1950
Los Angeles	1	2,479,015	1,970,358	Richmond	26	71,854	99,545
San Francisco	2	740,316	775,357	Compton	27	71,812	47,991
San Diego	3	573,224	334,387	San Mateo	28	69,870	41,782
Oakland	4	367,548	384,575	Pomona	29	67,157	35,405
Long Beach	5	344,168	250,767	Lakewood	30	67,126	—
San Jose	6	204,196	95,280	San Leandro	31	65,962	27,542
Sacramento	7	191,667	137,572	Alameda	32	63,855	64,430
Fresno	8	133,929	91,669	Inglewood	33	63,390	46,185
Glendale	9	119,442	95,702	Vallejo	34	60,877	26,038
Pasadena	10	116,407	104,577	Santa Clara	35	58,880	11,702
Berkeley	11	111,268	113,805	Santa Barbara	36	58,768	44,854
East Los Angeles	12	104,270	—	Bakersfield	37	56,848	34,784
Anaheim	13	104,184	14,556	Fullerton	38	56,180	13,958
Torrance	14	100,991	22,241	Alhambra	39	54,807	51,359
Santa Ana	15	100,350	45,533	South Gate	40	53,831	51,116
San Bernardino	16	91,922	63,058	Sunnyvale	41	52,898	9,829
Burbank	17	90,155	78,577	Palo Alto	42	52,287	25,475
Norwalk	18	88,739	—	West Covina	43	50,645	4,499
Stockton	19	86,321	70,853	Pico–Rivera	44	49,150	—
Riverside	20	84,332	46,764	Redondo Beach	45	46,986	25,226
Garden Grove	21	84,238	—	Ontario	46	46,617	22,872
Santa Monica	22	83,249	71,595	Buena Park	47	46,401	—
Downey	23	82,505	—	Redwood City	48	46,290	25,544
Arden–Arcade	24	73,352	—	Bellflower	49	44,846	—
Hayward	25	72,700	14,272	Daly City	50	44,791	15,191

TWENTY LEADING URBANIZED AREAS

AREA	RANK	1960	AREA	RANK	1960
Los Angeles–Long Beach	1	6,488,791	Santa Barbara	11	72,740
San Francisco–Oakland	2	2,430,663	Monterey–Seaside	12	70,187
San Diego	3	836,175	Modesto	13	62,473
San Jose	4	602,805	Oxnard–Port Hueneme	14	53,717
Sacramento	5	451,920	Salinas–Alisal	15	45,430
San Bernardino–Riverside	6	377,531	Santa Rosa	16	38,798
Fresno	7	213,444	Santa Cruz	17	36,809
Pomona–Ontario	8	186,547	Eureka	18	36,323
Bakersfield	9	141,763	Marysville–Yuba City	19	35,224
Stockton	10	141,604	Ventura	20	35,065

APPENDIX F:: AGRICULTURE

Agriculture was the predominant factor in the growth of California population for eighty years after the heyday of gold. Besides employment for disenchanted miners, farming and ranching provided many opportunities for newly immigrating landowners and laborers; they also furnished enticing advertisement of the state's charms to prospective tourists, senior citizens, and investors. Agriculture has stimulated other facets of the California economy such as transportation. Until World War II agricultural processing was the leading industrial type and constituted a voracious consumer of such items as fuels and electricity, container wares (from forests, tin plate mills, and glass factories), fertilizers, insecticides, and machinery. As late as 1950 agriculture accounted for 90 percent of California's water consumption.

Agriculture still occupies a basic position in the California economy although it is less dominant today than at any time since the Gold Rush. Agricultural products annually exceed the value of all gold mined since 1849 and surpass the combined annual revenues derived from minerals, lumber, and fish. California is the nation's leading agricultural state; hence, it is not surprising that food processing ranks second (after aerospace industries) in value and employment among major industrial types. In its related aspects agriculture is a common concern even of urban Californians. Understandably there is keen debate on such issues as relative rural and urban representation in the state Senate, the welfare of the large farm labor force, agricultural versus urban land zoning, and regulations governing size of farms.

EVOLUTION

The first two centuries of California agriculture have been characterized by three distinct agricultural types: (1) livestock ranching, (2) dry farming, and (3) irrigation. There has also been repeated struggle with drought and partial concern for specialty products for export. Ever expanding irrigation has perhaps been the most far-reaching trend during this

Fig. F-1. SELECTED AGRICULTURAL DATA.

VALUE OF PRODUCT (MILLIONS OF DOLLARS)	1920	1930	1940	1950	1960
Fruits (incl. nuts & berries)	276	295	158	394	585
Vegetables (incl. potatoes)	66	104	112	343	511
Cotton	11	26	27	196	305
Feed crops (incl. alfalfa, wheat, barley, corn, sorghum)	172	101	68	202	295
Miscellaneous crops	99	60	57	241	348
Total crop value	624	586	422	1376	2044
Dairy products	151	222	170	676	1103
Cattle sold	—	—	63	230	522
Chicken eggs	22	46	23	84	114
Livestock totals	173	268	256	990	1739
Percent of farms irrigated	57	63	61	66	75
Number of farms (in thousands)	118	136	133	137	99
Cropland (millions of acres)	11.9	11.4	12.9	14.3	12.9
Average farm size (acres)	250	224	230	267	372
Percent of harvested cropland irrigated	—	—	57	67	78
Farms over 1000 acres	4906	—	5265	6001	6012
Cropland contained (millions of acres)	4.6	—	6.0	6.9	7.1

interval; it has permitted increased population while farms have become smaller and more numerous until recent decades; output has likewise increased (Fig. F-1). The three agricultural types have existed side-by-side throughout the post-Indian occupance of California; yet each in turn has had its period of definite dominance.

THE LIVESTOCK ERA

California land-use was largely pastoral until the Gold Rush—such a scheme was logical in a dry-summer land inhabited by a Hispanic culture. Cattle grazed on vast properties; hence, rural population density was low. Tallow and hides were the chief exports, and meat and other products were largely wasted. Unprecedented drought in the 1860's and coming of Yankee farmers ended the dominance of livestock ranching. Grazing persists to the present, however, as the most widespread form of productive land-use in the state, and huge livestock properties are still of considerable number.

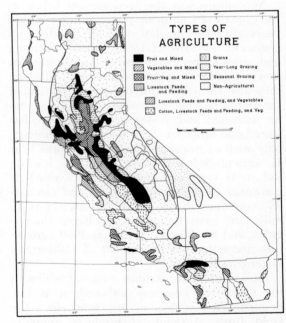

Fig. F-2. GENERALIZED TYPES OF AGRICULTURE.

472 :: APPENDIX F

THE DRY-FARMING ERA

American farmers soon substituted wheat and barley for native pasture and beef cattle over considerable tracts where soil and climate assured reasonable yields. As with livestock ranching, grain farming was wholly dependent upon winter and spring rains; landholdings remained relatively large and population density low. Ease of storage and handling facilitated export by ship at a time when overland transportation would have prohibited marketing elsewhere. California briefly became the first-ranking wheat state and is still the leading barley state. Wheat and barley have generally been evicted from choicer lands suitable for irrigation, yet they still occupy larger acreages than any other crop category. Both grains are now consumed largely within California, primarily as livestock feeds. Wine grapes, another important crop raised without benefit of irrigation during early American times, likewise yielded a product adapted to slow, nonrefrigerated handling. Most California grape production, however, belongs to a later period.

THE IRRIGATION ERA

Irrigated acreage remained limited even after statehood (despite evidence of its value from the Mission gardens) until rail linkage between California and eastern markets encouraged expansion. Such technical improvements as mechanical pumps and refrigerator cars were also invaluable factors; yet the inertia prompted by (1) litigation over water rights, (2) higher initial costs of irrigation facilities, and (3) uncertainties as to crop varieties and consumer response, remained. Half of California's present irrigated acreage was developed between 1890 and 1930, primarily upon the basis of orchard and vineyard products. As farms increased in number the average size tended to diminish notably. "Cheap" foreign labor for harvests was sought—Oriental, Hindus, Sikhs, Mexicans, and Filipinos were encouraged to immigrate. California's agricultural renown derives particularly from this golden age so that by 1930 fruits, grapes, and nuts alone accounted for over half of the state's crop value. Additional water supplies were made available in the 1940's by the Central Valley Project and the All-American Canal system; hence irrigated acreage has again increased. Less than 10 percent of California's area is irrigated crop land; yet this small portion includes the majority of the farms and cultivated acreage as well as value of crop output.

CONTEMPORARY ASPECTS

No other state approaches California in variety of agricultural commodities or in total value of product. Like other aspects of the Golden State's economy, rural land-use is characterized by diverse and complex patterns.

FARMS AND FARMLAND

Total cultivated land in California has continued to expand although at an irregular pace influenced by reclamation progress and federal control programs (Fig. F-1). An increasing proportion of farms and cropland is irrigated—the share now exceeds 75 percent. By contrast the number of individual farms reached its all-time peak during the 1930's. More recently properties of all sizes and all major types (including smaller part-time farms) have decreased. Size of the holding is related more to type of product than to other factors; present averages are (1) livestock ranches, 4300 acres; (2) cash-grain farms, 988 acres; (3) cotton farms, 400 acres; (4) vegetable farms, 278 acres; (5) dairies, 196 acres; (6) fruit and nut farms, 94 acres; (7) poultry farms, 37 acres. The average size of both irrigated and nonirrigated properties has enlarged notably since World War II; this trend is common in most of the leading agricultural counties. Holdings over 1000 acres particularly have increased their share of California cropland and now contain 46 percent of the total. These larger units are predominantly livestock and feed producers, but they also compose over half the state's cotton and rice operations.

AGRICULTURE : : 473

FARMERS

Personnel directly involved in California agriculture is extremely mobile in employment and residence. Some 20 percent of all "farmers" do not reside on their lands, and 40 percent have off-the-farm employment at least four months yearly. The majority of the farms utilize some hired labor—less than half these workers are permanent; the remainder are divided between local and nonlocal residents. During *peak harvest* months (September and October) the labor force more than doubles; nearly 300,000 temporary workers are hired in comparison to less than 90,000 during the slack season (March and April). Recently Mexican nationals and other foreign contract workers have composed about 16 percent of all farm labor during peak months. The number of hired workers did not decline appreciably in the 1950's, despite the trend toward mechanization; labor costs continue to form the largest single expense category for California farmers. Deliberate efforts are underway to automate the harvest of such crops as asparagus, tomatoes, grapes, prunes, and walnuts.

MARKETS

California still depends significantly upon the rest of the United States for disposal of its farm products despite the rising consumption of its own expanding population. An estimated 40 percent of its agriculture, thus committed, has remained consistent in recent years. About 80 percent of the canned fruits and vegetables and approximately two thirds of the fresh produce are shipped out of state. Such exports are based partly on California's status as supplier of near-monopoly commodities like dates, almonds, artichokes, lemons, figs, olives, garlic, English walnuts, figs, and Brussels sprouts. For crops grown more widely in the nation California farmers depend upon seasonal "gaps" elsewhere. Thus the Golden State is the chief supplier of the nation's late-spring potatoes while accounting for only a modest share of the total national potato production annually. The rigorously commercialized nature of fruit and vegetable marketing has stimulated grower organization to achieve quality control and operating efficiencies. California agriculture is noted especially for its use of growers' marketing associations, farmers' cooperative bargaining associations, and government marketing orders as well as corporate-like groups and other grower-shipper combinations. Since the 1930's the federal government has been an important "consumer" of California agriculture—both directly and indirectly. Price supports and other direct payments relate specifically to production of cotton, rice, wheat, barley, hops, flaxseed, sugar beets, and dry beans—the list is variable in time. Federal acreage controls also affect other crops, such as alfalfa, which are voluntarily expanded and contracted with the directly controlled crops. Federal tariff policies, size-quality standards, and subsidy for overseas exports form important but fluctuating influences on the composition of California agriculture.

COMMODITIES

California agriculture is legendary for the variety of its products. Many of its crops are unique in the nation, while most commodities raised elsewhere in the United States are grown also in the Golden State. Among the nation's major crops *only* tobacco, soybeans, and peanuts are *insignificant* here. And the variety of California commodities is ever enlarging. Since 1955 the State Agricultural Extension Service has added twenty items to its list of "commercial crops . . . produced in considerable volume," bringing the total to 289. From another vantage the trend is toward lesser diversity. Since 1940 cattle and cotton have accounted for greatly expanded shares of farm output; if market milk is added, these three ranking commodities alone account for over 40 percent of California's farm income in comparison to 24 percent in 1940. No other individual item totals more than 5 percent of the state's agricultural income; hence a grouping of similar products is essential for a comprehensive overview of California land-use. In order of value, major groups are (1) livestock, (2) fruits, (3) vegetables, and (4) cotton.

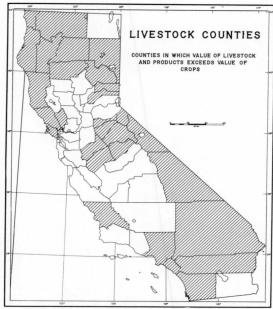

Fig. F-3. RELATIVE LIVESTOCK–CROP VALUES, BY COUNTY.

LIVESTOCK AND LIVESTOCK PRODUCTS

Fresh beef, milk, and eggs are increasingly consumed as California population expands; perishability, coupled with distance from the Middlewestern farm belt, has encouraged local production in increased volume. This circumstance applies to a lesser degree to many other livestock products. Feed production to support the additional livestock also increases, with more emphasis upon cultivated crops such as barley and irrigated hay; grazing lands reached their peak carrying capacity many years ago. By-products of California's abundant harvests of fruits, sugar beets, rice, cotton, and other crops have further encouraged the feeding of livestock concentrates.

Although much of California can be used to raise livestock, production is particularly dominant in two environments: (1) climatically handicapped and (2) urban fringes (Figs. F-2 and F-3). Income from livestock and products exceeds crops in nearly half the state's counties, many with habitats too cold or too rugged for high-value cropping—"cultivated land" there commonly is devoted to growth of supplemental feed. By contrast districts peripheral to large cities, where smaller poultry, dairy, and cattle feeding establishments abound, are supported from feeds from less congested localities. Between these two environmental extremes are the rich cultivated valleys such as Imperial, Salinas, and San Joaquin where high-value export crops normally take precedence. These lowlands generally have greater livestock emphasis on beef cattle and sheep feeding, manufacturing milk, and turkey and broiler raising than do the metropolitan fringes where fresh milk and eggs are dominant.

FRUITS AND NUTS

Orchard and vineyard products, although still a major component of California agriculture, have diminished relatively since the 1930's. Bearing acreage reached its peak in 1929, and 1945 was the year of maximum production. Marketing is hampered by the delay between planting and the first harvest and by inflexible production from year to year; cycles of overplanting and resultant bust-boom conditions have been characteristic. Specific setbacks have resulted from loss of overseas markets for raisins and other dried fruits, Florida's output of citrus concentrations (especially frozen orange juice), and urbanization of prune, apricot, and citrus orchards. Some fruits and nuts have been expanding significantly; among them have been walnuts, almonds, plums, cling peaches, and grapes.

It was noted earlier that orchards and vineyards were the support of earlier irrigation agriculture. They were located where soils, climate, and water supply were superior—especially on gently sloping alluvial plains of the eastern Central Valley and in many outer lowlands from the Russian River Valley to San Diego County (Fig. F-4). Anchored by superior incomes and perhaps by sheer inertia, and constituting a way of life, these well-established orchards and vineyards have persisted in their location despite California's shifting agricultural emphasis.

Within major fruit districts of the state individual crops tend to be strongly localized,

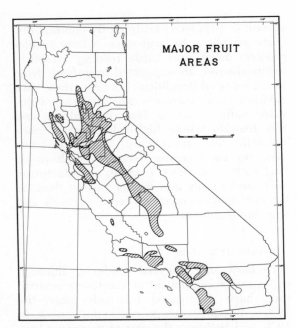

Fig. F-4. MAJOR FRUIT AREAS.

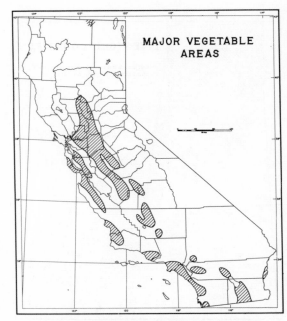

Fig. F-5. MAJOR VEGETABLE AREAS.

particularly because of microclimates. Examples include peaches in the Feather River Valley, the Modesto District, and the Kaweah Delta (Fig. 9-15); raisins around Fresno; figs near Fresno and Merced (Fig. 9-31); olives around Corning, Oroville, and Lindsay (Fig. 9-35); apricots, prunes, and plums in the Santa Clara Valley (Figs. 8-11 and 8-13); cherries around San Jose and Stockton (Fig. 9-24); lemons in Santa Barbara, Ventura, and San Diego counties (Fig. 7-45); pears in the Sierra Nevada foothills and dates in the Coachella Valley. These areal specializations permit more efficient use of harvest, processing, and shipping facilities, which are complex and expensive for many fruits and nuts.

VEGETABLES

California vegetable growing has traditionally been surpassed by fruit raising; however, expansion in recent decades has notably reduced this difference. The vegetable group consists essentially of annual perishable crops. Production is carefully timed to marketing; hence important melon and potato crops are included with this heterogeneous category. Export value of fresh vegetables now nearly

doubles that of fresh fruits. Besides primary dependence upon out-of-state consumption and perishability, vegetables share other traits with the fruits: climatic sensitivity, intensive application of labor and high output per acre, and variety of crops that compose the group. Tomatoes and lettuce are dominant and account for nearly 40 percent of vegetable value and acreage. A partial listing of California's contribution to the nation's fresh produce supply reflects the diversity: 100 percent of the artichokes and garlic; 88 percent of the Brussels sprouts; 63 percent of the lettuce; 62 percent of the broccoli; 55 percent of the celery; 45 percent of the cauliflower; 43 percent of the asparagus; 42 percent of the cantaloupes; and 41 percent of the carrots.

Vegetable farming in California is notable for its proportion of smaller properties. The 38 percent of vegetable farms with less than 50 acres prevails on expensive lands fringing urban areas; some are so small that horses are still used. Nearly the same proportion of vegetable farms are single-family operations without additional labor. The third of the growers belonging to minority ethnic groups include many Japanese who returned to this pursuit after their temporary eviction during World War II. High tenancy forms another distinctive feature of California truck farming: nearly 30 percent of the operators rent; another 40 percent are only part owners. Renting, quite common with larger operations, reflects "newness" and the desire of many growers to retain utmost year-to-year flexibility of activity. Production for processing or for fresh export to distant markets originates on larger units sufficiently removed from metropolitan areas to reduce land costs appreciably.

Vegetables are grown widely in milder winter districts of California (Figs. 9-37 and F-5). Districts of fruit and vegetable production tend to coincide, but locally vegetables are usually relegated to lower-lying (heavier) soils. On expanding urban peripheries, however, truck crops often persist long after orchard displacement. The season of harvest is often the crucial location factor. Thus potatoes are raised in such climatically different districts as Tule Lake and the Salinas Valley (Fig. 9-45), broccoli along the Santa Cruz Coast and in Imperial Valley, and tomatoes in the Sacramento Valley and the San Diego Coast—*at different seasons*. Lettuce is harvested throughout the year somewhere in California (Fig. 8-9). For many crops localities are selected whose climate favors harvest during the slack seasons elsewhere in the nation, as was noted earlier with potatoes.

A fifth of California's vegetables are processed locally and assembly of such materials as water, sugar, and containers, availability of labor, disposal of waste, and momentum of early start are major locational considerations. Vegetables for processing tend to be raised near factories that consume them—historically around the Bay Area and in adjacent sections of the Great Central Valley. For these crops, notably asparagus and summer tomatoes, successful out-of-state sale depends more on high yields, over-all production efficiency, and "brand names" than upon harvest season.

COTTON

This commodity has increased spectacularly since World War II to become California's leading crop in value. Despite its varied usage, the bulk of production is shipped to eastern textile mills after local ginning and compressing. Cotton has been a federally supported crop since the 1930's; yet its production in California expanded earlier, stimulated by growing industrial consumption and high Golden State yields. In recent years, federal quotas, established on state-by-state basis reflecting historic acreage, coupled with the support-price system that helps sustain marginal farmers in the South, has delayed more rapid expansion in California. Availability of virgin lands with level surfaces, in huge parcels suited to mechanized harvest, has given California major competitive advantages. Storability helps minimize isolation from eastern consumers.

Cotton is strongly localized, with definite climatic limitations outside the southern San Joaquin Valley and the southeastern desert (Figs. F-2 and 9-39). In both areas introduction of cotton was favored by abundance of relatively cheap land; subsequent competition from high-value vegetables has hampered continued expansion in the Imperial Valley. In the San Joaquin, cotton tends to be "king"— other products commonly are subordinate even if important. Feeds like barley and alfalfa, and to a lesser extent vegetables, are commonly associated "cotton-belt" filler crops, which help to defray investment in irrigation facilities, improve the soil, and provide alternative income in years when cotton quotas are reduced. Cattle feeding, another common enterprise in cotton districts, reflects the presence of abundant feeds. Cotton farms average 400 acres; however, 140 properties exceed 2000 acres—the initial cost of deep-well irrigation in the western San Joaquin Valley favors large-scale operations.

Products unrelated to the four groups just described furnish a tenth of California's farm income. They include the expanding cut-flower gardening, traditionally confined to coastal valleys, particularly near San Francisco and Los Angeles markets; rice, associated with water-plentiful bottomlands of the Great Central Valley (Fig. 9-11); and sugar beets (Fig. 9-8), an expanding crop since the 1920's which reflects locations of expensive refineries in the Imperial, Santa Maria, Salinas, San Joaquin, and Sacramento valleys.

BIBLIOGRAPHY

Compilation of a bibliography of the Golden State is a bewildering and frustrating task; thousands of books and articles have been written about California. Much geographic investigation, in the form of graduate studies, remains unpublished.

The following abbreviations have been used with bibliographic items:

AAAG	Annals of the Association of American Geographers
ACE	U. S. Army Corps of Engineers
AGS	American Geographical Society
ACSC	Automobile Club of Southern California
BCCGT	Bulletin, California Council of Geography Teachers
CA	California Agriculture
CDMG	California Division of Mines and Geology
CDWR	California Department of Water Resources
CF	California Farmer
CG	The California Geographer

The bibliography has been reviewed by Clarence F. McIntosh, Chico State College.

CHS	California Historical Society
CSAA	California State Automobile Association
CSCC	California State Chamber of Commerce
CSC	Chico State College
CWRB	California Water Resources Board
EG	Economic Geography
GPO	Government Printing Office, Washington, D. C.
GR	Geographical Review
H	Holiday magazine
HF	Haynes Foundation, Los Angeles
HL	Huntington Library, San Marino
JG	Journal of Geography
LPC	Lane Publishing Company, Menlo Park
M	Motorland magazine
MA	unpublished Master of Arts thesis
MIS	Mineral Information Service
MWR	Monthly Weather Review
NGM	National Geographic Magazine
PB	Pacific Books, Palo Alto
PD	Pacific Discovery
PG	The Professional Geographer
Ph.D.	unpublished Ph.D. dissertation
PHR	Pacific Historical Review
PS,FRES	Pacific Southwest, Forest Range and Experiment Station, Berkeley

RPC	Roberts Publishing Company, Northridge, California
S	Sunset magazine
SC	Sierra Club, San Francisco
SFNB	Security First National Bank, Los Angeles
SPP	San Pascual Press, Pasadena
SSR	Sociology and Social Research
SU	Stanford University
SUP	Stanford University Press
TITC	Title Insurance and Trust Company, Los Angeles
UC	University of California, Berkeley
UCLA	University of California, Los Angeles

UC,AES	University of California, Agricultural Experiment Station
UCP	University of California Press
UCPG	University of California, Publications in Geography
USDA	United States Department of Agriculture
USFS	United States Forest Service
USGS	United States Geological Survey
W	Westways magazine
WSP	Water-Supply Paper
YAPCG	Yearbook, Association of Pacific Coast Geographers

GENERAL SOURCES

Material appears regularly in the metropolitan newspapers and magazines (see *Readers' Guide*). *California State Publications* (issued monthly and annually) is voluminous. *Westways* (predecessor: *Touring Topics*), *Motorland,* and *Sunset* regularly provide timely articles. L. C. Powell describes new publications in his column "Western Books and Writers" in *Westways. Current Geographical Publications* (AGS) lists California items.

GENERAL WORKS

Several college-level geographic textbooks have been published. C. M. Zierer, editor, and thirty-one collaborators, *California and the Southwest* (Wiley, 1956), is systematic as is R. W. Durrenberger, *The Geography of California in Essays and Readings* (RPC, 1959), which also has short regional sections. P. F. Griffin and R. N. Young, *California, the New Empire State* (Fearon, 1957), is regional. D. W. Lantis, *California* (Doubleday, 1958), and I. Stone *et al.*, "The Call of California," *Life* (Oct. 19, 1962, entire issue) reflect the continued outpouring of shorter and more popular accounts. Geographically oriented are C. McWilliams, *California: The Great Exception* (Wyn, 1949), and W. W. Robinson, *Land in California* (UCP, 1948).

"Classic" guidebooks include A. Drury, *California, an Intimate Guide* (Harper, 1947), and Federal Writers' Project, *California, A Guide to the Golden State* (Hastings House, rev., 1954). More recent are Sunset Books' *Northern California* and *Southern California* (LPC, both 1959); A. Hepburn, *Complete Guide to Northern California* and *Complete Guide to Southern California* (Doubleday, both 1962); and *California-Nevada Tour Book* (American Automobile Association, annual revisions).

Also helpful are *California Statistical Abstract* (California Economic Development Agency, Sacramento, 1961) and *California Blue Book* (State Printer, Sacramento, annual)—the latter adds a section "Economic Survey of California" every fourth year, also published separately by CSCC; and A. Stone, ed., *California Information Almanac* (California Almanac Co., Lakewood), issued intermittently since 1947.

Political aspects are found in such materials as W. W. Crouch *et al.*, *California Government and Politics* (Prentice-Hall, 1956); B. L. Hyink *et al.*, *Politics and Government in California* (Crowell, 1959); H. A. Turner and J. A. Vieg, *The Government and Politics of California* (McGraw-Hill, 1960).

MAPS AND ATLASES

Complete large-scale map coverage is provided by the thirty sheets compiled by Army Map Service, 1942-1958, published by USGS. Hundreds of larger-scale topographic quadrangles are published by USGS. ACSC and CSAA publish numerous local-area highway maps. The standard geographical atlas is R. W. Durrenberger, *Patterns on the Land* (RPC, 1960). Map listings are found in *Sources of California Maps* (CSCC, 1961); E. L. Chapin, Jr., *A Selected Bibliography of Southern California Maps* (UCP, 1953); and C. I. Wheat, *Mapping the Transmississippi West, 1540-1861* (Institute of Historical Cartography, San Francisco, 1957), 5 vols.

PHYSICAL ENVIRONMENT
CLIMATE

For "feeling," read G. R. Stewart, *Storm* (Modern Library, 1947). Statistical data include *Cli-*

mate and Man, Yearbook for 1941 (USDA); U.S. Weather Bureau, Climates of the States: California, in series, "Climatography of the United States," no. 60-4 (GPO, Dec. 1959), and Climatic Summary of the United States—Supplement for 1931 through 1952. California, in series, "Climatography of the United States," no. 11-4 (GPO, reprinted 1958).

The Köppen system is presented by R. J. Russell, "Climates of California," UCPG, 2:2 (1926, reprinted 1938), 73-84. See also P. Meigs III, Climates of California, "Science Guide for Elementary Schools," vol. 5 (California Dept. of Education, 1938); Durrenberger, op. cit., general sources; and C. Patton, "The Climates of California According to C. Warren Thornthwaite's Classification of 1948" MA (UC, 1951).

Other references include Chap. 4, in Zierer, op. cit., general sources; J. Kesseli, "The Climates of California According to the Köppen Classification," GR, 32 (1942), 476-480; H. P. Bailey, "Proposal for a Modification of Köppen's Definition of Dry Climates," YAPCG, 10 (1948), 33-38; M. H. Kimball and F. A. Brooks, "Plantclimates of California," CA (May 1959), 7-12; and H. R. Byers, "Characteristic Weather Phenomena of California," Mass. Instit. of Technology, Meteor. Papers, 1 (1931), 1-54.

LANDFORMS

The standard source is N. E. A. Hinds, Evolution of the California Landscape, Bull. 158 (CDMG, 1952). Still relevant is N. M. Fenneman, Physiography of Western United States (Wiley, 1931). The classic geology is R. Reed, Geology of California (Amer. Assn. Petroleum Geol., Tulsa, 1933, reprinted 1951). W. J. Miller, California Through the Ages (Westernlore, 1957) is more recent. For structure see A. J. Eardley, Structural Geology of North America (Harper and Row, 1951 and 1962). Publications of California Division of Mines and Geology contain related information, especially MIS (monthly) as do dozens of USGS bulletins and water-supply papers; consult Publications of the Geological Survey (GPO, 1963). Geologic Map of California (CDMG), twenty-seven sheets, is being prepared; initial sheets appeared in 1958. Under general sources see Durrenberger, op. cit., and Chap. 2 in Zierer, op. cit.

SOILS

Standard sources include R. E. Storie and W. W. Weir, Generalized Soil Map of California, manual 6, with map (UC,AES, 1953), and R.

E. Storie, Revision of Soil-Rating Chart, UC,AES, leaflet 122 (1959); also see Chap. 6, in Zierer, op. cit., general sources, and H. Jenny et al., "Exploring the Soils of California," Bull. 155 (CDMG, 1951). Land-capability classification with map is given in L. R. Wohletz and E. F. Dolder, Know California's Land (Calif. Dept. of Natural Resources and U.S. Soil Conservation Service, 1952). The Soil Conservation Service (USDA) has prepared Soil Surveys for many areas of California—some in collaboration with UC,AES.

VEGETATION

Descriptions of vegetation types are presented in Durrenberger, op. cit., and Chap. 7 in Zierer, op. cit., general sources. The standard reference map of vegetation is Vegetation Types of California (Calif. Forest and Range Experiment Station, Berkeley, 1945). H. A. Jensen included this map in "A System for Classifying Vegetation in California," Calif. Fish and Game, 33 (Oct. 1947), 199-266. Basic manuals of botany are W. L. Jepson, A Manual of the Flowering Plants of California (Student Bookstore, UC, 1923) and P. Munz and D. D. Keck, A California Flora (UCP, 1959). A map of forest types, Timber Croplands of California, was issued by USFS (PS,FRES, Jan. 1945). L. T. Burcham, California Range Lands (Calif. Div. of Forestry, 1957) has good information about vegetation distribution.

WATER RESOURCES

C. F. Cole, "California's Water Requirements," JG, 59 (1960), 268-270, is succinct. More exhaustive is S. T. Harding, Water in California (N. P. Publications, Palo Alto, 1960). See The California Water Plan, Bull. 3 (1957) and other publications of CDWR; also W. A. Hutchins (Calif. State Engineer), The California Law of Water Rights (Sacramento, 1956) and Water Resources Development in California (ACE, San Francisco, 1959).

POPULATION

Statistics come from United States Census of Population, 1960: California (U.S. Bureau of the Census, 1961), especially sections entitled "Number of Inhabitants," "General Population Characteristics," and "General Social and Economic Characteristics."

A comprehensive study of California population is W. S. Thompson's *Growth and Changes in California's Population* (HF, 1955), summarized as *Californians—Who, Whence, Whither* by Kathleen Doyle in 1956. Growth and migration is described by M. S. Gordon, *Employment and Population Growth* (UCP, 1954). "Farm Population of California" is described by V. Fuller, CA (Nov. and Dec. 1954; Jan. 1955). A recent appraisal is H. F. Gregor's "Spatial Disharmonies in California Population Growth," GR, 53 (Jan. 1963), 100-122.

On statewide distribution: W. C. Calef, "The Distribution of the Population of California, 1940" MA (UCLA, 1942); J. E. Trotter, "Distribution of Population in California in 1950" MA (U. of Chicago, 1953); and "The Population of California: 1950-1961," Karinen and Lantis, abstracted in AAAG, 51 (Dec. 1961), 413-414.

HISTORY

A voluminous literature has been written on California history. The "classic" is H. H. Bancroft, *History of California* (San Francisco, 1884-1890, 7 vols.). Standard one-volume works include J. W. Caughey, *California* (Prentice-Hall, second edition, 1953), and Andrew F. Rolle, *California, A History* (Crowell, 1963); both contain well-selected bibliographies. The two volumes by R. G. Cleland, *From Wilderness to Empire, A History of California, 1542-1900* (Knopf, 1944) and *California in Our Time, 1900-1940* (Knopf, 1947) are well known. Regular additions to the literature appear in PHR, CHS *Quarterly* and the *Historical Society of Southern California's Publications* and *Quarterly*. A number of local historical societies also contribute many additions. Many histories of individual counties have been prepared; some are cited with chapter bibliographies.

For local orientation see M. B. Hoover, H. E. and E. G. Rensch, *Historic Spots in California* (SUP, rev., 1948); E. G. Gudde, *California Place Names* (UCP, rev., 1960); and R. L. Gentilcore, "Missions and Mission Lands of Alta California," AAAG, 51 (March 1961), 46-72.

ECONOMIC ASPECTS

Much economic information is found on the financial pages of daily newspapers, national news magazines, and annual reports of corporations. See R. K. Arnold, *The California Economy, 1947-1980* (Stanford Research Institute, 1960), and business reviews, such as *Monthly Summary of Business Conditions in Southern California* (SFNB), *Business Review* (Wells Fargo Bank, San Francisco), and *Monthly Review* (Federal Reserve Bank of San Francisco). Many trade journals give pertinent information. See also *Western Resources Handbook* (Stanford Research Institute, 1957).

FORESTRY

The USFS–PS,FRES publishes regular literature on this topic. See Chap. 18, in Zierer, *op. cit.*, general sources. Such trade organizations as the California Redwood Association (San Francisco) and Western Pine Association (Portland, Ore.) are helpful. See also S. T. Dana and M. Krueger, *California Lands* (American Forestry Assn., 1958).

MINING

The publications of the CDMG are basic, especially the monthly MIS and *Mineral Commodities of California, Bull.* 176 (1957).

AGRICULTURE

A standard reference is C. B. Hutchison, *California Agriculture* (UCP, 1946). Among publications of the Division of Agricultural Sciences, University of California, sources include *Trends for Major California Crops, Circular* 488 (1960), by G. W. Dean and C. O. McCorkle, Jr.; A. Shultis, *Farming in California, Circular* 474 (1959); G. W. Dean and C. O. McCorkle, Jr., *Projections Relating to California Agriculture in 1975, Bull.* 778 (1961); and the earlier *Types of Farming in California, Analyzed by Enterprises,* by L. A. Crawford and E. Hurd, Bull. 654 (1941). The UC, Division of Agricultural Sciences, has a monthly journal, CA. See farm magazines, *California Farmer* and *California Farm Bureau Monthly* (Berkeley). Also recommended are the Annual Reports assembled by county Agricultural Commissioners. See also H. F. Gregor, "The Geographic Dynamism of California Market Gardening," YAPCG, 18 (1956), 28-35, and "Local-Supply Agriculture of California," AAAG, 47 (Sept. 1957), 267-276.

FISHING

The recommended source is the California Department of Fish and Game, and its publication, *California Fish and Game.* An older source is C.

M. Zierer, "The Fishery Industry in California," *Scot. Geog. Mag.*, 51 (March 1935), 65-83.

MANUFACTURING

Geographic sources include J. J. Parsons, "California Manufacturing," GR, 39 (1949), 229-241, and several chapters in Zierer, *op. cit.*, general sources. Current magazines contain a plethora of articles; an example is J. Fischer, "Money Bait," *Harper's* (Sept. 1961), 10-16, on "growth" industries. Studies of corporations include C. M. Coleman, *P. G. and E. of California* (McGraw-Hill, 1952), and M. and B. R. James, *Biography of a Bank: The Story of Bank of America, NT and SA* (Harper, 1954).

TRANSPORTATION

See appropriate chapters (30 and 31) in Zierer, *op. cit.*, general sources, and *California Highways and Public Works*. Evolution of highways is reviewed in W (Dec. 1950) and by B. Blow, *California Highways* (Crocker, San Francisco, 1920). *The Southern Pacific's First Century* (Southern Pacific Public Relations Department, San Francisco, 1955) gives a brief account. See also M. Armitage, *Operations Santa Fe; Atchison, Topeka, and Santa Fe Railway System* (Duell, Sloan and Pearce, 1948). On air transport, see outdated *California Airports* (Calif. State Reconstruction and Re-Employment Commission, Sacramento, 1947).

TOURISM

See Chap. 23, in Zierer, *op. cit.*, general sources, and C. M. Zierer, "Tourism and Recreation in the West," GR, 42 (1952), 462-481, and a two-volume study, *California Public Outdoor Recreation Plan* (Sacramento, 1960). Lane's *State Parks of California* (LPC, 1961) provides an account of these facilities. See also K. Decker, *The Tourist Industry in California* (UC, Bureau of Public Administration, 1955). W. F. Heald, "Motoring under the Arc of the Fabulous Southwest," W (Sept. 1953, entire issue), describes favorite spots; see also *Public Campgrounds on the National Forests in California* (USFS, 1960).

CULTURE

Literature on this subject is so diverse that it becomes difficult to cite most appropriate examples. See J. W. Caughey, "California in Third Dimension," PHR, 28 (May 1959), 111-129, and

J. and L. R. Caughey, *California Heritage* (Ward Ritchie Press, Los Angeles, 1962). Also F. Walker, *San Francisco's Literary Frontier* (Knopf, 1939), and *A Literary History of Southern California* (UCP, 1950). M. Nishi's Ph.D, "Changing Occupance of the Japanese in Los Angeles County" (U. of Washington, 1955), is concerned with a specific group. C. Lindsay, *The Natives are Restless* (New York, 1960), scoffs at Southern California culture in general.

The California Indian has been relatively well investigated; the classic work is A. L. Kroeber, *Handbook of the Indians of California* (*Bull.* 78, Bur. of Amer. Ethnol., Smithsonian Institute; lithograph reprint by California Book Company, Berkeley, 1953). More recent are Chap. 10, Zierer, *op. cit.*, general sources; R. F. Heizer and M. A. Whipple, *The California Indians: A Source Book* (UCP, 1951); and *Indians of California* (American Friends Service Committee, San Francisco, 1957).

THE NORTHEAST (CHAPTER 1)

The environment has been investigated by M. A. Peacock, "The Modoc Lava Field, Northern California," GR, 21 (1931), 259-276; R. J. Russell "The Landforms of Surprise Valley," UCPG, 2 (1926), 323-358; *Anon.*, "Geology of Northeastern California," MIS, 12 (June 1959), 1-7; and H. Williams, *Geology of the Macdoel Quadrangle, Bull.* 151, CDMG (1949).

W. N. Davis, Jr., "California East of the Sierra: A Study in Economic Sectionalism," Ph.D (UC, 1942), and two recent geographic studies enrich the literature: R. W. Pease, "Geography of Modoc County, California, Past, Present and Future," Ph.D (UCLA, 1960), to appear in UCPG, and R. Middleton, "Honey Lake Basin, Ecumene of Northeast California," MA (CSC, in progress, 1963).

Also see B. E. Thomas, in "The California-Nevada Boundary," AAAG, 42 (March 1952), 51-68; *Northeastern Counties Investigation, Bull.* 58 (CDWR, June 1960); A. Powers, *Redwood Country* (Duell, Sloan and Pearce, 1949), espec. 189-194 and 283-284; G. Wilson *et al.*, *Drainage-Salinity Investigation of the Tulelake Lease Lands*, UC,AES, *Bull.* 779 (1961); and R. H. May and W. F. Heald, "California's Hidden Mountains," PD, 15 (Jan.-Feb. 1962), 22-26.

THE TRANS-SIERRA
(CHAPTER 2)

The lure of Death Valley accounts for an impressive literature. Geographers have contributed R. M. Glendinning, "The Role of Death Valley," EG, 16 (1940), 299-311, and A. Court, "How Hot is Death Valley?" GR, 39 (April 1949), 214-220. Other sources include W. A. Chalfant, *Death Valley, the Facts* (SUP, 1951); G. P. Putnam, *Death Valley and Its Country* (Duell, Sloan and Pearce, 1946); J. Schaefer, "Death Valley," H, 28 (Aug. 1960), 44ff; Federal Writers' Project, *Death Valley* (Houghton Mifflin, 1939); *Anon.*, "Death Valley," MIS, 11 (Oct. 1958), 1-9; and R. Kirk, *Exploring Death Valley* (SUP), 1956.

Sources on mining include W. E. Ver Planck, "Soda Ash Industry of Owens Lake, 1887-1959," MIS, 12 (Oct. 1959), 1-6, and *Anon.*, "Bishop District, California," MIS, 10 (Sept. 1957), 1-4.

Owens Valley has been described by R. E. Baugh, "Changes in Land Utilization in the Bishop Area, Owens Valley, California," EG, 13 (1937), 17-34, and by D. L. Goldman, "Owens Valley and Its Water," MA (UCLA, 1961). W. A. Chalfant tells *The Story of Inyo* (Chalfant, Bishop, rev. 1933); see also R. Nadeau, *The Water Seekers* (Doubleday, 1950), 21-115.

Fringe-area investigations include E. W. Kersten, Jr., "Settlements and Economic Life in the Walker River Country of California and Nevada," Ph.D (U. of Nebraska, 1961); C. B. Beaty, "Gradational Processes in the White Mountains of California and Nevada" Ph.D (UC, 1960); and E. M. Cain, *The Story of Bodie* (Fearon, 1956).

THE MOJAVE DESERT
(CHAPTER 3)

For impression, read E. Corle, *Desert Country* (Duell, Sloan and Pearce, 1941).

Landforms are described by D. F. Hewett, Chap. 2, 5-20, in R. H. Jahns, ed., *Geology of Southern California, Bull.* 170, Pt. I (CDMG, 1954); D. G. Thompson, *The Mohave Desert Region, California,* WSP 578 (USGS, 1929); and R. P. Blanc and G. B. Cleveland, "Pleistocene Lakes of Southeastern California," MIS, 14 (April and May 1961), 1-8 and 1-6. Local climatic investigation is given by R. F. Logan, "Winter Tem-

peratures of a Mid-Latitude Desert Mountain Range," GR, 51 (1961), 236-252. For wild animals see Chap. 8, Zierer, *op. cit.*, general sources. See also M. E. Parsons, *The Wild Flowers of California* (California Academy of Sciences, San Francisco, 1955). For over-all physical presentation, E. C. Jaeger, *The California Deserts* (SUP, 3rd ed., 1955).

On mining see W. F. Foshag, "Saline Lakes of the Mohave Desert Region," *Econ. Geology,* 21 (1926), 56-64; W. Calef, "The Salines of Southeastern California," EG, 27 (1951), 43-64; *Anon.*, "Element of Tomorrow," *Time* (June 10, 1957), 88-89; *Anon.*, "Boron," MIS, 10 (Oct. 1957), 1-5; F. J. Taylor, "World's Richest Mineral Stock Pile," *Saturday Even. Post* (March 5, 1949), 26-27ff; M. R. Wynn, *Desert Bonanza* (M. W. Samelson, Culver City, Calif., 1949); *Anon.*, "Potash," MIS, 11 (April 1958), 1-6; O. E. Bowen and C. H. Gray, Jr., "The Portland Cement Industry in California—1962," MIS, 15 (July and Aug. 1962), 1-7 and 1-11; and W. E. Ver Planck, "History of Mining in Northeastern San Bernardino County," MIS, 14 (Sept. 1961), 1-8.

For water problem see J. H. Snyder, *Ground-Water Overdraft in Antelope Valley* (UC, Ground Water Studies, Giannini Foundation, no. 2); *Mojave River, California* ACE (86th Cong., 1st Sess., HD 164, 1959); and E. Hyatt, *Mojave River Investigation* (CDWR, Bull. 47, 1934).

Graduate research in geography includes R. E. Baugh, "The Antelope Valley," Ph.D (Clark U., 1926); J. J. Garrison, "An Analysis of the Livelihood Pattern of the Mojave Desert," Ph.D (UCLA, 1960); K. W. Rumage, "The Palo Verde Valley—A Geographic Analysis of Land-Use Development in the Lower Colorado River Valley, California," Ph.D (UCLA, 1956); and C. G. Lade, Jr., "Lucerne Valley, California—Agricultural Land Use as Related to the Physical Setting," MA (UCLA, 1953).

On changing and expanding use see R. F. Logan, "The Shifting Patterns of Travel in the Southwest Deserts" (abstract), AAAG, 45 (June 1955), 199, and "Suburbia in the Desert" (abstract), AAAG, 46 (June 1956), 259; K. R. Schneider, "Urbanization in the California Desert: Signs of Ultimate Dispersion," *Jour., Amer. Instit. of Planners,* 28 (Feb. 1962), 18-23; E. C. Jaeger, "Monument of the Joshuas," PD, 8 (May-June 1955), 10-21; H. C. James, "Our Deserts Are Not Expendible," *Nature Mag.,* 48 (Nov. 1955), 482-484ff; and J. Garrison, "Barstow, California: A Transportation Focus in a Desert Environment," EG, 29 (April 1953), 159-167.

For specific areas see L. R. O'Neal, *A Peculiar Piece of Desert* (Westernlore, 1957); *Anon., The Antelope Valley* (Southern California Edison Co., Los Angeles 1961); and J. Ball, Jr., *Edwards: Flight Test Center of the U.S.A.F.* (Duell, Sloan and Pearce, 1962).

THE COLORADO DESERT (CHAPTER 4)

Scope of the literature is suggested by E. I. Edwards, *Desert Voices: A Descriptive Bibliography* (Westernlore, 1958).

On environment see T. W. Dibblee, Jr., "Geology of the Imperial Valley Region, California," 21-28, in R. H. Jahns, ed., *Geology of Southern California, Vol. 1, Bull.* 170 (CDMG, 1954); J. S. Brown, *The Salton Sea Region, California,* USGS (WSP 497, 1923); K. Bryan, "Physiographic Study in the Salton Sea Region," GR, 21 (April 1931), 153; F. B. Kniffen, "The Natural Landscape of the Colorado Delta," UCPG, 5 (1932); F. Shreve, *Vegetation of the Sonoran Desert* (Carnegie Institute of Washington, 1951); and G. Sykes, "The Delta and Estuary of the Colorado River," GR, 16 (April 1926), 232-255.

Sources on floods and watering the Desert include P. L. Kleinsorge, *The Boulder Canyon Project. Historical and Economic Aspects* (SUP, 1941); R. A. Nadeau, *The Water Seekers* (Doubleday, 1950), 137-281; H. T. Cory, *Imperial Valley and the Salton Sea* (1907); W. L. Thomas, Jr., "Competition for a Desert Lake: the Salton Sea, California," CG, 2 (1961), 31-40; and *The Colorado River* (U.S. Dept. of Interior, Washington, 1946).

Graduate research in geography includes R. A. Kennelly, "The California-Mexico Boundary as a Factor in Areal Differentiation," MA (State U. of Iowa, 1950); R. W. Stanley, "Political Geography of the Yuma Border District," Ph.D (UCLA, 1954); P. G. Curti, "The Borrego Valley, California: The Birth of a Desert Community," MA (UCLA, 1955); T. H. Mahmud, "Processing and Marketing Aspects of the Date Industry in the Coachella Valley, California," MA (UCLA, 1958); H. H. Blossom, "Agricultural Development of the Coachella Valley," MA (UC, 1959); W. I. Darnell, "The Imperial Valley: Its Physical and Cultural Geography," MA (San Diego State College, 1959); T. A. Jensen, "Palm Springs, California, Its Evolution and Function,"

MA (UCLA, 1954); J. M. Khalaf, "The Water Resources of the Lower Colorado Basin," Ph.D (U. of Chicago, 1951); and F. B. Kniffen, "The Delta Country of the Colorado," Ph.D (UC, 1930).

O. B. Tout describes settlement in *The First Thirty Years* (1931). A more recent impression is C. H. Steere, *Imperial and Coachella Valleys* (SUP, 1953); see also R. M. Glendinning, "Desert Contrasts Illustrated by the Coachella Valley," GR, 39 (1949), 221-229.

On farming see N. L. McFarlane *et al., California Desert Agriculture* (UC,AES, circ. 464, 1957); H. F. Gregor, "An Evaluation of Oasis Agriculture," YAPCG, 21 (1959), 39-50; R. A. Kennelly, "Cattle Feeding in the Imperial Valley," YAPCG, 22 (1960), 50-56; and G. D. Peterson, Jr., *et al.,* in *Cotton Production in the Lower Desert Valleys of California* (UC,AES, circ. 508, 1962). On agricultural labor see P. S. Taylor, *Mexican Labor in the United States* (UCP, 1928-1934), and E. C. McDonagh, "Attitudes towards Ethnic Farm Workers in the Coachella Valley," SSR 40 (Sept.-Oct. 1955), 10-18.

For recreational aspects see H. Parker, *Anza-Borrego Desert Guide Book* (Desert Magazine Press, Palm Desert, 1957); R. Carson, "The Bountiful Desert of California," H (Feb. 1962), 66-74; and M. Sutherland, "Californians Escape to the Desert," NGM (Nov. 1957), 675-724.

THE SIERRA NEVADA (CHAPTER 5)

R. Peattie, ed., *The Sierra Nevada: The Range of Light* (Vanguard, 1947) whets one's enthusiasm, as do J. R. Challacombe, "The Fabulous Sierra Nevada," NGM, 105 (1954), 825-844, and W. Stegner, "America's Mightiest Playground," H (July 1956), 35-43ff. See also W. S. Lee, *The Sierra* (Putnam's, 1961).

Environmental studies include T. I. Storer and R. L. Usinger, *Sierra Nevada Natural History* (UCP, 1963); F. E. Matthes, "Reconnaissance of the Geomorphology and Glacial Geology of San Juan Basin, Sierra Nevada, California" (USGS, *Prof. Paper* 329, 1960); J. E. Kesseli, "Studies in the Pleistocene Glaciation of the Sierra Nevada, California," UCPG, 6-8 (1941), 315-362; D. H. Miller, "Snow Cover and Climate in the Sierra Nevada, California," UCPG, 11 (1955), 1-218; and *Survey of Mountainous Areas* (CDWR, Bull.

56, 1955), 16-24. A classic is J. Muir, *The Mountains of California* (Century, 1894); for an appreciation of Muir, see J. Leighly, "John Muir's Image of the West," AAAG, 48 (Dec. 1958), 309-318. See also M. Sprague, "Monthly and Seasonal Distribution of Snowfall in California," MWR, 62 (Dec. 1934), 438-481.

Transportation literature includes G. Stewart, *Donner Pass and Those Who Crossed It* (CHS, 1960), *Ordeal by Hunger* (Holt, 1936), and *The California Trail* (McGraw-Hill, 1962); O. Lewis, *The Big Four* (Knopf, 1938); R. L. Behme, "Keddie's Impossible Dream," W (Dec. 1958), 16-17; D. N. Deane, *Sierra Railway* (Howell-North, 1960); G. Stewart, *U.S. 40;* and C. J. Todd, "The Sierra Nevada: a Transportation Barrier," MA (UCLA, 1949).

Literature on the High Sierra includes *Sportsman's Atlas: The High Sierra and its Environs* (LPC, 1955); J. Wampler and W. Heald, *High Sierra Mountain Wonderland* (Wampler, Berkeley, 1960); P. E. Estes, "Recreational Uses of the High Sierra," MA (UCLA, 1953); J. Y. Vernon, "Recreation and Water Supply in the Upper Basin of the Tuolumne River, California," MA (UCLA, 1951); and D. R. Brower, "Sierra High Trip," NGM 105 (June 1954), 844-868. Guides include W. A. Starr, *Guide to the John Muir Trail* (SC, 5th ed., 1953); H. Voge, ed., *A Climber's Guide to the High Sierra* (SC, 1954); and D. R. Brower, ed., *Going Light—with backpack or burro* (SC, 1958).

Material on the Eastern Slope is less exhaustive; see D. Goldman, "Landscape, Water and Outdoor Recreation in the Eastern Sierra," CG, 3 (1962), 41-46; R. D. Orser, "The eastern slope of the high Sierra as a recreation area," MA (UC, 1961); and G. Schumacher *et al., The Mammoth Lakes Sierra* (SC, 1959).

Material on the Southern Prongs is limited; see A. Woodward, *The Story of El Tejon* (Los Angeles, 1942); H. O. Weight, "The Lost Gold of Havilah," W (Feb. 1957), 2-3; and P. and E. Jenkins in "Along the Forks of the Kern River," W (April 1957), 24-25.

Extensive writing on the Park Belt is evidenced in F. P. Farquhar, *Yosemite, The Big Trees and the High Sierra: A Selective Bibliography* (UCP, 1948); D. Yeager, *National Parks in California* (LPC, 1959); F. E. Matthes, *Sequoia National Park, a Geological Album* (UCP, 1956) and *The Incomparable Valley, A Geologic Interpretation of the Yosemite* (UCP, 1950); J. R. White, *Sequoia and the Kings Canyon National Parks* (SUP, 1954); W. Fry and J. R. White, *Big Trees* (SUP, 1938); J. M. Kauffmann, "Giant Sequoias Draw Millions to California Parks," NGM (Aug. 1959), 147-187; V. and A. Adams, *Yosemite Valley* (SUP, 1952); and C. P. Russell, *One Hundred Years in Yosemite* (UCP, 1947).

The Foothills has been well investigated, evidenced by C. I. Wheat, *Books of the California Gold Rush* (Colt Press, San Francisco, 1949) and *The Maps of the California Gold Region* (Grabhorn Press, San Francisco, 1942). See also R. E. Baugh, "Mother Lode, 1949," YAPCG, 11 (1949), 3-18; *Anon., Gold Rush Country* (LPC, 1957); *Geologic Guidebook along Highway 49—Sierran Gold Belt: The Mother Lode Country* (CDMG, Bull. 141, 1948); R. W. Paul, *California Gold* (Harvard U. Press, 1947); J. W. Caughey, *Gold is the Cornerstone* (UCP, 1948); and J. H. Jackson, *Anybody's Gold: the Story of California's Mining Towns* (Appleton-Century-Crofts, 1941). R. A. Rydell, *Cape Horn to the Pacific: the Rise and Decline of an Ocean Highway* (UCP, 1952), gets the miners to California; and J. A. McGowan, "Freighting to the Mines in California," Ph.D (UC, 1949), describes commerce into the Foothills. See also D. Teeguarden *et al., Timber Marketing and Land Ownership in the Central Sierra Nevada Region* (UC,AES, Bull. 774, 1960).

In the Northern Sierra best known and best investigated is the Donner-Tahoe area: *Anon.,* "Winter Sports," M (Jan.-Feb. 1961), 12-19; E. B. Scott, *The Saga of Lake Tahoe* (Sierra-Tahoe Pub. Co., Crystal Bay, Nev., 1957); and G. H. and B. M. Hinkle, *Sierra Nevada Lakes* (Bobbs-Merrill, 1949). D. R. Lane describes less well-known "Yuba River Region," M (Sept.-Oct. 1959), 12-17. Investigation of Paradise is presented by W. C. McKain, Jr., "The Social Participation of Old People in a California Retirement Community," Ph.D (Harvard U., 1947); see also R. Pillsbury, "The Apples of Paradise," senior thesis (CSC, 1962). Importance of water to foothill utilization is seen in K. Lucas, "A Study of Water Problems and Land Use of the Oroville-Wyandotte Irrigation District," MA (CSC, 1960). For agricultural utilization, D. Weeks *et al., Land Utilization in the Northern Sierra Nevada* (UCP, 1943).

On regional prospects see *Economic Potentials of the Sierra Nevada Mountain Counties* (California Senate, Fact-Finding Committee on Commerce and Economic Development, Sacramento, 1959).

THE SOUTHERN CASCADE
(CHAPTER 6)

The literature is modest. R. Peattie, ed., *The Cascade* (Vanguard), is more concerned with Oregon and Washington. See also A. Powers, *Redwood Country* (Duell, Sloan and Pearce, 1949), 157-167; R. O. and V. Case, *Lost Mountains: the Story of the Cascades* (Doubleday, Doran, 1945); *Northeastern Counties Investigation* (CDWR, *Bull.* 58, 1960).

The physical environment is described by J. S. Diller, "Volcanic History of Lassen Peak," *Science*, 43 (May 26, 1916), 727-733; H. Williams, "A recent volcanic eruption near Lassen Peak, California" (UC, Dept. Geolog. Sci., *Bull.* 17, 1928, 241-263); and "The history and character of volcanic domes" (UC, Dept. of Geolog. Sci., *Bull.*, 21, 1932, 51-146).

On other aspects see W. H. Hutchinson, *California Heritage, A History of Northern California Lumbering* (Diamond National, Chico, 1957); R. W. Cox, "Westwood, California," MA (UC, 1934); and L. J. Haueter, "Westwood, California: The Life and Death of a Lumbertown," MA (UC, 1956).

Geographic research includes V. G. Holbrook, "The Agricultural Geography of Shasta Valley," MA (U. of Oregon, 1955), and W. E. Scott, "The agricultural geography of Indian Valley, Plumas County, California," MA (CSC, 1953).

See also W. F. Heald, "The Fires of Lassen," PD (Jan.-Feb. 1962), 22-26, and H. Hayden, "Lakes of the Caribou," W (Feb. 1958), 20-21.

SOUTHERN CALIFORNIA
(CHAPTER 7)

Southern California constitutes a primary concentration of professional geographers within the United States, yet voids remain in the literature. Besides Chap. 1, 1-60, in Griffin and Young, *op. cit.*, general sources, approximations to comprehensive summations are W. L. Thomas, Jr., ed., *Man, Time, and Space in Southern California*, AAAG, *supplement*, 49:3 (Sept. 1959); and C. McWilliams, *Southern California Country* (Duell, Sloan and Pearce, 1946).

The most comprehensive geological survey has been cited: Jahns, ed., *Geology of Southern California*. Climatic investigations include H. C. Coffin, "Marine influence on the climate of Southern California in Summer," Ph.D (UC, 1961); A. Campbell, "The Santa Ana or Desert Winds," MWR, 34 (Oct. 1906), 465, and "Sonora Storms

and Sonora Clouds of California," MWR, 34 (Oct. 1906), 464-465; H. B. Lynch, *Rainfall and Stream Run-off in Southern California since 1769* (Metropolitan Water District, Los Angeles, 1931); L. Sergius, "The Santa Ana," *Weatherwise*, 5 (June 1952), 66-68; and F. A. Young, "Desert Winds in Southern California," MWR, 59 (Oct. 1931), 380-382.

For historical background see J. W. Caughey, *The Indians of Southern California in 1852* (Plantin Press, Los Angeles, 1952); R. G. Cleland, *The Cattle on a Thousand Hills* (HL, 1951); C. Nordhoff, *California: for Health, Pleasure and Residence* (Harper, 1874); W. W. Robinson, *Panorama—a Picture History of Southern California* (TITC, 1953); G. S. Dumke, *The Boom of the Eighties in Southern California* (HL, 1944); E. Corle, *The Royal Highway* (Bobbs-Merrill, 1949); R. H. Dana, *Two Years Before the Mast* (Harper, 1840); J. E. Bauer, *The Health Seekers of Southern California, 1870-1900* (HL, 1960); J. A. Graves, *My 70 Years in Southern California: 1857-1927* (Times-Mirror Press, Los Angeles, 1954); and R. V. Hine, *California's Utopian Colonies* (HL, 1953).

SAN DIEGO COUNTRY

For ancient man see G. F. Carter, *Pleistocene Man at San Diego* (Johns Hopkins Press, Baltimore, 1957). On settlement see A. M. Suhl, "Historical Geography of San Diego," MA (UC, 1928) and *San Diego, A California City* (American Guide Series, San Diego, 1937). More recent are J. W. Noble, "San Diego Grows Up," H (Dec. 1957), 56-61ff, and B. Ballantine, "The Sunniest End of California," H (Feb. 1963), 22ff. R. Bigger *et al.*, *Metropolitan Coast: San Diego and Orange Counties, California* (Bureau of Governmental Research, UCLA, 1958) describes the South Coast. G. Chenkin, "The Port of San Diego," MA (SU, 1959) considers an expanding seaport. R. V. Henson, "Mission Valley, San Diego County, California, a Study of Changing Land-use from 1769 to 1960," MA (UCLA, 1960) investigates a segment of the expanding metropolis. A coastal town is described by D. Clark, "La Jolla, a Gem of the California Coast," NGM, 102 (Dec. 1952), 755-782, and *Anon.*, "The Big Sun Spot," H (Oct. 1956), 106ff. A well-known mission has been studied by M. Walder, "The Historical Geography of Mission San Juan Capistrano, California," MA (UCLA, 1958). Agricultural specialization is considered by D. I. Eidemiller, "Economic Geography of Avocado Growing in San Diego County," MA (UC, 1950). F. E. Heston, "Growth of Urbanism on the Southern California Coast from

Newport to Del Mar," MA (UCLA, 1950), describes contemporary utilization of the South Coast. Large-scale ranching is described by R. G. Cleland, *The Irvine Ranch of Orange County: 1810-1950* (HL, 1953). J. Van der Veer gives a feeling for the Back Country in "Foothills," in R. Peattie, ed., *The Pacific Coast Ranges* (Vanguard, 1946), 103-134.

THE LOS ANGELES LOWLANDS

There is a plethora of works. See J. G. Layne, *Books of the Los Angeles District* (Glen Dawson, Los Angeles, 1950). Brief accounts include D. W. Lantis, *Los Angeles* (Doubleday, 1960); R. de Roos, "Los Angeles," NGM, 122 (Oct. 1962), 451-502; Anon., "The Astounding World of Los Angeles," H (Oct. 1957, entire issue); and D. W. Lantis and J. W. Reith, "Los Angeles," *Focus*, 12 (May 1962).

For background see W. W. Robinson, *The Old Spanish and Mexican Ranchos of Los Angeles County*, 1937, *The Old Spanish and Mexican Ranchos of Orange County*, 1954 (both TITC), and *Ranchos Become Cities* (SPP, 1939); also R. Bigger and J. D. Kitchen, *How the Cities Grew* (HF, 1952); and A. L. Gray, Jr., "Los Angeles: Urban Prototype," *Land Econ.*, 35 (1959), 232-242.

THE CITY OF LOS ANGELES

A doctoral dissertation, A. Wagner, *Los Angeles* (Bibliographisches Instit. Ag., Leipzig, 1935) was never published in English. In need of a genuine revision is American Guide Series, *Los Angeles, A Guide to the City and Its Environs* (Hastings House, 1941); more recent is M. Scott, *Metropolitan Los Angeles, One Community* (HF, 1949). Origins are given by R. E. Baugh, "The Site of Early Los Angeles," EG, 18 (1942), 87-96; R. Nadeau, *City Makers* (Doubleday, 1948), later updated his account in *Los Angeles from Mission to Modern Metropolis* (Longmans, Green, 1960). Other historical accounts include J. Baur and R. E. Belous, *Los Angeles: 1900-1961* (History Division, Los Angeles County Museum, 1961); W. W. Robinson, *Los Angeles from the Days of the Pueblo* (CHS and LPC, 1959); B. Duncan et al., "Patterns of City Growth (Los Angeles)," *Am. Jour. Sociol.*, 67 (1962), 418-429; and G. W. Robbins and L. D. Tilton, eds., *Los Angeles: Preface to a Master Plan* (Pacific Southwest Academy, Los Angeles, 1941).

"Smog problem" literature includes J. W. Reith, "Los Angeles Smog," YAPCG, 13 (1951), 24-31; M. Neiburger, "Weather Modification and Smog," *Science*, 126 (Oct. 4, 1957), 637-645; and L. B. Hitchcock and H. G. Marcus, "Some Scientific Aspects of the Urban Air Pollution Problems," *Sci. Mon.*, 81 (July 1955), 10-21. On another problem: W. M. Davis, "The Long Beach Earthquake," GR, 24 (Jan. 1934), 1-11.

Material on industrial activity: Anon., "The Undiscovered City," *Fortune* (June 1949), 76-82ff, is still useful. Pertinent issues of *Monthly Summary of Business Conditions in Southern California* (SFNB) include "Electronics Industry in Southern California" (Sept. 1959); "Reduction in Aircraft Employment Offsets Gains in Other Lines" (Oct. 1960); "Motion Picture Production and Distribution" (March 1960); and "The Suburbanization of Department Stores Sales" (Dec. 1959). See also W. G. Cunningham, *The Aircraft Industry: A Study in Industrial Location* (Morrison, Los Angeles, 1951). C. M. Zierer describes oil fields in "An Ephemeral Type of Industrial Land Occupance," AAAG, 26 (1936), 126-156. See pertinent chapters (24, 25, 26, 27, 28, 29), Zierer, *op. cit.*, general sources.

Geographers have overlooked transportation; an exception is J. Kemler, "Railway Entrances and Exits to Los Angeles," EG, 16 (1940), 312-314.

Sources on water include E. L. Bogart, *Water Problems of Southern California* (U. of Illinois, Urbana, 1934); V. Ostrom, *Water and Politics: A Study of Water Policies and Administration in the Development of Los Angeles* (HF, 1953); R. Nadeau, *The Water Seekers* (Doubleday, 1950); J. F. Poland, *Geology, Hydrology and Chemical Character of ground-water in the Torrance-Santa Monica Area, California* (USGS, WP 1461, 1959) and *Los Angeles County Land and Water Use Survey* (CWRB, Bull. 24, 1955).

On local minerals see J. W. Reith, "The Supply of Fuel and Power for Los Angeles," *Northwestern University, Studies in Geography*, 6 (1962), 79-91; Anon., "Offshore Geology and Oil Resources," MIS, 12 (May 1959), 1-8; and T. E. Gay, Jr., "Sand and Gravel," in *Mineral Commodities of California* (CDMG, Bull. 176, 1957), 511-517.

THE COASTAL PLAIN

For an overview see *The Southwest Area* (1961) and *The Southeast Area, An Area Land-Use Plan* (1959), Los Angeles County Regional Planning Commission. Anon., "Central City Area" (1959 Accomplishments, Los Angeles City Planning Commission), 12-16, has eleven worthwhile maps. R. Gillingham, in *The Rancho San Pedro* (Dominguez Estate Co., Los Angeles, 1961), traces successive use of the oldest rancho.

Unique aspects of Coast Plain geography presented in graduate studies: D. J. LeFevre, "Geographic Aspects of the Private Swimming Pool Industry in Los Angeles," MA (UCLA, 1960); D. R. Radell, "'Mom 'N Pop' Grocery Stores in the Boyle Heights Section of Los Angeles, California," MA (Los Angeles State College, 1961); N. Dlin, "Some Cultural and Geographical Aspects of the Christian Lebanese in Metropolitan Los Angeles," MA (UCLA, 1961); and L. D. Esterin, "The Miracle Mile: An Example of De-Centralization," MA (UCLA, 1955).

For the motion picture industry see C. M. Zierer: "Hollywood—World Center of Motion Picture Production," *Ann. Am. Acad. Pol. & Soc. Sci.* (Nov. 1947), 12-17; L. Jacobs, *The Rise of the American Film, A Critical History* (1939); Chap. 26, Zierer, *op. cit.*, general sources; H. Powdermaker, *Hollywood, the Dream Factory* (London, 1951); and R. Carson, "Haunted Hollywood," H (Oct. 1957), 68-72ff.

A glimpse of Beverly Hills: D. Dabney, "Beverly Hills, California: An Exclusive Residential Enclave" (abstract), YAPCG, 15 (1953), 39-40.

For the Santa Monica Littoral see W. W. Robinson and L. C. Powell, *The Malibu* (Dawson's Book Shop, Los Angeles, 1958); C. R. Stapleton, "Recreation and Its Problems on the Santa Monica–Venice Shoreline, Southern California," MA (UCLA, 1952); J. Backhouse, "Functional Differentiation in Santa Monica, California," MA (UCLA, 1961); A. C. Gerlach, "The Growth of El Segundo," EG, 16 (April 1940). Earlier use of the Palos Verdes is described by H. F. Raup, "Land Use and Water Supply Problems in Southern California: Market Gardens of the Palos Verdes Hills," GR, 26 (April 1936), 264-269.

On the central section of the Coastal Plain see R. Horvath, "The Functions of Santa Fe Springs," MA (UCLA, 1961), and H. J. Nelson, "The Vernon Area, California," AAAG, 42 (1952), 177-191.

On dairying see G. J. Fielding, "Dairying in the Los Angeles Milkshed: Factors Affecting Character and Location," Ph.D (UCLA, 1962) and "Dairying in Cities Designed to Keep People Out," PG, 14 (Jan. 1962), 12-17; B. L. Anderson and E. Boersma, "Changing Location Factors in the Los Angeles Milkshed," CG, 3 (1962), 47-54; and L. B. Fletcher and C. O. McCorkle, Jr., *Growth and Adjustment of the Los Angeles Milkshed* (UC,AES, Bull. 787, 1962).

For Long Beach and the harbors see G. J. Foster, "Tidewater Industrial Sites at Los Angeles–Long Beach Harbor, California," MA (UCLA, 1953); E. H. Draine, "A Geographic Study of Land Subsidence in the Long Beach Harbor Area," MA (UCLA, 1958); and R. M. Roesti, "Economic Analysis of Factors Underlying Pricing in the Southern California Tuna Canning Industry," Ph.D (U. of So. Calif., 1960).

For the Southeast see H. F. Raup, "The German Colonization of Anaheim, California," UCPG, 6:123-146; A. W. Carthew, "The Lower Basin of the Santa Ana River," MA (UC, 1931); *The Southeast Area: An Area Land-Use Plan* (Los Angeles County Regional Planning Commission, 1959); and *The Growth and Dynamic Stature of Orange County* (SFNB, 1961).

THE SAN FERNANDO VALLEY

W. W. Robinson, *The Story of San Fernando Valley* (TITC, 1961), and L. E. Guzman, "San Fernando Valley: Two Hundred Years in Transition," CG, 3 (1962), 55-58, provide overviews. See also G. R. Pappas, "The San Fernando Valley: A Socio-Geographic Study of a Modern Fringe Area," Ph.D (U. of Maryland, 1952); *The Growth and Economic Stature of the San Fernando Valley* (SFNB, 1960); A. E. Izzard, Jr., "The Factors Influencing the Electronics Industry in the San Fernando Valley," MA (UCLA, 1961); G. J. Foster and H. J. Nelson, *Ventura Boulevard: A String-type Shopping Street* (Real Estate Research Program, UCLA, 1958); and C. M. Zierer, "San Fernando—a Type of Southern California Town," AAAG, 24 (1934), 1-28.

THE SAN GABRIEL VALLEY

History is traced by W. W. Robinson, *Pasadena* (TITC, 1955), and I. M. Shrode, "The Sequent Occupance of the Rancho Azua de Duarte," Ph.D (U. of Chicago, 1948). See also B. H. Takisawa, "West Covina, California: Differentiation of a Suburb from Central Cities with Emphasis on Land Use," MA (UCLA, 1962), and *The East San Gabriel Valley* (Los Angeles County Regional Planning Commission, 1956).

VALLEY OF THE SOUTH
(INLAND EMPIRE)

W. W. Robinson provides evolution in *The Story of Riverside County* (TITC, 1957) and in *The Story of San Bernardino County* (TITC, 1958). See also G. W. and H. P. Beattie, *Heritage of the Valley, San Bernardino's First Century* (SPP, 1939); R. L. Gentilcore, "Ontario, California and the Agricultural Boom of the 1880's," *Agri. History,* 34 (April 1960), 77-87; and H. F. Raup, "San Bernardino, California, a Pass-site

City," UCPG, 8 (1940), 1-64. G. K. Douglass, *Developing the Inland Empire* (Southern California Research Council, Los Angeles, Ninth annual report, 1962), reviews prospects. See also N. Nichols, Jr., "Land Utilization on the Cucamonga Alluvial Fan, California," MA (Clark U., 1950), and J. L. Banks, Jr., "The Upper Santa Ana River Watershed, California: Water Resources," MA (UCLA, 1949).

On citrus see H. Webber *et al.*, *The Citrus Industry* (UCP, 2 vol., 1943-1948); C. M. Zierer, "The Citrus Fruit Industry of the Los Angeles Basin," EG, 10 (Jan. 1934), 53-73; and S. Hoos and J. N. Boles, *Oranges and Orange Products* (UC,AES, Bull. 731, 1953).

THE SAN JACINTO BASIN

H. F. Raup, "Land-Use and Water-Supply Problems in Southern California: The Case of Perris Valley," GR, 22 (April 1932), 270-278, describes earlier condition; also see R. Pease, "Problems of Recreational Land Use of the Elsinore Basin of Southern California," MA (UCLA, 1946), and R. Whittington, "Hemet–San Jacinto, A Geographic Survey of an Agricultural Valley," MA (UCLA, 1951).

OXNARD PLAIN

W. W. Robinson provides a history, *The Story of Ventura County* (TITC); C. M. Zierer, "The Ventura Area of Southern California," *Bull., Geog. Soc. of Philadelphia*, 30 (1932), 26-57, made an earlier investigation. Portions of H. F. Gregor, "Changing Agricultural Patterns in the Oxnard Plain," Ph.D (UCLA, 1950), are published: "A Sample Study of the California Ranch," AAAG, 41 (1951), 281-294; "The Southern California Water Problem in the Oxnard Area," GR, 42 (1952), 16-36; and "Agricultural Shifts in the Ventura Lowland," EG, 29 (1953), 340-361. Other doctoral studies are G. M. Reith, "Ventura, Life Story of a City," Ph.D (Clark U., 1962), and R. W. Durrenberger, "Climate as a Factor in the Production of Lemons in California," Ph.D (UCLA, 1955). See also *Ventura County Investigation* (CWRB, Bull. 12, 1955).

THE SANTA BARBARA COAST

For background, J. E. Upson *et al.*, *Geology and Ground-Water Resources of Santa Barbara County* (USCG, WSP 1108, 1951); B. Willis, "A Study of the Santa Barbara Earthquake of June 29, 1925," *Seismological Soc. of Am. Bull.*, 15 (1925), 255-278; and earlier occupancy, M. W.

Mikesell, "The Santa Barbara Area, California, a Study of Changing Cultural Patterns Prior to 1865," MA (UCLA), 1953. For recent use see J. D. Blick, "The Carpinteria Area: A Study in Land Use," MA (UCLA, 1950); Southern California Writers' Project, *Santa Barbara* (Hastings House, 1941); *The Growth and Economic Stature of Santa Barbara County, interim study* (SFNB, 1961); and J. D. Weaver, "Santa Barbara: Dilemma in Paradise," H (June 1961), 83-86ff.

TRANSVERSE RANGES

Geographic research includes H. P. Bailey, "Physical Geography of the San Gabriel Mountains," Ph.D (UCLA, 1950); J. Thompson, "The Settlement Geography of the San Gorgonio Pass Area," MA (UC, 1951); J. H. Le Resche, "The Lower Ventura Valley, California: a Study in Changing Occupance," MA (UCLA, 1951); E. G. Bjelland, "Ojai Valley: A Geographic Study," MA (UCLA, 1951); J. S. Carroll, "Elizabeth Lake–Leonis Valley Area," MA (UCLA, 1948); and J. L. Place, "The Pacific Face of the Santa Monica Mountains, Southern California: a geographic interpretation," MA (UCLA, 1952).

Other sources include R. G. Cleland, *The Place Called Sespe* (HL, 1957); R. M. Glendinning, "The Simi Valley," *Geog. Jour.*, 92 (Dec. 1938), 45; and R. E. Harrington, *Early Days in Simi Valley* (private, 1961).

CHANNEL ISLANDS

For setting see Chap. 9, Zierer, *op. cit.*, general sources, and K. O. Emery, *The Sea Off Southern California: a Modern Habitat of Petroleum* (Wiley, 1960).

E. Warren, Jr., gives a brief description in "California's Ranches in the Sky," NGM (Aug. 1958), 256-283. Longer works include C. Hillinger, *The California Islands* (Academy Press, Los Angeles, 1958), and D. Gleason, *Islands and Ports of California* (Devin-Adair, Los Angeles, 1957).

Descriptions of individual islands include S. O'Dell, *Island of the Blue Dolphins* (Houghton Mifflin, 1960); J. H. Winslow, "San Nicolas Island, Ventura County, California," (*Library Summary*, U. of Calif. at Riverside, no. 22, 1960); W. F. Heald, "Seagoing National Monument," PD, 10 (Jan.-Feb. 1957), 11-14; W. M. Woodbridge, "Santa Cruz—an Island Museum," PD, 7 (Jan.-Feb., 1954), 18-21; and W. W. Robinson, *Catalina Island* (TITC, 1951).

THE CENTRAL COAST (CHAPTER 8)

A summation of landforms is presented by G. B. Oakeshott, "Geologic Sketches of the Southern Coast Ranges," MIS, 13 (Jan. 1960), 1-13. See also B. Willis, "The San Andreas Rift, California," *Jour. of Geology*, 46 (1938), 793-827.

Chapters 2 and 3, Griffin and Young, *op. cit.*, general sources, afford the best regional description in geography. More pertinent farther north, R. Peattie, ed., *The Pacific Coast Ranges* (Vanguard, 1946) has value, espec. 341-346, 361-363, and 366-371.

OUTER LOWLANDS

For Lompoc-Santa Ynez, see H. D. Wilson, Jr., *Ground-water appraisal of Santa Ynez River Basin, Santa Barbara County, California, 1945-1952* (USGS, WSP 1467, 1959), and J. F. Gaines and S. F. Norsworthy, *Vegetation and Agricultural Crops of the Point Arguello Naval Missile Facility and Vicinity* (U. of Calif. at Riverside, 1960).

For the Santa Maria Valley see V. F. Carlson, *This is our Valley* (Westernlore, 1959), and C. H. MacFadden, "The Santa Maria Valley, Santa Barbara County, California," Ph.D (U. of Michigan, 1948).

Sources for the Salinas Valley include J. Steinbeck, *East of Eden* (Viking, 1952); R. H. Allen, "Economic History of Agriculture in Monterey County, California, During the American Period," Ph.D (UC); and A. B. Fisher, *The Salinas—Upside Down River* (Farrar and Rinehart, 1945). See also P. F. Griffin and C. L. White, "Lettuce Industry of the Salinas Valley," *Sci. Mon.*, 81 (1955), 77-84; and C. N. Beard, "Land Forms and Land Use East of Monterey Bay," EG, 24 (Oct. 1948), 286-295.

On Santa Clara Valley see J. O. M. Broek, *The Santa Clara Valley, California: A Study in Landscape Changes* (Utrecht, 1932); E. N. Torbert, "The Specialized Commercial Agriculture of the Northern Santa Clara Valley," GR, 26 (April 1936), 247-263; and F. M. MacGraw, "The Santa Clara Valley: an Historical and Geographical Appraisal," MA (SU, 1961). G. Cunningham, "The Tin Can Industry in California," YAPCG, 15 (1953), 11-17, has relevancy, as does J. Foytik, *Trends and Outlook, California Plum Industry* (UC,AES, Circ. 493, 1961).

THE INTERIOR BASINS

Literature is modest despite R. L. Chatham, "The Geography of San Benito County, California: A Regional Plan for Development," Ph.D (SU, 1962). For general impressions see *Anon.*, "Instead of the freeway," S (March 1963), 86-91, and *Anon.*, "San Juan Bautista," M (Oct. 1962), 14-16. Also R. F. Logan, "The Cuyama: Land of Dramatic Change" (abstract), YAPCG, 13 (1951), 45; and J. E. Upson and G. F. Worts, Jr., *Ground-water in the Cuyama Valley, California* (USGS, WSP 1110-B, 1951).

THE RANGES

The more northerly ranges are obviously better known. On vegetation see *Area and Ownership of Forest Land in Santa Cruz County* (PS, FRES, For. Surv. Release no. 21, 1953); W. C. Robison, "Historical Geography of the Santa Cruz Mountain Redwoods," MA (UC, 1949); and J. H. Thomas, *Flora of the Santa Cruz Mountains of California* (SUP, 1961). Also see J. W. Coulter, "Land Utilization in the Santa Lucia Region," GR, 20 (July 1930), 469-479.

THE COAST

On climate: H. R. Byers, "Summer Sea Fogs of the Central California Coast," UCPG, 3 (1930), 291-338; R. W. Richardson, "Summer Air Transport along the Coast of Central California: A Micro-climatic Study of a Wind Gap and Some Observed Effects of Wind on Trees," Ph.D (UC, 1943); and H. U. Sverdrup, "The California Current," *Science in the University* (UCP, 1944). Also see F. Cameron, "California's Wonderful One," NGM (Nov. 1959), 571-617; *Anon.*, "The Cultured Coast of Monterey," H (Dec. 1959), 82-87; and O. Lewis, *Fabulous San Simeon* (CHS, 1958).

For the Monterey Peninsula see American Guide Series, *Monterey Peninsula* (J. L. Delkin, SU, 2nd ed., 1948); *Monterey Bay, California*, ACE (86th Cong., 1st sess., HD 219, 1959); and C. M. Wilson, "Port of Monterey and vicinity," EG, 23 (July 1947), 199-219. G. T. Renner III has investigated the western flank of the Santa Cruz Mountains, "Geography of the Western Littoral of the Peninsula of Central California," MA (T.C., Columbia, 1950)—abstracted as "The Halfmoon Bay Littoral of Central California," JG, 53 (1954), 164-171.

THE BAY AREA

Physical introduction is afforded by *Geologic Guidebook of the San Francisco Bay Counties* (CDMG, Bull. 154, 1951); C. P. Patton, "Climatology of Summer Fogs in the San Francisco Bay

Area," UCPG, 10 (1956), 113-200; and H. E. Root, "San Francisco, the Air-Conditioned City," *Weatherwise*, 13 (April 1960), 47-54.

On the Bay itself H. Gilliam, *San Francisco Bay* (Doubleday, 1957); J. W. Noble, "San Francisco Bay," H, 20 (Aug. 1956), 26-35ff; C. E. Erickson, *Sunset Sportsman Atlas, San Francisco Bay and Delta Area* (LPC, 1952); and C. M. Wilson, "The Treacherous Farallones," *Americas*, 7 (June 1955), 26-30.

Planner M. Scott reviews evolution in *The San Francisco Bay Area, A Metropolis in Perspective* (UCP, 1956). See also American Guide Series, *San Francisco* (Hastings House, rev., 1947); F. Shor, "Boom on San Francisco Bay," NGM, 110 (Aug. 1956), 181-226; *Anon.*, "California's New Boom Area," *Bus. Week* (Apr. 2, 1960), 51ff; and R. N. Young and P. F. Griffin, "Recent Land-Use Changes in the San Francisco Bay Area," GR, 47 (1957), 396-405. Also *Future Development of the San Francisco Bay Area, 1960-2020* (U.S. Dept. of Commerce, Office of Area Development, 2 vol., 1959).

SAN FRANCISCO

See E. Rostlund, "Geographic Setting of San Francisco," JG, 54 (1955), 441-448, and H. F. Raup, "The Delayed Discovery of San Francisco Bay," CHSQ, 27, 289-296. The best geographic summary is J. J. Parsons, *San Francisco* (Doubleday, 1957). See also *Anon.*, "San Francisco," H (April 1961, entire issue) and the entire issue of *Westways* (March 1962). Also J. W. Noble, "San Francisco," H (Dec. 1956), 18ff; G. Atherton, *My San Francisco* (Bobbs-Merrill, 1946); H. Caen, *Baghdad by the Bay* (Doubleday, 1949); and J. C. Altrocchi, *The Spectacular San Franciscans* (Dutton, 1949); *Growth of the San Francisco Bay Area Core* (Real Estate Research Report 8, UC, Bureau of Bus. and Econ. Research, 1956); and W. Bronson, *The Earth Shook, the Sky Burned* (Doubleday, 1959).

THE EAST BAY

Literature includes J. W. Noble, "Oakland," H, 21 (Feb. 1957), 58-62; American Guide Series, *Berkeley: the First Seventy-Five Years* (Berkeley, 1940); J. L. Pimsleur, "The Battle of Berkeley," *This Week* (San Francisco Chronicle, March 17, 1963), 3-16; and D. Goodan and T. C. Shatto, "Changing Land Use in Ignacio Valley, California," EG, 24 (Jan. 1948), 135-148.

THE PENINSULA

See R. M. Newcomb, "Some Contrasts in the Features of the Physical Landscapes of the Southern San Francisco Peninsula," MA (UCLA, 1951); and C. L. White and H. M. Foote, "The Unorthodox San Francisco Bay Area Electronics Industry," JG, 59 (1960), 251-258.

THE SOUTH BAY

Several articles have concerned urbanization in northern Santa Clara Valley. See D. E. Sopher, "Postwar Urbanization of the Santa Clara Valley," BCCGT, 4 (April 1957), 13-17; P. F. Griffin and R. L. Chatham, "Urban Impact on Agriculture in Santa Clara County," AAAG, 48 (Sept. 1958), 195-208; and E. C. Moores, "Land Use Planning and the Consumer: A Study of Shopping Centers in the Santa Clara Valley, California," MA (SU, 1961).

MARIN PENINSULA

Literature includes *Anon.*, "Sausalito," H (May 1958), 67ff; H. Gilliam, *Island in Time: The Point Reyes Peninsula* (SC, 1962); and R. A. Ellefsen, "Displacement of Dairy Land by Subdivision Encroachment in the San Francisco Bay Area," MA (Clark U., 1959).

NORTH BAY

Investigations include W. J. Ketteringham, "The Settlement Geography of the Napa Valley," MA (SU, 1961) and P. Marr, "Industrial Development of North Bay Counties," MA (UC, 1955), abstracted as "The Transportation Factor in Industrial Location: an Historic Appraisal of the San Francisco North Bay Area," BCCGT, 4 (April 1957), 2-9.

GREAT CENTRAL VALLEY (CHAPTER 9)

An introduction is provided by F. Simpich, "California's Central Valley," NGM, 90 (Nov. 1946), 645-664.

For environmental overview, *Anon.*, *Central Valley Basin* (U.S. Dept. of the Interior, 1949). Physiographic studies include F. H. Olmstead and G. H. Davis, *Geologic Features and Ground-Water Storage Capacity of the Sacramento Valley, California* (USGS, WSP 1497, 1961), and G. H. Davis *et al.*, *Ground-Water Conditions and Storage Capacity in the San Joaquin Valley, California* (USGS, WSP 1469, 1959). K. Thompson describes vegetation in "Riparian Forests of the Sacramento Valley," AAAG, 51 (Sept. 1961), 294-315. H. J. Wood, "The Agricultural Value of California Soils," GR, 29 (1939), 310-313, contains maps of the Valley. C. F. Cole, "The Salt and Sodium Affected Soils of the Eastern San Joaquin Valley," YAPCG, 20 (1958), 27-34, considers soil conditions.

Background includes D. C. Cutter, "Spanish Exploration of California's Central Valley," Ph.D (UC, 1952) and *The Diary of Ensign Gabriel Moraga's Expedition of Discovery in the Sacramento Valley, 1808* (Glen Dawson, Los Angeles, 1957); and J. P. Zollinger in *Sutter, the Man and his Empire* (Oxford University Press, 1939). Historical accounts include J. A. McGowan, *History of the Sacramento Valley* (Lewis Hist. Pub. Co., New York, 1961) 3 vol., and W. Smith, *Garden of the Sun* (M. Hardison, Fresno, 3rd ed., 1956).

December tragedy is depicted by S. Pierson, dir., *The Big Flood, California 1955* (Calif. Disaster Office, Sacramento, 1956). K. Thompson, "Historic Flooding in the Sacramento Valley," PHR, 29 (Nov. 1960), 349-360, provides a longer range view. For effect of mining methods see R. L. Kelley, *Gold vs. Grain, the hydraulic mining controversy in California's Sacramento Valley* (Clark, Glendale, 1959).

There is much literature on water development: *Central Valley Basin* (U.S. Dept. of the Interior, Washington, 1949); P. Meigs, "Water Planning in the Great Central Valley," GR, 29 (1939), 252-273; S. Downey, *They Would Rule the Valley* (publ. by author, San Francisco, 1947); R. de Roos, *The Thirsty Land* (SUP, 1948); and P. S. Taylor, "Central Valley Project: Water and Land," *West. Polit. Qtr.*, 2 (1949), 229-253. Other studies by Taylor include "Destruction of Federal Reclamation Policy? The Ivanhoe Case," *Stanford Law Review*, 10 (Dec. 1957), 76-111; and "Excess Land Law: Pressure vs. Principle," *Calif. Law Review*, 47 (Aug. 1959), 499-541. Also see *The California Water Plan* (CDWR, Bull. 3, 1957); *The Delta and the Delta Water Project* (CDWR, Jan. 1960); and A. D. Angel, "Political and Administrative Aspects of the Central Valley Project of California," Ph.D (UCLA, 1944).

Literature on farm labor includes C. McWilliams, *Factories in the Field* (Little, Brown, 1939) and *Ill Fares the Land* (Little, Brown, 1944); J. Steinbeck, *The Grapes of Wrath* (Viking, 1939); W. H. Camp, *Skip to My Lou; Agricultural Labor in the San Joaquin Valley* (Governor of California, Committee to Survey the Agricultural Labor Resources of the San Joaquin Valley, Sacramento, 1951); and E. Galarza, *Strangers in our Fields* (U.S. section, U.S.-Mex. Trade Union Committee, Washington, 1956). On mechanization see A. H. Higbee, "Agricultural Implement Industry of California," MA (SU, 1956), and *Anon.*, "Invention Sprouts on California's Farms," *Fortune* (Jan. 1963), 90-99.

THE SACRAMENTO VALLEY

J. Dana, *The Sacramento* (Rinehart, 1939), *The Sacramento River Basin* (CDWR, Bull. 26, 1933), and *Sacramento River*, ACE (84th Cong., 2d sess., HD 272, 1955) provide introductions.

On the era of wheat farming see M. H. Saunders, "California Wheat, 1867-1910: Influence of Transportation on the Export Trade and Location of Producing Areas," MA (UC, 1960); J. D. Hicks, *The Populist Movement* (1931); and R. Paul, "Great California Grain War," PHR, 27 (Nov. 1958), 331-349.

Literature on *Anderson Valley* and the *West Side* is negligible. See C. Curran, "The Corning Area," senior thesis (CSC, 1961).

THE VALLEY TROUGH

On river transportation: J. MacMullen, *Paddle-Wheel Days of California* (SUP, 1944), and G. C. Shaw, "History of Steamboating on the Upper Sacramento River, 1848-1862," MA (CSC, 1963). A river town is described by C. H. Hisken, *Tehama, Little City of Big Trees* (Exposition, 1948).

On rice see W. M. Covington, "Rice Farming in the Sacramento Valley," BCCGT, 6 (1959), 23-25; N. A. Bleyhl, "A History of the Production and Marketing of Rice in California," Ph.D (U of Minn., 1955); and G. R. Sitton, "California Rice Industry," Ph.D (SU, 1954).

THE EAST SIDE

Much of the findings of R. P. Lowry, "Who Runs this Town? A Study of the Quality of Public Life in the Changing Small Community," Ph.D (UC, 1962), abstracted as "The Function of Alienation in Leadership," SSR, 46 (July 1962), 426-435, referent to Chico, would be applicable to other towns; the same comment applies to B. Ogilvie, "Unincorporated Urban Settlement in Butte County," Ph.D (Clark U., 1955).

On Sacramento see B. E. Tsagris and R. K. Coe, *Changing Pattern of Industrialization, Land Use and Values, Sacramento Metropolitan Area, 1950-1961* (Calif. Div. of Real Estate, June 1962), and K. Thompson, "Prospects for the Port of Sacramento," *Southwestern Soc. Sci. Qtr.*, 39 (1958), 133-144.

THE DELTA LANDS

A good portrayal is provided by J. Thompson, "The Settlement Geography of the Sacramento–San Joaquin Delta," Ph.D (SU, 1957), abstracted with same title, BCCGT, 4 (1956), 3-7, and M. H. McClain, "The Distribution of Asparagus Production in the Sacramento–San Joaquin Delta," MA (UC, 1954). Also see C. E. Erickson, *Sunset Sportsman Atlas—San Francisco Bay and Delta Area* (LPC, 1952). J. J. Parsons, "The Natural Gas Supply of California," *Land Economics,* 34 (Feb. 1958), 19-36, includes other regions; see also *Geologic Guide to the Gas and Oil Fields of Northern California* (CDMG, Bull. 181, 1962).

THE SAN JOAQUIN VALLEY

P. M. Bartz, in her published dissertation, *Ground Water in California: the Present State of its Investigation* (UCP, 1949), considered water needs. See also *The San Joaquin River Basin* (CDWR, Bull. 2, 1934).

THE EAST SIDE

Geographic research includes R. E. Copley, "An Historical Geography of the Dairy Industry of Stanislaus County, California," MA (UC, 1961); J. C. Graham, "The Settlement of Merced County, California," MA (UCLA, 1957); G. D. Aumack, "A Geographic Study of the Tulare County Citrus Belt," MA (UCLA, 1939); W. G. Byron, "A Geographic Analysis of the Porterville Area, California," MA (UCLA, 1951); J. Viletto, Jr., "Ecological Crop Geography of the Orange in California," M.Sc. (Penn State U., 1961); and A. Karperos, "A Survey of the California Wine Industry: Its Distribution and Location," MA (UCLA, 1952). C. F. Cole, "Rural Occupance Patterns in the Great Valley Portion of Fresno County, California," Ph.D (U. of Nebr., 1950), has particular value.

Investigation in allied fields includes D. D. M. Kesseli, "The Railroad as an Agency of Settlement in California, 1870-1890," MA (UC); B. F. Rhodes, Jr., "The Thirsty Land: the Modesto Irrigation District," Ph.D (UC, 1943); N. P. Hardeman, "History of the Inland Seaport of Stockton," Ph.D (UC, 1952); and A. P. Beltrami, "The Modesto Irrigation District," MA (UC, 1957).

Agricultural studies include a geographic "classic" by C. C. Colby, "The California Raisin Industry," AAAG, 14 (1924), 49-108; K. Thompson, "Location and Relocation of a Tree Crop—English Walnuts in California," EG, 37 (April 1961), 133-149; P. F. Griffin, "The California Olive Industry," JG, 54 (1955), 429-440; D. Taylor, "Growth of Tulare's Citrus Industry," CF (Oct. 6, 1962), 10-11, and O. D. Forker, "The Challenge to California's Dairy Industry," *Calif. Monthly* (July-Aug. 1962), 7ff.

Other literature includes *Anon., The Growth and Economic Stature of Fresno, Tulare, Kern, and Kings Counties* (SFNB, 1961), and W. R. Goldschmidt, *As You Sow* (Harcourt, Brace, 1947).

THE WEST SIDE

Geographic investigation includes J. D. Blick, "An Analysis of Cotton Production in the San Joaquin Valley," Ph.D (UCLA, 1956), and E. Meier, "Irrigation in West Fresno County," MA (U. of No. Dak., 1955). In allied fields see W. D. Lawrence, "Henry Miller and the San Joaquin Valley," MA (UC, 1933), and E. E. Martin, "Development of Wheat Culture in the San Joaquin Valley," MA (UC, 1924).

On cotton see *Anon.,* "California's Cotton Rush," *Fortune* (May 1949), 85-89ff, and D. C. Large, "Cotton in the San Joaquin Valley: A Study of Government in Agriculture," GR, 47 (1957), 365-380. For other crops see S. N. Dicken, "Dry Farming in the San Joaquin Valley," EG, 8 (1932), 94-99, and J. C. Lingle, "The Vegetable Areas of America—California's Central Valley," *Amer. Vegetable Grower* (Feb. 1957), 16-17ff.

THE SOUTH END

Literature includes K. Douglas, *Selected Large-Scale Farming Enterprises in California* (73rd Cong., 3d sess., purs. to Sen. Res. 266, 74th Cong., Pt. 62, 1940); *Anon.,* "Joseph DiGiorgio," *Fortune* (Aug. 1946); P. J. Fitzgerald, *Kern County Land Company: a Story of Science and Finance* (2nd ed., 1939); H. W. Wills, "Large-Scale Farm Operations in the upper San Joaquin Valley, California," MA (UCLA, 1953); and W. W. Robinson, *The Story of Kern County* (TITC, 1961).

For the California oil industry, sources include Chap. 20 in Zierer, *op. cit.,* general sources; O. P. Jenkins *et al., Geologic Formations and economic development of the oil and gas fields of California* (CDMG, *Bull.* 118, 1943) *Anon.,* "Petroleum in California," MIS (March 1958); California Division of Oil and Gas, *Summary of Operations, California Oil Fields* (annual); and F. Latta, *Black Gold in the San Joaquin* (Caxton, 1949).

THE NORTHWEST (CHAPTER 10)

For general impression see Peattie, ed., *The Pacific Coast Ranges* (Vanguard, 1946), espec.

59-65, and "North Coast Area," Chap. 3 (Bull. 2, vol. 1, CWRB, 1955).

On landforms, see W. P. Irwin, *Geologic Reconnaissance of the Northern Coast Ranges and Klamath Mountains, California* (CDMG, Bull. 179, 1960); also a series of USGS *Water-Supply Papers:* 1297 (1955); 1427 (1958); 1462 and 1470 (1959); 1495 (1960); 1576-C (1961).

For a glimpse of lumbering, see Chap. 18 in Zierer, *op. cit.*, general sources, and E. Fritz's source book, *California Coast Redwood—an Annotated Bibliography* (Recorder-Sunset Press, San Francisco, 1957); also H. J. Vaux, *Young-Growth Timber Taxation in Mendocino County* (UC,AES, Bull. 789, 1961) and "Timber in Humboldt County," CA (Jan. 1955), 4-5. The publications of the Pacific Southwest (formerly California) Forest and Range Experiment Station, Berkeley are valuable, including *Tech. Paper* 2 (1953), *Tech. Paper* 7 (1954), *Forest Survey Release* 19 (1953), *Misc. Paper* 25 (1958), *Misc. Paper* 38 (1959), *Forest Surv. Release* 20 (1953), and *Forest Surv. Release* 35 (1958).

THE NORTH COAST

J. W. Hoover, "The Littoral of Northern California as a geographic province," GR, 23 (1933), 217-229, reflects the paucity of published geographic investigation. H. Eder is preparing a dissertation on Humboldt and Del Norte counties at UCLA (in progress, 1963). O. C. Coy, *The Humboldt Bay Region:1850-1875* (Calif. State Hist. Assn., Los Angeles, 1924) gives background.

Investigation farther south includes A. E. Karinen, "Historical Geography of the Mendocino Coast," MA (UC, 1948); M. E. Trussell, "Settlement of Bodega Bay Region," MA (UC, 1960); and P. Wagner, "Russian Exploration in North America," MA (UC, 1950).

See also D. Jennings, "The Friendly Train Called Skunk," NGM (May 1959), 720-734; P. Casamajor, *Timber Marketing and Land Ownership in Mendocino County* (UC,AES, *Bull.* 772, 1960); *Anon.*, "Mendocino County," M (Sept.-Oct. 1961), 10-13; *Anon.*, "Mendocino," S (Oct. 1962), 74-81; and C. Mohler, "North Coast Adventure," W (Feb. 1958), 4-5.

THE REDWOOD HEARTLAND

For impression see Powers, *Redwood Country* (Duell, Sloan and Pearce, 1949), espec. 93-101 and 110-125. E. R. Schlappi describes a dramatic endeavor in "Saving the Redwoods,"

MA (UC, 1959). See also G. Leatherwood, "Redwood Highway," *Calif. High. and Publ. Works,* 35 (May-June 1956), 25-28ff, and *Eel River,* ACE (85th Cong., 1st sess., HD 80, 1957).

THE SOUTHERN VALLEYS

H. F. Raup and W. B. Pounds, Jr., "Northernmost Spanish Frontier in California," CHSQ, 32 (March 1953), 43-48, provides a background. See also H. H. Arnold, "My Life in the Valley of the Moon," NGM, 94 (Dec. 1948), 689-716, and "Wildlife in and near the Valley of the Moon," NGM, 97 (March 1950), 400-414; and J. R. McNitt, "Geothermal Power," MIS, 13 (March 1960), 1-9.

On Napa Valley see W. J. Ketteringham, "The Settlement Geography of Napa Valley," MA (SU, 1961). A novel pertinent to this area is A. N. T. Hobart, *The Cup and the Sword* (Bobbs-Merrill, 1942). For grape growing and wine see *Anon.*, "The North Coast Wine Country," S (Sept. 1959), 49-55; J. D. Weaver, "The Vineyards of California," H (Sept. 1961), 44-49ff; V. P. Carosso, *The California Wine Industry, 1830-1895: A Study of the Formative Years* (UCP, 1951); and M. F. K. Fisher and M. Yavno, *The Story of Wine in California* (UCP, 1962).

LAKE COUNTY

The geographic reference is F. J. Simoons, "The Clear Lake Upland of California," MA (UC, 1952). See also H. K. Mauldin, *Your Lakes, Valleys and Mountains, History of Lake County* (East Wind Printers, San Francisco, 1960). The views of W. M. Davis, "Lakes of California," *Calif. Jour. Mines and Geol.*, 29 (Jan. 1934), 175-236, regarding the origin of Clear Lake have been disputed.

KLAMATH COUNTRY

Literature is restricted chiefly to articles in *Westways* and *Sunset*. Graduate studies in history include E. Anderson, "The Hoopa Valley Indian Reservation in Northwestern California: A Study of its Origins," MA (UC, 1956). Life along the Klamath River is told by S. W. Patterson, *Dear Mad'm* (Norton, 1956).

Literature on recreation includes *Anon.*, "The Trinity Alps—a pocket-size Sierra flanked by a pocket-size Mother Lode," S (Aug. 1955), 36-39; *Anon.*, "Into the rugged heartland of California's Trinity Alps," S (July 1958), 46-51; Round Valley is described by R. H. Dillon, "The Valley of Tall Grass," W (Jan. 1960), 30-31.

INDEX